Operations Management: BUS 4110

Custom Edition

David R. Anderson | Dennis J. Sweeney | Thomas A. Williams | Jeffrey D. Camm | Kipp Martin

CENGAGE
Learning

Australia • Brazil • Japan • Korea • Mexico • Singapore • Spain • United Kingdom • United States

CENGAGE
Learning·

Operations Management: BUS 4110, Custom Edition

An Introduction to Management Science: Quantitative Approached to Decision Making, Revised 13th Edition

David R. Anderson | Dennis J. Sweeney | Thomas A. Williams | Jeffrey D. Camm | Kipp Martin

ExamView® and ExamView Pro® are registered trademarks of FSCreations, Inc. Windows is a registered trademark of the Microsoft Corporation used herein under license. Macintosh and Power Macintosh are registered trademarks of Apple Computer, Inc. used herein under license.

Executive Editors:
Maureen Staudt
Michael Stranz

Senior Project Development Manager:
Linda deStefano

Marketing Specialist:
Courtney Sheldon

Senior Production/Manufacturing Manager:
Donna M. Brown

Production Editorial Manager:
Kim Fry

Sr. Rights Acquisition Account Manager:
Todd Osborne

For product information and technology assistance, contact us at
Cengage Learning Customer & Sales Support, 1-800-354-9706

For permission to use material from this text or product, submit all requests online at **cengage.com/permissions**
Further permissions questions can be emailed to
permissionrequest@cengage.com

This book contains select works from existing Cengage Learning resources and was produced by Cengage Learning Custom Solutions for collegiate use. As such, those adopting and/or contributing to this work are responsible for editorial content accuracy, continuity and completeness.

Compilation © 2012 Cengage Learning
ISBN-13: 978-1-285-13000-2

ISBN-10: 1-285-13000-6

Cengage Learning
5191 Natorp Boulevard
Mason, Ohio 45040
USA

Cengage Learning is a leading provider of customized learning solutions with office locations around the globe, including Singapore, the United Kingdom, Australia, Mexico, Brazil, and Japan. Locate your local office at:
international.cengage.com/region.
Cengage Learning products are represented in Canada by Nelson Education, Ltd.
For your lifelong learning solutions, visit **www.cengage.com/custom.**
Visit our corporate website at **www.cengage.com.**

Printed in the United States of America

Brief Contents

CHAPTER 1

Introduction

CONTENTS

Management science, an approach to decision making based on the scientific method, makes extensive use of quantitative analysis. A variety of names exists for the body of knowledge involving quantitative approaches to decision making; in addition to management science, two other widely known and accepted names are operations research and decision science. Today, many use the terms *management science, operations research,* and *decision science* interchangeably.

The scientific management revolution of the early 1900s, initiated by Frederic W. Taylor, provided the foundation for the use of quantitative methods in management. But modern management science research is generally considered to have originated during the World War II period, when teams were formed to deal with strategic and tactical problems faced by the military. These teams, which often consisted of people with diverse specialties (e.g., mathematicians, engineers, and behavioral scientists), were joined together to solve a common problem by utilizing the scientific method. After the war, many of these team members continued their research in the field of management science.

According to Irv Lustig of IBM ILOG, Inc., solution methods developed today are 10,000 times faster than the ones used 15 years ago.

Two developments that occurred during the post–World War II period led to the growth and use of management science in nonmilitary applications. First, continued research resulted in numerous methodological developments. Probably the most significant development was the discovery by George Dantzig, in 1947, of the simplex method for solving linear programming problems. At the same time these methodological developments were taking place, digital computers prompted a virtual explosion in computing power. Computers enabled practitioners to use the methodological advances to solve a large variety of problems. The computer technology explosion continues, and personal computers can now be used to solve problems larger than those solved on mainframe computers in the 1990s.

As stated in the Preface, the purpose of the text is to provide students with a sound conceptual understanding of the role that management science plays in the decision-making process. We also said that the text is applications oriented. To reinforce the applications nature of the text and provide a better understanding of the variety of applications in which management science has been used successfully, Management Science in Action articles are presented throughout the text. Each Management Science in Action article summarizes an application of management science in practice. The first Management Science in Action in this chapter, Revenue Management at American Airlines, describes one of the most significant applications of management science in the airline industry.

MANAGEMENT SCIENCE IN ACTION

REVENUE MANAGEMENT AT AMERICAN AIRLINES*

One of the great success stories in management science involves the work done by the operations research (OR) group at American Airlines. In 1982, Thomas M. Cook joined a group of 12 operations research analysts at American Airlines. Under Cook's guidance, the OR group quickly grew to a staff of 75 professionals who developed models and conducted studies to support senior management decision making. Today the OR group is called Sabre and employs 10,000 professionals worldwide.

One of the most significant applications developed by the OR group came about because of the deregulation of the airline industry in the late 1970s. As a result of deregulation, a number of low-cost airlines were able to move into the market by selling seats at a fraction of the price charged by established carriers such as American Airlines. Facing the question of how to compete, the OR group suggested offering different fare classes (discount and full fare) and in the process created a new area of management science referred to as yield or revenue management.

The OR group used forecasting and optimization techniques to determine how many seats to sell at a discount and how many seats to hold for full fare. Although the initial implementation was relatively crude, the group continued to improve the forecasting and optimization models that drive the system and to obtain better data. Tom Cook counts at least four basic generations of revenue management during his tenure. Each produced in excess of $100 million in incremental profitability over its predecessor. This revenue management system at American Airlines generates nearly $1 billion annually in incremental revenue.

Today, virtually every airline uses some sort of revenue management system. The cruise, hotel, and car rental industries also now apply revenue management methods, a further tribute to the pioneering efforts of the OR group at American Airlines and its leader, Thomas M. Cook.

*Based on Peter Horner, "The Sabre Story," *OR/MS Today* (June 2000).

1.1 PROBLEM SOLVING AND DECISION MAKING

Problem solving can be defined as the process of identifying a difference between the actual and the desired state of affairs and then taking action to resolve the difference. For problems important enough to justify the time and effort of careful analysis, the problem-solving process involves the following seven steps:

1. Identify and define the problem.
2. Determine the set of alternative solutions.
3. Determine the criterion or criteria that will be used to evaluate the alternatives.
4. Evaluate the alternatives.
5. Choose an alternative.
6. Implement the selected alternative.
7. Evaluate the results to determine whether a satisfactory solution has been obtained.

Decision making is the term generally associated with the first five steps of the problem-solving process. Thus, the first step of decision making is to identify and define the problem. Decision making ends with the choosing of an alternative, which is the act of making the decision.

Let us consider the following example of the decision-making process. For the moment assume that you are currently unemployed and that you would like a position that will lead to a satisfying career. Suppose that your job search has resulted in offers from companies in Rochester, New York; Dallas, Texas; Greensboro, North Carolina; and Pittsburgh, Pennsylvania. Thus, the alternatives for your decision problem can be stated as follows:

1. Accept the position in Rochester.
2. Accept the position in Dallas.
3. Accept the position in Greensboro.
4. Accept the position in Pittsburgh.

The next step of the problem-solving process involves determining the criteria that will be used to evaluate the four alternatives. Obviously, the starting salary is a factor of some importance. If salary were the only criterion of importance to you, the alternative selected as "best" would be the one with the highest starting salary. Problems in which the objective is to find the best solution with respect to one criterion are referred to as **single-criterion decision problems.**

Suppose that you also conclude that the potential for advancement and the location of the job are two other criteria of major importance. Thus, the three criteria in your decision problem are starting salary, potential for advancement, and location. Problems that involve more than one criterion are referred to as **multicriteria decision problems.**

The next step of the decision-making process is to evaluate each of the alternatives with respect to each criterion. For example, evaluating each alternative relative to the

TABLE 1.1   DATA FOR THE JOB EVALUATION DECISION-MAKING PROBLEM

Alternative	Starting Salary	Potential for Advancement	Job Location
1. Rochester	$48,500	Average	Average
2. Dallas	$46,000	Excellent	Good
3. Greensboro	$46,000	Good	Excellent
4. Pittsburgh	$47,000	Average	Good

starting salary criterion is done simply by recording the starting salary for each job alternative. Evaluating each alternative with respect to the potential for advancement and the location of the job is more difficult to do, however, because these evaluations are based primarily on subjective factors that are often difficult to quantify. Suppose for now that you decide to measure potential for advancement and job location by rating each of these criteria as poor, fair, average, good, or excellent. The data that you compile are shown in Table 1.1.

You are now ready to make a choice from the available alternatives. What makes this choice phase so difficult is that the criteria are probably not all equally important, and no one alternative is "best" with regard to all criteria. Although we will present a method for dealing with situations like this one later in the text, for now let us suppose that after a careful evaluation of the data in Table 1.1, you decide to select alternative 3; alternative 3 is thus referred to as the **decision.**

At this point in time, the decision-making process is complete. In summary, we see that this process involves five steps:

1. Define the problem.
2. Identify the alternatives.
3. Determine the criteria.
4. Evaluate the alternatives.
5. Choose an alternative.

Note that missing from this list are the last two steps in the problem-solving process: implementing the selected alternative and evaluating the results to determine whether a satisfactory solution has been obtained. This omission is not meant to diminish the importance of each of these activities, but to emphasize the more limited scope of the term *decision making* as compared to the term *problem solving.* Figure 1.1 summarizes the relationship between these two concepts.

1.2   QUANTITATIVE ANALYSIS AND DECISION MAKING

Consider the flowchart presented in Figure 1.2. Note that it combines the first three steps of the decision-making process under the heading of "Structuring the Problem" and the latter two steps under the heading "Analyzing the Problem." Let us now consider in greater detail how to carry out the set of activities that make up the decision-making process.

Figure 1.3 shows that the analysis phase of the decision-making process may take two basic forms: qualitative and quantitative. Qualitative analysis is based primarily on the manager's judgment and experience; it includes the manager's intuitive "feel" for the problem and is more an art than a science. If the manager has had experience with similar

FIGURE 1.1   THE RELATIONSHIP BETWEEN PROBLEM SOLVING
AND DECISION MAKING

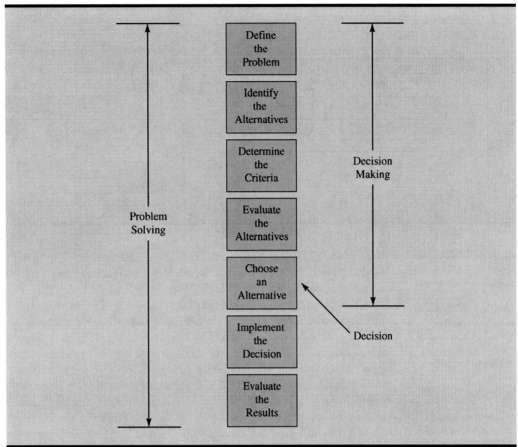

problems or if the problem is relatively simple, heavy emphasis may be placed upon a qualitative analysis. However, if the manager has had little experience with similar problems, or if the problem is sufficiently complex, then a quantitative analysis of the problem can be an especially important consideration in the manager's final decision.

When using the quantitative approach, an analyst will concentrate on the quantitative facts or data associated with the problem and develop mathematical expressions that

FIGURE 1.2   AN ALTERNATE CLASSIFICATION OF THE DECISION-MAKING PROCESS

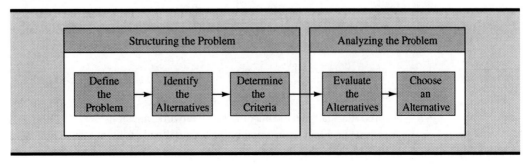

FIGURE 1.3   THE ROLE OF QUALITATIVE AND QUANTITATIVE ANALYSIS

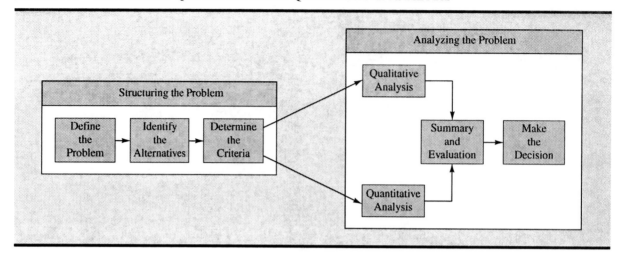

Quantitative methods are especially helpful with large, complex problems. For example, in the coordination of the thousands of tasks associated with landing Apollo 11 safely on the moon, quantitative techniques helped to ensure that more than 300,000 pieces of work performed by more than 400,000 people were integrated smoothly.

describe the objectives, constraints, and other relationships that exist in the problem. Then, by using one or more quantitative methods, the analyst will make a recommendation based on the quantitative aspects of the problem.

Although skills in the qualitative approach are inherent in the manager and usually increase with experience, the skills of the quantitative approach can be learned only by studying the assumptions and methods of management science. A manager can increase decision-making effectiveness by learning more about quantitative methodology and by better understanding its contribution to the decision-making process. A manager who is knowledgeable in quantitative decision-making procedures is in a much better position to compare and evaluate the qualitative and quantitative sources of recommendations and ultimately to combine the two sources in order to make the best possible decision.

The box in Figure 1.3 entitled "Quantitative Analysis" encompasses most of the subject matter of this text. We will consider a managerial problem, introduce the appropriate quantitative methodology, and then develop the recommended decision.

In closing this section, let us briefly state some of the reasons why a quantitative approach might be used in the decision-making process:

Try Problem 4 to test your understanding of why quantitative approaches might be needed in a particular problem.

1. The problem is complex, and the manager cannot develop a good solution without the aid of quantitative analysis.
2. The problem is especially important (e.g., a great deal of money is involved), and the manager desires a thorough analysis before attempting to make a decision.
3. The problem is new, and the manager has no previous experience from which to draw.
4. The problem is repetitive, and the manager saves time and effort by relying on quantitative procedures to make routine decision recommendations.

1.3   QUANTITATIVE ANALYSIS

From Figure 1.3, we see that quantitative analysis begins once the problem has been structured. It usually takes imagination, teamwork, and considerable effort to transform a rather general problem description into a well-defined problem that can be approached via quantitative analysis. The more the analyst is involved in the process of structuring the problem, the more likely the ensuing quantitative analysis will make an important contribution to the decision-making process.

To successfully apply quantitative analysis to decision making, the management scientist must work closely with the manager or user of the results. When both the management scientist and the manager agree that the problem has been adequately structured, work can begin on developing a model to represent the problem mathematically. Solution procedures can then be employed to find the best solution for the model. This best solution for the model then becomes a recommendation to the decision maker. The process of developing and solving models is the essence of the quantitative analysis process.

Model Development

Models are representations of real objects or situations and can be presented in various forms. For example, a scale model of an airplane is a representation of a real airplane. Similarly, a child's toy truck is a model of a real truck. The model airplane and toy truck are examples of models that are physical replicas of real objects. In modeling terminology, physical replicas are referred to as **iconic models.**

A second classification includes models that are physical in form but do not have the same physical appearance as the object being modeled. Such models are referred to as **analog models.** The speedometer of an automobile is an analog model; the position of the needle on the dial represents the speed of the automobile. A thermometer is another analog model representing temperature.

A third classification of models—the type we will primarily be studying—includes representations of a problem by a system of symbols and mathematical relationships or expressions. Such models are referred to as **mathematical models** and are a critical part of any quantitative approach to decision making. For example, the total profit from the sale of a product can be determined by multiplying the profit per unit by the quantity sold. If we let x represent the number of units sold and P the total profit, then, with a profit of \$10 per unit, the following mathematical model defines the total profit earned by selling x units:

$$P = 10x \qquad (1.1)$$

The purpose, or value, of any model is that it enables us to make inferences about the real situation by studying and analyzing the model. For example, an airplane designer might test an iconic model of a new airplane in a wind tunnel to learn about the potential flying characteristics of the full-size airplane. Similarly, a mathematical model may be used to make inferences about how much profit will be earned if a specified quantity of a particular product is sold. According to the mathematical model of equation (1.1), we would expect selling three units of the product ($x = 3$) would provide a profit of $P = 10(3) = \$30$.

In general, experimenting with models requires less time and is less expensive than experimenting with the real object or situation. A model airplane is certainly quicker and less expensive to build and study than the full-size airplane. Similarly, the mathematical model in equation (1.1) allows a quick identification of profit expectations without actually requiring the manager to produce and sell x units. Models also have the advantage of reducing the risk associated with experimenting with the real situation. In particular, bad designs or bad decisions that cause the model airplane to crash or a mathematical model to project a \$10,000 loss can be avoided in the real situation.

The value of model-based conclusions and decisions is dependent on how well the model represents the real situation. The more closely the model airplane represents the real

Herbert A. Simon, a Nobel Prize winner in economics and an expert in decision making, said that a mathematical model does not have to be exact; it just has to be close enough to provide better results than can be obtained by common sense.

airplane, the more accurate the conclusions and predictions will be. Similarly, the more closely the mathematical model represents the company's true profit-volume relationship, the more accurate the profit projections will be.

Because this text deals with quantitative analysis based on mathematical models, let us look more closely at the mathematical modeling process. When initially considering a managerial problem, we usually find that the problem definition phase leads to a specific objective, such as maximization of profit or minimization of cost, and possibly a set of restrictions or **constraints,** such as production capacities. The success of the mathematical model and quantitative approach will depend heavily on how accurately the objective and constraints can be expressed in terms of mathematical equations or relationships.

A mathematical expression that describes the problem's objective is referred to as the **objective function.** For example, the profit equation $P = 10x$ would be an objective function for a firm attempting to maximize profit. A production capacity constraint would be necessary if, for instance, 5 hours are required to produce each unit and only 40 hours of production time are available per week. Let x indicate the number of units produced each week. The production time constraint is given by

$$5x \leq 40 \qquad (1.2)$$

The value of $5x$ is the total time required to produce x units; the symbol $\leq$ indicates that the production time required must be less than or equal to the 40 hours available.

The decision problem or question is the following: How many units of the product should be scheduled each week to maximize profit? A complete mathematical model for this simple production problem is

$$\text{Maximize} \qquad P = 10x \quad \text{objective function}$$
$$\text{subject to (s.t.)}$$
$$\left. \begin{array}{r} 5x \leq 40 \\ x \geq 0 \end{array} \right\} \text{constraints}$$

The $x \geq 0$ constraint requires the production quantity x to be greater than or equal to zero, which simply recognizes the fact that it is not possible to manufacture a negative number of units. The optimal solution to this model can be easily calculated and is given by $x = 8$, with an associated profit of \$80. This model is an example of a linear programming model. In subsequent chapters we will discuss more complicated mathematical models and learn how to solve them in situations where the answers are not nearly so obvious.

In the preceding mathematical model, the profit per unit (\$10), the production time per unit (5 hours), and the production capacity (40 hours) are environmental factors that are not under the control of the manager or decision maker. Such environmental factors, which can affect both the objective function and the constraints, are referred to as **uncontrollable inputs** to the model. Inputs that are controlled or determined by the decision maker are referred to as **controllable inputs** to the model. In the example given, the production quantity x is the controllable input to the model. Controllable inputs are the decision alternatives specified by the manager and thus are also referred to as the **decision variables** of the model.

Once all controllable and uncontrollable inputs are specified, the objective function and constraints can be evaluated and the output of the model determined. In this sense, the output of the model is simply the projection of what would happen if those particular

FIGURE 1.4 FLOWCHART OF THE PROCESS OF TRANSFORMING MODEL INPUTS INTO OUTPUT

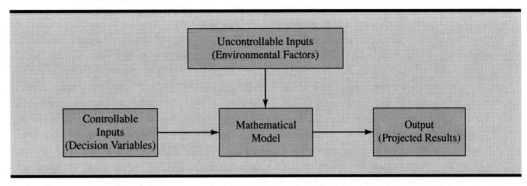

environmental factors and decisions occurred in the real situation. A flowchart of how controllable and uncontrollable inputs are transformed by the mathematical model into output is shown in Figure 1.4. A similar flowchart showing the specific details of the production model is shown in Figure 1.5.

As stated earlier, the uncontrollable inputs are those the decision maker cannot influence. The specific controllable and uncontrollable inputs of a model depend on the particular problem or decision-making situation. In the production problem, the production time available (40) is an uncontrollable input. However, if it were possible to hire more employees or use overtime, the number of hours of production time would become a controllable input and therefore a decision variable in the model.

Uncontrollable inputs can either be known exactly or be uncertain and subject to variation. If all uncontrollable inputs to a model are known and cannot vary, the model is referred to as a **deterministic model.** Corporate income tax rates are not under the influence of the manager and thus constitute an uncontrollable input in many decision models. Because these rates are known and fixed (at least in the short run), a mathematical model with corporate income tax rates as the only uncontrollable input would be a deterministic

FIGURE 1.5 FLOWCHART FOR THE PRODUCTION MODEL

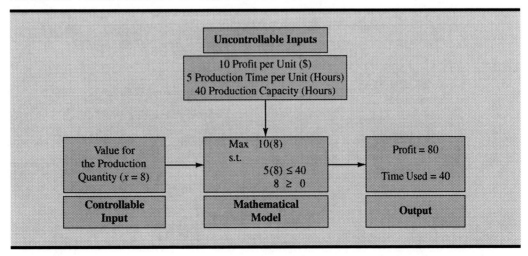

model. The distinguishing feature of a deterministic model is that the uncontrollable input values are known in advance.

If any of the uncontrollable inputs are uncertain and subject to variation, the model is referred to as a **stochastic** or **probabilistic model.** An uncontrollable input to many production planning models is demand for the product. A mathematical model that treats future demand—which may be any of a range of values—with uncertainty would be called a stochastic model. In the production model, the number of hours of production time required per unit, the total hours available, and the unit profit were all uncontrollable inputs. Because the uncontrollable inputs were all known to take on fixed values, the model was deterministic. If, however, the number of hours of production time per unit could vary from 3 to 6 hours depending on the quality of the raw material, the model would be stochastic. The distinguishing feature of a stochastic model is that the value of the output cannot be determined even if the value of the controllable input is known because the specific values of the uncontrollable inputs are unknown. In this respect, stochastic models are often more difficult to analyze.

Data Preparation

Another step in the quantitative analysis of a problem is the preparation of the data required by the model. Data in this sense refer to the values of the uncontrollable inputs to the model. All uncontrollable inputs or data must be specified before we can analyze the model and recommend a decision or solution for the problem.

In the production model, the values of the uncontrollable inputs or data were $10 per unit for profit, 5 hours per unit for production time, and 40 hours for production capacity. In the development of the model, these data values were known and incorporated into the model as it was being developed. If the model is relatively small and the uncontrollable input values or data required are few, the quantitative analyst will probably combine model development and data preparation into one step. In these situations the data values are inserted as the equations of the mathematical model are developed.

However, in many mathematical modeling situations, the data or uncontrollable input values are not readily available. In these situations the management scientist may know that the model will need profit per unit, production time, and production capacity data, but the values will not be known until the accounting, production, and engineering departments can be consulted. Rather than attempting to collect the required data as the model is being developed, the analyst will usually adopt a general notation for the model development step, and then a separate data preparation step will be performed to obtain the uncontrollable input values required by the model.

Using the general notation

$$c = \text{profit per unit}$$
$$a = \text{production time in hours per unit}$$
$$b = \text{production capacity in hours}$$

the model development step of the production problem would result in the following general model:

$$\text{Max} \quad cx$$
$$\text{s.t.}$$
$$ax \leq b$$
$$x \geq 0$$

A separate data preparation step to identify the values for c, a, and b would then be necessary to complete the model.

Many inexperienced quantitative analysts assume that once the problem has been defined and a general model developed, the problem is essentially solved. These individuals tend to believe that data preparation is a trivial step in the process and can be easily handled by clerical staff. Actually, this assumption could not be further from the truth, especially with large-scale models that have numerous data input values. For example, a small linear programming model with 50 decision variables and 25 constraints could have more than 1300 data elements that must be identified in the data preparation step. The time required to prepare these data and the possibility of data collection errors will make the data preparation step a critical part of the quantitative analysis process. Often, a fairly large database is needed to support a mathematical model, and information systems specialists may become involved in the data preparation step.

Model Solution

Once the model development and data preparation steps are completed, we can proceed to the model solution step. In this step, the analyst will attempt to identify the values of the decision variables that provide the "best" output for the model. The specific decision-variable value or values providing the "best" output will be referred to as the **optimal solution** for the model. For the production problem, the model solution step involves finding the value of the production quantity decision variable x that maximizes profit while not causing a violation of the production capacity constraint.

One procedure that might be used in the model solution step involves a trial-and-error approach in which the model is used to test and evaluate various decision alternatives. In the production model, this procedure would mean testing and evaluating the model under various production quantities or values of x. Note, in Figure 1.5, that we could input trial values for x and check the corresponding output for projected profit and satisfaction of the production capacity constraint. If a particular decision alternative does not satisfy one or more of the model constraints, the decision alternative is rejected as being **infeasible,** regardless of the objective function value. If all constraints are satisfied, the decision alternative is **feasible** and a candidate for the "best" solution or recommended decision. Through this trial-and-error process of evaluating selected decision alternatives, a decision maker can identify a good—and possibly the best—feasible solution to the problem. This solution would then be the recommended decision for the problem.

Table 1.2 shows the results of a trial-and-error approach to solving the production model of Figure 1.5. The recommended decision is a production quantity of 8 because the feasible solution with the highest projected profit occurs at $x = 8$.

Although the trial-and-error solution process is often acceptable and can provide valuable information for the manager, it has the drawbacks of not necessarily providing the best solution and of being inefficient in terms of requiring numerous calculations if many decision alternatives are tried. Thus, quantitative analysts have developed special solution procedures for many models that are much more efficient than the trial-and-error approach. Throughout this text, you will be introduced to solution procedures that are applicable to the specific mathematical models that will be formulated. Some relatively small models or problems can be solved by hand computations, but most practical applications require the use of a computer.

Model development and model solution steps are not completely separable. An analyst will want both to develop an accurate model or representation of the actual problem situation and to be able to find a solution to the model. If we approach the model development

TABLE 1.2   TRIAL-AND-ERROR SOLUTION FOR THE PRODUCTION MODEL OF FIGURE 1.5

Decision Alternative (Production Quantity) x	Projected Profit	Total Hours of Production	Feasible Solution? (Hours Used ≤ 40)
0	0	0	Yes
2	20	10	Yes
4	40	20	Yes
6	60	30	Yes
8	80	40	Yes
10	100	50	No
12	120	60	No

step by attempting to find the most accurate and realistic mathematical model, we may find the model so large and complex that it is impossible to obtain a solution. In this case, a simpler and perhaps more easily understood model with a readily available solution procedure is preferred even if the recommended solution is only a rough approximation of the best decision. As you learn more about quantitative solution procedures, you will have a better idea of the types of mathematical models that can be developed and solved.

Try Problem 8 to test your understanding of the concept of a mathematical model and what is referred to as the optimal solution to the model.

After a model solution is obtained, both the management scientist and the manager will be interested in determining how good the solution really is. Even though the analyst has undoubtedly taken many precautions to develop a realistic model, often the goodness or accuracy of the model cannot be assessed until model solutions are generated. Model testing and validation are frequently conducted with relatively small "test" problems that have known or at least expected solutions. If the model generates the expected solutions, and if other output information appears correct, the go-ahead may be given to use the model on the full-scale problem. However, if the model test and validation identify potential problems or inaccuracies inherent in the model, corrective action, such as model modification and/or collection of more accurate input data, may be taken. Whatever the corrective action, the model solution will not be used in practice until the model has satisfactorily passed testing and validation.

Report Generation

An important part of the quantitative analysis process is the preparation of managerial reports based on the model's solution. In Figure 1.3, we see that the solution based on the quantitative analysis of a problem is one of the inputs the manager considers before making a final decision. Thus, the results of the model must appear in a managerial report that can be easily understood by the decision maker. The report includes the recommended decision and other pertinent information about the results that may be helpful to the decision maker.

A Note Regarding Implementation

As discussed in Section 1.2, the manager is responsible for integrating the quantitative solution with qualitative considerations in order to make the best possible decision. After completing the decision-making process, the manager must oversee the implementation and follow-up evaluation of the decision. The manager should continue to monitor the contribution of the model during the implementation and follow-up. At times this process may lead to requests for model expansion or refinement that will cause the management scientist to return to an earlier step of the quantitative analysis process.

Successful implementation of results is of critical importance to the management scientist as well as the manager. If the results of the quantitative analysis process are not correctly implemented, the entire effort may be of no value. It doesn't take too many unsuccessful implementations before the management scientist is out of work. Because implementation often requires people to do things differently, it often meets with resistance. People want to know, "What's wrong with the way we've been doing it?" and so on. One of the most effective ways to ensure successful implementation is to include users throughout the modeling process. A user who feels a part of identifying the problem and developing the solution is much more likely to enthusiastically implement the results. The success rate for implementing the results of a management science project is much greater for those projects characterized by extensive user involvement. The Management Science in Action, Quantitative Analysis at Merrill Lynch, discusses some of the reasons behind the success Merrill Lynch realized from using quantitative analysis.

MANAGEMENT SCIENCE IN ACTION

QUANTITATIVE ANALYSIS AT MERRILL LYNCH*

Merrill Lynch, a brokerage and financial services firm with more than 56,000 employees in 45 countries, serves its client base through two business units. The Merrill Lynch Corporate and Institutional Client Group serves more than 7000 corporations, institutions, and governments. The Merrill Lynch Private Client Group (MLPC) serves approximately 4 million households, as well as 225,000 small to mid-sized businesses and regional financial institutions, through more than 14,000 financial consultants in 600-plus branch offices. The management science group, established in 1986, has been part of MLPC since 1991. The mission of this group is to provide high-end quantitative analysis to support strategic management decisions and to enhance the financial consultant–client relationship.

The management science group has successfully implemented models and developed systems for asset allocation, financial planning, marketing information technology, database marketing, and portfolio performance measurement. Although technical expertise and objectivity are clearly important factors in any analytical group, the management science group attributes much of its success to communications skills, teamwork, and consulting skills.

Each project begins with face-to-face meetings with the client. A proposal is then prepared to outline the background of the problem, the objectives of the project, the approach, the required resources, the time schedule, and the implementation issues. At this stage, analysts focus on developing solutions that provide significant value and are easily implemented.

As the work progresses, frequent meetings keep the clients up to date. Because people with different skills, perspectives, and motivations must work together for a common goal, teamwork is essential. The group's members take classes in team approaches, facilitation, and conflict resolution. They possess a broad range of multifunctional and multidisciplinary capabilities and are motivated to provide solutions that focus on the goals of the firm. This approach to problem solving and the implementation of quantitative analysis has been a hallmark of the management science group. The impact and success of the group translates into hard dollars and repeat business. The group received the annual Edelman award given by the Institute for Operations Research and the Management Sciences for effective use of management science for organizational success.

*Based on Russ Labe, Raj Nigam, and Steve Spence, "Management Science at Merrill Lynch Private Client Group," *Interfaces* 29, no. 2 (March/April 1999): 1–14.

NOTES AND COMMENTS

1. Developments in computer technology have increased the availability of management science techniques to decision makers. Many software packages are now available for personal computers. Microsoft Excel, and LINGO are widely used in management science courses and in industry.

2. Various chapter appendices provide step-by-step instructions for using Excel and LINGO to solve problems in the text. Microsoft Excel has become the most used analytical modeling software in business and industry. We recommend that you read Appendix A, Building Spreadsheet Models, located in the back of this text.

1.4   MODELS OF COST, REVENUE, AND PROFIT

Some of the most basic quantitative models arising in business and economic applications are those involving the relationship between a volume variable—such as production volume or sales volume—and cost, revenue, and profit. Through the use of these models, a manager can determine the projected cost, revenue, and/or profit associated with an established production quantity or a forecasted sales volume. Financial planning, production planning, sales quotas, and other areas of decision making can benefit from such cost, revenue, and profit models.

Cost and Volume Models

The cost of manufacturing or producing a product is a function of the volume produced. This cost can usually be defined as a sum of two costs: fixed cost and variable cost. **Fixed cost** is the portion of the total cost that does not depend on the production volume; this cost remains the same no matter how much is produced. **Variable cost,** on the other hand, is the portion of the total cost that is dependent on and varies with the production volume. To illustrate how cost and volume models can be developed, we will consider a manufacturing problem faced by Nowlin Plastics.

Nowlin Plastics produces a variety of compact disc (CD) storage cases. Nowlin's best-selling product is the CD-50, a slim, plastic CD holder with a specially designed lining that protects the optical surface of the disc. Several products are produced on the same manufacturing line, and a setup cost is incurred each time a changeover is made for a new product. Suppose that the setup cost for the CD-50 is $3000. This setup cost is a fixed cost that is incurred regardless of the number of units eventually produced. In addition, suppose that variable labor and material costs are $2 for each unit produced. The cost-volume model for producing x units of the CD-50 can be written as

$$C(x) = 3000 + 2x \tag{1.3}$$

where

$$x = \text{production volume in units}$$
$$C(x) = \text{total cost of producing } x \text{ units}$$

Once a production volume is established, the model in equation (1.3) can be used to compute the total production cost. For example, the decision to produce $x = 1200$ units would result in a total cost of $C(1200) = 3000 + 2(1200) = \$5400$.

Marginal cost is defined as the rate of change of the total cost with respect to production volume. That is, it is the cost increase associated with a one-unit increase in the production volume. In the cost model of equation (1.3), we see that the total cost $C(x)$ will increase by \$2 for each unit increase in the production volume. Thus, the marginal cost is \$2. With more complex total cost models, marginal cost may depend on the production volume. In such cases, we could have marginal cost increasing or decreasing with the production volume x.

Revenue and Volume Models

Management of Nowlin Plastics will also want information on the projected revenue associated with selling a specified number of units. Thus, a model of the relationship between revenue and volume is also needed. Suppose that each CD-50 storage unit sells for \$5. The model for total revenue can be written as

$$R(x) = 5x \tag{1.4}$$

where

$$x = \text{sales volume in units}$$
$$R(x) = \text{total revenue associated with selling } x \text{ units}$$

Marginal revenue is defined as the rate of change of total revenue with respect to sales volume. That is, it is the increase in total revenue resulting from a one-unit increase in sales volume. In the model of equation (1.4), we see that the marginal revenue is \$5. In this case, marginal revenue is constant and does not vary with the sales volume. With more complex models, we may find that marginal revenue increases or decreases as the sales volume x increases.

Profit and Volume Models

One of the most important criteria for management decision making is profit. Managers need to be able to know the profit implications of their decisions. If we assume that we will only produce what can be sold, the production volume and sales volume will be equal. We can combine equations (1.3) and (1.4) to develop a profit-volume model that will determine the total profit associated with a specified production-sales volume. Total profit, denoted $P(x)$, is total revenue minus total cost; therefore, the following model provides the total profit associated with producing and selling x units:

$$P(x) = R(x) - C(x)$$
$$= 5x - (3000 + 2x) = -3000 + 3x \tag{1.5}$$

Thus, the profit-volume model can be derived from the revenue-volume and cost-volume models.

Breakeven Analysis

Using equation (1.5), we can now determine the total profit associated with any production volume *x*. For example, suppose that a demand forecast indicates that 500 units of the product can be sold. The decision to produce and sell the 500 units results in a projected profit of

$$P(500) = -3000 + 3(500) = -1500$$

In other words, a loss of $1500 is predicted. If sales are expected to be 500 units, the manager may decide against producing the product. However, a demand forecast of 1800 units would show a projected profit of

$$P(1800) = -3000 + 3(1800) = 2400$$

This profit may be enough to justify proceeding with the production and sale of the product.

We see that a volume of 500 units will yield a loss, whereas a volume of 1800 provides a profit. The volume that results in total revenue equaling total cost (providing $0 profit) is called the **breakeven point.** If the breakeven point is known, a manager can quickly infer that a volume above the breakeven point will result in a profit, whereas a volume below the breakeven point will result in a loss. Thus, the breakeven point for a product provides valuable information for a manager who must make a yes/no decision concerning production of the product.

Let us now return to the Nowlin Plastics example and show how the total profit model in equation (1.5) can be used to compute the breakeven point. The breakeven point can be found by setting the total profit expression equal to zero and solving for the production volume. Using equation (1.5), we have

$$P(x) = -3000 + 3x = 0$$
$$3x = 3000$$
$$x = 1000$$

Try Problem 12 to test your ability to determine the breakeven point for a quantitative model.

With this information, we know that production and sales of the product must be greater than 1000 units before a profit can be expected. The graphs of the total cost model, the total revenue model, and the location of the breakeven point are shown in Figure 1.6. In Appendix 1.1 we also show how Excel can be used to perform a breakeven analysis for the Nowlin Plastics production example.

1.5   MANAGEMENT SCIENCE TECHNIQUES

In this section we present a brief overview of the management science techniques covered in this text. Over the years, practitioners have found numerous applications for the following techniques:

Linear Programming   Linear programming is a problem-solving approach developed for situations involving maximizing or minimizing a linear function subject to linear constraints that limit the degree to which the objective can be pursued. The production model developed in Section 1.3 (see Figure 1.5) is an example of a simple linear programming model.

Integer Linear Programming   Integer linear programming is an approach used for problems that can be set up as linear programs, with the additional requirement that some or all of the decision variables be integer values.

FIGURE 1.6   GRAPH OF THE BREAKEVEN ANALYSIS FOR NOWLIN PLASTICS

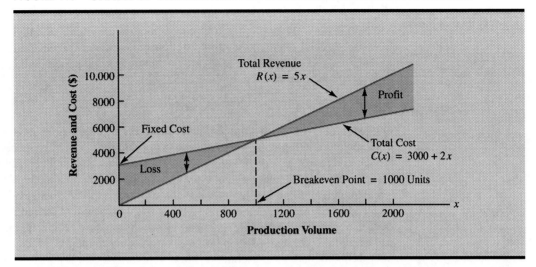

Distribution and Network Models   A network is a graphical description of a problem consisting of circles called nodes that are interconnected by lines called arcs. Specialized solution procedures exist for these types of problems, enabling us to quickly solve problems in such areas as transportation system design, information system design, and project scheduling.

Nonlinear Programming   Many business processes behave in a nonlinear manner. For example, the price of a bond is a nonlinear function of interest rates; the quantity demanded for a product is usually a nonlinear function of the price. Nonlinear programming is a technique that allows for maximizing or minimizing a nonlinear function subject to nonlinear constraints.

Project Scheduling: PERT/CPM   In many situations, managers are responsible for planning, scheduling, and controlling projects that consist of numerous separate jobs or tasks performed by a variety of departments, individuals, and so forth. The PERT (Program Evaluation and Review Technique) and CPM (Critical Path Method) techniques help managers carry out their project scheduling responsibilities.

Inventory Models   Inventory models are used by managers faced with the dual problems of maintaining sufficient inventories to meet demand for goods and, at the same time, incurring the lowest possible inventory holding costs.

Waiting-Line or Queueing Models   Waiting-line or queueing models have been developed to help managers understand and make better decisions concerning the operation of systems involving waiting lines.

Simulation   Simulation is a technique used to model the operation of a system. This technique employs a computer program to model the operation and perform simulation computations.

Decision Analysis   Decision analysis can be used to determine optimal strategies in situations involving several decision alternatives and an uncertain or risk-filled pattern of events.

Goal Programming   Goal programming is a technique for solving multicriteria decision problems, usually within the framework of linear programming.

Analytic Hierarchy Process   This multicriteria decision-making technique permits the inclusion of subjective factors in arriving at a recommended decision.

Forecasting   Forecasting methods are techniques that can be used to predict future aspects of a business operation.

Markov Process Models   Markov process models are useful in studying the evolution of certain systems over repeated trials. For example, Markov processes have been used to describe the probability that a machine, functioning in one period, will function or break down in another period.

Methods Used Most Frequently

Our experience as both practitioners and educators has been that the most frequently used management science techniques are linear programming, integer programming, network models (including transportation and transshipment models), and simulation. Depending upon the industry, the other methods in the preceding list are used more or less frequently.

Helping to bridge the gap between the manager and the management scientist is a major focus of the text. We believe that the barriers to the use of management science can best be removed by increasing the manager's understanding of how management science can be applied. The text will help you develop an understanding of which management science techniques are most useful, how they are used, and, most importantly, how they can assist managers in making better decisions.

The Management Science in Action, Impact of Operations Research on Everyday Living, describes some of the many ways quantitative analysis affects our everyday lives.

MANAGEMENT SCIENCE IN ACTION

IMPACT OF OPERATIONS RESEARCH ON EVERYDAY LIVING*

Mark Eisner, associate director of the School of Operations Research and Industrial Engineering at Cornell University, once said that operations research "is probably the most important field nobody's ever heard of." The impact of operations research on everyday living over the past 20 years is substantial.

Suppose you schedule a vacation to Florida and use Orbitz to book your flights. An algorithm developed by operations researchers will search among millions of options to find the cheapest fare. Another algorithm will schedule the flight crews and aircraft used by the airline. If you rent a car in Florida, the price you pay for the car is determined by a mathematical model that seeks to maximize revenue for the car rental firm. If you do some shopping on your trip and decide to ship your purchases home using UPS, another algorithm tells UPS which truck to put the packages on, the route the truck should follow, and where the packages should be placed on the truck to minimize loading and unloading time.

If you enjoy watching college basketball, operations research plays a role in which games you see. Michael Trick, a professor at the Tepper School of Business at Carnegie-Mellon, designed a system for scheduling each year's Atlantic Coast Conference men's and women's basketball games. Even though it might initially appear that scheduling 16 games among the nine men's teams would be easy, it requires sorting through hundreds of millions of possible combinations of possible schedules. Each of those possibilities entails some desirable and some undesirable characteristics. For example, you do not want to schedule too many consecutive home games, and you want to ensure that each team plays the same number of weekend games.

*Based on Virginia Postrel, "Operations Everything," *The Boston Globe,* June 27, 2004.

NOTES AND COMMENTS

The Institute for Operations Research and the Management Sciences (INFORMS) and the Decision Sciences Institute (DSI) are two professional societies that publish journals and newsletters dealing with current research and applications of operations research and management science techniques.

SUMMARY

This text is about how management science may be used to help managers make better decisions. The focus of this text is on the decision-making process and on the role of management science in that process. We discussed the problem orientation of this process and in an overview showed how mathematical models can be used in this type of analysis.

The difference between the model and the situation or managerial problem it represents is an important point. Mathematical models are abstractions of real-world situations and, as such, cannot capture all the aspects of the real situation. However, if a model can capture the major relevant aspects of the problem and can then provide a solution recommendation, it can be a valuable aid to decision making.

One of the characteristics of management science that will become increasingly apparent as we proceed through the text is the search for a best solution to the problem. In carrying out the quantitative analysis, we shall be attempting to develop procedures for finding the "best" or optimal solution.

GLOSSARY

Problem solving The process of identifying a difference between the actual and the desired state of affairs and then taking action to resolve the difference.

Decision making The process of defining the problem, identifying the alternatives, determining the criteria, evaluating the alternatives, and choosing an alternative.

Single-criterion decision problem A problem in which the objective is to find the "best" solution with respect to just one criterion.

Multicriteria decision problem A problem that involves more than one criterion; the objective is to find the "best" solution, taking into account all the criteria.

Decision The alternative selected.

Model A representation of a real object or situation.

Iconic model A physical replica, or representation, of a real object.

Analog model Although physical in form, an analog model does not have a physical appearance similar to the real object or situation it represents.

Mathematical model Mathematical symbols and expressions used to represent a real situation.

Constraints Restrictions or limitations imposed on a problem.

Objective function A mathematical expression that describes the problem's objective.

Uncontrollable inputs The environmental factors or inputs that cannot be controlled by the decision maker.

Controllable inputs The inputs that are controlled or determined by the decision maker.

Decision variable Another term for controllable input.

Deterministic model A model in which all uncontrollable inputs are known and cannot vary.

Stochastic (probabilistic) model A model in which at least one uncontrollable input is uncertain and subject to variation; stochastic models are also referred to as probabilistic models.

Optimal solution   The specific decision-variable value or values that provide the "best" output for the model.

Infeasible solution   A decision alternative or solution that does not satisfy one or more constraints.

Feasible solution   A decision alternative or solution that satisfies all constraints.

Fixed cost   The portion of the total cost that does not depend on the volume; this cost remains the same no matter how much is produced.

Variable cost   The portion of the total cost that is dependent on and varies with the volume.

Marginal cost   The rate of change of the total cost with respect to volume.

Marginal revenue   The rate of change of total revenue with respect to volume.

Breakeven point   The volume at which total revenue equals total cost.

PROBLEMS

1. Define the terms *management science* and *operations research*.

2. List and discuss the steps of the decision-making process.

3. Discuss the different roles played by the qualitative and quantitative approaches to managerial decision making. Why is it important for a manager or decision maker to have a good understanding of both of these approaches to decision making?

4. A firm just completed a new plant that will produce more than 500 different products, using more than 50 different production lines and machines. The production scheduling decisions are critical in that sales will be lost if customer demands are not met on time. If no individual in the firm has experience with this production operation and if new production schedules must be generated each week, why should the firm consider a quantitative approach to the production scheduling problem?

5. What are the advantages of analyzing and experimenting with a model as opposed to a real object or situation?

6. Suppose that a manager has a choice between the following two mathematical models of a given situation: (a) a relatively simple model that is a reasonable approximation of the real situation, and (b) a thorough and complex model that is the most accurate mathematical representation of the real situation possible. Why might the model described in part (a) be preferred by the manager?

7. Suppose you are going on a weekend trip to a city that is d miles away. Develop a model that determines your round-trip gasoline costs. What assumptions or approximations are necessary to treat this model as a deterministic model? Are these assumptions or approximations acceptable to you?

8. Recall the production model from Section 1.3:

$$\text{Max} \quad 10x$$
$$\text{s.t.}$$
$$5x \leq 40$$
$$x \geq 0$$

Suppose the firm in this example considers a second product that has a unit profit of $5 and requires 2 hours of production time for each unit produced. Use y as the number of units of product 2 produced.

a. Show the mathematical model when both products are considered simultaneously.
b. Identify the controllable and uncontrollable inputs for this model.
c. Draw the flowchart of the input-output process for this model (see Figure 1.5).
d. What are the optimal solution values of x and y?
e. Is the model developed in part (a) a deterministic or a stochastic model? Explain.

9. Suppose we modify the production model in Section 1.3 to obtain the following mathematical model:

$$\text{Max} \quad 10x$$
$$\text{s.t.}$$
$$ax \leq 40$$
$$x \geq 0$$

where a is the number of hours of production time required for each unit produced. With $a = 5$, the optimal solution is $x = 8$. If we have a stochastic model with $a = 3, a = 4, a = 5$, or $a = 6$ as the possible values for the number of hours required per unit, what is the optimal value for x? What problems does this stochastic model cause?

10. A retail store in Des Moines, Iowa, receives shipments of a particular product from Kansas City and Minneapolis. Let

$$x = \text{number of units of the product received from Kansas City}$$
$$y = \text{number of units of the product received from Minneapolis}$$

a. Write an expression for the total number of units of the product received by the retail store in Des Moines.
b. Shipments from Kansas City cost $0.20 per unit, and shipments from Minneapolis cost $0.25 per unit. Develop an objective function representing the total cost of shipments to Des Moines.
c. Assuming the monthly demand at the retail store is 5000 units, develop a constraint that requires 5000 units to be shipped to Des Moines.
d. No more than 4000 units can be shipped from Kansas City, and no more than 3000 units can be shipped from Minneapolis in a month. Develop constraints to model this situation.
e. Of course, negative amounts cannot be shipped. Combine the objective function and constraints developed to state a mathematical model for satisfying the demand at the Des Moines retail store at minimum cost.

11. For most products, higher prices result in a decreased demand, whereas lower prices result in an increased demand. Let

$$d = \text{annual demand for a product in units}$$
$$p = \text{price per unit}$$

Assume that a firm accepts the following price-demand relationship as being realistic:

$$d = 800 - 10p$$

where p must be between $20 and $70.
a. How many units can the firm sell at the $20 per-unit price? At the $70 per-unit price?
b. Show the mathematical model for the total revenue (TR), which is the annual demand multiplied by the unit price.

c. Based on other considerations, the firm's management will only consider price alternatives of $30, $40, and $50. Use your model from part (b) to determine the price alternative that will maximize the total revenue.

d. What are the expected annual demand and the total revenue corresponding to your recommended price?

12. The O'Neill Shoe Manufacturing Company will produce a special-style shoe if the order size is large enough to provide a reasonable profit. For each special-style order, the company incurs a fixed cost of $1000 for the production setup. The variable cost is $30 per pair, and each pair sells for $40.

a. Let x indicate the number of pairs of shoes produced. Develop a mathematical model for the total cost of producing x pairs of shoes.

b. Let P indicate the total profit. Develop a mathematical model for the total profit realized from an order for x pairs of shoes.

c. How large must the shoe order be before O'Neill will break even?

13. Micromedia offers computer training seminars on a variety of topics. In the seminars each student works at a personal computer, practicing the particular activity that the instructor is presenting. Micromedia is currently planning a two-day seminar on the use of Microsoft Excel in statistical analysis. The projected fee for the seminar is $300 per student. The cost for the conference room, instructor compensation, lab assistants, and promotion is $4800. Micromedia rents computers for its seminars at a cost of $30 per computer per day.

a. Develop a model for the total cost to put on the seminar. Let x represent the number of students who enroll in the seminar.

b. Develop a model for the total profit if x students enroll in the seminar.

c. Micromedia has forecasted an enrollment of 30 students for the seminar. How much profit will be earned if their forecast is accurate?

d. Compute the breakeven point.

14. Eastman Publishing Company is considering publishing a paperback textbook on spreadsheet applications for business. The fixed cost of manuscript preparation, textbook design, and production setup is estimated to be $80,000. Variable production and material costs are estimated to be $3 per book. Demand over the life of the book is estimated to be 4000 copies. The publisher plans to sell the text to college and university bookstores for $20 each.

a. What is the breakeven point?

b. What profit or loss can be anticipated with a demand of 4000 copies?

c. With a demand of 4000 copies, what is the minimum price per copy that the publisher must charge to break even?

d. If the publisher believes that the price per copy could be increased to $25.95 and not affect the anticipated demand of 4000 copies, what action would you recommend? What profit or loss can be anticipated?

15. Preliminary plans are under way for the construction of a new stadium for a major league baseball team. City officials have questioned the number and profitability of the luxury corporate boxes planned for the upper deck of the stadium. Corporations and selected individuals may buy the boxes for $100,000 each. The fixed construction cost for the upper-deck area is estimated to be $1,500,000, with a variable cost of $50,000 for each box constructed.

a. What is the breakeven point for the number of luxury boxes in the new stadium?

b. Preliminary drawings for the stadium show that space is available for the construction of up to 50 luxury boxes. Promoters indicate that buyers are available and that all 50 could be sold if constructed. What is your recommendation concerning the construction of luxury boxes? What profit is anticipated?

16. Financial Analysts, Inc., is an investment firm that manages stock portfolios for a number of clients. A new client is requesting that the firm handle an $80,000 portfolio. As an initial investment strategy, the client would like to restrict the portfolio to a mix of the following two stocks:

Stock	Price/ Share	Maximum Estimated Annual Return/Share	Possible Investment
Oil Alaska	$50	$6	$50,000
Southwest Petroleum	$30	$4	$45,000

Let

$$x = \text{number of shares of Oil Alaska}$$
$$y = \text{number of shares of Southwest Petroleum}$$

a. Develop the objective function, assuming that the client desires to maximize the total annual return.
b. Show the mathematical expression for each of the following three constraints:
   (1) Total investment funds available are $80,000.
   (2) Maximum Oil Alaska investment is $50,000.
   (3) Maximum Southwest Petroleum investment is $45,000.

Note: Adding the $x \geq 0$ and $y \geq 0$ constraints provides a linear programming model for the investment problem. A solution procedure for this model will be discussed in Chapter 2.

17. Models of inventory systems frequently consider the relationships among a beginning inventory, a production quantity, a demand or sales, and an ending inventory. For a given production period j, let

$$s_{j-1} = \text{ending inventory from the previous period (beginning inventory for period } j\text{)}$$
$$x_j = \text{production quantity in period } j$$
$$d_j = \text{demand in period } j$$
$$s_j = \text{ending inventory for period } j$$

a. Write the mathematical relationship or model that describes how these four variables are related.
b. What constraint should be added if production capacity for period j is given by C_j?
c. What constraint should be added if inventory requirements for period j mandate an ending inventory of at least I_j?

Case Problem   SCHEDULING A GOLF LEAGUE

Chris Lane, the head professional at Royal Oak Country Club, must develop a schedule of matches for the couples' golf league that begins its season at 4:00 P.M. tomorrow. Eighteen couples signed up for the league, and each couple must play every other couple over the course of the 17-week season. Chris thought it would be fairly easy to develop a schedule, but after working on it for a couple of hours, he has been unable to come up with a schedule. Because Chris must have a schedule ready by tomorrow afternoon, he asked you to help him. A possible complication is that one of the couples told Chris that they may have to cancel for the season. They told Chris they will let him know by 1:00 P.M. tomorrow whether they will be able to play this season.

Managerial Report

Prepare a report for Chris Lane. Your report should include, at a minimum, the following items:

1. A schedule that will enable each of the 18 couples to play every other couple over the 17-week season.
2. A contingency schedule that can be used if the couple that contacted Chris decides to cancel for the season.

Appendix 1.1   USING EXCEL FOR BREAKEVEN ANALYSIS

In Section 1.4 we introduced the Nowlin Plastics production example to illustrate how quantitative models can be used to help a manager determine the projected cost, revenue, and/or profit associated with an established production quantity or a forecasted sales volume. In this appendix we introduce spreadsheet applications by showing how to use Microsoft Excel to perform a quantitative analysis of the Nowlin Plastics example.

Refer to the worksheet shown in Figure 1.7. We begin by entering the problem data into the top portion of the worksheet. The value of 3000 in cell B3 is the fixed cost, the value

FIGURE 1.7   FORMULA WORKSHEET FOR THE NOWLIN PLASTICS PRODUCTION EXAMPLE

	A	B
1	**Nowlin Plastics**	
2		
3	**Fixed Cost**	3000
4		
5	**Variable Cost Per Unit**	2
6		
7	**Selling Price Per Unit**	5
8		
9		
10	**Models**	
11		
12	**Production Volume**	800
13		
14	**Total Cost**	=B3+B5*B12
15		
16	**Total Revenue**	=B7*B12
17		
18	**Total Profit (Loss)**	=B16-B14

of 2 in cell B5 is the variable labor and material costs per unit, and the value of 5 in cell B7 is the selling price per unit. As discussed in Appendix A, whenever we perform a quantitative analysis using Excel, we will enter the problem data in the top portion of the worksheet and reserve the bottom portion for model development. The label "Models" in cell A10 helps to provide a visual reminder of this convention.

Cell B12 in the models portion of the worksheet contains the proposed production volume in units. Because the values for total cost, total revenue, and total profit depend upon the value of this decision variable, we have placed a border around cell B12 and screened the cell for emphasis. Based upon the value in cell B12, the cell formulas in cells B14, B16, and B18 are used to compute values for total cost, total revenue, and total profit (loss), respectively. First, recall that the value of total cost is the sum of the fixed cost (cell B3) and the total variable cost. The total variable cost—the product of the variable cost per unit (cell B5) and the production volume (cell B12)—is given by B5*B12. Thus, to compute the value of total cost we entered the formula =B3+B5*B12 in cell B14. Next, total revenue is the product of the selling price per unit (cell B7) and the number of units produced (cell B12), which is entered in cell B16 as the formula =B7*B12. Finally, the total profit (or loss) is the difference between the total revenue (cell B16) and the total cost (cell B14). Thus, in cell B18 we have entered the formula =B16-B14. The worksheet shown in Figure 1.8 shows the formulas used to make these computations; we refer to it as a formula worksheet.

To examine the effect of selecting a particular value for the production volume, we entered a value of 800 in cell B12. The worksheet shown in Figure 1.8 shows the values obtained by the formulas; a production volume of 800 units results in a total cost of $4600, a total revenue of $4000, and a loss of $600. To examine the effect of other production volumes, we only need to enter a different value into cell B12. To examine the

FIGURE 1.8   SOLUTION USING A PRODUCTION VOLUME OF 800 UNITS FOR THE
NOWLIN PLASTICS PRODUCTION EXAMPLE

Nowlin

	A	B
1	**Nowlin Plastics**	
2		
3	**Fixed Cost**	$3,000
4		
5	**Variable Cost Per Unit**	$2
6		
7	**Selling Price Per Unit**	$5
8		
9		
10	**Models**	
11		
12	**Production Volume**	800
13		
14	**Total Cost**	$4,600
15		
16	**Total Revenue**	$4,000
17		
18	**Total Profit (Loss)**	−$600

effect of different costs and selling prices, we simply enter the appropriate values in the data portion of the worksheet; the results will be displayed in the model section of the worksheet.

In Section 1.4 we illustrated breakeven analysis. Let us now see how Excel's Goal Seek tool can be used to compute the breakeven point for the Nowlin Plastics production example.

Determining the Breakeven Point Using Excel's Goal Seek Tool

The breakeven point is the production volume that results in total revenue equal to total cost and hence a profit of $0. One way to determine the breakeven point is to use a trial-and-error approach. For example, in Figure 1.8 we saw that a trial production volume of 800 units resulted in a loss of $600. Because this trial solution resulted in a loss, a production volume of 800 units cannot be the breakeven point. We could continue to experiment with other production volumes by simply entering different values into cell B12 and observing the resulting profit or loss in cell B18. A better approach is to use Excel's Goal Seek tool to determine the breakeven point.

Excel's Goal Seek tool allows the user to determine the value for an input cell that will cause the value of a related output cell to equal some specified value (called the *goal*). In the case of breakeven analysis, the "goal" is to set Total Profit to zero by "seeking" an appropriate value for Production Volume. Goal Seek will allow us to find the value of production volume that will set Nowlin Plastics' total profit to zero. The following steps describe how to use Goal Seek to find the breakeven point for Nowlin Plastics:

Step 1. Select the **Data** tab at the top of the Ribbon
Step 2. Select **What-If Analysis** in the **Data Tools** group
Step 3. Select **Goal Seek** in What-if Analysis
Step 4. When the **Goal Seek** dialog box appears:
  Enter B18 in the **Set cell** box
  Enter 0 in the **To value** box
  Enter B12 in the **By changing cell** box
  Click **OK**

FIGURE 1.9   GOAL SEEK DIALOG BOX FOR THE NOWLIN PLASTICS
             PRODUCTION EXAMPLE

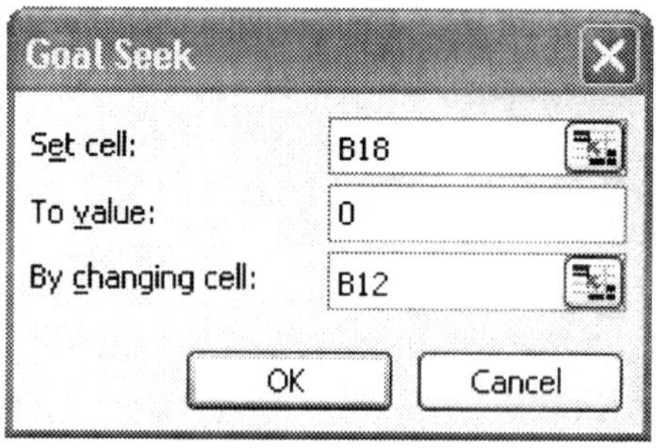

FIGURE 1.10   BREAKEVEN POINT FOUND USING EXCEL'S GOAL SEEK TOOL
FOR THE NOWLIN PLASTICS PRODUCTION EXAMPLE

	A	B
1	**Nowlin Plastics**	
2		
3	**Fixed Cost**	$3,000
4		
5	**Variable Cost Per Unit**	$2
6		
7	**Selling Price Per Unit**	$5
8		
9		
10	**Models**	
11		
12	**Production Volume**	1000
13		
14	**Total Cost**	$5,000
15		
16	**Total Revenue**	$5,000
17		
18	**Total Profit (Loss)**	$0

The completed Goal Seek dialog box is shown in Figure 1.9, and the worksheet obtained after selecting **OK** is shown in Figure 1.10. The Total Profit in cell B18 is zero, and the Production Volume in cell B12 has been set to the breakeven point of 1000.

CHAPTER 2

An Introduction to Linear Programming

CONTENTS

Linear programming is a problem-solving approach developed to help managers make decisions. Numerous applications of linear programming can be found in today's competitive business environment. For instance, Eastman Kodak uses linear programming to determine where to manufacture products throughout their worldwide facilities, and GE Capital uses linear programming to help determine optimal lease structuring. Marathon Oil Company uses linear programming for gasoline blending and to evaluate the economics of a new terminal or pipeline. The Management Science in Action, Timber Harvesting Model at MeadWestvaco Corporation, provides another example of the use of linear programming. Later in the chapter another Management Science in Action illustrates how the Hanshin Expressway Public Corporation uses linear programming for traffic control on an urban toll expressway in Osaka, Japan.

To illustrate some of the properties that all linear programming problems have in common, consider the following typical applications:

1. A manufacturer wants to develop a production schedule and an inventory policy that will satisfy sales demand in future periods. Ideally, the schedule and policy will enable the company to satisfy demand and at the same time *minimize* the total production and inventory costs.

2. A financial analyst must select an investment portfolio from a variety of stock and bond investment alternatives. The analyst would like to establish the portfolio that *maximizes* the return on investment.

3. A marketing manager wants to determine how best to allocate a fixed advertising budget among alternative advertising media such as radio, television, newspaper, and magazine. The manager would like to determine the media mix that *maximizes* advertising effectiveness.

4. A company has warehouses in a number of locations throughout the United States. For a set of customer demands, the company would like to determine how much each warehouse should ship to each customer so that total transportation costs are *minimized*.

MANAGEMENT SCIENCE IN ACTION

TIMBER HARVESTING MODEL AT MEADWESTVACO CORPORATION*

MeadWestvaco Corporation is a major producer of premium papers for periodicals, books, commercial printing, and business forms. The company also produces pulp and lumber, designs and manufactures packaging systems for beverage and other consumables markets, and is a world leader in the production of coated board and shipping containers. Quantitative analyses at MeadWestvaco are developed and implemented by the company's Decision Analysis Department. The department assists decision makers by providing them with analytical tools of quantitative methods as well as personal analysis and recommendations.

MeadWestvaco uses quantitative models to assist with the long-range management of the company's timberland. Through the use of large-scale linear programs, timber harvesting plans are developed to cover a substantial time horizon. These models consider wood market conditions, mill pulpwood requirements, harvesting capacities, and general forest management principles. Within these constraints, the model arrives at an optimal harvesting and purchasing schedule based on discounted cash flow. Alternative schedules reflect changes in the various assumptions concerning forest growth, wood availability, and general economic conditions.

Quantitative methods are also used in the development of the inputs for the linear programming models. Timber prices and supplies as well as mill requirements must be forecast over the time horizon, and advanced sampling techniques are used to evaluate land holdings and to project forest growth. The harvest schedule is then developed using quantitative methods.

*Based on information provided by Dr. Edward P. Winkofsky.

Linear programming was initially referred to as "programming in a linear structure." In 1948 Tjalling Koopmans suggested to George Dantzig that the name was much too long; Koopmans suggested shortening it to linear programming. George Dantzig agreed and the field we now know as linear programming was named.

These examples are only a few of the situations in which linear programming has been used successfully, but they illustrate the diversity of linear programming applications. A close scrutiny reveals one basic property they all have in common. In each example, we were concerned with *maximizing* or *minimizing* some quantity. In example 1, the manufacturer wanted to minimize costs; in example 2, the financial analyst wanted to maximize return on investment; in example 3, the marketing manager wanted to maximize advertising effectiveness; and in example 4, the company wanted to minimize total transportation costs. *In all linear programming problems, the maximization or minimization of some quantity is the objective.*

All linear programming problems also have a second property: restrictions, or **constraints,** that limit the degree to which the objective can be pursued. In example 1, the manufacturer is restricted by constraints requiring product demand to be satisfied and by the constraints limiting production capacity. The financial analyst's portfolio problem is constrained by the total amount of investment funds available and the maximum amounts that can be invested in each stock or bond. The marketing manager's media selection decision is constrained by a fixed advertising budget and the availability of the various media. In the transportation problem, the minimum-cost shipping schedule is constrained by the supply of product available at each warehouse. *Thus, constraints are another general feature of every linear programming problem.*

2.1   A SIMPLE MAXIMIZATION PROBLEM

Par, Inc., is a small manufacturer of golf equipment and supplies whose management has decided to move into the market for medium- and high-priced golf bags. Par's distributor is enthusiastic about the new product line and has agreed to buy all the golf bags Par produces over the next three months.

After a thorough investigation of the steps involved in manufacturing a golf bag, management determined that each golf bag produced will require the following operations:

1. Cutting and dyeing the material
2. Sewing
3. Finishing (inserting umbrella holder, club separators, etc.)
4. Inspection and packaging

The director of manufacturing analyzed each of the operations and concluded that if the company produces a medium-priced standard model, each bag will require $7/10$ hour in the cutting and dyeing department, $1/2$ hour in the sewing department, 1 hour in the finishing department, and $1/10$ hour in the inspection and packaging department. The more expensive deluxe model will require 1 hour for cutting and dyeing, $5/6$ hour for sewing, $2/3$ hour for finishing, and $1/4$ hour for inspection and packaging. This production information is summarized in Table 2.1.

Par's production is constrained by a limited number of hours available in each department. After studying departmental workload projections, the director of manufacturing estimates that 630 hours for cutting and dyeing, 600 hours for sewing, 708 hours for finishing, and 135 hours for inspection and packaging will be available for the production of golf bags during the next three months.

The accounting department analyzed the production data, assigned all relevant variable costs, and arrived at prices for both bags that will result in a profit contribution[1] of $10 for

[1]From an accounting perspective, profit contribution is more correctly described as the contribution margin per bag; for example, overhead and other shared costs have not been allocated.

TABLE 2.1   PRODUCTION REQUIREMENTS PER GOLF BAG

Department	Production Time (hours)	
	Standard Bag	Deluxe Bag
Cutting and Dyeing	$7/10$	1
Sewing	$1/2$	$5/6$
Finishing	1	$2/3$
Inspection and Packaging	$1/10$	$1/4$

It is important to understand that we are maximizing profit contribution, not profit. Overhead and other shared costs must be deducted before arriving at a profit figure.

every standard bag and $9 for every deluxe bag produced. Let us now develop a mathematical model of the Par, Inc., problem that can be used to determine the number of standard bags and the number of deluxe bags to produce in order to maximize total profit contribution.

Problem Formulation

Problem formulation, or **modeling,** is the process of translating the verbal statement of a problem into a mathematical statement. Formulating models is an art that can only be mastered with practice and experience. Even though every problem has some unique features, most problems also have common features. As a result, *some* general guidelines for model formulation can be helpful, especially for beginners. We will illustrate these general guidelines by developing a mathematical model for the Par, Inc., problem.

Understand the Problem Thoroughly   We selected the Par, Inc., problem to introduce linear programming because it is easy to understand. However, more complex problems will require much more thinking in order to identify the items that need to be included in the model. In such cases, read the problem description quickly to get a feel for what is involved. Taking notes will help you focus on the key issues and facts.

Describe the Objective   The objective is to maximize the total contribution to profit.

Describe Each Constraint   Four constraints relate to the number of hours of manufacturing time available; they restrict the number of standard bags and the number of deluxe bags that can be produced.

Constraint 1:   Number of hours of cutting and dyeing time used must be less than or equal to the number of hours of cutting and dyeing time available.

Constraint 2:   Number of hours of sewing time used must be less than or equal to the number of hours of sewing time available.

Constraint 3:   Number of hours of finishing time used must be less than or equal to the number of hours of finishing time available.

Constraint 4:   Number of hours of inspection and packaging time used must be less than or equal to the number of hours of inspection and packaging time available.

Define the Decision Variables   The controllable inputs for Par, Inc., are (1) the number of standard bags produced, and (2) the number of deluxe bags produced. Let

$$S = \text{number of standard bags}$$
$$D = \text{number of deluxe bags}$$

In linear programming terminology, S and D are referred to as the **decision variables.**

Write the Objective in Terms of the Decision Variables Par's profit contribution comes from two sources: (1) the profit contribution made by producing S standard bags, and (2) the profit contribution made by producing D deluxe bags. If Par makes $10 for every standard bag, the company will make $10S$ if S standard bags are produced. Also, if Par makes $9 for every deluxe bag, the company will make $9D$ if D deluxe bags are produced. Thus, we have

$$\text{Total Profit Contribution} = 10S + 9D$$

Because the objective—maximize total profit contribution—is a function of the decision variables S and D, we refer to $10S + 9D$ as the *objective function*. Using "Max" as an abbreviation for maximize, we write Par's objective as follows:

$$\text{Max } 10S + 9D$$

Write the Constraints in Terms of the Decision Variables

Constraint 1:

$$\begin{pmatrix} \text{Hours of cutting and} \\ \text{dyeing time used} \end{pmatrix} \leq \begin{pmatrix} \text{Hours of cutting and} \\ \text{dyeing time available} \end{pmatrix}$$

Every standard bag Par produces will use $7/10$ hour cutting and dyeing time; therefore, the total number of hours of cutting and dyeing time used in the manufacture of S standard bags is $7/10 S$. In addition, because every deluxe bag produced uses 1 hour of cutting and dyeing time, the production of D deluxe bags will use $1D$ hours of cutting and dyeing time. Thus, the total cutting and dyeing time required for the production of S standard bags and D deluxe bags is given by

$$\text{Total hours of cutting and dyeing time used} = 7/10 S + 1D$$

The units of measurement on the left-hand side of the constraint must match the units of measurement on the right-hand side.

The director of manufacturing stated that Par has at most 630 hours of cutting and dyeing time available. Therefore, the production combination we select must satisfy the requirement

$$7/10 S + 1D \leq 630 \tag{2.1}$$

Constraint 2:

$$\begin{pmatrix} \text{Hours of sewing} \\ \text{time used} \end{pmatrix} \leq \begin{pmatrix} \text{Hours of sewing} \\ \text{time available} \end{pmatrix}$$

From Table 2.1, we see that every standard bag manufactured will require $1/2$ hour for sewing, and every deluxe bag will require $5/6$ hour for sewing. Because 600 hours of sewing time are available, it follows that

$$1/2 S + 5/6 D \leq 600 \tag{2.2}$$

Constraint 3:

$$\left(\begin{array}{c}\text{Hours of finishing}\\\text{time used}\end{array}\right) \leq \left(\begin{array}{c}\text{Hours of finishing}\\\text{time available}\end{array}\right)$$

Every standard bag manufactured will require 1 hour for finishing, and every deluxe bag will require $\frac{2}{3}$ hour for finishing. With 708 hours of finishing time available, it follows that

$$1S + \tfrac{2}{3}D \leq 708 \tag{2.3}$$

Constraint 4:

$$\left(\begin{array}{c}\text{Hours of inspection and}\\\text{packaging time used}\end{array}\right) \leq \left(\begin{array}{c}\text{Hours of inspection and}\\\text{packaging time available}\end{array}\right)$$

Every standard bag manufactured will require $\frac{1}{10}$ hour for inspection and packaging, and every deluxe bag will require $\frac{1}{4}$ hour for inspection and packaging. Because 135 hours of inspection and packaging time are available, it follows that

$$\tfrac{1}{10}S + \tfrac{1}{4}D \leq 135 \tag{2.4}$$

We have now specified the mathematical relationships for the constraints associated with the four departments. Have we forgotten any other constraints? Can Par produce a negative number of standard or deluxe bags? Clearly, the answer is no. Thus, to prevent the decision variables S and D from having negative values, two constraints,

$$S \geq 0 \quad \text{and} \quad D \geq 0 \tag{2.5}$$

must be added. These constraints ensure that the solution to the problem will contain nonnegative values for the decision variables and are thus referred to as the **nonnegativity constraints.** Nonnegativity constraints are a general feature of all linear programming problems and may be written in the abbreviated form:

$$S, D \geq 0$$

Try Problem 24(a) to test your ability to formulate a mathematical model for a maximization linear programming problem with less-than-or-equal-to constraints.

Mathematical Statement of the Par, Inc., Problem

The mathematical statement or mathematical formulation of the Par, Inc., problem is now complete. We succeeded in translating the objective and constraints of the problem into a set of mathematical relationships referred to as a **mathematical model.** The complete mathematical model for the Par problem is as follows:

$$
\begin{aligned}
\text{Max} \quad & 10S + 9D \\
\text{subject to (s.t.)} \quad & \\
& \tfrac{7}{10}S + 1D \le 630 \quad \text{Cutting and dyeing} \\
& \tfrac{1}{2}S + \tfrac{5}{6}D \le 600 \quad \text{Sewing} \\
& 1S + \tfrac{2}{3}D \le 708 \quad \text{Finishing} \\
& \tfrac{1}{10}S + \tfrac{1}{4}D \le 135 \quad \text{Inspection and packaging} \\
& S, D \ge 0
\end{aligned}
\tag{2.6}
$$

Our job now is to find the product mix (i.e., the combination of S and D) that satisfies all the constraints and, at the same time, yields a value for the objective function that is greater than or equal to the value given by any other feasible solution. Once these values are calculated, we will have found the optimal solution to the problem.

This mathematical model of the Par problem is **a linear programming model,** or **linear program.** The problem has the objective and constraints that, as we said earlier, are common properties of all *linear* programs. But what is the special feature of this mathematical model that makes it a linear program? The special feature that makes it a linear program is that the objective function and all constraint functions are linear functions of the decision variables.

Mathematical functions in which each variable appears in a separate term and is raised to the first power are called **linear functions.** The objective function ($10S + 9D$) is linear because each decision variable appears in a separate term and has an exponent of 1. The amount of production time required in the cutting and dyeing department ($\tfrac{7}{10}S + 1D$) is also a linear function of the decision variables for the same reason. Similarly, the functions on the left-hand side of all the constraint inequalities (the constraint functions) are linear functions. Thus, the mathematical formulation of this problem is referred to as a linear program.

Try Problem 1 to test your ability to recognize the types of mathematical relationships that can be found in a linear program.

Linear *programming* has nothing to do with computer programming. The use of the word *programming* here means "choosing a course of action." Linear programming involves choosing a course of action when the mathematical model of the problem contains only linear functions.

NOTES AND COMMENTS

1. The three assumptions necessary for a linear programming model to be appropriate are proportionality, additivity, and divisibility. *Proportionality* means that the contribution to the objective function and the amount of resources used in each constraint are proportional to the value of each decision variable. *Additivity* means that the value of the objective function and the total resources used can be found by summing the objective function contribution and the resources used for all decision variables. *Divisibility* means that the decision variables are continuous. The divisibility assumption plus the nonnegativity constraints mean that decision variables can take on any value greater than or equal to zero.

2. Management scientists formulate and solve a variety of mathematical models that contain an objective function and a set of constraints. Models of this type are referred to as *mathematical programming models.* Linear programming models are a special type of mathematical programming model in that the objective function and all constraint functions are linear.

2.2 GRAPHICAL SOLUTION PROCEDURE

A linear programming problem involving only two decision variables can be solved using a graphical solution procedure. Let us begin the graphical solution procedure by developing a graph that displays the possible solutions (S and D values) for the Par problem. The graph (Figure 2.1) will have values of S on the horizontal axis and values of D on the vertical axis. Any point on the graph can be identified by the S and D values, which indicate the position of the point along the horizontal and vertical axes, respectively. Because every point (S, D) corresponds to a possible solution, every point on the graph is called a *solution point*. The solution point where $S = 0$ and $D = 0$ is referred to as the origin. Because S and D must be nonnegative, the graph in Figure 2.1 only displays solutions where $S \geq 0$ and $D \geq 0$.

Earlier, we saw that the inequality representing the cutting and dyeing constraint is

$$\tfrac{7}{10}S + 1D \leq 630$$

To show all solution points that satisfy this relationship, we start by graphing the solution points satisfying the constraint as an equality. That is, the points where $\tfrac{7}{10}S + 1D = 630$. Because the graph of this equation is a line, it can be obtained by identifying two points that satisfy the equation and then drawing a line through the points. Setting $S = 0$ and solving for D, we see that the point ($S = 0$, $D = 630$) satisfies the equation. To find a second point satisfying this equation, we set $D = 0$ and solve for S. By doing so, we obtain

FIGURE 2.1   SOLUTION POINTS FOR THE TWO-VARIABLE PAR, INC., PROBLEM

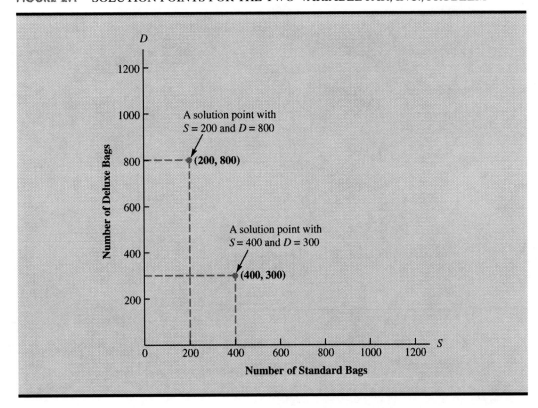

$\frac{7}{10}S + 1(0) = 630$, or $S = 900$. Thus, a second point satisfying the equation is ($S = 900$, $D = 0$). Given these two points, we can now graph the line corresponding to the equation

$$\frac{7}{10}S + 1D = 630$$

This line, which will be called the cutting and dyeing *constraint line,* is shown in Figure 2.2. We label this line "C & D" to indicate that it represents the cutting and dyeing constraint line.

Recall that the inequality representing the cutting and dyeing constraint is

$$\frac{7}{10}S + 1D \leq 630$$

Can you identify all of the solution points that satisfy this constraint? Because all points on the line satisfy $\frac{7}{10}S + 1D = 630$, we know any point on this line must satisfy the constraint. But where are the solution points satisfying $\frac{7}{10}S + 1D < 630$? Consider two solution points: ($S = 200$, $D = 200$) and ($S = 600$, $D = 500$). You can see from Figure 2.2 that the first solution point is below the constraint line and the second is above the constraint line. Which of these solutions will satisfy the cutting and dyeing constraint? For the point ($S = 200$, $D = 200$), we see that

$$\frac{7}{10}S + 1D = \frac{7}{10}(200) + 1(200) = 340$$

FIGURE 2.2   THE CUTTING AND DYEING CONSTRAINT LINE

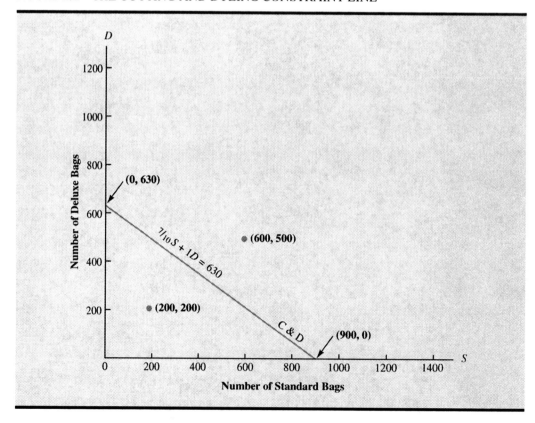

Because the 340 hours is less than the 630 hours available, the ($S = 200, D = 200$) production combination, or solution point, satisfies the constraint. For the point ($S = 600, D = 500$), we have

$$\tfrac{7}{10}S + 1D = \tfrac{7}{10}(600) + 1(500) = 920$$

The 920 hours is greater than the 630 hours available, so the ($S = 600, D = 500$) solution point does not satisfy the constraint and is thus not feasible.

Can you graph a constraint line and find the solution points that are feasible? Try Problem 2.

If a solution point is not feasible for a particular constraint, then all other solution points on the same side of that constraint line are not feasible. If a solution point is feasible for a particular constraint, then all other solution points on the same side of the constraint line are feasible for that constraint. Thus, one has to evaluate the constraint function for only one solution point to determine which side of a constraint line is feasible. In Figure 2.3 we indicate all points satisfying the cutting and dyeing constraint by the shaded region.

We continue by identifying the solution points satisfying each of the other three constraints. The solutions that are feasible for each of these constraints are shown in Figure 2.4.

Four separate graphs now show the feasible solution points for each of the four constraints. In a linear programming problem, we need to identify the solution points that satisfy *all* the constraints *simultaneously*. To find these solution points, we can draw all four constraints on one graph and observe the region containing the points that do in fact satisfy all the constraints simultaneously.

FIGURE 2.3 FEASIBLE SOLUTIONS FOR THE CUTTING AND DYEING CONSTRAINT, REPRESENTED BY THE SHADED REGION

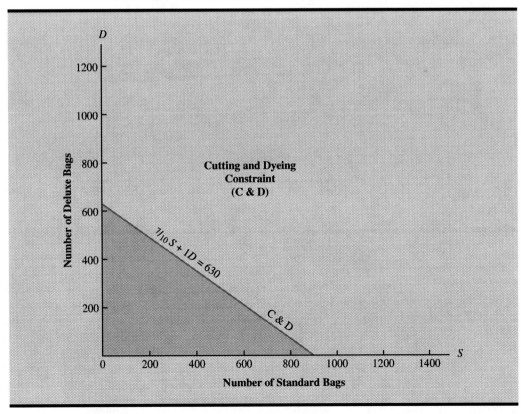

FIGURE 2.4   FEASIBLE SOLUTIONS FOR THE SEWING, FINISHING, AND INSPECTION AND PACKAGING CONSTRAINTS, REPRESENTED BY THE SHADED REGIONS

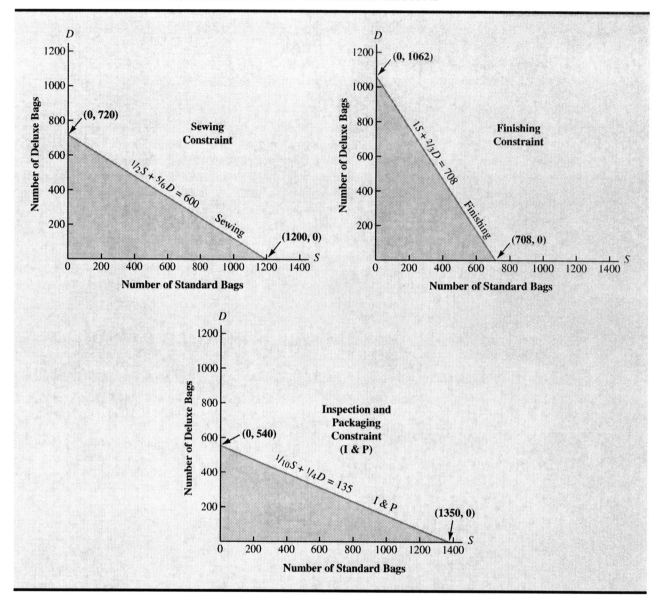

Try Problem 7 to test your ability to find the feasible region given several constraints.

The graphs in Figures 2.3 and 2.4 can be superimposed to obtain one graph with all four constraints. This combined-constraint graph is shown in Figure 2.5. The shaded region in this figure includes every solution point that satisfies all the constraints simultaneously. Solutions that satisfy all the constraints are termed **feasible solutions,** and the shaded region is called the feasible solution region, or simply the **feasible region.** Any solution point on the boundary of the feasible region or within the feasible region is a *feasible solution point.*

Now that we have identified the feasible region, we are ready to proceed with the graphical solution procedure and find the optimal solution to the Par, Inc., problem. Recall that the optimal solution for a linear programming problem is the feasible solution that provides

FIGURE 2.5 COMBINED-CONSTRAINT GRAPH SHOWING THE FEASIBLE REGION FOR THE PAR, INC., PROBLEM

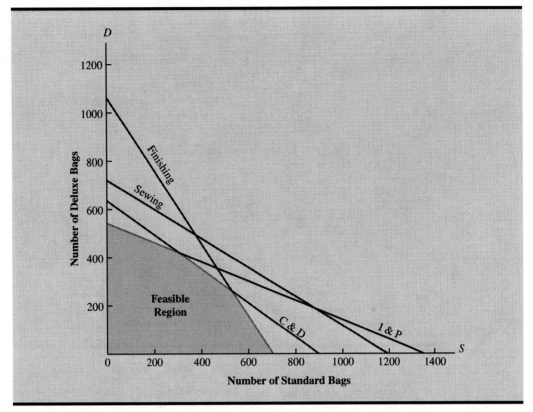

the best possible value of the objective function. Let us start the optimizing step of the graphical solution procedure by redrawing the feasible region on a separate graph. The graph is shown in Figure 2.6.

One approach to finding the optimal solution would be to evaluate the objective function for each feasible solution; the optimal solution would then be the one yielding the largest value. The difficulty with this approach is the infinite number of feasible solutions; thus, because one cannot possibly evaluate an infinite number of feasible solutions, this trial-and-error procedure cannot be used to identify the optimal solution.

Rather than trying to compute the profit contribution for each feasible solution, we select an arbitrary value for profit contribution and identify all the feasible solutions (S, D) that yield the selected value. For example, which feasible solutions provide a profit contribution of $1800? These solutions are given by the values of S and D in the feasible region that will make the objective function

$$10S + 9D = 1800$$

This expression is simply the equation of a line. Thus, all feasible solution points (S, D) yielding a profit contribution of $1800 must be on the line. We learned earlier in this section how to graph a constraint line. The procedure for graphing the profit or objective function line is the same. Letting $S = 0$, we see that D must be 200; thus, the solution

FIGURE 2.6   FEASIBLE REGION FOR THE PAR, INC., PROBLEM

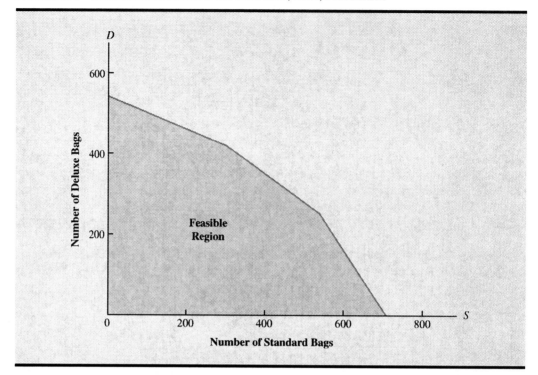

point ($S = 0$, $D = 200$) is on the line. Similarly, by letting $D = 0$, we see that the solution point ($S = 180$, $D = 0$) is also on the line. Drawing the line through these two points identifies all the solutions that have a profit contribution of $1800. A graph of this profit line is presented in Figure 2.7.

Because the objective is to find the feasible solution yielding the largest profit contribution, let us proceed by selecting higher profit contributions and finding the solutions yielding the selected values. For instance, let us find all solutions yielding profit contributions of $3600 and $5400. To do so, we must find the S and D values that are on the following lines:

$$10S + 9D = 3600$$

and

$$10S + 9D = 5400$$

Using the previous procedure for graphing profit and constraint lines, we draw the $3600 and $5400 profit lines as shown on the graph in Figure 2.8. Although not all solution points on the $5400 profit line are in the feasible region, at least some points on the line are, and it is therefore possible to obtain a feasible solution that provides a $5400 profit contribution.

Can we find a feasible solution yielding an even higher profit contribution? Look at Figure 2.8, and see what general observations you can make about the profit lines already drawn. Note the following: (1) the profit lines are *parallel* to each other, and (2) higher

FIGURE 2.7 $1800 PROFIT LINE FOR THE PAR, INC., PROBLEM

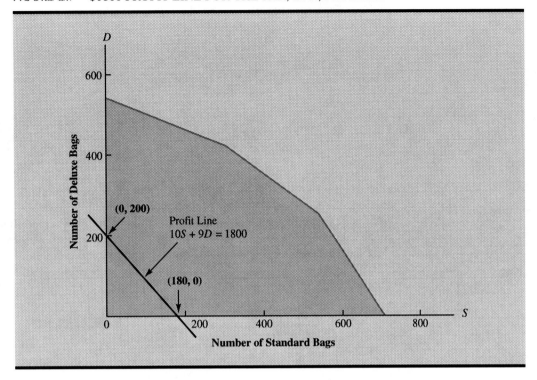

FIGURE 2.8 SELECTED PROFIT LINES FOR THE PAR, INC., PROBLEM

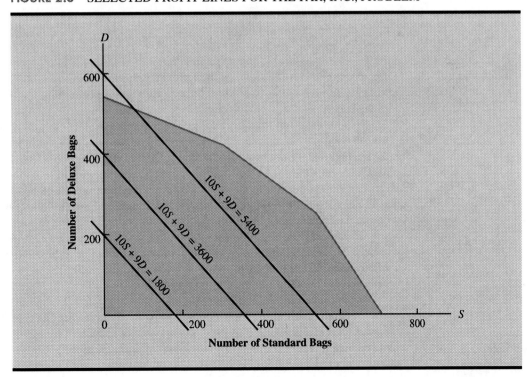

profit lines are obtained as we move farther from the origin. These observations can also be expressed algebraically. Let P represent total profit contribution. The objective function is

$$P = 10S + 9D$$

Solving for D in terms of S and P, we obtain

$$9D = -10S + P$$
$$D = -\tfrac{10}{9}S + \tfrac{1}{9}P \qquad (2.7)$$

Equation (2.7) is the *slope-intercept form* of the linear equation relating S and D. The coefficient of S, $-\tfrac{10}{9}$, is the slope of the line, and the term $\tfrac{1}{9}P$ is the D intercept (i.e., the value of D where the graph of equation (2.7) crosses the D axis). Substituting the profit contributions of $P = 1800$, $P = 3600$, and $P = 5400$ into equation (2.7) yields the following slope-intercept equations for the profit lines shown in Figure 2.8:

For $P = 1800$,

$$D = -\tfrac{10}{9}S + 200$$

For $P = 3600$,

$$D = -\tfrac{10}{9}S + 400$$

For $P = 5400$,

$$D = -\tfrac{10}{9}S + 600$$

Can you graph the profit line for a linear program? Try Problem 6.

The slope $(-\tfrac{10}{9})$ is the same for each profit line because the profit lines are parallel. Further, we see that the D intercept increases with larger profit contributions. Thus, higher profit lines are farther from the origin.

Because the profit lines are parallel and higher profit lines are farther from the origin, we can obtain solutions that yield increasingly larger values for the objective function by continuing to move the profit line farther from the origin in such a fashion that it remains parallel to the other profit lines. However, at some point we will find that any further outward movement will place the profit line completely outside the feasible region. Because solutions outside the feasible region are unacceptable, the point in the feasible region that lies on the highest profit line is the optimal solution to the linear program.

You should now be able to identify the optimal solution point for this problem. Use a ruler or the edge of a piece of paper, and move the profit line as far from the origin as you can. What is the last point in the feasible region that you reach? This point, which is the optimal solution, is shown graphically in Figure 2.9.

The optimal values of the decision variables are the S and D values at the optimal solution. Depending on the accuracy of the graph, you may or may not be able to determine the *exact* S and D values. Based on the graph in Figure 2.9, the best we can do is conclude that the optimal production combination consists of approximately 550 standard bags (S) and approximately 250 deluxe bags (D).

FIGURE 2.9 OPTIMAL SOLUTION FOR THE PAR, INC., PROBLEM

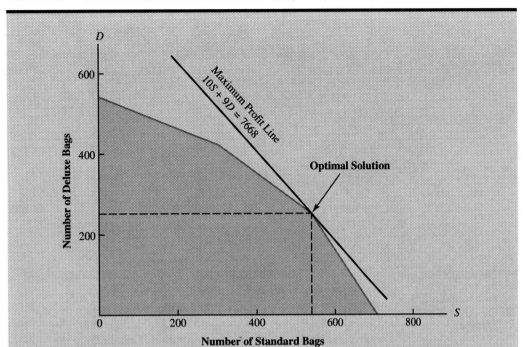

A closer inspection of Figures 2.5 and 2.9 shows that the optimal solution point is at the intersection of the cutting and dyeing and the finishing constraint lines. That is, the optimal solution point is on both the cutting and dyeing constraint line

$$\frac{7}{10}S + 1D = 630 \tag{2.8}$$

and the finishing constraint line

$$1S + \frac{2}{3}D = 708 \tag{2.9}$$

Thus, the optimal values of the decision variables S and D must satisfy both equations (2.8) and (2.9) simultaneously. Using equation (2.8) and solving for S gives

$$\frac{7}{10}S = 630 - 1D$$

or

$$S = 900 - \frac{10}{7}D \tag{2.10}$$

Substituting this expression for S into equation (2.9) and solving for D provides the following:

$$1(900 - {}^{10}\!/_{7}D) + {}^{2}\!/_{3}D = 708$$
$$900 - {}^{10}\!/_{7}D + {}^{2}\!/_{3}D = 708$$
$$900 - {}^{30}\!/_{21}D + {}^{14}\!/_{21}D = 708$$
$$-{}^{16}\!/_{21}D = -192$$
$$D = \frac{192}{{}^{16}\!/_{21}} = 252$$

Using $D = 252$ in equation (2.10) and solving for S, we obtain

$$S = 900 - {}^{10}\!/_{7}(252)$$
$$= 900 - 360 = 540$$

Although the optimal solution to the Par, Inc., problem consists of integer values for the decision variables, this result will not always be the case.

The exact location of the optimal solution point is $S = 540$ and $D = 252$. Hence, the optimal production quantities for Par, Inc., are 540 standard bags and 252 deluxe bags, with a resulting profit contribution of $10(540) + 9(252) = \$7668$.

For a linear programming problem with two decision variables, the exact values of the decision variables can be determined by first using the graphical solution procedure to identify the optimal solution point and then solving the two simultaneous constraint equations associated with it.

A Note on Graphing Lines

Try Problem 10 to test your ability to use the graphical solution procedure to identify the optimal solution and find the exact values of the decision variables at the optimal solution.

An important aspect of the graphical method is the ability to graph lines showing the constraints and the objective function of the linear program. The procedure we used for graphing the equation of a line is to find any two points satisfying the equation and then draw the line through the two points. For the Par, Inc., constraints, the two points were easily found by first setting $S = 0$ and solving the constraint equation for D. Then we set $D = 0$ and solved for S. For the cutting and dyeing constraint line

$$ {}^{7}\!/_{10}S + 1D = 630 $$

this procedure identified the two points $(S = 0, D = 630)$ and $(S = 900, D = 0)$. The cutting and dyeing constraint line was then graphed by drawing a line through these two points.

All constraints and objective function lines in two-variable linear programs can be graphed if two points on the line can be identified. However, finding the two points on the line is not always as easy as shown in the Par, Inc., problem. For example, suppose a company manufactures two models of a small handheld computer: the Assistant (A) and the Professional (P). Management needs 50 units of the Professional model for its own sales-force, and expects sales of the Professional to be at most one-half of the sales of the Assistant. A constraint enforcing this requirement is

$$P - 50 \leq \tfrac{1}{2}A$$

or

$$2P - 100 \leq A$$

or

$$2P - A \leq 100$$

Using the equality form and setting $P = 0$, we find the point ($P = 0, A = -100$) is on the constraint line. Setting $A = 0$, we find a second point ($P = 50, A = 0$) on the constraint line. If we have drawn only the nonnegative ($P \geq 0, A \geq 0$) portion of the graph, the first point ($P = 0, A = -100$) cannot be plotted because $A = -100$ is not on the graph. Whenever we have two points on the line but one or both of the points cannot be plotted in the nonnegative portion of the graph, the simplest approach is to enlarge the graph. In this example, the point ($P = 0, A = -100$) can be plotted by extending the graph to include the negative A axis. Once both points satisfying the constraint equation have been located, the line can be drawn. The constraint line and the feasible solutions for the constraint $2P - A \leq 100$ are shown in Figure 2.10.

As another example, consider a problem involving two decision variables, R and T. Suppose that the number of units of R produced had to be at least equal to the number of units of T produced. A constraint enforcing this requirement is

$$R \geq T$$

or

$$R - T \geq 0$$

FIGURE 2.10   FEASIBLE SOLUTIONS FOR THE CONSTRAINT $2P - A \leq 100$

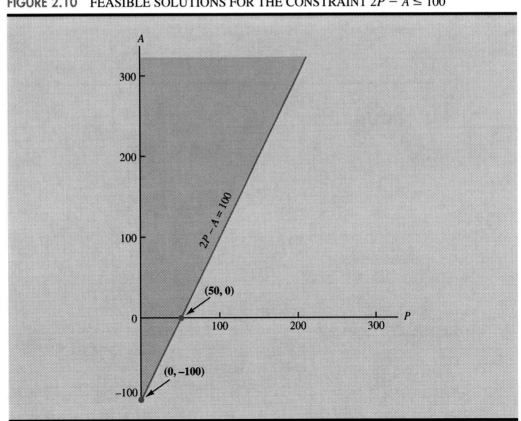

Can you graph a constraint line when the origin is on the constraint line? Try Problem 5.

To find all solutions satisfying the constraint as an equality, we first set $R = 0$ and solve for T. This result shows that the origin ($T = 0$, $R = 0$) is on the constraint line. Setting $T = 0$ and solving for R provides the same point. However, we can obtain a second point on the line by setting T equal to any value other than zero and then solving for R. For instance, setting $T = 100$ and solving for R, we find that the point ($T = 100$, $R = 100$) is on the line. With the two points ($R = 0$, $T = 0$) and ($R = 100$, $T = 100$), the constraint line $R - T = 0$ and the feasible solutions for $R - T \geq 0$ can be plotted as shown in Figure 2.11.

Summary of the Graphical Solution Procedure for Maximization Problems

For additional practice in using the graphical solution procedure, try Problem 24(b), 24(c), and 24(d).

As we have seen, the graphical solution procedure is a method for solving two-variable linear programming problems such as the Par, Inc., problem. The steps of the graphical solution procedure for a maximization problem are summarized here:

1. Prepare a graph of the feasible solutions for each of the constraints.
2. Determine the feasible region by identifying the solutions that satisfy all the constraints simultaneously.
3. Draw an objective function line showing the values of the decision variables that yield a specified value of the objective function.
4. Move parallel objective function lines toward larger objective function values until further movement would take the line completely outside the feasible region.
5. Any feasible solution on the objective function line with the largest value is an optimal solution.

FIGURE 2.11   FEASIBLE SOLUTIONS FOR THE CONSTRAINT $R - T \geq 0$

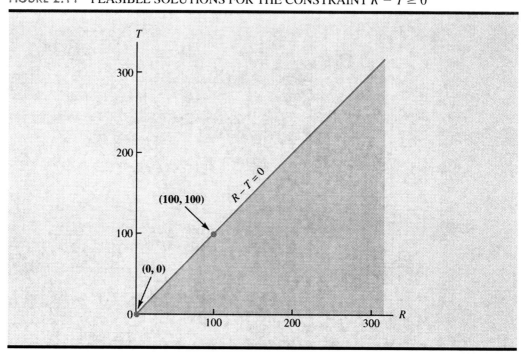

Slack Variables

In addition to the optimal solution and its associated profit contribution, Par's management will probably want information about the production time requirements for each production operation. We can determine this information by substituting the optimal solution values ($S = 540$, $D = 252$) into the constraints of the linear program.

Constraint	Hours Required for $S = 540$ and $D = 252$	Hours Available	Unused Hours
Cutting and dyeing	$\frac{7}{10}(540) + 1(252) = 630$	630	0
Sewing	$\frac{1}{2}(540) + \frac{5}{6}(252) = 480$	600	120
Finishing	$1(540) + \frac{2}{3}(252) = 708$	708	0
Inspection and packaging	$\frac{1}{10}(540) + \frac{1}{4}(252) = 117$	135	18

Thus, the complete solution tells management that the production of 540 standard bags and 252 deluxe bags will require all available cutting and dyeing time (630 hours) and all available finishing time (708 hours), while $600 - 480 = 120$ hours of sewing time and $135 - 117 = 18$ hours of inspection and packaging time will remain unused. The 120 hours of unused sewing time and 18 hours of unused inspection and packaging time are referred to as *slack* for the two departments. In linear programming terminology, any unused capacity for a ≤ constraint is referred to as the *slack* associated with the constraint.

Can you identify the slack associated with a constraint? Try Problem 24(e).

Often variables, called **slack variables,** are added to the formulation of a linear programming problem to represent the slack, or idle capacity. Unused capacity makes no contribution to profit; thus, slack variables have coefficients of zero in the objective function. After the addition of four slack variables, denoted S_1, S_2, S_3, and S_4, the mathematical model of the Par, Inc., problem becomes

$$\text{Max} \quad 10S + 9D + 0S_1 + 0S_2 + 0S_3 + 0S_4$$

s.t.

$$\frac{7}{10}S + 1D + 1S_1 \qquad\qquad\qquad = 630$$
$$\frac{1}{2}S + \frac{5}{6}D \qquad + 1S_2 \qquad\qquad = 600$$
$$1S + \frac{2}{3}D \qquad\qquad + 1S_3 \qquad = 708$$
$$\frac{1}{10}S + \frac{1}{4}D \qquad\qquad\qquad + 1S_4 = 135$$
$$S, D, S_1, S_2, S_3, S_4 \geq 0$$

Can you write a linear program in standard form? Try Problem 18.

Whenever a linear program is written in a form with all constraints expressed as equalities, it is said to be written in **standard form.**

Referring to the standard form of the Par, Inc., problem, we see that at the optimal solution ($S = 540$ and $D = 252$), the values for the slack variables are

Constraint	Value of Slack Variable
Cutting and dyeing	$S_1 = 0$
Sewing	$S_2 = 120$
Finishing	$S_3 = 0$
Inspection and packaging	$S_4 = 18$

Could we have used the graphical solution to provide some of this information? The answer is yes. By finding the optimal solution point on Figure 2.5, we can see that the cutting and dyeing and the finishing constraints restrict, or *bind,* the feasible region at this point. Thus, this solution requires the use of all available time for these two operations. In other words, the graph shows us that the cutting and dyeing and the finishing departments will have zero slack. On the other hand, the sewing and the inspection and packaging constraints are not binding the feasible region at the optimal solution, which means we can expect some unused time or slack for these two operations.

As a final comment on the graphical analysis of this problem, we call your attention to the sewing capacity constraint as shown in Figure 2.5. Note, in particular, that this constraint did not affect the feasible region. That is, the feasible region would be the same whether the sewing capacity constraint were included or not, which tells us that enough sewing time is available to accommodate any production level that can be achieved by the other three departments. The sewing constraint does not affect the feasible region and thus cannot affect the optimal solution; it is called a **redundant constraint.**

NOTES AND COMMENTS

1. In the standard-form representation of a linear programming model, the objective function coefficients for slack variables are zero. This zero coefficient implies that slack variables, which represent unused resources, do not affect the value of the objective function. However, in some applications, unused resources can be sold and contribute to profit. In such cases, the corresponding slack variables become decision variables representing the amount of unused resources to be sold. For each of these variables, a nonzero coefficient in the objective function would reflect the profit associated with selling a unit of the corresponding resource.

2. Redundant constraints do not affect the feasible region; as a result, they can be removed from a linear programming model without affecting the optimal solution. However, if the linear programming model is to be re-solved later, changes in some of the data might make a previously redundant constraint a binding constraint. Thus, we recommend keeping all constraints in the linear programming model even though at some point in time one or more of the constraints may be redundant.

2.3   EXTREME POINTS AND THE OPTIMAL SOLUTION

Suppose that the profit contribution for Par's standard golf bag is reduced from \$10 to \$5 per bag, while the profit contribution for the deluxe golf bag and all the constraints remain unchanged. The complete linear programming model of this new problem is identical to the mathematical model in Section 2.1, except for the revised objective function:

$$\text{Max } 5S + 9D$$

How does this change in the objective function affect the optimal solution to the Par, Inc., problem? Figure 2.12 shows the graphical solution of this new problem with the revised objective function. Note that without any change in the constraints, the feasible region does not change. However, the profit lines have been altered to reflect the new objective function.

By moving the profit line in a parallel manner toward higher profit values, we find the optimal solution as shown in Figure 2.12. The values of the decision variables at this point

FIGURE 2.12   OPTIMAL SOLUTION FOR THE PAR, INC., PROBLEM WITH AN OBJECTIVE FUNCTION OF $5S + 9D$

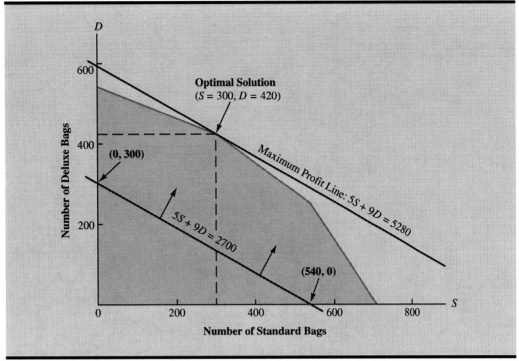

are $S = 300$ and $D = 420$. The reduced profit contribution for the standard bag caused a change in the optimal solution. In fact, as you may have suspected, we are cutting back the production of the lower-profit standard bags and increasing the production of the higher-profit deluxe bags.

What observations can you make about the location of the optimal solutions in the two linear programming problems solved thus far? Look closely at the graphical solutions in Figures 2.9 and 2.12. Notice that the optimal solutions occur at one of the vertices, or "corners," of the feasible region. In linear programming terminology, these vertices are referred to as the **extreme points** of the feasible region. The Par, Inc., feasible region has five vertices, or five extreme points (see Figure 2.13). We can now formally state our observation about the location of optimal solutions as follows:

For additional practice in identifying the extreme points of the feasible region and determining the optimal solution by computing and comparing the objective function value at each extreme point, try Problem 13.

> The optimal solution to a linear program can be found at an extreme point of the feasible region.[2]

This property means that if you are looking for the optimal solution to a linear program, you do not have to evaluate all feasible solution points. In fact, you have to consider

---

[2]We will discuss in Section 2.6 the two special cases (infeasibility and unboundedness) in linear programming that have no optimal solution, and for which this statement does not apply.

FIGURE 2.13   THE FIVE EXTREME POINTS OF THE FEASIBLE REGION
FOR THE PAR, INC., PROBLEM

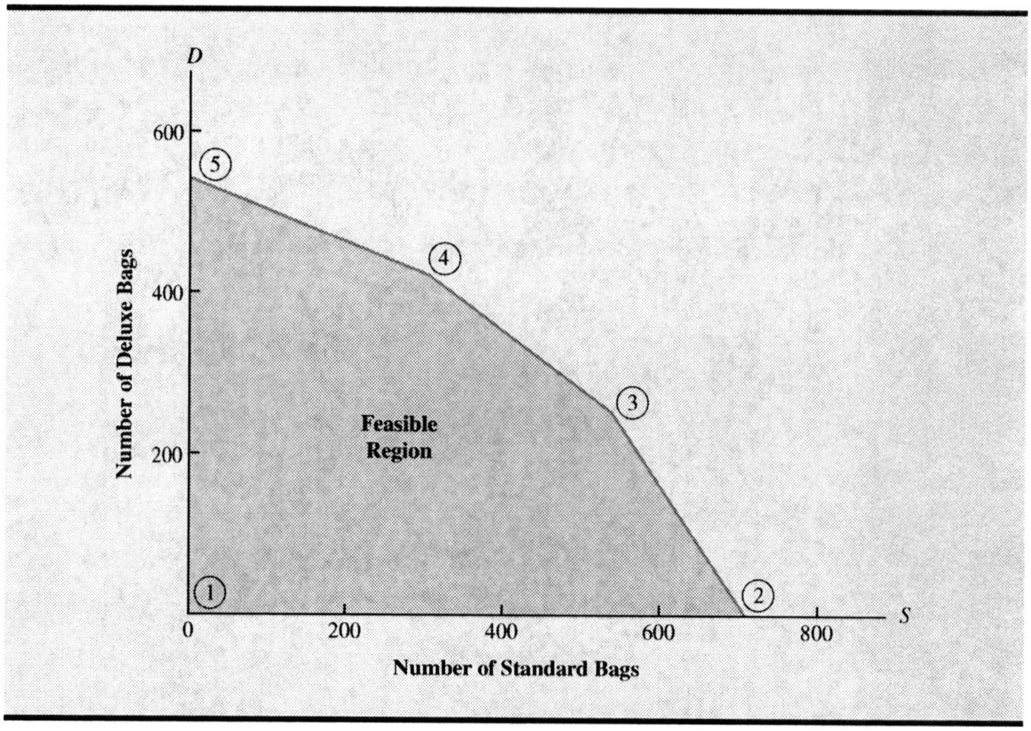

only the feasible solutions that occur at the extreme points of the feasible region. Thus, for the Par, Inc., problem, instead of computing and comparing the profit contributions for all feasible solutions, we can find the optimal solution by evaluating the five extreme-point solutions and selecting the one that provides the largest profit contribution. Actually, the graphical solution procedure is nothing more than a convenient way of identifying an optimal extreme point for two-variable problems.

2.4   COMPUTER SOLUTION OF THE PAR, INC., PROBLEM

In January 1952 the first successful computer solution of a linear programming problem was performed on the SEAC (Standards Eastern Automatic Computer). The SEAC, the first digital computer built by the National Bureau of Standards under U.S. Air Force sponsorship, had a 512-word memory and magnetic tape for external storage.

Computer programs designed to solve linear programming problems are now widely available. After a short period of familiarization with the specific features of the package, users are able to solve linear programming problems with few difficulties. Problems involving thousands of variables and thousands of constraints are now routinely solved with computer packages. Some of the leading commercial packages include CPLEX, Gurobi, LINGO, MOSEK, Risk Solver for Excel, and Xpress-MP. Packages are also available for free download. A good example is Clp (COIN-OR linear programming).

The solution to Par, Inc. is shown in Figure 2.14. The authors have chosen to make this book flexible and not rely on a specific linear programming package. Hence, the output in Figure 2.14 is generic and is not an actual printout from a particular software package. The output provided in Figure 2.14 is typical of most linear programming packages. We use this output format throughout the text. At the website for this course two linear programming packages are provided. A description of the packages is provided in the appendices. In Appendix 2.1 we show how to solve the Par, Inc., problem using LINGO. In Appendix 2.2 we

FIGURE 2.14   THE SOLUTION FOR THE PAR, INC., PROBLEM

WEB file

Par

```
Optimal Objective Value =                    7668.00000

        Variable                Value             Reduced Cost
     --------------        --------------      ------------------
           S                 540.00000                 0.00000
           D                 252.00000                 0.00000

       Constraint           Slack/Surplus           Dual Value
     --------------        --------------      ------------------
           1                   0.00000                 4.37500
           2                 120.00000                 0.00000
           3                   0.00000                 6.93750
           4                  18.00000                 0.00000

                         Objective         Allowable          Allowable
        Variable        Coefficient         Increase           Decrease
     ----------       -------------      ----------         ----------
           S             10.00000          3.50000            3.70000
           D              9.00000          5.28571            2.33333

                             RHS           Allowable          Allowable
        Constraint          Value           Increase           Decrease
     ----------       -------------      ----------         ----------
           1             630.00000         52.36364          134.40000
           2             600.00000          Infinite         120.00000
           3             708.00000        192.00000          128.00000
           4             135.00000          Infinite          18.00000
```

show how to formulate a spreadsheet model for the Par, Inc., problem and use Excel Solver to solve the problem.

Interpretation of Computer Output

Let us look more closely at the output in Figure 2.14 and interpret the computer solution provided for the Par, Inc., problem. The optimal solution to this problem will provide a profit of $7668. Directly below the objective function value, we find the values of the decision variables at the optimal solution. We have $S = 540$ standard bags and $D = 252$ deluxe bags as the optimal production quantities.

Recall that the Par, Inc., problem had four less-than-or-equal-to constraints corresponding to the hours available in each of four production departments. The information shown in the Slack/Surplus column provides the value of the slack variable for each of the departments. This information is summarized here:

Constraint Number	Constraint Name	Slack
1	Cutting and dyeing	0
2	Sewing	120
3	Finishing	0
4	Inspection and packaging	18

From this information, we see that the binding constraints (the cutting and dyeing and the finishing constraints) have zero slack at the optimal solution. The sewing department has 120 hours of slack or unused capacity, and the inspection and packaging department has 18 hours of slack or unused capacity.

The rest of the output in Figure 2.14 can be used to determine how changes in the input data impact the optimal solution. We shall defer discussion of reduced costs, dual values, allowable increases and decreases of objective function coefficients and right-hand-side values until Chapter 3, when we study the topic of sensitivity analysis.

NOTES AND COMMENTS

Linear programming solvers are now a standard feature of most spreadsheet packages. In Appendix 2.2 we show how spreadsheets can be used to solve linear programs by using Excel to solve the Par, Inc., problem.

2.5   A SIMPLE MINIMIZATION PROBLEM

M&D Chemicals produces two products that are sold as raw materials to companies manufacturing bath soaps and laundry detergents. Based on an analysis of current inventory levels and potential demand for the coming month, M&D's management specified that the combined production for products A and B must total at least 350 gallons. Separately, a major customer's order for 125 gallons of product A must also be satisfied. Product A requires 2 hours of processing time per gallon and product B requires 1 hour of processing time per gallon. For the coming month, 600 hours of processing time are available. M&D's objective is to satisfy these requirements at a minimum total production cost. Production costs are $2 per gallon for product A and $3 per gallon for product B.

To find the minimum-cost production schedule, we will formulate the M&D Chemicals problem as a linear program. Following a procedure similar to the one used for the Par, Inc., problem, we first define the decision variables and the objective function for the problem. Let

$$A = \text{number of gallons of product A}$$
$$B = \text{number of gallons of product B}$$

With production costs at $2 per gallon for product A and $3 per gallon for product B, the objective function that corresponds to the minimization of the total production cost can be written as

$$\text{Min } 2A + 3B$$

Next, consider the constraints placed on the M&D Chemicals problem. To satisfy the major customer's demand for 125 gallons of product A, we know A must be at least 125. Thus, we write the constraint

$$1A \geq 125$$

For the combined production for both products, which must total at least 350 gallons, we can write the constraint

$$1A + 1B \geq 350$$

Finally, for the limitation of 600 hours on available processing time, we add the constraint

$$2A + 1B \leq 600$$

After adding the nonnegativity constraints ($A, B \geq 0$), we arrive at the following linear program for the M&D Chemicals problem:

Min $2A + 3B$
s.t.

$1A$	≥ 125	Demand for product A
$1A + 1B$	≥ 350	Total production
$2A + 1B$	≤ 600	Processing time
$A, B \geq 0$		

Because the linear programming model has only two decision variables, the graphical solution procedure can be used to find the optimal production quantities. The graphical solution procedure for this problem, just as in the Par problem, requires us to first graph the constraint lines to find the feasible region. By graphing each constraint line separately and then checking points on either side of the constraint line, the feasible solutions for each constraint can be identified. By combining the feasible solutions for each constraint on the same graph, we obtain the feasible region shown in Figure 2.15.

FIGURE 2.15   THE FEASIBLE REGION FOR THE M&D CHEMICALS PROBLEM

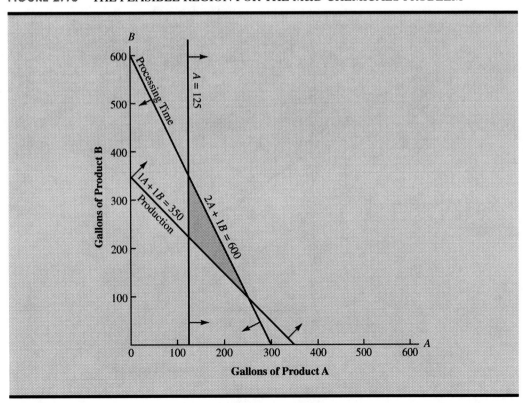

To find the minimum-cost solution, we now draw the objective function line corresponding to a particular total cost value. For example, we might start by drawing the line $2A + 3B = 1200$. This line is shown in Figure 2.16. Clearly, some points in the feasible region would provide a total cost of $1200. To find the values of A and B that provide smaller total cost values, we move the objective function line in a lower left direction until, if we moved it any farther, it would be entirely outside the feasible region. Note that the objective function line $2A + 3B = 800$ intersects the feasible region at the extreme point $A = 250$ and $B = 100$. This extreme point provides the minimum-cost solution with an objective function value of 800. From Figures 2.15 and 2.16, we can see that the total production constraint and the processing time constraint are binding. Just as in every linear programming problem, the optimal solution occurs at an extreme point of the feasible region.

Summary of the Graphical Solution Procedure for Minimization Problems

Can you use the graphical solution procedure to determine the optimal solution for a minimization problem? Try Problem 31.

The steps of the graphical solution procedure for a minimization problem are summarized here:

1. Prepare a graph of the feasible solutions for each of the constraints.
2. Determine the feasible region by identifying the solutions that satisfy all the constraints simultaneously.

FIGURE 2.16   GRAPHICAL SOLUTION FOR THE M&D CHEMICALS PROBLEM

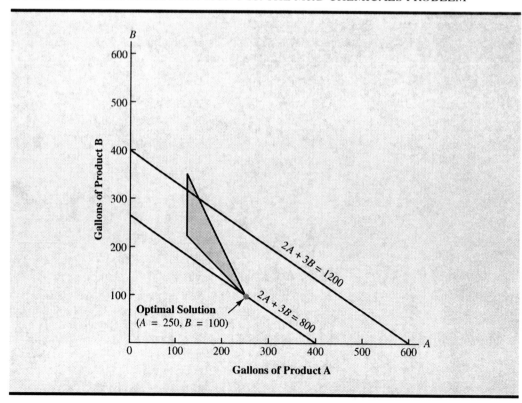

3. Draw an objective function line showing the values of the decision variables that yield a specified value of the objective function.
4. Move parallel objective function lines toward smaller objective function values until further movement would take the line completely outside the feasible region.
5. Any feasible solution on the objective function line with the smallest value is an optimal solution.

Surplus Variables

The optimal solution to the M&D Chemicals problem shows that the desired total production of $A + B = 350$ gallons has been achieved by using all available processing time of $2A + 1B = 2(250) + 1(100) = 600$ hours. In addition, note that the constraint requiring that product A demand be met has been satisfied with $A = 250$ gallons. In fact, the production of product A exceeds its minimum level by $250 - 125 = 125$ gallons. This excess production for product A is referred to as *surplus*. In linear programming terminology, any excess quantity corresponding to a $\geq$ constraint is referred to as surplus.

Recall that with a $\leq$ constraint, a slack variable can be added to the left-hand side of the inequality to convert the constraint to equality form. With a $\geq$ constraint, a **surplus variable** can be subtracted from the left-hand side of the inequality to convert the constraint to equality form. Just as with slack variables, surplus variables are given a coefficient of zero in the objective function because they have no effect on its value. After including two surplus variables, S_1 and S_2, for the $\geq$ constraints and one slack variable, S_3, for the $\leq$ constraint, the linear programming model of the M&D Chemicals problem becomes

$$\text{Min} \quad 2A + 3B + 0S_1 + 0S_2 + 0S_3$$
$$\text{s.t.}$$
$$
\begin{aligned}
1A \quad\quad\;\; - 1S_1 \quad\quad\quad\quad\;\; &= 125 \\
1A + 1B \quad\;\; - 1S_2 \quad\quad\;\; &= 350 \\
2A + 1B \quad\quad\quad\;\; + 1S_3 &= 600 \\
A, B, S_1, S_2, S_3 &\geq 0
\end{aligned}
$$

Try Problem 35 to test your ability to use slack and surplus variables to write a linear program in standard form.

All the constraints are now equalities. Hence, the preceding formulation is the standard-form representation of the M&D Chemicals problem. At the optimal solution of $A = 250$ and $B = 100$, the values of the surplus and slack variables are as follows:

Constraint	Value of Surplus or Slack Variables
Demand for product A	$S_1 = 125$
Total production	$S_2 = 0$
Processing time	$S_3 = 0$

Refer to Figures 2.15 and 2.16. Note that the zero surplus and slack variables are associated with the constraints that are binding at the optimal solution—that is, the total production and processing time constraints. The surplus of 125 units is associated with the nonbinding constraint on the demand for product A.

In the Par, Inc., problem all the constraints were of the $\leq$ type, and in the M&D Chemicals problem the constraints were a mixture of $\geq$ and $\leq$ types. The number and types of constraints encountered in a particular linear programming problem depend on the specific conditions existing in the problem. Linear programming problems may have some $\leq$ constraints, some $=$ constraints, and some $\geq$ constraints. For an equality constraint, feasible solutions must lie directly on the constraint line.

Try Problem 34 to practice solving a linear program with all three constraint forms.

An example of a linear program with two decision variables, G and H, and all three constraint forms is given here:

$$\text{Min} \quad 2G + 2H$$
$$\text{s.t.}$$
$$1G + 3H \leq 12$$
$$3G + 1H \geq 13$$
$$1G - 1H = 3$$
$$G, H \geq 0$$

The standard-form representation of this problem is

$$\text{Min} \quad 2G + 2H + 0S_1 + 0S_2$$
$$\text{s.t.}$$
$$1G + 3H + 1S_1 \qquad\qquad = 12$$
$$3G + 1H \qquad - 1S_2 = 13$$
$$1G - 1H \qquad\qquad = 3$$
$$G, H, S_1, S_2 \geq 0$$

The standard form requires a slack variable for the $\leq$ constraint and a surplus variable for the $\geq$ constraint. However, neither a slack nor a surplus variable is required for the third constraint because it is already in equality form.

When solving linear programs graphically, it is not necessary to write the problem in its standard form. Nevertheless, you should be able to compute the values of the slack and surplus variables and understand what they mean, because the values of slack and surplus variables are included in the computer solution of linear programs.

A final point: The standard form of the linear programming problem is equivalent to the original formulation of the problem. That is, the optimal solution to any linear programming problem is the same as the optimal solution to the standard form of the problem. The standard form has not changed the basic problem; it has only changed how we write the constraints for the problem.

Computer Solution of the M&D Chemicals Problem

The optimal solution to M&D is given in Figure 2.17. The computer output shows that the minimum-cost solution yields an objective function value of $800. The values of the decision variables show that 250 gallons of product A and 100 gallons of product B provide the minimum-cost solution.

The Slack/Surplus column shows that the $\geq$ constraint corresponding to the demand for product A (see constraint 1) has a surplus of 125 units. This column tells us that production of product A in the optimal solution exceeds demand by 125 gallons. The Slack/Surplus values are zero for the total production requirement (constraint 2) and the processing time limitation (constraint 3), which indicates that these constraints are binding at the optimal solution. We will discuss the rest of the computer output that appears in Figure 2.17 in Chapter 3 when we study the topic of sensitivity analysis.

FIGURE 2.17   THE SOLUTION FOR THE M&D CHEMICALS PROBLEM

```
Optimal Objective Value =                    800.00000

           Variable                 Value              Reduced Cost
       ---------------        ---------------        ----------------
              A                  250.00000                0.00000
              B                  100.00000                0.00000

           Constraint            Slack/Surplus           Dual Value
       ---------------        ---------------        ----------------
              1                  125.00000                0.00000
              2                    0.00000                4.00000
              3                    0.00000               -1.00000

                          Objective          Allowable           Allowable
           Variable       Coefficient        Increase            Decrease
       ----------       -----------        ----------        ----------
              A            2.00000           1.00000             Infinite
              B            3.00000           Infinite            1.00000

                             RHS              Allowable           Allowable
           Constraint      Value             Increase            Decrease
       ----------       -----------        ----------        ----------
              1          125.00000          125.00000            Infinite
              2          350.00000          125.00000           50.00000
              3          600.00000          100.00000          125.00000
```

WEB file

M&D

2.6   SPECIAL CASES

In this section we discuss three special situations that can arise when we attempt to solve linear programming problems.

Alternative Optimal Solutions

From the discussion of the graphical solution procedure, we know that optimal solutions can be found at the extreme points of the feasible region. Now let us consider the special case in which the optimal objective function line coincides with one of the binding constraint lines on the boundary of the feasible region. We will see that this situation can lead to the case of **alternative optimal solutions; in** such cases, more than one solution provides the optimal value for the objective function.

To illustrate the case of alternative optimal solutions, we return to the Par, Inc., problem. However, let us assume that the profit for the standard golf bag (S) has been decreased to $6.30. The revised objective function becomes $6.3S + 9D$. The graphical solution of this problem is shown in Figure 2.18. Note that the optimal solution still occurs at an extreme point. In fact, it occurs at two extreme points: extreme point ④ ($S = 300, D = 420$) and extreme point ③ ($S = 540, D = 252$).

The objective function values at these two extreme points are identical; that is,

$$6.3S + 9D = 6.3(300) + 9(420) = 5670$$

FIGURE 2.18 PAR, INC., PROBLEM WITH AN OBJECTIVE FUNCTION OF $6.3S + 9D$
(ALTERNATIVE OPTIMAL SOLUTIONS)

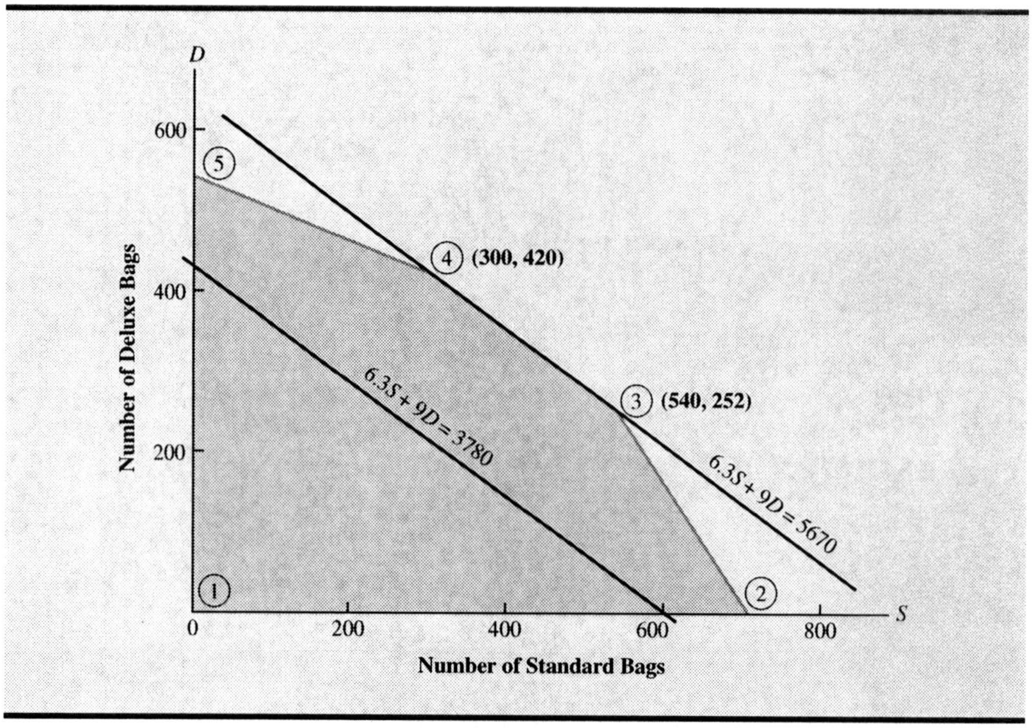

and

$$6.3S + 9D = 6.3(540) + 9(252) = 5670$$

Furthermore, any point on the line connecting the two optimal extreme points also provides an optimal solution. For example, the solution point ($S = 420$, $D = 336$), which is halfway between the two extreme points, also provides the optimal objective function value of

$$6.3S + 9D = 6.3(420) + 9(336) = 5670$$

A linear programming problem with alternative optimal solutions is generally a good situation for the manager or decision maker. It means that several combinations of the decision variables are optimal and that the manager can select the most desirable optimal solution. Unfortunately, determining whether a problem has alternative optimal solutions is not a simple matter.

Infeasibility

Infeasibility means that no solution to the linear programming problem satisfies all the constraints, including the nonnegativity conditions. Graphically, infeasibility means that a feasible region does not exist; that is, no points satisfy all the constraints and the nonnegativity conditions simultaneously. To illustrate this situation, let us look again at the problem faced by Par, Inc.

Problems with no feasible solution do arise in practice, most often because management's expectations are too high or because too many restrictions have been placed on the problem.

Suppose that management specified that at least 500 of the standard bags and at least 360 of the deluxe bags must be manufactured. The graph of the solution region may now be constructed to reflect these new requirements (see Figure 2.19). The shaded area in the lower

FIGURE 2.19 NO FEASIBLE REGION FOR THE PAR, INC., PROBLEM WITH MINIMUM PRODUCTION REQUIREMENTS OF 500 STANDARD AND 360 DELUXE BAGS

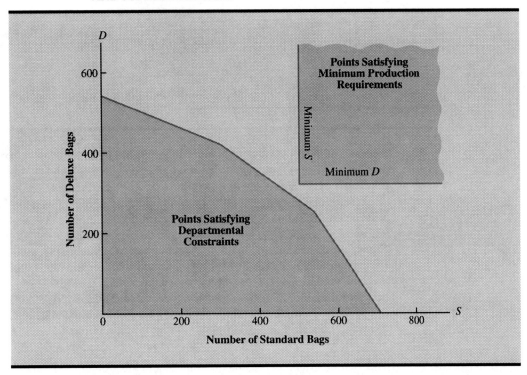

left-hand portion of the graph depicts those points satisfying the departmental constraints on the availability of time. The shaded area in the upper right-hand portion depicts those points satisfying the minimum production requirements of 500 standard and 360 deluxe bags. But no points satisfy both sets of constraints. Thus, we see that if management imposes these minimum production requirements, no feasible region exists for the problem.

How should we interpret infeasibility in terms of this current problem? First, we should tell management that given the resources available (i.e., production time for cutting and dyeing, sewing, finishing, and inspection and packaging), it is not possible to make 500 standard bags and 360 deluxe bags. Moreover, we can tell management exactly how much of each resource must be expended to make it possible to manufacture 500 standard and 360 deluxe bags. Table 2.2 shows the minimum amounts of resources that must be available, the amounts currently available, and additional amounts that would be required to accomplish this level of production. Thus, we need 80 more hours for cutting and dyeing, 32 more hours for finishing, and 5 more hours for inspection and packaging to meet management's minimum production requirements.

If, after reviewing this information, management still wants to manufacture 500 standard and 360 deluxe bags, additional resources must be provided. Perhaps by hiring another person to work in the cutting and dyeing department, transferring a person from elsewhere in the plant to work part-time in the finishing department, or having the sewing people help out periodically with the inspection and packaging, the resource requirements can be met. As you can see, many possibilities are available for corrective management action, once we discover the lack of a feasible solution. The important thing to realize is that linear programming

TABLE 2.2   RESOURCES NEEDED TO MANUFACTURE 500 STANDARD BAGS
AND 360 DELUXE BAGS

Operation	Minimum Required Resources (hours)	Available Resources (hours)	Additional Resources Needed (hours)
Cutting and dyeing	$\frac{7}{10}(500) + 1(360) = 710$	630	80
Sewing	$\frac{1}{2}(500) + \frac{5}{6}(360) = 550$	600	None
Finishing	$1(500) + \frac{2}{3}(360) = 740$	708	32
Inspection and packaging	$\frac{1}{10}(500) + \frac{1}{4}(360) = 140$	135	5

analysis can help determine whether management's plans are feasible. By analyzing the problem using linear programming, we are often able to point out infeasible conditions and initiate corrective action.

Whenever you attempt to solve a problem that is infeasible using either LINGO or Excel Solver, you will get an error message indicating that the problem is infeasible. In this case you know that no solution to the linear programming problem will satisfy all constraints, including the nonnegativity conditions. Careful inspection of your formulation is necessary to try to identify why the problem is infeasible. In some situations, the only reasonable approach is to drop one or more constraints and re-solve the problem. If you are able to find an optimal solution for this revised problem, you will know that the constraint(s) that was omitted, in conjunction with the others, is causing the problem to be infeasible.

Unbounded

The solution to a maximization linear programming problem is **unbounded** if the value of the solution may be made infinitely large without violating any of the constraints; for a minimization problem, the solution is unbounded if the value may be made infinitely small. This condition might be termed *managerial utopia;* for example, if this condition were to occur in a profit maximization problem, the manager could achieve an unlimited profit.

However, in linear programming models of real problems, the occurrence of an unbounded solution means that the problem has been improperly formulated. We know it is not possible to increase profits indefinitely. Therefore, we must conclude that if a profit maximization problem results in an unbounded solution, the mathematical model doesn't represent the real-world problem sufficiently. Usually, what has happened is that a constraint has been inadvertently omitted during problem formulation.

As an illustration, consider the following linear program with two decision variables, X and Y:

$$\text{Max} \quad 20X + 10Y$$
$$\text{s.t.}$$
$$1X \qquad\qquad \geq 2$$
$$1Y \leq 5$$
$$X, Y \geq 0$$

In Figure 2.20 we graphed the feasible region associated with this problem. Note that we can only indicate part of the feasible region because the feasible region extends indefinitely in the direction of the X axis. Looking at the objective function lines in Figure 2.20, we see that the solution to this problem may be made as large as we desire. That is, no matter what solution we pick, we will always be able to reach some feasible solution with a larger value. Thus, we say that the solution to this linear program is *unbounded.*

FIGURE 2.20   EXAMPLE OF AN UNBOUNDED PROBLEM

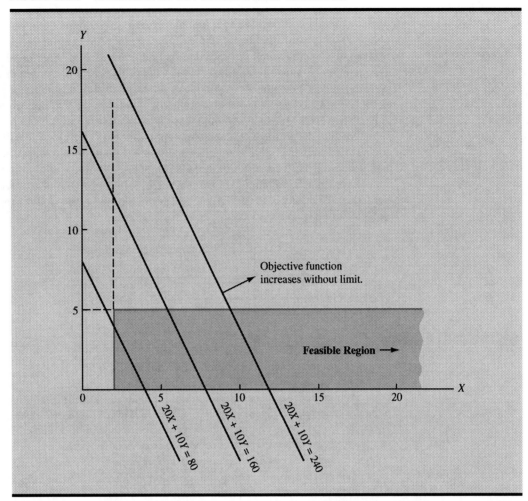

Can you recognize whether a linear program involves alternative optimal solutions or infeasibility, or is unbounded? Try Problems 42 and 43.

Whenever you attempt to solve a problem that is unbounded using either LINGO or Excel Solver you will get a message telling you that the problem is unbounded. Because unbounded solutions cannot occur in real problems, the first thing you should do is to review your model to determine whether you incorrectly formulated the problem. In many cases, this error is the result of inadvertently omitting a constraint during problem formulation.

NOTES AND COMMENTS

1. Infeasibility is independent of the objective function. It exists because the constraints are so restrictive that no feasible region for the linear programming model is possible. Thus, when you encounter infeasibility, making changes in the coefficients of the objective function will not help; the problem will remain infeasible.

2. The occurrence of an unbounded solution is often the result of a missing constraint. However, a change in the objective function may cause a previously unbounded problem to become bounded with an optimal solution. For example, the graph in Figure 2.20 shows an unbounded solution for the objective function Max $20X + 10Y$. However, changing the objective function to Max $-20X - 10Y$ will provide the optimal solution $X = 2$ and $Y = 0$ even though no changes have been made in the constraints.

2.7   GENERAL LINEAR PROGRAMMING NOTATION

In this chapter we showed how to formulate linear programming models for the Par, Inc., and M&D Chemicals problems. To formulate a linear programming model of the Par, Inc., problem we began by defining two decision variables: S = number of standard bags and D = number of deluxe bags. In the M&D Chemicals problem, the two decision variables were defined as A = number of gallons of product A and B = number of gallons of product B. We selected decision-variable names of S and D in the Par, Inc., problem and A and B in the M&D Chemicals problem to make it easier to recall what these decision variables represented in the problem. Although this approach works well for linear programs involving a small number of decision variables, it can become difficult when dealing with problems involving a large number of decision variables.

A more general notation that is often used for linear programs uses the letter x with a subscript. For instance, in the Par, Inc., problem, we could have defined the decision variables as follows:

$$x_1 = \text{number of standard bags}$$
$$x_2 = \text{number of deluxe bags}$$

In the M&D Chemicals problem, the same variable names would be used, but their definitions would change:

$$x_1 = \text{number of gallons of product A}$$
$$x_2 = \text{number of gallons of product B}$$

A disadvantage of using general notation for decision variables is that we are no longer able to easily identify what the decision variables actually represent in the mathematical model. However, the advantage of general notation is that formulating a mathematical model for a problem that involves a large number of decision variables is much easier. For instance, for a linear programming model with three decision variables, we would use variable names of x_1, x_2, and x_3; for a problem with four decision variables, we would use variable names of x_1, x_2, x_3, and x_4, and so on. Clearly, if a problem involved 1000 decision variables, trying to identify 1000 unique names would be difficult. However, using the general linear programming notation, the decision variables would be defined as $x_1, x_2, x_3, \ldots, x_{1000}$.

To illustrate the graphical solution procedure for a linear program written using general linear programming notation, consider the following mathematical model for a maximization problem involving two decision variables:

$$\text{Max} \quad 3x_1 + 2x_2$$
$$\text{s.t.}$$
$$2x_1 + 2x_2 \leq 8$$
$$1x_1 + 0.5x_2 \leq 3$$
$$x_1, x_2 \geq 0$$

We must first develop a graph that displays the possible solutions (x_1 and x_2 values) for the problem. The usual convention is to plot values of x_1 along the horizontal axis and values of x_2 along the vertical axis. Figure 2.21 shows the graphical solution for this two-variable problem. Note that for this problem the optimal solution is $x_1 = 2$ and $x_2 = 2$, with an objective function value of 10.

FIGURE 2.21   GRAPHICAL SOLUTION OF A TWO-VARIABLE LINEAR PROGRAM WITH GENERAL NOTATION

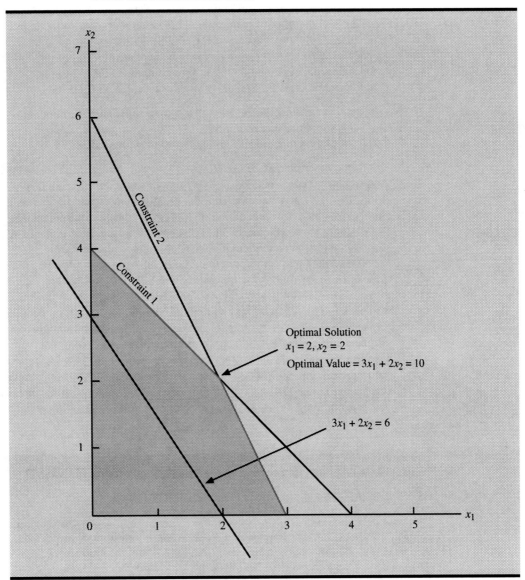

Using general linear programming notation, we can write the standard form of the preceding linear program as follows:

$$\text{Max}\quad 3x_1 + 2x_2 + 0s_1 + 0s_2$$

s.t.

$$2x_1 + 2x_2 + 1s_1 \qquad\quad = 8$$
$$1x_1 + 0.5x_2 + \qquad\quad 1s_2 = 3$$
$$x_1, x_2, s_1, s_2 \geq 0$$

Thus, at the optimal solution $x_1 = 2$ and $x_2 = 2$; the values of the slack variables are $s_1 = s_2 = 0$.

SUMMARY

We formulated linear programming models for two problems: the Par, Inc., maximization problem and the M&D Chemicals minimization problem. For both problems we showed a graphical solution procedure and provided a computer solution to the problem in a generic solution table. In formulating a mathematical model of these problems, we developed a general definition of a linear programming model.

A linear programming model is a mathematical model with the following characteristics:

1. A linear objective function that is to be maximized or minimized
2. A set of linear constraints
3. Variables that are all restricted to nonnegative values

Slack variables may be used to write less-than-or-equal-to constraints in equality form and surplus variables may be used to write greater-than-or-equal-to constraints in equality form. The value of a slack variable can usually be interpreted as the amount of unused resource, whereas the value of a surplus variable indicates the amount over and above some stated minimum requirement. When all constraints have been written as equalities, the linear program has been written in its standard form.

If the solution to a linear program is infeasible or unbounded, no optimal solution to the problem can be found. In the case of infeasibility, no feasible solutions are possible, whereas, in the case of an unbounded solution, the objective function can be made infinitely large for a maximization problem and infinitely small for a minimization problem. In the case of alternative optimal solutions, two or more optimal extreme points exist, and all the points on the line segment connecting them are also optimal.

This chapter concludes with a section showing how to write a linear program using general linear programming notation. The Management Science in Action, Using Linear Programming for Traffic Control, provides another example of the widespread use of linear programming. In the next two chapters we will see many more applications of linear programming.

MANAGEMENT SCIENCE IN ACTION

USING LINEAR PROGRAMMING FOR TRAFFIC CONTROL*

The Hanshin Expressway was the first urban toll expressway in Osaka, Japan. Although in 1964 its length was only 2.3 kilometers, today it is a large-scale urban expressway network of 200 kilometers. The Hanshin Expressway provides service for the Hanshin (Osaka-Kobe) area, the second-most populated area in Japan. An average of 828,000 vehicles use the expressway each day, with daily traffic sometimes exceeding 1 million vehicles. In 1990, the Hanshin Expressway Public Corporation started using an automated traffic control system in order to maximize the number of vehicles flowing into the expressway network.

The automated traffic control system relies on two control methods: (1) limiting the number of cars that enter the expressway at each entrance ramp; and (2) providing drivers with up-to-date and accurate traffic information, including expected travel times and information about accidents. The approach used to limit the number of vehicles depends upon whether the expressway is in a normal or steady state of operation, or whether some type of unusual event, such as an accident or a breakdown, has occurred.

In the first phase of the steady-state case, the Hanshin system uses a linear programming model to maximize the total number of vehicles entering the system, while preventing traffic congestion and adverse effects on surrounding road networks. The data that drive the linear programming model are collected from detectors installed every 500 meters along the expressway and at all entrance and exit ramps. Every five minutes the real-time data collected from the detectors are used to update the model coefficients, and a new linear program computes the maximum number of vehicles the expressway can accommodate.

The automated traffic control system has been successful. According to surveys, traffic control decreased the length of congested portions of the expressway by 30% and the duration by 20%. It proved to be extremely cost effective, and drivers consider it an indispensable service.

*Based on T. Yoshino, T. Sasaki, and T. Hasegawa, "The Traffic-Control System on the Hanshin Expressway," *Interfaces* (January/February 1995): 94–108.

GLOSSARY

Constraint An equation or inequality that rules out certain combinations of decision variables as feasible solutions.

Problem formulation The process of translating the verbal statement of a problem into a mathematical statement called the *mathematical model.*

Decision variable A controllable input for a linear programming model.

Nonnegativity constraints A set of constraints that requires all variables to be nonnegative.

Mathematical model A representation of a problem where the objective and all constraint conditions are described by mathematical expressions.

Linear programming model A mathematical model with a linear objective function, a set of linear constraints, and nonnegative variables.

Linear program Another term for linear programming model.

Linear functions Mathematical expressions in which the variables appear in separate terms and are raised to the first power.

Feasible solution A solution that satisfies all the constraints.

Feasible region The set of all feasible solutions.

Slack variable A variable added to the left-hand side of a less-than-or-equal-to constraint to convert the constraint into an equality. The value of this variable can usually be interpreted as the amount of unused resource.

Standard form A linear program in which all the constraints are written as equalities. The optimal solution of the standard form of a linear program is the same as the optimal solution of the original formulation of the linear program.

Redundant constraint A constraint that does not affect the feasible region. If a constraint is redundant, it can be removed from the problem without affecting the feasible region.

Extreme point Graphically speaking, extreme points are the feasible solution points occurring at the vertices or "corners" of the feasible region. With two-variable problems, extreme points are determined by the intersection of the constraint lines.

Surplus variable A variable subtracted from the left-hand side of a greater-than-or-equal-to constraint to convert the constraint into an equality. The value of this variable can usually be interpreted as the amount over and above some required minimum level.

Alternative optimal solutions The case in which more than one solution provides the optimal value for the objective function.

Infeasibility The situation in which no solution to the linear programming problem satisfies all the constraints.

Unbounded If the value of the solution may be made infinitely large in a maximization linear programming problem or infinitely small in a minimization problem without violating any of the constraints, the problem is said to be unbounded.

PROBLEMS

1. Which of the following mathematical relationships could be found in a linear programming model, and which could not? For the relationships that are unacceptable for linear programs, state why.
   a. $-1A + 2B \leq 70$
   b. $2A - 2B = 50$
   c. $1A - 2B^2 \leq 10$
   d. $3\sqrt{A} + 2B \geq 15$
   e. $1A + 1B = 6$
   f. $2A + 5B + 1AB \leq 25$

2. Find the solutions that satisfy the following constraints:
   a. $4A + 2B \leq 16$
   b. $4A + 2B \geq 16$
   c. $4A + 2B = 16$

3. Show a separate graph of the constraint lines and the solutions that satisfy each of the following constraints:
   a. $3A + 2B \leq 18$
   b. $12A + 8B \geq 480$
   c. $5A + 10B = 200$

4. Show a separate graph of the constraint lines and the solutions that satisfy each of the following constraints:
   a. $3A - 4B \geq 60$
   b. $-6A + 5B \leq 60$
   c. $5A - 2B \leq 0$

5. Show a separate graph of the constraint lines and the solutions that satisfy each of the following constraints:
   a. $A \geq 0.25 (A + B)$
   b. $B \leq 0.10 (A + B)$
   c. $A \leq 0.50 (A + B)$

6. Three objective functions for linear programming problems are $7A + 10B$, $6A + 4B$, and $-4A + 7B$. Show the graph of each for objective function values equal to 420.

7. Identify the feasible region for the following set of constraints:

$$0.5A + 0.25B \geq 30$$
$$1A + \quad 5B \geq 250$$
$$0.25A + \quad 0.5B \leq 50$$
$$A, B \geq 0$$

8. Identify the feasible region for the following set of constraints:

$$2A - 1B \leq 0$$
$$-1A + 1.5B \leq 200$$
$$A, B \geq 0$$

9. Identify the feasible region for the following set of constraints:

$$3A - 2B \geq 0$$
$$2A - 1B \leq 200$$
$$1A \leq 150$$
$$A, B \geq 0$$

10. For the linear program

$$\text{Max} \quad 2A + 3B$$

s.t.

$$1A + 2B \leq 6$$
$$5A + 3B \leq 15$$
$$A, B \geq 0$$

find the optimal solution using the graphical solution procedure. What is the value of the objective function at the optimal solution?

11. Solve the following linear program using the graphical solution procedure:

$$\text{Max} \quad 5A + 5B$$

s.t.

$$1A \quad\quad\quad \leq 100$$
$$1B \leq 80$$
$$2A + 4B \leq 400$$
$$A, B \geq 0$$

12. Consider the following linear programming problem:

$$\text{Max} \quad 3A + 3B$$

s.t.

$$2A + 4B \leq 12$$
$$6A + 4B \leq 24$$
$$A, B \geq 0$$

a. Find the optimal solution using the graphical solution procedure.
b. If the objective function is changed to $2A + 6B$, what will the optimal solution be?
c. How many extreme points are there? What are the values of A and B at each extreme point?

13. Consider the following linear program:

$$\text{Max} \quad 1A + 2B$$

s.t.

$$1A \quad\quad\quad \leq 5$$
$$1B \leq 4$$
$$2A + 2B = 12$$
$$A, B \geq 0$$

a. Show the feasible region.
b. What are the extreme points of the feasible region?
c. Find the optimal solution using the graphical procedure.

14. RMC, Inc., is a small firm that produces a variety of chemical products. In a particular production process, three raw materials are blended (mixed together) to produce two products: a fuel additive and a solvent base. Each ton of fuel additive is a mixture of $\frac{2}{5}$ ton of material 1 and $\frac{3}{5}$ of material 3. A ton of solvent base is a mixture of $\frac{1}{2}$ ton of material 1, $\frac{1}{5}$ ton of material 2, and $\frac{3}{10}$ ton of material 3. After deducting relevant costs, the profit contribution is $40 for every ton of fuel additive produced and $30 for every ton of solvent base produced.

RMC's production is constrained by a limited availability of the three raw materials. For the current production period, RMC has available the following quantities of each raw material:

Raw Material	Amount Available for Production
Material 1	20 tons
Material 2	5 tons
Material 3	21 tons

Assuming that RMC is interested in maximizing the total profit contribution, answer the following:
a. What is the linear programming model for this problem?
b. Find the optimal solution using the graphical solution procedure. How many tons of each product should be produced, and what is the projected total profit contribution?
c. Is there any unused material? If so, how much?
d. Are any of the constraints redundant? If so, which ones?

15. Refer to the Par, Inc., problem described in Section 2.1. Suppose that Par's management encounters the following situations:
a. The accounting department revises its estimate of the profit contribution for the deluxe bag to $18 per bag.
b. A new low-cost material is available for the standard bag, and the profit contribution per standard bag can be increased to $20 per bag. (Assume that the profit contribution of the deluxe bag is the original $9 value.)
c. New sewing equipment is available that would increase the sewing operation capacity to 750 hours. (Assume that $10A + 9B$ is the appropriate objective function.) If each of these situations is encountered separately, what is the optimal solution and the total profit contribution?

16. Refer to the feasible region for Par, Inc., problem in Figure 2.13.
a. Develop an objective function that will make extreme point ⑤ the optimal extreme point.
b. What is the optimal solution for the objective function you selected in part (a)?
c. What are the values of the slack variables associated with this solution?

17. Write the following linear program in standard form:

$$\text{Max} \quad 5A + 2B$$
$$\text{s.t.}$$
$$1A - 2B \leq 420$$
$$2A + 3B \leq 610$$
$$6A - 1B \leq 125$$
$$A, B \geq 0$$

18. For the linear program

$$\text{Max} \quad 4A + 1B$$
$$\text{s.t.}$$
$$10A + 2B \leq 30$$
$$3A + 2B \leq 12$$
$$2A + 2B \leq 10$$
$$A, B \geq 0$$

a. Write this problem in standard form.
b. Solve the problem using the graphical solution procedure.
c. What are the values of the three slack variables at the optimal solution?

19. Given the linear program

$$\text{Max} \quad 3A + 4B$$
$$\text{s.t.}$$
$$-1A + 2B \leq 8$$
$$1A + 2B \leq 12$$
$$2A + 1B \leq 16$$
$$A, B \geq 0$$

a. Write the problem in standard form.
b. Solve the problem using the graphical solution procedure.
c. What are the values of the three slack variables at the optimal solution?

20. For the linear program

$$\text{Max} \quad 3A + 2B$$
$$\text{s.t.}$$
$$A + B \geq 4$$
$$3A + 4B \leq 24$$
$$A \geq 2$$
$$A - B \leq 0$$
$$A, B \geq 0$$

a. Write the problem in standard form.
b. Solve the problem.
c. What are the values of the slack and surplus variables at the optimal solution?

21. Consider the following linear program:

$$\text{Max} \quad 2A + 3B$$
$$\text{s.t.}$$

$$5A + 5B \leq 400 \quad \text{Constraint 1}$$
$$-1A + 1B \leq 10 \quad \text{Constraint 2}$$
$$1A + 3B \geq 90 \quad \text{Constraint 3}$$
$$A, B \geq 0$$

Figure 2.22 shows a graph of the constraint lines.
a. Place a number (1, 2, or 3) next to each constraint line to identify which constraint it represents.
b. Shade in the feasible region on the graph.
c. Identify the optimal extreme point. What is the optimal solution?
d. Which constraints are binding? Explain.
e. How much slack or surplus is associated with the nonbinding constraint?

22. Reiser Sports Products wants to determine the number of All-Pro (A) and College (C) footballs to produce in order to maximize profit over the next four-week planning horizon. Constraints affecting the production quantities are the production capacities in three departments: cutting and dyeing; sewing; and inspection and packaging. For

FIGURE 2.22   GRAPH OF THE CONSTRAINT LINES FOR EXERCISE 21

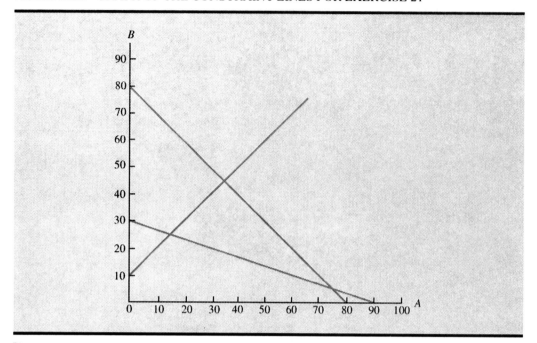

the four-week planning period, 340 hours of cutting and dyeing time, 420 hours of sewing time, and 200 hours of inspection and packaging time are available. All-Pro footballs provide a profit of $5 per unit and College footballs provide a profit of $4 per unit. The linear programming model with production times expressed in minutes is as follows:

$$\text{Max} \quad 5A + 4C$$

s.t.

$$12A + 6C \leq 20{,}400 \quad \text{Cutting and dyeing}$$
$$9A + 15C \leq 25{,}200 \quad \text{Sewing}$$
$$6A + 6C \leq 12{,}000 \quad \text{Inspection and packaging}$$
$$A, C \geq 0$$

A portion of the graphical solution to the Reiser problem is shown in Figure 2.23.
a.   Shade the feasible region for this problem.
b.   Determine the coordinates of each extreme point and the corresponding profit. Which extreme point generates the highest profit?
c.   Draw the profit line corresponding to a profit of $4000. Move the profit line as far from the origin as you can in order to determine which extreme point will provide the optimal solution. Compare your answer with the approach you used in part (b).
d.   Which constraints are binding? Explain.
e.   Suppose that the values of the objective function coefficients are $4 for each All-Pro model produced and $5 for each College model. Use the graphical solution procedure to determine the new optimal solution and the corresponding value of profit.

FIGURE 2.23   PORTION OF THE GRAPHICAL SOLUTION FOR EXERCISE 22

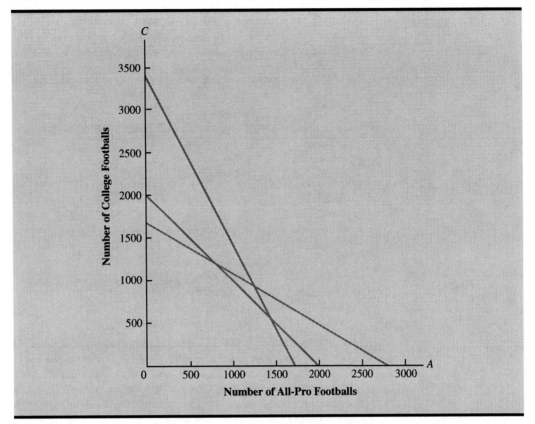

23. Embassy Motorcycles (EM) manufacturers two lightweight motorcycles designed for easy handling and safety. The EZ-Rider model has a new engine and a low profile that make it easy to balance. The Lady-Sport model is slightly larger, uses a more traditional engine, and is specifically designed to appeal to women riders. Embassy produces the engines for both models at its Des Moines, Iowa, plant. Each EZ-Rider engine requires 6 hours of manufacturing time and each Lady-Sport engine requires 3 hours of manufacturing time. The Des Moines plant has 2100 hours of engine manufacturing time available for the next production period. Embassy's motorcycle frame supplier can supply as many EZ-Rider frames as needed. However, the Lady-Sport frame is more complex and the supplier can only provide up to 280 Lady-Sport frames for the next production period. Final assembly and testing requires 2 hours for each EZ-Rider model and 2.5 hours for each Lady-Sport model. A maximum of 1000 hours of assembly and testing time are available for the next production period. The company's accounting department projects a profit contribution of $2400 for each EZ-Rider produced and $1800 for each Lady-Sport produced.

   a. Formulate a linear programming model that can be used to determine the number of units of each model that should be produced in order to maximize the total contribution to profit.

   b. Solve the problem graphically. What is the optimal solution?

   c. Which constraints are binding?

24. Kelson Sporting Equipment, Inc., makes two different types of baseball gloves: a regular model and a catcher's model. The firm has 900 hours of production time available in its cutting and sewing department, 300 hours available in its finishing department, and 100 hours available in its packaging and shipping department. The production time requirements and the profit contribution per glove are given in the following table:

| | Production Time (hours) | | | |
Model	Cutting and Sewing	Finishing	Packaging and Shipping	Profit/Glove
Regular model	1	$\frac{1}{2}$	$\frac{1}{8}$	$5
Catcher's model	$\frac{3}{2}$	$\frac{1}{3}$	$\frac{1}{4}$	$8

Assuming that the company is interested in maximizing the total profit contribution, answer the following:
a. What is the linear programming model for this problem?
b. Find the optimal solution using the graphical solution procedure. How many gloves of each model should Kelson manufacture?
c. What is the total profit contribution Kelson can earn with the given production quantities?
d. How many hours of production time will be scheduled in each department?
e. What is the slack time in each department?

25. George Johnson recently inherited a large sum of money; he wants to use a portion of this money to set up a trust fund for his two children. The trust fund has two investment options: (1) a bond fund and (2) a stock fund. The projected returns over the life of the investments are 6% for the bond fund and 10% for the stock fund. Whatever portion of the inheritance he finally decides to commit to the trust fund, he wants to invest at least 30% of that amount in the bond fund. In addition, he wants to select a mix that will enable him to obtain a total return of at least 7.5%.
a. Formulate a linear programming model that can be used to determine the percentage that should be allocated to each of the possible investment alternatives.
b. Solve the problem using the graphical solution procedure.

26. The Sea Wharf Restaurant would like to determine the best way to allocate a monthly advertising budget of $1000 between newspaper advertising and radio advertising. Management decided that at least 25% of the budget must be spent on each type of media, and that the amount of money spent on local newspaper advertising must be at least twice the amount spent on radio advertising. A marketing consultant developed an index that measures audience exposure per dollar of advertising on a scale from 0 to 100, with higher values implying greater audience exposure. If the value of the index for local newspaper advertising is 50 and the value of the index for spot radio advertising is 80, how should the restaurant allocate its advertising budget in order to maximize the value of total audience exposure?
a. Formulate a linear programming model that can be used to determine how the restaurant should allocate its advertising budget in order to maximize the value of total audience exposure.
b. Solve the problem using the graphical solution procedure.

27. Blair & Rosen, Inc. (B&R), is a brokerage firm that specializes in investment portfolios designed to meet the specific risk tolerances of its clients. A client who contacted B&R this past week has a maximum of $50,000 to invest. B&R's investment advisor decides to recommend a portfolio consisting of two investment funds: an Internet fund and a Blue

Chip fund. The Internet fund has a projected annual return of 12%, whereas the Blue Chip fund has a projected annual return of 9%. The investment advisor requires that at most $35,000 of the client's funds should be invested in the Internet fund. B&R services include a risk rating for each investment alternative. The Internet fund, which is the more risky of the two investment alternatives, has a risk rating of 6 per thousand dollars invested. The Blue Chip fund has a risk rating of 4 per thousand dollars invested. For example, if $10,000 is invested in each of the two investment funds, B&R's risk rating for the portfolio would be 6(10) + 4(10) = 100. Finally, B&R developed a questionnaire to measure each client's risk tolerance. Based on the responses, each client is classified as a conservative, moderate, or aggressive investor. Suppose that the questionnaire results classified the current client as a moderate investor. B&R recommends that a client who is a moderate investor limit his or her portfolio to a maximum risk rating of 240.

a. What is the recommended investment portfolio for this client? What is the annual return for the portfolio?

b. Suppose that a second client with $50,000 to invest has been classified as an aggressive investor. B&R recommends that the maximum portfolio risk rating for an aggressive investor is 320. What is the recommended investment portfolio for this aggressive investor? Discuss what happens to the portfolio under the aggressive investor strategy.

c. Suppose that a third client with $50,000 to invest has been classified as a conservative investor. B&R recommends that the maximum portfolio risk rating for a conservative investor is 160. Develop the recommended investment portfolio for the conservative investor. Discuss the interpretation of the slack variable for the total investment fund constraint.

28. Tom's, Inc., produces various Mexican food products and sells them to Western Foods, a chain of grocery stores located in Texas and New Mexico. Tom's, Inc., makes two salsa products: Western Foods Salsa and Mexico City Salsa. Essentially, the two products have different blends of whole tomatoes, tomato sauce, and tomato paste. The Western Foods Salsa is a blend of 50% whole tomatoes, 30% tomato sauce, and 20% tomato paste. The Mexico City Salsa, which has a thicker and chunkier consistency, consists of 70% whole tomatoes, 10% tomato sauce, and 20% tomato paste. Each jar of salsa produced weighs 10 ounces. For the current production period, Tom's, Inc., can purchase up to 280 pounds of whole tomatoes, 130 pounds of tomato sauce, and 100 pounds of tomato paste; the price per pound for these ingredients is $0.96, $0.64, and $0.56, respectively. The cost of the spices and the other ingredients is approximately $0.10 per jar. Tom's, Inc., buys empty glass jars for $0.02 each, and labeling and filling costs are estimated to be $0.03 for each jar of salsa produced. Tom's contract with Western Foods results in sales revenue of $1.64 for each jar of Western Foods Salsa and $1.93 for each jar of Mexico City Salsa.

a. Develop a linear programming model that will enable Tom's to determine the mix of salsa products that will maximize the total profit contribution.

b. Find the optimal solution.

29. AutoIgnite produces electronic ignition systems for automobiles at a plant in Cleveland, Ohio. Each ignition system is assembled from two components produced at AutoIgnite's plants in Buffalo, New York, and Dayton, Ohio. The Buffalo plant can produce 2000 units of component 1, 1000 units of component 2, or any combination of the two components each day. For instance, 60% of Buffalo's production time could be used to produce component 1 and 40% of Buffalo's production time could be used to produce component 2; in this case, the Buffalo plant would be able to produce 0.6(2000) = 1200 units of component 1 each day and 0.4(1000) = 400 units of component 2 each day. The Dayton plant can produce 600 units of component 1, 1400 units of component 2, or any combination of the two components each day. At the end of each day, the component production at Buffalo and Dayton is sent to Cleveland for assembly of the ignition systems on the following workday.

a. Formulate a linear programming model that can be used to develop a daily production schedule for the Buffalo and Dayton plants that will maximize daily production of ignition systems at Cleveland.
b. Find the optimal solution.

30. A financial advisor at Diehl Investments identified two companies that are likely candidates for a takeover in the near future. Eastern Cable is a leading manufacturer of flexible cable systems used in the construction industry, and ComSwitch is a new firm specializing in digital switching systems. Eastern Cable is currently trading for $40 per share, and ComSwitch is currently trading for $25 per share. If the takeovers occur, the financial advisor estimates that the price of Eastern Cable will go to $55 per share and ComSwitch will go to $43 per share. At this point in time, the financial advisor has identified ComSwitch as the higher risk alternative. Assume that a client indicated a willingness to invest a maximum of $50,000 in the two companies. The client wants to invest at least $15,000 in Eastern Cable and at least $10,000 in ComSwitch. Because of the higher risk associated with ComSwitch, the financial advisor has recommended that at most $25,000 should be invested in ComSwitch.
a. Formulate a linear programming model that can be used to determine the number of shares of Eastern Cable and the number of shares of ComSwitch that will meet the investment constraints and maximize the total return for the investment.
b. Graph the feasible region.
c. Determine the coordinates of each extreme point.
d. Find the optimal solution.

31. Consider the following linear program:

$$\text{Min} \quad 3A + 4B$$
$$\text{s.t.}$$
$$1A + 3B \geq 6$$
$$1A + 1B \geq 4$$
$$A, B \geq 0$$

Identify the feasible region and find the optimal solution using the graphical solution procedure. What is the value of the objective function?

32. Identify the three extreme-point solutions for the M&D Chemicals problem (see Section 2.5). Identify the value of the objective function and the values of the slack and surplus variables at each extreme point.

33. Consider the following linear programming problem:

$$\text{Min} \quad A + 2B$$
$$\text{s.t.}$$
$$A + 4B \leq 21$$
$$2A + B \geq 7$$
$$3A + 1.5B \leq 21$$
$$-2A + 6B \geq 0$$
$$A, B \geq 0$$

a. Find the optimal solution using the graphical solution procedure and the value of the objective function.
b. Determine the amount of slack or surplus for each constraint.
c. Suppose the objective function is changed to max $5A + 2B$. Find the optimal solution and the value of the objective function.

34. Consider the following linear program:

$$\text{Min} \quad 2A + 2B$$

s.t.

$$1A + 3B \leq 12$$
$$3A + 1B \geq 13$$
$$1A - 1B = 3$$
$$A, B \geq 0$$

a. Show the feasible region.
b. What are the extreme points of the feasible region?
c. Find the optimal solution using the graphical solution procedure.

35. For the linear program

$$\text{Min} \quad 6A + 4B$$

s.t.

$$2A + 1B \geq 12$$
$$1A + 1B \geq 10$$
$$1B \leq 4$$
$$A, B \geq 0$$

a. Write the problem in standard form.
b. Solve the problem using the graphical solution procedure.
c. What are the values of the slack and surplus variables?

36. As part of a quality improvement initiative, Consolidated Electronics employees complete a three-day training program on teaming and a two-day training program on problem solving. The manager of quality improvement has requested that at least 8 training programs on teaming and at least 10 training programs on problem solving be offered during the next six months. In addition, senior-level management has specified that at least 25 training programs must be offered during this period. Consolidated Electronics uses a consultant to teach the training programs. During the next quarter, the consultant has 84 days of training time available. Each training program on teaming costs $10,000 and each training program on problem solving costs $8000.
a. Formulate a linear programming model that can be used to determine the number of training programs on teaming and the number of training programs on problem solving that should be offered in order to minimize total cost.
b. Graph the feasible region.
c. Determine the coordinates of each extreme point.
d. Solve for the minimum cost solution.

37. The New England Cheese Company produces two cheese spreads by blending mild cheddar cheese with extra sharp cheddar cheese. The cheese spreads are packaged in 12-ounce containers, which are then sold to distributors throughout the Northeast. The Regular blend contains 80% mild cheddar and 20% extra sharp, and the Zesty blend contains 60% mild cheddar and 40% extra sharp. This year, a local dairy cooperative offered to provide up to 8100 pounds of mild cheddar cheese for $1.20 per pound and up to 3000 pounds of extra sharp cheddar cheese for $1.40 per pound. The cost to blend and package the cheese spreads, excluding the cost of the cheese, is $0.20 per container. If each container of Regular is sold for $1.95 and each container of Zesty is sold for $2.20, how many containers of Regular and Zesty should New England Cheese produce?

38. Applied Technology, Inc. (ATI), produces bicycle frames using two fiberglass materials that improve the strength-to-weight ratio of the frames. The cost of the standard grade material is $7.50 per yard and the cost of the professional grade material is $9.00 per yard. The standard and professional grade materials contain different amounts of fiberglass, carbon fiber, and Kevlar as shown in the following table:

	Standard Grade	Professional Grade
Fiberglass	84%	58%
Carbon fiber	10%	30%
Kevlar	6%	12%

ATI signed a contract with a bicycle manufacturer to produce a new frame with a carbon fiber content of at least 20% and a Kevlar content of not greater than 10%. To meet the required weight specification, a total of 30 yards of material must be used for each frame.

a. Formulate a linear program to determine the number of yards of each grade of fiberglass material that ATI should use in each frame in order to minimize total cost. Define the decision variables and indicate the purpose of each constraint.

b. Use the graphical solution procedure to determine the feasible region. What are the coordinates of the extreme points?

c. Compute the total cost at each extreme point. What is the optimal solution?

d. The distributor of the fiberglass material is currently overstocked with the professional grade material. To reduce inventory, the distributor offered ATI the opportunity to purchase the professional grade for $8 per yard. Will the optimal solution change?

e. Suppose that the distributor further lowers the price of the professional grade material to $7.40 per yard. Will the optimal solution change? What effect would an even lower price for the professional grade material have on the optimal solution? Explain.

39. Innis Investments manages funds for a number of companies and wealthy clients. The investment strategy is tailored to each client's needs. For a new client, Innis has been authorized to invest up to $1.2 million in two investment funds: a stock fund and a money market fund. Each unit of the stock fund costs $50 and provides an annual rate of return of 10%; each unit of the money market fund costs $100 and provides an annual rate of return of 4%.

The client wants to minimize risk subject to the requirement that the annual income from the investment be at least $60,000. According to Innis's risk measurement system, each unit invested in the stock fund has a risk index of 8, and each unit invested in the money market fund has a risk index of 3; the higher risk index associated with the stock fund simply indicates that it is the riskier investment. Innis's client also specified that at least $300,000 be invested in the money market fund.

a. Determine how many units of each fund Innis should purchase for the client to minimize the total risk index for the portfolio.

b. How much annual income will this investment strategy generate?

c. Suppose the client desires to maximize annual return. How should the funds be invested?

40. Photo Chemicals produces two types of photographic developing fluids. Both products cost Photo Chemicals $1 per gallon to produce. Based on an analysis of current inventory levels and outstanding orders for the next month, Photo Chemicals' management specified that at least 30 gallons of product 1 and at least 20 gallons of product 2 must be produced during the next two weeks. Management also stated that an existing inventory of highly perishable raw material required in the production of both fluids must be used within the

next two weeks. The current inventory of the perishable raw material is 80 pounds. Although more of this raw material can be ordered if necessary, any of the current inventory that is not used within the next two weeks will spoil—hence, the management requirement that at least 80 pounds be used in the next two weeks. Furthermore, it is known that product 1 requires 1 pound of this perishable raw material per gallon and product 2 requires 2 pounds of the raw material per gallon. Because Photo Chemicals' objective is to keep its production costs at the minimum possible level, the firm's management is looking for a minimum cost production plan that uses all the 80 pounds of perishable raw material and provides at least 30 gallons of product 1 and at least 20 gallons of product 2. What is the minimum cost solution?

41. Southern Oil Company produces two grades of gasoline: regular and premium. The profit contributions are $0.30 per gallon for regular gasoline and $0.50 per gallon for premium gasoline. Each gallon of regular gasoline contains 0.3 gallons of grade A crude oil and each gallon of premium gasoline contains 0.6 gallons of grade A crude oil. For the next production period, Southern has 18,000 gallons of grade A crude oil available. The refinery used to produce the gasolines has a production capacity of 50,000 gallons for the next production period. Southern Oil's distributors have indicated that demand for the premium gasoline for the next production period will be at most 20,000 gallons.

    a. Formulate a linear programming model that can be used to determine the number of gallons of regular gasoline and the number of gallons of premium gasoline that should be produced in order to maximize total profit contribution.

    b. What is the optimal solution?

    c. What are the values and interpretations of the slack variables?

    d. What are the binding constraints?

 42. Does the following linear program involve infeasibility, unbounded, and/or alternative optimal solutions? Explain.

$$\text{Max} \quad 4A + 8B$$
$$\text{s.t.}$$
$$2A + 2B \leq 10$$
$$-1A + 1B \geq 8$$
$$A, B \geq 0$$

 43. Does the following linear program involve infeasibility, unbounded, and/or alternative optimal solutions? Explain.

$$\text{Max} \quad 1A + 1B$$
$$\text{s.t.}$$
$$8A + 6B \geq 24$$
$$2B \geq 4$$
$$A, B \geq 0$$

44. Consider the following linear program:

$$\text{Max} \quad 1A + 1B$$
$$\text{s.t.}$$
$$5A + 3B \leq 15$$
$$3A + 5B \leq 15$$
$$A, B \geq 0$$

a. What is the optimal solution for this problem?

b. Suppose that the objective function is changed to $1A + 2B$. Find the new optimal solution.

45. Consider the following linear program:

$$\text{Max} \quad 1A - 2B$$
$$\text{s.t.}$$
$$-4A + 3B \le 3$$
$$1A - 1B \le 3$$
$$A, B \ge 0$$

a. Graph the feasible region for the problem.

b. Is the feasible region unbounded? Explain.

c. Find the optimal solution.

d. Does an unbounded feasible region imply that the optimal solution to the linear program will be unbounded?

46. The manager of a small independent grocery store is trying to determine the best use of her shelf space for soft drinks. The store carries national and generic brands and currently has 200 square feet of shelf space available. The manager wants to allocate at least 60% of the space to the national brands and, regardless of the profitability, allocate at least 10% of the space to the generic brands. How many square feet of space should the manager allocate to the national brands and the generic brands under the following circumstances?

a. The national brands are more profitable than the generic brands.

b. Both brands are equally profitable.

c. The generic brand is more profitable than the national brand.

47. Discuss what happens to the M&D Chemicals problem (see Section 2.5) if the cost per gallon for product A is increased to $3.00 per gallon. What would you recommend? Explain.

48. For the M&D Chemicals problem in Section 2.5, discuss the effect of management's requiring total production of 500 gallons for the two products. List two or three actions M&D should consider to correct the situation you encounter.

49. PharmaPlus operates a chain of 30 pharmacies. The pharmacies are staffed by licensed pharmacists and pharmacy technicians. The company currently employs 85 full-time equivalent pharmacists (combination of full time and part time) and 175 full-time equivalent technicians. Each spring management reviews current staffing levels and makes hiring plans for the year. A recent forecast of the prescription load for the next year shows that at least 250 full-time equivalent employees (pharmacists and technicians) will be required to staff the pharmacies. The personnel department expects 10 pharmacists and 30 technicians to leave over the next year. To accommodate the expected attrition and prepare for future growth, management stated that at least 15 new pharmacists must be hired. In addition, PharmaPlus's new service quality guidelines specify no more than two technicians per licensed pharmacist. The average salary for licensed pharmacists is $40 per hour and the average salary for technicians is $10 per hour.

a. Determine a minimum-cost staffing plan for PharmaPlus. How many pharmacists and technicians are needed?

b. Given current staffing levels and expected attrition, how many new hires (if any) must be made to reach the level recommended in part (a)? What will be the impact on the payroll?

50. Expedition Outfitters manufactures a variety of specialty clothing for hiking, skiing, and mountain climbing. Its management decided to begin production on two new parkas designed

for use in extremely cold weather: the Mount Everest Parka and the Rocky Mountain Parka. The manufacturing plant has 120 hours of cutting time and 120 hours of sewing time available for producing these two parkas. Each Mount Everest Parka requires 30 minutes of cutting time and 45 minutes of sewing time, and each Rocky Mountain Parka requires 20 minutes of cutting time and 15 minutes of sewing time. The labor and material cost is $150 for each Mount Everest Parka and $50 for each Rocky Mountain Parka, and the retail prices through the firm's mail order catalog are $250 for the Mount Everest Parka and $200 for the Rocky Mountain Parka. Because management believes that the Mount Everest Parka is a unique coat that will enhance the image of the firm, they specified that at least 20% of the total production must consist of this model. Assuming that Expedition Outfitters can sell as many coats of each type as it can produce, how many units of each model should it manufacture to maximize the total profit contribution?

51. English Motors, Ltd. (EML), developed a new all-wheel-drive sports utility vehicle. As part of the marketing campaign, EML produced a video tape sales presentation to send to both owners of current EML four-wheel-drive vehicles as well as to owners of four-wheel-drive sports utility vehicles offered by competitors; EML refers to these two target markets as the current customer market and the new customer market. Individuals who receive the new promotion video will also receive a coupon for a test drive of the new EML model for one weekend. A key factor in the success of the new promotion is the response rate, the percentage of individuals who receive the new promotion and test drive the new model. EML estimates that the response rate for the current customer market is 25% and the response rate for the new customer market is 20%. For the customers who test drive the new model, the sales rate is the percentage of individuals that make a purchase. Marketing research studies indicate that the sales rate is 12% for the current customer market and 20% for the new customer market. The cost for each promotion, excluding the test drive costs, is $4 for each promotion sent to the current customer market and $6 for each promotion sent to the new customer market. Management also specified that a minimum of 30,000 current customers should test drive the new model and a minimum of 10,000 new customers should test drive the new model. In addition, the number of current customers who test drive the new vehicle must be at least twice the number of new customers who test drive the new vehicle. If the marketing budget, excluding test drive costs, is $1.2 million, how many promotions should be sent to each group of customers in order to maximize total sales?

52. Creative Sports Design (CSD) manufactures a standard-size racket and an oversize racket. The firm's rackets are extremely light due to the use of a magnesium-graphite alloy that was invented by the firm's founder. Each standard-size racket uses 0.125 kilograms of the alloy and each oversize racket uses 0.4 kilograms; over the next two-week production period only 80 kilograms of the alloy are available. Each standard-size racket uses 10 minutes of manufacturing time and each oversize racket uses 12 minutes. The profit contributions are $10 for each standard-size racket and $15 for each oversize racket, and 40 hours of manufacturing time are available each week. Management specified that at least 20% of the total production must be the standard-size racket. How many rackets of each type should CSD manufacture over the next two weeks to maximize the total profit contribution? Assume that because of the unique nature of their products, CSD can sell as many rackets as they can produce.

53. Management of High Tech Services (HTS) would like to develop a model that will help allocate their technicians' time between service calls to regular contract customers and new customers. A maximum of 80 hours of technician time is available over the two-week planning period. To satisfy cash flow requirements, at least $800 in revenue (per technician) must be generated during the two-week period. Technician time for regular customers generates $25 per hour. However, technician time for new customers only

generates an average of $8 per hour because in many cases a new customer contact does not provide billable services. To ensure that new customer contacts are being maintained, the technician time spent on new customer contacts must be at least 60% of the time spent on regular customer contacts. Given these revenue and policy requirements, HTS would like to determine how to allocate technician time between regular customers and new customers so that the total number of customers contacted during the two-week period will be maximized. Technicians require an average of 50 minutes for each regular customer contact and 1 hour for each new customer contact.

    a.   Develop a linear programming model that will enable HTS to allocate technician time between regular customers and new customers.

    b.   Find the optimal solution.

54.   Jackson Hole Manufacturing is a small manufacturer of plastic products used in the automotive and computer industries. One of its major contracts is with a large computer company and involves the production of plastic printer cases for the computer company's portable printers. The printer cases are produced on two injection molding machines. The M-100 machine has a production capacity of 25 printer cases per hour, and the M-200 machine has a production capacity of 40 cases per hour. Both machines use the same chemical material to produce the printer cases; the M-100 uses 40 pounds of the raw material per hour and the M-200 uses 50 pounds per hour. The computer company asked Jackson Hole to produce as many of the cases during the upcoming week as possible; it will pay $18 for each case Jackson Hole can deliver. However, next week is a regularly scheduled vacation period for most of Jackson Hole's production employees; during this time, annual maintenance is performed for all equipment in the plant. Because of the downtime for maintenance, the M-100 will be available for no more than 15 hours, and the M-200 will be available for no more than 10 hours. However, because of the high setup cost involved with both machines, management requires that, each machine must be operated for at least 5 hours. The supplier of the chemical material used in the production process informed Jackson Hole that a maximum of 1000 pounds of the chemical material will be available for next week's production; the cost for this raw material is $6 per pound. In addition to the raw material cost, Jackson Hole estimates that the hourly cost of operating the M-100 and the M-200 are $50 and $75, respectively.

    a.   Formulate a linear programming model that can be used to maximize the contribution to profit.

    b.   Find the optimal solution.

55.   The Kartick Company is trying to determine how much of each of two products to produce over the coming planning period. There are three departments, A, B and C, with limited labor hours available in each department. Each product must be processed by each department and the per-unit requirements for each product, labor hours available, and per-unit profit are as shown below.

	Labor required in each department		
	Product (hrs./unit)		**Labor Hours**
Department	**Product 1**	**Product 2**	**Available**
A	1.00	0.30	100
B	0.30	0.12	36
C	0.15	0.56	50
Profit Contribution	$33.00	$24.00	

A linear program for this situation is as follows:

Let
$$x_1 = \text{the amount of product 1 to produce}$$
$$x_2 = \text{the amount of product 2 to produce}$$

Maximize $33\,x_1 + 24\,x_2$

s.t.

$$1.0\,x_1 + .30\,x_2 \le 100 \quad \text{Department A}$$
$$.30\,x_1 + .12\,x_2 \le 36 \quad \text{Department B}$$
$$.15\,x_1 + .56\,x_2 \le 50 \quad \text{Department C}$$
$$x_1, x_2 \ge 0$$

Mr. Kartick (the owner) used trial and error with a spreadsheet model to arrive at a solution. His proposed solution is $x_1 = 75$ and $x_2 = 60$, as shown below in Figure 2.24. He said he felt his proposed solution is optimal.

Is his solution optimal? Without solving the problem, explain why you believe this solution is optimal or not optimal.

FIGURE 2.24   MR. KARTICK'S TRIAL-AND-ERROR MODEL

	A	B	C	D	E
1	**Kartick**				
2	**Data**				
3				Hours	
4	Department	Prod 1	Prod 2	Available	
5	A	1.00	0.30	100	
6	B	0.30	0.12	36	
7	C	0.15	0.56	50	
8	Per unit				
9	Contribution	$33.00	$24.00		
10					
11	**Decisions**				
12					
13		Prod 1	Prod 2		
14	Quantity	75	60		
15					
16					
17	**Model**				
18		Hours	Unused		
19	Department	Used	Hours		
20	A	93	7		
21	B	29.7	6.3		
22	C	44.85	5.15		
23					
24	Contribution	$3,915.00			

56.   Assume you are given a minimization linear program that has an optimal solution. The problem is then modified by changing an equality constraint in the problem to a less-than-or-equal-to constraint. Is it possible that the modified problem is infeasible? Answer yes or no and justify.

57.   Assume you are given a minimization linear program that has an optimal solution. The problem is then modified by changing a greater-than-or-equal-to constraint in the problem to a less-than-or-equal-to constraint. Is it possible that the modified problem is infeasible? Answer yes or no and justify.

58.   A consultant was hired to build an optimization model for a large marketing research company. The model is based on a consumer survey that was taken in which each person was asked to rank 30 new products in descending order based on their likelihood of purchasing the product. The consultant was assigned the task of building a model that selects the minimum number of products (which would then be introduced into the marketplace) such that the first, second, and third choice of every subject in the survey is included in the list of selected products. While building a model to figure out which products to introduce, the consultant's boss walked up to her and said: "Look, if the model tells us we need to introduce more than 15 products, then add a constraint which limits the number of new products to 15 or less. It's too expensive to introduce more than 15 new products." Evaluate this statement in terms of what you have learned so far about constrained optimization models.

Case Problem 1   WORKLOAD BALANCING

Digital Imaging (DI) produces photo printers for both the professional and consumer markets. The DI consumer division recently introduced two photo printers that provide color prints rivaling those produced by a professional processing lab. The DI-910 model can produce a 4" × 6" borderless print in approximately 37 seconds. The more sophisticated and faster DI-950 can even produce a 13" × 19" borderless print. Financial projections show profit contributions of $42 for each DI-910 and $87 for each DI-950.

The printers are assembled, tested, and packaged at DI's plant located in New Bern, North Carolina. This plant is highly automated and uses two manufacturing lines to produce the printers. Line 1 performs the assembly operation with times of 3 minutes per DI-910 printer and 6 minutes per DI-950 printer. Line 2 performs both the testing and packaging operations. Times are 4 minutes per DI-910 printer and 2 minutes per DI-950 printer. The shorter time for the DI-950 printer is a result of its faster print speed. Both manufacturing lines are in operation one 8-hour shift per day.

Managerial Report

Perform an analysis for Digital Imaging in order to determine how many units of each printer to produce. Prepare a report to DI's president presenting your findings and recommendations. Include (but do not limit your discussion to) a consideration of the following:

1.   The recommended number of units of each printer to produce to maximize the total contribution to profit for an 8-hour shift. What reasons might management have for not implementing your recommendation?

2.   Suppose that management also states that the number of DI-910 printers produced must be at least as great as the number of DI-950 units produced. Assuming that the objective is to maximize the total contribution to profit for an 8-hour shift, how many units of each printer should be produced?

3. Does the solution you developed in part (2) balance the total time spent on line 1 and the total time spent on line 2? Why might this balance or lack of it be a concern to management?
4. Management requested an expansion of the model in part (2) that would provide a better balance between the total time on line 1 and the total time on line 2. Management wants to limit the difference between the total time on line 1 and the total time on line 2 to 30 minutes or less. If the objective is still to maximize the total contribution to profit, how many units of each printer should be produced? What effect does this workload balancing have on total profit in part (2)?
5. Suppose that in part (1) management specified the objective of maximizing the total number of printers produced each shift rather than total profit contribution. With this objective, how many units of each printer should be produced per shift? What effect does this objective have on total profit and workload balancing?

For each solution that you develop, include a copy of your linear programming model and graphical solution in the appendix to your report.

Case Problem 2   PRODUCTION STRATEGY

Better Fitness, Inc. (BFI), manufactures exercise equipment at its plant in Freeport, Long Island. It recently designed two universal weight machines for the home exercise market. Both machines use BFI-patented technology that provides the user with an extremely wide range of motion capability for each type of exercise performed. Until now, such capabilities have been available only on expensive weight machines used primarily by physical therapists.

At a recent trade show, demonstrations of the machines resulted in significant dealer interest. In fact, the number of orders that BFI received at the trade show far exceeded its manufacturing capabilities for the current production period. As a result, management decided to begin production of the two machines. The two machines, which BFI named the BodyPlus 100 and the BodyPlus 200, require different amounts of resources to produce.

The BodyPlus 100 consists of a frame unit, a press station, and a pec-dec station. Each frame produced uses 4 hours of machining and welding time and 2 hours of painting and finishing time. Each press station requires 2 hours of machining and welding time and 1 hour of painting and finishing time, and each pec-dec station uses 2 hours of machining and welding time and 2 hours of painting and finishing time. In addition, 2 hours are spent assembling, testing, and packaging each BodyPlus 100. The raw material costs are $450 for each frame, $300 for each press station, and $250 for each pec-dec station; packaging costs are estimated to be $50 per unit.

The BodyPlus 200 consists of a frame unit, a press station, a pec-dec station, and a leg-press station. Each frame produced uses 5 hours of machining and welding time and 4 hours of painting and finishing time. Each press station requires 3 hours machining and welding time and 2 hours of painting and finishing time, each pec-dec station uses 2 hours of machining and welding time and 2 hours of painting and finishing time, and each leg-press station requires 2 hours of machining and welding time and 2 hours of painting and finishing time. In addition, 2 hours are spent assembling, testing, and packaging each Body-Plus 200. The raw material costs are $650 for each frame, $400 for each press station, $250 for each pec-dec station, and $200 for each leg-press station; packaging costs are estimated to be $75 per unit.

For the next production period, management estimates that 600 hours of machining and welding time, 450 hours of painting and finishing time, and 140 hours of assembly, testing, and packaging time will be available. Current labor costs are $20 per hour for machining and welding time, $15 per hour for painting and finishing time, and $12 per hour for assembly, testing, and packaging time. The market in which the two machines must compete suggests a retail price of $2400 for the BodyPlus 100 and $3500 for the BodyPlus 200, although some flexibility may be available to BFI because of the unique capabilities of the new machines. Authorized BFI dealers can purchase machines for 70% of the suggested retail price.

BFI's president believes that the unique capabilities of the BodyPlus 200 can help position BFI as one of the leaders in high-end exercise equipment. Consequently, he has stated that the number of units of the BodyPlus 200 produced must be at least 25% of the total production.

Managerial Report

Analyze the production problem at Better Fitness, Inc., and prepare a report for BFI's president presenting your findings and recommendations. Include (but do not limit your discussion to) a consideration of the following items:

1. What is the recommended number of BodyPlus 100 and BodyPlus 200 machines to produce?
2. How does the requirement that the number of units of the BodyPlus 200 produced be at least 25% of the total production affect profits?
3. Where should efforts be expended in order to increase profits?

Include a copy of your linear programming model and graphical solution in an appendix to your report.

Case Problem 3   HART VENTURE CAPITAL

Hart Venture Capital (HVC) specializes in providing venture capital for software development and Internet applications. Currently HVC has two investment opportunities: (1) Security Systems, a firm that needs additional capital to develop an Internet security software package, and (2) Market Analysis, a market research company that needs additional capital to develop a software package for conducting customer satisfaction surveys. In exchange for Security Systems stock, the firm has asked HVC to provide $600,000 in year 1, $600,000 in year 2, and $250,000 in year 3 over the coming three-year period. In exchange for their stock, Market Analysis has asked HVC to provide $500,000 in year 1, $350,000 in year 2, and $400,000 in year 3 over the same three-year period. HVC believes that both investment opportunities are worth pursuing. However, because of other investments, they are willing to commit at most $800,000 for both projects in the first year, at most $700,000 in the second year, and $500,000 in the third year.

HVC's financial analysis team reviewed both projects and recommended that the company's objective should be to maximize the net present value of the total investment in Security Systems and Market Analysis. The net present value takes into account the estimated value of the stock at the end of the three-year period as well as the capital outflows that are necessary during each of the three years. Using an 8% rate of return, HVC's financial analysis team estimates that 100% funding of the Security Systems project has a net present value of $1,800,000, and 100% funding of the Market Analysis project has a net present value of $1,600,000.

HVC has the option to fund any percentage of the Security Systems and Market Analysis projects. For example, if HVC decides to fund 40% of the Security Systems project, investments of 0.40($600,000) = $240,000 would be required in year 1, 0.40($600,000) = $240,000 would be required in year 2, and 0.40($250,000) = $100,000 would be required in year 3. In this case, the net present value of the Security Systems project would be 0.40($1,800,000) = $720,000. The investment amounts and the net present value for partial funding of the Market Analysis project would be computed in the same manner.

Managerial Report

Perform an analysis of HVC's investment problem and prepare a report that presents your findings and recommendations. Include (but do not limit your discussion to) a consideration of the following items:

1. What is the recommended percentage of each project that HVC should fund and the net present value of the total investment?
2. What capital allocation plan for Security Systems and Market Analysis for the coming three-year period and the total HVC investment each year would you recommend?
3. What effect, if any, would HVC's willingness to commit an additional $100,000 during the first year have on the recommended percentage of each project that HVC should fund?
4. What would the capital allocation plan look like if an additional $100,000 is made available?
5. What is your recommendation as to whether HVC should commit the additional $100,000 in the first year?

Provide model details and relevant computer output in a report appendix.

Appendix 2.1   SOLVING LINEAR PROGRAMS WITH LINGO

LINGO is a product of LINDO Systems. It was developed by Linus E. Schrage and Kevin Cunningham at the University of Chicago.

In this appendix we describe how to use LINGO to solve the Par, Inc., problem. When you start LINGO, two windows are immediately displayed. The outer or main frame window contains all the command menus and the command toolbar. The smaller window is the model window; this window is used to enter and edit the linear programming model you want to solve. The first item we enter into the model window is the objective function. Recall that the objective function for the Par, Inc., problem is Max $10S + 9D$. Thus, in the first line of the LINGO model window, we enter the following expression:

$$\text{MAX} = 10*S + 9*D;$$

Note that in LINGO the symbol * is used to denote multiplication and that the objective function line ends with a semicolon. In general, each mathematical expression (objective function and constraints) in LINGO is terminated with a semicolon.

Next, we press the enter key to move to a new line. The first constraint in the Par, Inc., problem is $0.7S + 1D \leq 630$. Thus, in the second line of the LINGO model window we enter the following expression:

$$0.7*S + 1*D <= 630$$

Note that LINGO interprets the $<=$ symbol as $\leq$. Alternatively, we could enter $<$ instead of $<=$. As was the case when entering the objective function, a semicolon is required at the end of the first constraint. Pressing the enter key moves us to a new line as we continue the process by entering the remaining constraints as shown here:

$$0.5*S + \tfrac{5}{6}*D <= 600$$
$$1*S + \tfrac{2}{3}*D <= 708$$
$$0.1*S + 0.25*D <= 135$$

The model window will now appear as follows:

$$MAX = 10*S + 9*D$$
$$0.7*S + 1*D <= 630$$
$$0.5*S + \tfrac{5}{6}*D <= 600$$
$$1*S + \tfrac{2}{3}*D <= 708$$
$$0.1*S + 0.25*D <= 135$$

When entering a fraction into LINGO it is not necessary to convert the fraction into an equivalent or rounded decimal number. For example, simply enter the fraction $\tfrac{2}{3}$ into LINGO as $\tfrac{2}{3}$ and do not worry about converting to a decimal or how many decimal places to use. Enter $\tfrac{7}{10}$ either as $\tfrac{7}{10}$ or .7. Let LINGO act as a calculator for you.

LINGO is very flexible about the format of an equation and it is not necessary to have the variables on the left hand side of an equation and the constant term on the right. For example,

$$0.7*S + 1*D <= 630$$

could also be entered as

$$0.7*S <= 630 - 1*D$$

This feature will be very useful later when writing models in a clear and understandable form. Finally, note that although we have expressly included a coefficient of 1 on the variable D above, this is not necessary. In LINGO, 1*D and D are equivalent.

If you make an error in entering the model, you can correct it at any time by simply positioning the cursor where you made the error and entering the necessary correction.

To solve the model, select the Solve command from the LINGO menu or press the Solve button on the toolbar at the top of the main frame window. LINGO will begin the solution process by determining whether the model conforms to all syntax requirements. If the LINGO model doesn't pass these tests, you will be informed by an error message. If LINGO does not find any errors in the model input, it will begin to solve the model. As part of the solution process, LINGO displays a Solver Status window that allows you to monitor the progress of the solver. LINGO displays the solution in a new window titled "Solution Report." The output that appears in the Solution Report window for the Par, Inc., problem is shown in Figure 2.25.

The first part of the output shown in Figure 2.25 indicates that an optimal solution has been found and that the value of the objective function is 7668. We see that the optimal solution is $S = 540$ and $D = 252$, and that the slack variables for the four constraints (rows 2–5) are 0, 120, 0, and 18. We will discuss the use of the information in the Reduced Cost column and the Dual Price column in Chapter 3 when we study the topic of sensitivity analysis.

FIGURE 2.25   PAR, INC., SOLUTION REPORT USING LINGO

```
Global optimal solution found.
Objective value:                              7668.000
Total solver iterations:                             2

             Variable              Value          Reduced Cost
          --------------      ---------------    -----------------
                     S           540.0000             0.000000
                     D           252.0000             0.000000

                  Row      Slack or Surplus          Dual Price
          --------------      ---------------    -----------------
                     1           7668.000             1.000000
                     2           0.000000             4.375000
                     3           120.0000             0.000000
                     4           0.000000             6.937500
                     5           18.00000             0.000000
```

Appendix 2.2   SOLVING LINEAR PROGRAMS WITH EXCEL

In this appendix we will use an Excel worksheet to solve the Par, Inc., linear programming problem. We will enter the problem data for the Par problem in the top part of the worksheet and develop the linear programming model in the bottom part of the worksheet.

Formulation

Whenever we formulate a worksheet model of a linear program, we perform the following steps:

Step 1. Enter the problem data in the top part of the worksheet.
Step 2. Specify cell locations for the decision variables.
Step 3. Select a cell and enter a formula for computing the value of the objective function.
Step 4. Select a cell and enter a formula for computing the left-hand side of each constraint.
Step 5. Select a cell and enter a formula for computing the right-hand side of each constraint.

The formula worksheet that we developed for the Par, Inc., problem using these five steps is shown in Figure 2.26. Note that the worksheet consists of two sections: a data section and a model section. The four components of the model are screened, and the cells reserved for the decision variables are enclosed in a boldface box. Figure 2.26 is called a formula worksheet because it displays the formulas that we have entered and not the values computed from those formulas. In a moment we will see how Excel's Solver is used to find the optimal solution to the Par, Inc., problem. But first, let's review each of the preceding steps as they apply to the Par, Inc., problem.

Step 1. Enter the problem data in the top part of the worksheet.
Cells B5:C8 show the production requirements per unit for each product. Note that in cells C6 and C7, we have entered the exact fractions. That is, in cell C6 we have entered $=5/6$ and in cell C7 we have entered $=2/3$.

FIGURE 2.26   FORMULA WORKSHEET FOR THE PAR, INC., PROBLEM

	A	B	C	D
1	Par, Inc.			
2				
3		**Production Time**		
4	**Operation**	**Standard**	**Deluxe**	**Time Available**
5	Cutting and Dyeing	0.7	1	630
6	Sewing	0.5	0.83333	600
7	Finishing	1	0.66667	708
8	Inspection and Packaging	0.1	0.25	135
9	**Profit Per Bag**	10	9	
10				
11				
12	**Model**			
13				
14		**Decision Variables**		
15		**Standard**	**Deluxe**	
16	**Bags Produced**			
17				
18	**Maximize Total Profit**	=B9*B16+C9*C16		
19				
20	**Constraints**	**Hours Used (LHS)**		**Hours Available (RHS)**
21	Cutting and Dyeing	=B5*B16+C5*C16	<=	=D5
22	Sewing	=B6*B16+C6*C16	<=	=D6
23	Finishing	=B7*B16+C7*C16	<=	=D7
24	Inspection and Packaging	=B8*B16+C8*C16	<=	=D8

Cells B9:C9 show the profit contribution per unit for the two products.
Cells D5:D8 show the number of hours available in each department.

Step 2. Specify cell locations for the decision variables.

Cell B16 will contain the number of standard bags produced, and cell C16 will contain the number of deluxe bags produced.

Step 3. Select a cell and enter a formula for computing the value of the objective function.

Cell B18: =B9*B16+C9*C16

Step 4. Select a cell and enter a formula for computing the left-hand side of each constraint.

With four constraints, we have

Cell B21: =B5*B16+C5*C16
Cell B22: =B6*B16+C6*C16
Cell B23: =B7*B16+C7*C16
Cell B24: =B8*B16+C8*C16

Step 5. Select a cell and enter a formula for computing the right-hand side of each constraint.

With four constraints, we have

Cell D21: =D5
Cell D22: =D6
Cell D23: =D7
Cell D24: =D8

Note that descriptive labels make the model section of the worksheet easier to read and understand. For example, we added "Standard," "Deluxe," and "Bags Produced" in rows 15 and 16 so that the values of the decision variables appearing in cells B16 and C16 can be easily interpreted. In addition, we entered "Maximize Total Profit" in cell A18 to indicate that the value of the objective function appearing in cell B18 is the maximum profit contribution. In the constraint section of the worksheet we added the constraint names as well as the "<=" symbols to show the relationship that exists between the left-hand side and the right-hand side of each constraint. Although these descriptive labels are not necessary to use Excel Solver to find a solution to the Par, Inc., problem, the labels make it easier for the user to understand and interpret the optimal solution.

Appendix A provides a discussion of how to properly build and structure a good spreadsheet model.

Excel Solution

The standard Excel Solver developed by Frontline Systems can be used to solve all of the linear programming problems presented in this text.

The following steps describe how Excel Solver can be used to obtain the optimal solution to the Par, Inc., problem:

Step 1. Select the **Data tab** on the **Ribbon**
Step 2. Select **Solver** from the **Analysis Group**
Step 3. When the **Solver Parameters** dialog box appears (see Figure 2.27):
  Enter B18 into the **Set Objective** box
  Select the **To: Max** option
  Enter B16:C16 into the **By Changing Variable Cells** box
Step 4. Select **Add**
  When the **Add Constraint** dialog box appears:
  Enter B21:B24 in the left-hand box of the **Cell Reference** area
  Select <= from the middle drop-down button.
  Enter D21:D24 in the **Constraint** area
  Click **OK**
Step 5. When the **Solver Parameters** dialog box reappears:
  Select the checkbox, **Make Unconstrained Variables Non-Negative**
Step 6. Select the **Select a Solving Method** drop-down button
  Select **Simplex LP**
Step 7. Choose **Solve**
Step 8. When the **Solver Results** dialog box appears:
  Select **Keep Solver Solution**
  Click **OK**

Figure 2.27 shows the completed **Solver Parameters** dialog box, and Figure 2.28 shows the optimal solution in the worksheet. The optimal solution of 540 standard bags and 252 deluxe bags is the same as we obtained using the graphical solution procedure. In addition to the output information shown in Figure 2.28, Solver has an option to provide sensitivity analysis information. We discuss sensitivity analysis in Chapter 3.

In Step 5 we selected the **Make Unconstrained Variables Non-Negative** checkbox to avoid having to enter nonnegativity constraints for the decision variables. In general, whenever we want to solve a linear programming model in which the decision variables are all restricted to be nonnegative, we will select this option. In addition, in Step 4 we entered all four less-than-or-equal-to constraints simultaneously by entering B21:B24 in the left-hand

FIGURE 2.27   SOLVER PARAMETERS DIALOG BOX FOR THE PAR, INC., PROBLEM

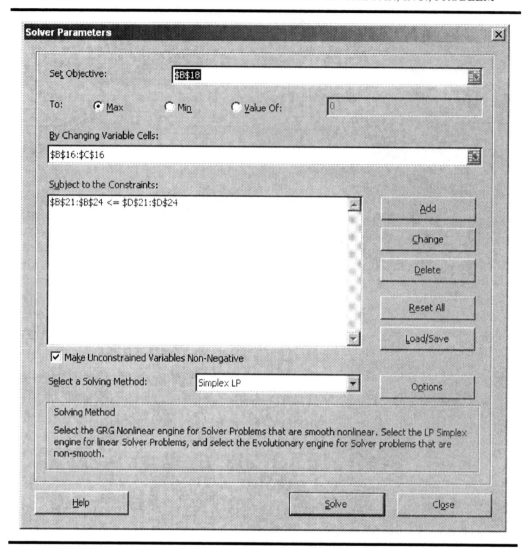

box of the **Cell Reference** area, selecting $<=$, and entering D21:D24 in the right-hand box. Alternatively, we could have entered the four constraints one at a time.

As a reminder, when entering a fraction into Excel, it is not necessary to convert the fraction into an equivalent or rounded decimal number. For example, simply enter the fraction $2/3$ into Excel as $=2/3$ and do not worry about converting to a decimal or how many decimal places to use. Enter $7/10$ either as $=7/10$ or $=.7$. When entering a fraction, the "$=$" sign is necessary; otherwise, Excel will treat the fraction as text rather than a number.

FIGURE 2.28   EXCEL SOLUTION FOR THE PAR, INC., PROBLEM

	A	B	C	D
4	Operation	Standard	Deluxe	Time Available
5	Cutting and Dyeing	0.7	1	630
6	Sewing	0.5	0.833333333	600
7	Finishing	1	0.666666667	708
8	Inspection and Packaging	0.1	0.25	135
9	Profit Per Bag	10	9	
10				
11				
12	Model			
13				
14		Decision Variables		
15		Standard	Deluxe	
16	Bags Produced	540.00000	252.00000	
17				
18	Maximize Total Profit	7668		
19				
20	Constraints	Hours Used (LHS)		Hours Available (RHS)
21	Cutting and Dyeing	630	<=	630
22	Sewing	480.00000	<=	600
23	Finishing	708	<=	708
24	Inspection and Packaging	117.00000	<=	135

CHAPTER 3

Linear Programming: Sensitivity Analysis and Interpretation of Solution

CONTENTS

Sensitivity analysis is the study of how the changes in the coefficients of an optimization model affect the optimal solution. Using sensitivity analysis, we can answer questions such as the following:

1. How will a change *in a coefficient of the objective function* affect the optimal solution?
2. How will a change in the *right-hand-side value for a constraint* affect the optimal solution?

Because sensitivity analysis is concerned with how these changes affect the optimal solution, the analysis does not begin until the optimal solution to the original linear programming problem has been obtained. For that reason, sensitivity analysis is often referred to as *postoptimality analysis.*

Our approach to sensitivity analysis parallels the approach used to introduce linear programming in Chapter 2. We begin by showing how a graphical method can be used to perform sensitivity analysis for linear programming problems with two decision variables. Then, we show how optimization software provides sensitivity analysis information.

Finally, we extend the discussion of problem formulation started in Chapter 2 by formulating and solving three larger linear programming problems. In discussing the solution for each of these problems, we focus on managerial interpretation of the optimal solution and sensitivity analysis information.

MANAGEMENT SCIENCE IN ACTION

ASSIGNING PRODUCTS TO WORLDWIDE FACILITIES AT EASTMAN KODAK*

One of the major planning issues at Eastman Kodak involves the determination of which products should be manufactured at Kodak's facilities located throughout the world. The assignment of products to facilities is called the "world load." In determining the world load, Kodak faces a number of interesting trade-offs. For instance, not all manufacturing facilities are equally efficient for all products, and the margins by which some facilities are better varies from product to product. In addition to manufacturing costs, the transportation costs and the effects of duty and duty drawbacks can significantly affect the allocation decision.

To assist in determining the world load, Kodak developed a linear programming model that accounts for the physical nature of the distribution problem and the various costs (manufacturing, transportation, and duties) involved. The model's objective is to minimize the total cost subject to constraints such as satisfying demand and capacity constraints for each facility.

The linear programming model is a static representation of the problem situation, and the real world is always changing. Thus, the linear programming model must be used in a dynamic way. For instance, when demand expectations change, the model can be used to determine the effect the change will have on the world load. Suppose that the currency of country A rises compared to the currency of country B. How should the world load be modified? In addition to using the linear programming model in a "how-to-react" mode, the model is useful in a more active mode by considering questions such as the following: Is it worthwhile for facility F to spend *d* dollars to lower the unit manufacturing cost of product P from *x* to *y*? The linear programming model helps Kodak evaluate the overall effect of possible changes at any facility.

In the final analysis, managers recognize that they cannot use the model by simply turning it on, reading the results, and executing the solution. The model's recommendation combined with managerial judgment provide the final decision.

*Based on information provided by Greg Sampson of Eastman Kodak.

Sensitivity analysis and the interpretation of the optimal solution are important aspects of applying linear programming. The Management Science in Action, Assigning Products to Worldwide Facilities at Eastman Kodak, shows some of the sensitivity analysis and interpretation issues encountered at Kodak in determining the optimal product assignments. Later in the chapter, other Management Science in Action articles illustrate how Performance Analysis Corporation uses sensitivity analysis as part of an evaluation model for a chain of fast-food outlets, how GE Plastics uses a linear programming model involving thousands of variables and constraints to determine optimal production quantities, how the Nutrition Coordinating Center of the University of Minnesota uses a linear programming model to estimate the nutrient amounts in new food products, and how Duncan Industries Limited's linear programming model for tea distribution convinced management of the benefits of using quantitative analysis techniques to support the decision-making process.

3.1 INTRODUCTION TO SENSITIVITY ANALYSIS

Sensitivity analysis is important to decision makers because real-world problems exist in a changing environment. Prices of raw materials change, product demand changes, companies purchase new machinery, stock prices fluctuate, employee turnover occurs, and so on. If a linear programming model has been used in such an environment, we can expect some of the coefficients to change over time. We will then want to determine how these changes affect the optimal solution to the original linear programming problem. Sensitivity analysis provides us with the information needed to respond to such changes without requiring the complete solution of a revised linear program.

Recall the Par, Inc., problem:

$$\text{Max} \quad 10S + 9D$$

s.t.

$$
\begin{aligned}
\tfrac{7}{10}S + 1D &\leq 630 \quad \text{Cutting and dyeing} \\
\tfrac{1}{2}S + \tfrac{5}{6}D &\leq 600 \quad \text{Sewing} \\
1S + \tfrac{2}{3}D &\leq 708 \quad \text{Finishing} \\
\tfrac{1}{10}S + \tfrac{1}{4}D &\leq 135 \quad \text{Inspection and packaging} \\
S, D &\geq 0
\end{aligned}
$$

The optimal solution, $S = 540$ standard bags and $D = 252$ deluxe bags, was based on profit contribution figures of $10 per standard bag and $9 per deluxe bag. Suppose we later learn that a price reduction causes the profit contribution for the standard bag to fall from $10 to $8.50. Sensitivity analysis can be used to determine whether the production schedule calling for 540 standard bags and 252 deluxe bags is still best. If it is, solving a modified linear programming problem with $8.50S + 9D$ as the new objective function will not be necessary.

Sensitivity analysis can also be used to determine which coefficients in a linear programming model are crucial. For example, suppose that management believes the $9 profit contribution for the deluxe bag is only a rough estimate of the profit contribution that will actually be obtained. If sensitivity analysis shows that 540 standard bags and 252 deluxe bags will be the optimal solution as long as the profit contribution for the deluxe bag is between $6.67 and $14.29, management should feel comfortable with the $9-per-bag estimate and the recommended production quantities. However, if sensitivity analysis shows that 540 standard bags and 252 deluxe bags will be the optimal solution only if the profit contribution for the deluxe bags is between $8.90 and $9.25, management may want to review the accuracy of the $9-per-bag estimate. Management would especially want to consider how the optimal production quantities should be revised if the profit contribution per deluxe bag were to drop.

Another aspect of sensitivity analysis concerns changes in the right-hand-side values of the constraints. Recall that in the Par, Inc., problem the optimal solution used all available time in the cutting and dyeing department and the finishing department. What would happen to the optimal solution and total profit contribution if Par could obtain additional quantities of either of these resources? Sensitivity analysis can help determine how much each additional hour of production time is worth and how many hours can be added before diminishing returns set in.

3.2 GRAPHICAL SENSITIVITY ANALYSIS

For linear programming problems with two decision variables, graphical solution methods can be used to perform sensitivity analysis on the objective function coefficients and the right-hand-side values for the constraints.

Objective Function Coefficients

Let us consider how changes in the objective function coefficients might affect the optimal solution to the Par, Inc., problem. The current contribution to profit is $10 per unit for the standard bag and $9 per unit for the deluxe bag. It seems obvious that an increase in the profit contribution for one of the bags might lead management to increase production of that bag, and a decrease in the profit contribution for one of the bags might lead management to decrease production of that bag. It is not as obvious, however, how much the profit contribution would have to change before management would want to change the production quantities.

The current optimal solution to this problem calls for producing 540 standard golf bags and 252 deluxe golf bags. The **range of optimality** for each objective function coefficient provides the range of values over which the current solution will remain optimal. Managerial attention should be focused on those objective function coefficients that have a narrow range of optimality and coefficients near the end points of the range. With these coefficients, a small change can necessitate modifying the optimal solution. Let us now compute the ranges of optimality for this problem.

Figure 3.1 shows the graphical solution. A careful inspection of this graph shows that as long as the slope of the objective function line is between the slope of line A (which coincides with the cutting and dyeing constraint line) and the slope of line B (which coincides with the finishing constraint line), extreme point ③ with $S = 540$ and $D = 252$ will be optimal. Changing an objective function coefficient for S or D will cause the slope of the objective function line to change. In Figure 3.1 we see that such changes cause the objective function line to rotate around extreme point ③. However, as long as the objective function line stays within the shaded region, extreme point ③ will remain optimal.

Rotating the objective function line *counterclockwise* causes the slope to become less negative, and the slope increases. When the objective function line rotates counterclockwise (slope increased) enough to coincide with line A, we obtain alternative optimal solutions between extreme points ③ and ④. Any further counterclockwise rotation of the objective function line will cause extreme point ③ to be nonoptimal. Hence, the slope of line A provides an upper limit for the slope of the objective function line.

Rotating the objective function line *clockwise* causes the slope to become more negative, and the slope decreases. When the objective function line rotates clockwise (slope decreases) enough to coincide with line B, we obtain alternative optimal solutions between extreme points ③ and ②. Any further clockwise rotation of the objective function line

The slope of the objective function line usually is negative; hence, rotating the objective function line clockwise makes the line steeper even though the slope is getting smaller (more negative).

FIGURE 3.1   GRAPHICAL SOLUTION OF PAR, INC., PROBLEM WITH SLOPE OF OBJECTIVE FUNCTION LINE BETWEEN SLOPES OF LINES A AND B; EXTREME POINT ③ IS OPTIMAL

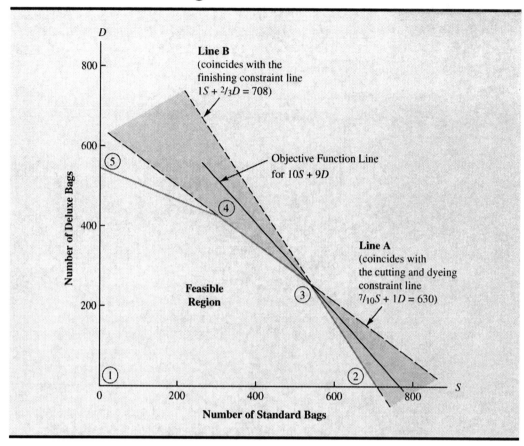

will cause extreme point ③ to be nonoptimal. Hence, the slope of line B provides a lower limit for the slope of the objective function line.

Thus, extreme point ③ will be the optimal solution as long as

Slope of line B ≤ slope of the objective function line ≤ slope of line A

In Figure 3.1 we see that the equation for line A, the cutting and dyeing constraint line, is as follows:

$$\tfrac{7}{10}S + 1D = 630$$

By solving this equation for D, we can write the equation for line A in its slope-intercept form, which yields

$$D = -\tfrac{7}{10}S + 630$$

Slope of   Intercept of
line A   line A on
            D axis

Thus, the slope for line A is $-\tfrac{7}{10}$, and its intercept on the D axis is 630.

The equation for line B in Figure 3.1 is

$$1S + \tfrac{2}{3}D = 708$$

Solving for D provides the slope-intercept form for line B. Doing so yields

$$\tfrac{2}{3}D = -1S + 708$$
$$D = -\tfrac{3}{2}S + 1062$$

Thus, the slope of line B is $-\tfrac{3}{2}$, and its intercept on the D axis is 1062.

Now that the slopes of lines A and B have been computed, we see that for extreme point ③ to remain optimal we must have

$$-\tfrac{3}{2} \leq \text{slope of objective function} \leq -\tfrac{7}{10} \qquad (3.1)$$

Let us now consider the general form of the slope of the objective function line. Let C_S denote the profit of a standard bag, C_D denote the profit of a deluxe bag, and P denote the value of the objective function. Using this notation, the objective function line can be written as

$$P = C_S S + C_D D$$

Writing this equation in slope-intercept form, we obtain

$$C_D D = -C_S S + P$$

and

$$D = -\frac{C_S}{C_D} S + \frac{P}{C_D}$$

Thus, we see that the slope of the objective function line is given by $-C_S/C_D$. Substituting $-C_S/C_D$ into expression (3.1), we see that extreme point ③ will be optimal as long as the following expression is satisfied:

$$-\tfrac{3}{2} \leq -\frac{C_S}{C_D} \leq -\tfrac{7}{10} \qquad (3.2)$$

To compute the range of optimality for the standard-bag profit contribution, we hold the profit contribution for the deluxe bag fixed at its initial value $C_D = 9$. Doing so in expression (3.2), we obtain

$$-\tfrac{3}{2} \leq -\frac{C_S}{9} \leq -\tfrac{7}{10}$$

From the left-hand inequality, we have

$$-\tfrac{3}{2} \leq -\frac{C_S}{9} \qquad \text{or} \qquad \tfrac{3}{2} \geq \frac{C_S}{9}$$

Thus,

$$\tfrac{27}{2} \geq C_S \qquad \text{or} \qquad C_S \leq \tfrac{27}{2} = 13.5$$

From the right-hand inequality, we have

$$-\frac{C_S}{9} \leq -\tfrac{7}{10} \qquad \text{or} \qquad \frac{C_S}{9} \geq \tfrac{7}{10}$$

Thus,

$$C_S \geq \tfrac{63}{10} \qquad \text{or} \qquad C_S \geq 6.3$$

Combining the calculated limits for C_S provides the following range of optimality for the standard-bag profit contribution:

$$6.3 \leq C_S \leq 13.5$$

In the original problem for Par, Inc., the standard bag had a profit contribution of $10. The resulting optimal solution was 540 standard bags and 252 deluxe bags. The range of optimality for C_S tells Par's management that, with other coefficients unchanged, the profit contribution for the standard bag can be anywhere between $6.30 and $13.50 and the production quantities of 540 standard bags and 252 deluxe bags will remain optimal. Note, however, that even though the production quantities will not change, the total profit contribution (value of objective function) will change due to the change in profit contribution per standard bag.

These computations can be repeated, holding the profit contribution for standard bags constant at $C_S = 10$. In this case, the range of optimality for the deluxe-bag profit contribution can be determined. Check to see that this range is $6.67 \leq C_D \leq 14.29$.

In cases where the rotation of the objective function line about an optimal extreme point causes the objective function line to become *vertical,* there will be either no upper limit or no lower limit for the slope as it appears in the form of expression (3.2). To show how this special situation can occur, suppose that the objective function for the Par, Inc., problem is $18C_S + 9C_D$; in this case, extreme point ② in Figure 3.2 provides the optimal solution. Rotating the objective function line counterclockwise around extreme point ② provides an upper limit for the slope when the objective function line coincides with line B. We showed previously that the slope of line B is $-\tfrac{3}{2}$, so the upper limit for the slope of the objective function line must be $-\tfrac{3}{2}$. However, rotating the objective function line clockwise results in the slope becoming more and more negative, approaching a value of minus infinity as the objective function line becomes vertical; in this case, the slope of the objective function has no lower limit. Using the upper limit of $-\tfrac{3}{2}$, we can write

$$-\frac{C_S}{C_D} \leq -\tfrac{3}{2}$$

Slope of the
objective function line

FIGURE 3.2 GRAPHICAL SOLUTION OF PAR, INC., PROBLEM WITH AN OBJECTIVE FUNCTION OF $18S + 9D$; OPTIMAL SOLUTION AT EXTREME POINT ②

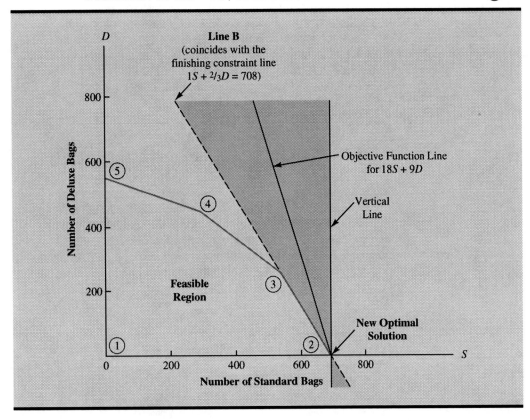

Following the previous procedure of holding C_D constant at its original value, $C_D = 9$, we have

$$-\frac{C_S}{9} \leq -\tfrac{3}{2} \quad \text{or} \quad \frac{C_S}{9} \geq \tfrac{3}{2}$$

Solving for C_S provides the following result:

$$C_S \geq \tfrac{27}{2} = 13.5$$

In reviewing Figure 3.2 we note that extreme point ② remains optimal for all values of C_S above 13.5. Thus, we obtain the following range of optimality for C_S at extreme point ②:

$$13.5 \leq C_S < \infty$$

Simultaneous Changes The range of optimality for objective function coefficients is only applicable for changes made to one coefficient at a time. All other coefficients are assumed to be fixed at their initial values. If two or more objective function coefficients are changed simultaneously, further analysis is necessary to determine whether the optimal solution will change. However, when solving two-variable problems graphically, expression (3.2) suggests an easy way to determine whether simultaneous changes in both objective function coefficients will cause a change in the optimal solution. Simply compute the slope of the objective function $(-C_S/C_D)$ for the new coefficient values. If this ratio is greater than or equal to the lower limit on the slope of the objective function and less than or equal to the upper limit, then the changes made will not cause a change in the optimal solution.

Consider changes in both of the objective function coefficients for the Par, Inc., problem. Suppose the profit contribution per standard bag is increased to $13 and the profit contribution per deluxe bag is simultaneously reduced to $8. Recall that the ranges of optimality for C_S and C_D (both computed in a one-at-a-time manner) are

$$6.3 \le C_S \le 13.5 \qquad (3.3)$$
$$6.67 \le C_D \le 14.29 \qquad (3.4)$$

For these ranges of optimality, we can conclude that changing either C_S to $13 or C_D to $8 (but not both) would not cause a change in the optimal solution of $S = 540$ and $D = 252$. But we cannot conclude from the ranges of optimality that changing both coefficients simultaneously would not result in a change in the optimal solution.

In expression (3.2) we showed that extreme point ③ remains optimal as long as

$$-\tfrac{3}{2} \le -\frac{C_S}{C_D} \le -\tfrac{7}{10}$$

If C_S is changed to 13 and simultaneously C_D is changed to 8, the new objective function slope will be given by

$$-\frac{C_S}{C_D} = -\frac{13}{8} = -1.625$$

Because this value is less than the lower limit of $-\tfrac{3}{2}$, the current solution of $S = 540$ and $D = 252$ will no longer be optimal. By re-solving the problem with $C_S = 13$ and $C_D = 8$, we will find that extreme point ② is the new optimal solution.

Looking at the ranges of optimality, we concluded that changing either C_S to $13 or C_D to $8 (but not both) would not cause a change in the optimal solution. But in recomputing the slope of the objective function with simultaneous changes for both C_S and C_D, we saw that the optimal solution did change. This result emphasizes the fact that a range of optimality, by itself, can only be used to draw a conclusion about changes made to *one objective function coefficient at a time.*

Right-Hand Sides

Let us now consider how a change in the right-hand side for a constraint may affect the feasible region and perhaps cause a change in the optimal solution to the problem. To illustrate this aspect of sensitivity analysis, let us consider what happens if an additional 10 hours of production time become available in the cutting and dyeing department of Par, Inc. The right-hand side of the cutting and dyeing constraint is changed from 630 to 640, and the constraint is rewritten as

$$\tfrac{7}{10}S + 1D \le 640$$

FIGURE 3.3   EFFECT OF A 10-UNIT CHANGE IN THE RIGHT-HAND SIDE
OF THE CUTTING AND DYEING CONSTRAINT

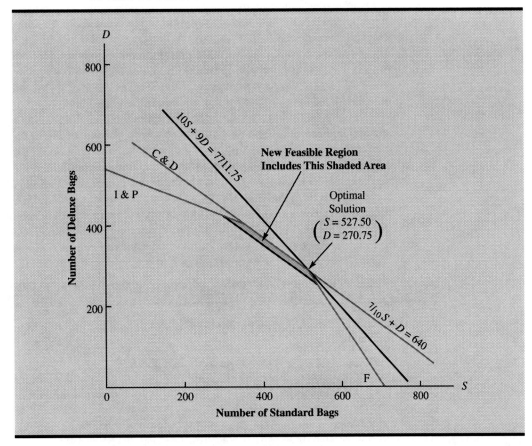

By obtaining an additional 10 hours of cutting and dyeing time, we expand the feasible region for the problem, as shown in Figure 3.3. With an enlarged feasible region, we now want to determine whether one of the new feasible solutions provides an improvement in the value of the objective function. Application of the graphical solution procedure to the problem with the enlarged feasible region shows that the extreme point with $S = 527.5$ and $D = 270.75$ now provides the optimal solution. The new value for the objective function is $10(527.5) + 9(270.75) = \$7711.75$, with an increase in profit of $\$7711.75 - \$7668.00 = \$43.75$. Thus, the increased profit occurs at a rate of $\$43.75/10$ hours $= \$4.375$ per hour added.

The *change* in the value of the optimal solution per unit increase in the right-hand side of the constraint is called the **dual value.** Here, the dual value for the cutting and dyeing constraint is $4.375; in other words, if we increase the right-hand side of the cutting and dyeing constraint by 1 hour, the value of the objective function will increase by $4.375. Conversely, if the right-hand side of the cutting and dyeing constraint were to decrease by 1 hour, the objective function would go down by $4.375. The dual value can generally be used to determine what will happen to the value of the objective function when we make a one-unit change in the right-hand side of a constraint.

We caution here that the value of the dual value may be applicable only for small changes in the right-hand side. As more and more resources are obtained and the right-hand-side value continues to increase, other constraints will become binding and limit the change in the value of the objective function. For example, in the problem for Par, Inc., we would eventually reach a point where more cutting and dyeing time would be of no value; it would occur at the point where the cutting and dyeing constraint becomes nonbinding. At this point, the dual value would equal zero. In the next section we will show how to determine the range of values for a right-hand side over which the dual value will accurately predict the improvement in the objective function. Finally, we note that the dual value for any nonbinding constraint will be zero because an increase in the right-hand side of such a constraint will affect only the value of the slack or surplus variable for that constraint.

The dual value is the change in the objective function value per unit increase in a constraint right-hand side. Suppose that we now solve a problem involving the minimization of total cost and that the value of the optimal solution is $100. Furthermore, suppose that the first constraint is a less-than-or-equal-to constraint and that this constraint is binding for the optimal solution. Increasing the right-hand side of this constraint makes the problem easier to solve. Thus, if the right-hand side of this binding constraint is increased by one unit, we expect the optimal objective function value to get better. In the case of a minimization problem, this means that the optimal objective function value gets smaller. If an increase in the right-hand side makes the optimal objective function value smaller, the dual value is negative.

MANAGEMENT SCIENCE IN ACTION

EVALUATING EFFICIENCY AT PERFORMANCE ANALYSIS CORPORATION*

Performance Analysis Corporation specializes in the use of management science to design more efficient and effective operations for a wide variety of chain stores. One such application uses linear programming methodology to provide an evaluation model for a chain of fast-food outlets.

According to the concept of Pareto optimality, a restaurant in a given chain is relatively inefficient if other restaurants in the same chain exhibit the following characteristics:

1. Operates in the same or worse environment
2. Produces at least the same level of *all* outputs
3. Utilizes no more of *any* resource and *less* of at least one of the resources

To determine which of the restaurants are Pareto inefficient, Performance Analysis Corporation developed and solved a linear programming model. Model constraints involve requirements concerning the minimum acceptable levels of output and conditions imposed by uncontrollable elements in the environment, and the objective function calls for the minimization of the resources necessary to produce the output. Solving the model produces the following output for each restaurant:

1. A score that assesses the level of so-called relative technical efficiency achieved by the particular restaurant over the time period in question
2. The reduction in controllable resources or the increase of outputs over the time period in question needed for an inefficient restaurant to be rated as efficient
3. A peer group of other restaurants with which each restaurant can be compared in the future

Sensitivity analysis provides important managerial information. For example, for each constraint concerning a minimum acceptable output level, the dual value tells the manager how much one more unit of output would change the efficiency measure.

The analysis typically identifies 40% to 50% of the restaurants as underperforming, given the previously stated conditions concerning the inputs available and outputs produced. Performance Analysis Corporation finds that if all the relative inefficiencies identified are eliminated simultaneously, corporate profits typically increase approximately 5% to 10%. This increase is truly substantial given the large scale of operations involved.

*Based on information provided by Richard C. Morey of Performance Analysis Corporation.

The Management Science in Action, Evaluating Efficiency at Performance Analysis Corporation, illustrates the use of dual values as part of an evaluation model for a chain of fast-food outlets. This type of model will be studied in more detail in Chapter 5 when we discuss an application referred to as data envelopment analysis.

NOTES AND COMMENTS

1. If two objective function coefficients change simultaneously, both may move outside their respective ranges of optimality and not affect the optimal solution. For instance, in a two-variable linear program, the slope of the objective function will not change at all if both coefficients are changed by the same percentage.

2. Some textbooks and optimization solvers, for example Excel Solver, use the term *shadow price* rather than dual value.

3.3   SENSITIVITY ANALYSIS: COMPUTER SOLUTION

In Section 2.4 we showed how to interpret the output of a linear programming solver. In this section we continue that discussion and show how to interpret the sensitivity analysis output. We use the Par, Inc., problem restated below.

$$\text{Max} \quad 10S + 9D$$

s.t.

$$\begin{aligned}
\tfrac{7}{10}S + 1D &\leq 630 \quad \text{Cutting and dyeing} \\
\tfrac{1}{2}S + \tfrac{5}{6}D &\leq 600 \quad \text{Sewing} \\
1S + \tfrac{2}{3}D &\leq 708 \quad \text{Finishing} \\
\tfrac{1}{10}S + \tfrac{1}{4}D &\leq 135 \quad \text{Inspection and packaging} \\
S, D &\geq 0
\end{aligned}$$

Let us demonstrate interpreting the sensitivity analysis by considering the solution to the Par, Inc., linear program shown in Figure 3.4.

Interpretation of Computer Output

In Section 2.4 we discussed the output in the top portion of Figure 3.4. We see that the optimal solution is $S = 540$ standard bags and $D = 252$ deluxe bags; the value of the optimal solution is $7668. Associated with each decision variable is reduced cost. We will interpret the reduced cost after our discussion on dual values.

Immediately following the optimal S and D values and the reduced cost information, the computer output provides information about the constraints. Recall that the Par, Inc., problem had four less-than-or-equal-to constraints corresponding to the hours available in each of four production departments. The information shown in the Slack/Surplus column provides the value of the slack variable for each of the departments. This information is summarized here:

Constraint Number	Constraint Name	Slack
1	Cutting and dyeing	0
2	Sewing	120
3	Finishing	0
4	Inspection and packaging	18

FIGURE 3.4   THE SOLUTION FOR THE PAR, INC., PROBLEM

Optimal Objective Value =   7668.00000

Variable	Value	Reduced Cost
S	540.00000	0.00000
D	252.00000	0.00000

Constraint	Slack/Surplus	Dual Value
1	0.00000	4.37500
2	120.00000	0.00000
3	0.00000	6.93750
4	18.00000	0.00000

Variable	Objective Coefficient	Allowable Increase	Allowable Decrease
S	10.00000	3.50000	3.70000
D	9.00000	5.28571	2.33333

Constraint	RHS Value	Allowable Increase	Allowable Decrease
1	630.00000	52.36364	134.40000
2	600.00000	Infinite	120.00000
3	708.00000	192.00000	128.00000
4	135.00000	Infinite	18.00000

Par

From this information, we see that the binding constraints (the cutting and dyeing and the finishing constraints) have zero slack at the optimal solution. The sewing department has 120 hours of slack, or unused capacity, and the inspection and packaging department has 18 hours of slack, or unused capacity.

The Dual Value column contains information about the marginal value of each of the four resources at the optimal solution. In Section 3.2 we defined the *dual value* as follows:

> The dual value associated with a constraint is the *change* in the optimal value of the solution per unit increase in the right-hand side of the constraint.

Try Problem 5 to test your ability to use computer output to determine the optimal solution and to interpret the dual values.

Thus, the nonzero dual values of 4.37500 for constraint 1 (cutting and dyeing constraint) and 6.93750 for constraint 3 (finishing constraint) tell us that an additional hour of cutting and dyeing time increases the value of the optimal solution by $4.37, and an additional hour of finishing time increases the value of the optimal solution by $6.94. Thus, if the cutting and dyeing time were increased from 630 to 631 hours, with all other coefficients in the problem remaining the same, Par's profit would be increased by $4.37, from $7668 to $7668 + $4.37 = $7672.37. A similar interpretation for the finishing constraint implies that an increase from 708 to 709 hours of available finishing time, with all other coefficients in the problem remaining the same, would increase Par's profit to $7668 + $6.94 = $7674.94. Because the sewing and the inspection and packaging constraints both have slack, or unused capacity, available, the dual values of zero show that additional hours of these two resources will not improve the value of the objective function.

Now that the concept of a dual value has been explained, we define the reduced cost associated with each variable. The **reduced cost** associated with a variable is equal to the dual value for the nonnegativity constraint associated with the variable. From Figure 3.4, we see that the reduced cost on variable S is zero and on variable D is zero. This makes sense. Consider variable S. The nonnegativity constraint is $S \geq 0$. The current value of S is 540, so changing the nonnegativity constraint to $S \geq 1$ has no effect on the optimal solution value. Because increasing the right-hand side by one unit has no effect on the optimal objective function value, the dual value (i.e., reduced cost) of this nonnegativity constraint is zero. A similar argument applies to variable D. In general, if a variable has a nonzero value in the optimal solution, then it will have a reduced cost equal to zero. Later in this section we give an example where the reduced cost of a variable is nonzero, and this example provides more insight on why the term *reduced cost* is used for the nonnegativity constraint dual value.

Referring again to the computer output in Figure 3.4, we see that after providing the constraint information on slack/surplus variables and dual values, the solution output provides ranges for the objective function coefficients and the right-hand sides of the constraints.

Considering the objective function coefficient range analysis, we see that variable S, which has a current profit coefficient of 10, has an *allowable increase* of 3.5 and an *allowable decrease* of 3.7. Therefore, as long as the profit contribution associated with the standard bag is between $10 – $3.7 = $6.30 and $10 + $3.5 = $13.50, the production of $S = 540$ standard bags and $D = 252$ deluxe bags will remain the optimal solution. Therefore, the range of optimality for the objective function coefficient on variable S is from 6.3 to 13.5. Note that the range of optimality is the same as obtained by performing graphical sensitivity analysis for C_S in Section 3.2.

Using the objective function coefficient range information for deluxe bags, we see the following range of optimality (after rounding to two decimal places):

$$9 - 2.33 = 6.67 \leq C_p \leq 9 + 5.29 = 14.29$$

This result tells us that as long as the profit contribution associated with the deluxe bag is between $6.67 and $14.29, the production of $S = 540$ standard bags and $D = 252$ deluxe bags will remain the optimal solution.

The final section of the computer output provides the allowable increase and allowable decrease in the right-hand sides of the constraints relative to the dual values holding. As long as the constraint right-hand side is not increased (decreased) by more than the allowable increase (decrease), the associated dual value gives the exact change in the value of the optimal solution per unit increase in the right-hand side. For example, let us consider the cutting and dyeing constraint with a current right-hand-side value of 630. Because the dual value for this constraint is $4.37, we can conclude that additional hours will increase the objective function by $4.37 per hour. It is also true that a reduction in the hours available will reduce the value of the objective function by $4.37 per hour. From the range information given, we see that the dual value of $4.37 has an allowable increase of 52.36364 and is therefore valid for right-hand side values up to 630 + 52.36364 = 682.363364. The allowable decrease is 134.4, so the dual value of $4.37 is valid for right-hand side values down to 630 – 134.4 = 495.6. A similar interpretation for the finishing constraint's right-hand

Try Problem 6 to test your ability to use computer output to determine the ranges of optimality and the ranges of feasibility.

side (constraint 3) shows that the dual value of $6.94 is applicable for increases up to 900 hours and decreases down to 580 hours.

As mentioned, the right-hand-side ranges provide limits within which the dual values give the exact change in the optimal objective function value. For changes outside the range, the problem must be re-solved to find the new optimal solution and the new dual value. We shall call the range over which the dual value is applicable the **range of feasibility.** The ranges of feasibility for the Par, Inc., problem are summarized here:

Constraint	Min RHS	Max RHS
Cutting and dyeing	495.6	682.4
Sewing	480.0	No upper limit
Finishing	580.0	900.0
Inspection and packaging	117.0	No upper limit

As long as the values of the right-hand sides are within these ranges, the dual values shown on the computer output will not change. Right-hand-side values outside these limits will result in changes in the dual value information.

Cautionary Note on the Interpretation of Dual Values

As stated previously, the dual value is the change in the value of the optimal solution per unit increase in the right-hand side of a constraint. When the right-hand side of the constraint represents the amount of a resource available, the associated dual value is often interpreted as the maximum amount one should be willing to pay for one additional unit of the resource. However, such an interpretation is not always correct. To see why, we need to understand the difference between sunk and relevant costs. A **sunk cost** is one that is not affected by the decision made. It will be incurred no matter what values the decision variables assume. A **relevant cost** is one that depends on the decision made. The amount of a relevant cost will vary depending on the values of the decision variables.

Let us reconsider the Par, Inc., problem. The amount of cutting and dyeing time available is 630 hours. The cost of the time available is a sunk cost if it must be paid regardless of the number of standard and deluxe golf bags produced. It would be a relevant cost if Par only had to pay for the number of hours of cutting and dyeing time actually used to produce golf bags. All relevant costs should be reflected in the objective function of a linear program. Sunk costs should not be reflected in the objective function. For Par, Inc., we have been assuming that the company must pay its employees' wages regardless of whether their time on the job is completely utilized. Therefore, the cost of the labor-hours resource for Par, Inc., is a sunk cost and has not been reflected in the objective function.

Only relevant costs should be included in the objective function.

When the cost of a resource is *sunk,* the dual value can be interpreted as the maximum amount the company should be willing to pay for one additional unit of the resource. When the cost of a resource used is relevant, the dual value can be interpreted as the amount by which the value of the resource exceeds its cost. Thus, when the resource cost is relevant, the dual value can be interpreted as the maximum premium over the normal cost that the company should be willing to pay for one unit of the resource.

The Modified Par, Inc., Problem

The graphical solution procedure is useful only for linear programs involving two decision variables. In practice, the problems solved using linear programming usually involve a large number of variables and constraints. For instance, the Management Science in Action, Determining Optimal Production Quantities at GE Plastics, describes how a linear programming model with 3100 variables and 1100 constraints was solved in less than 10 seconds to determine the optimal production quantities at GE Plastics. In this section we discuss the formulation and computer solution for two linear programs with three decision variables. In doing so, we will show how to interpret the reduced-cost portion of the computer output.

The original Par, Inc., problem is restated as follows:

$$\text{Max} \quad 10S + 9D$$

s.t.

$$\frac{7}{10}S + 1D \leq 630 \quad \text{Cutting and dyeing}$$
$$\frac{1}{2}S + \frac{5}{6}D \leq 600 \quad \text{Sewing}$$
$$1S + \frac{2}{3}D \leq 708 \quad \text{Finishing}$$
$$\frac{1}{10}S + \frac{1}{4}D \leq 135 \quad \text{Inspection and packaging}$$
$$S, D \geq 0$$

Recall that S is the number of standard golf bags produced and D is the number of deluxe golf bags produced. Suppose that management is also considering producing a lightweight model designed specifically for golfers who prefer to carry their bags. The design department estimates that each new lightweight model will require 0.8 hours for cutting and dyeing, 1 hour for sewing, 1 hour for finishing, and 0.25 hours for inspection and packaging. Because of the unique capabilities designed into the new model, Par's management feels they will realize a profit contribution of $12.85 for each lightweight model produced during the current production period.

Let us consider the modifications in the original linear programming model that are needed to incorporate the effect of this additional decision variable. We will let L denote the number of lightweight bags produced. After adding L to the objective function and to each of the four constraints, we obtain the following linear program for the modified problem:

$$\text{Max} \quad 10S + 9D + 12.85L$$

s.t.

$$\frac{7}{10}S + 1D + 0.8L \leq 630 \quad \text{Cutting and dyeing}$$
$$\frac{1}{2}S + \frac{5}{6}D + 1L \leq 600 \quad \text{Sewing}$$
$$1S + \frac{2}{3}D + 1L \leq 708 \quad \text{Finishing}$$
$$\frac{1}{10}S + \frac{1}{4}D + \frac{1}{4}L \leq 135 \quad \text{Inspection and packaging}$$
$$S, D, L \geq 0$$

Figure 3.5 shows the solution to the modified problem. We see that the optimal solution calls for the production of 280 standard bags, 0 deluxe bags, and 428 of the new lightweight bags; the value of the optimal solution is $8299.80.

Let us now look at the information contained in the Reduced Cost column. Recall that the reduced costs are the dual values of the corresponding nonnegativity constraints. As the computer output shows, the reduced costs for S and L are zero because these decision variables already have positive values in the optimal solution. However, the reduced cost for decision variable D is −1.15. The interpretation of this number is that if the production of deluxe bags is increased from the current level of 0 to 1, then the optimal objective function value will decrease by 1.15. Another interpretation is that if we "reduce the cost" of deluxe bags by 1.15 (i.e., increase the contribution margin by 1.15), then there is an optimal solution where we produce a nonzero number of deluxe bags.

FIGURE 3.5   SOLUTION FOR THE MODIFIED PAR, INC., PROBLEM

WEB file

Parmod

```
Optimal Objective Value =        8299.80000

        Variable              Value           Reduced Cost
        --------          --------------      --------------
           S                 280.00000              0.00000
           D                   0.00000             -1.15000
           L                 428.00000              0.00000

        Constraint         Slack/Surplus          Dual Value
        --------          --------------         -----------
           1                  91.60000              0.00000
           2                  32.00000              0.00000
           3                   0.00000              8.10000
           4                   0.00000             19.00000

                        Objective         Allowable         Allowable
        Variable       Coefficient         Increase          Decrease
        --------       -----------        ----------        ----------
           S            10.00000            2.07000           4.86000
           D             9.00000            1.15000           Infinite
           L            12.85000           12.15000           0.94091

                           RHS             Allowable         Allowable
        Constraint        Value             Increase          Decrease
        --------       -----------        ----------        ----------
           1            630.00000           Infinite          91.60000
           2            600.00000           Infinite          32.00000
           3            708.00000          144.63158         168.00000
           4            135.00000            9.60000          64.20000
```

Suppose we increase the coefficient of D by exactly $1.15 so that the new value is $9 + $1.15 = $10.15 and then re-solve. Figure 3.6 shows the new solution. Note that although D assumes a positive value in the new solution, the value of the optimal solution has not changed. In other words, increasing the profit contribution of D by *exactly* the amount of the reduced cost has resulted in alternative optimal solutions. Depending on the computer software package used to optimize this model, you may or may not see D assume a positive value if you re-solve the problem with an objective function coefficient of exactly 10.15 for D—that is, the software package may show a different alternative optimal solution. However, if the profit contribution of D is increased by *more than* $1.15, then D will not remain at zero in the optimal solution.

We also note from Figure 3.6 that the dual values for constraints 3 and 4 are 8.1 and 19, respectively, indicating that these two constraints are binding in the optimal solution. Thus, each additional hour in the finishing department would increase the value of the optimal solution by $8.10, and each additional hour in the inspection and packaging department would increase the value of the optimal solution by $19.00. Because of a slack of 91.6 hours in the cutting and dyeing department and 32 hours in the sewing department (see Figure 3.6), management might want to consider the possibility of utilizing these unused labor-hours in the finishing or inspection and packaging departments. For example, some of the employees

FIGURE 3.6   SOLUTION FOR THE MODIFIED PAR, INC., PROBLEM WITH THE COEFFICIENT OF D INCREASED BY $1.15

```
Optimal Objective Value =         8299.80000

        Variable              Value            Reduced Cost
      --------------     --------------      ----------------

          S                403.78378            0.00000
          D                222.81081            0.00000
          L                155.67568            0.00000

       Constraint        Slack/Surplus          Dual Value
      --------------     --------------      ----------------

          1                  0.00000            0.00000
          2                 56.75676            0.00000
          3                  0.00000            8.10000
          4                  0.00000           19.00000
```

Variable	Objective Coefficient	Allowable Increase	Allowable Decrease
S	10.00000	2.51071	0.00000
D	10.15000	5.25790	0.00000
L	12.85000	0.00000	2.19688

Constraint	RHS Value	Allowable Increase	Allowable Decrease
1	630.00000	52.36364	91.60000
2	600.00000	Infinite	56.75676
3	708.00000	144.63158	128.00000
4	135.00000	16.15385	18.00000

in the cutting and dyeing department could be used to perform certain operations in either the finishing department or the inspection and packaging department. In the future, Par's management may want to explore the possibility of cross-training employees so that unused capacity in one department could be shifted to other departments. In the next chapter we will consider similar modeling situations.

NOTES AND COMMENTS

1. Computer software packages for solving linear programs are readily available. Most of these provide the optimal solution, dual or shadow price information, the range of optimality for the objective function coefficients, and the range of feasibility for the right-hand sides. The labels used for the ranges of optimality and feasibility may vary, but the meaning is the same as what we have described here.

2. Whenever one of the right-hand sides is at an end point of its range of feasibility, the dual and shadow prices only provide one-sided information. In this case, they only predict the change in the optimal value of the objective function for changes toward the interior of the range.

(continued)

3. A condition called *degeneracy* can cause a subtle difference in how we interpret changes in the objective function coefficients beyond the end points of the range of optimality. Degeneracy occurs when the dual value equals zero for one of the binding constraints. Degeneracy does not affect the interpretation of changes toward the interior of the range of optimality. However, when degeneracy is present, changes beyond the end points of the range do not necessarily mean a different solution will be optimal. From a practical point of view, changes beyond the end points of the range of optimality necessitate re-solving the problem.

4. Managers are frequently called on to provide an economic justification for new technology. Often the new technology is developed, or purchased, in order to conserve resources. The dual value can be helpful in such cases because it can be used to determine the savings attributable to the new technology by showing the savings per unit of resource conserved.

MANAGEMENT SCIENCE IN ACTION

DETERMINING OPTIMAL PRODUCTION QUANTITIES AT GE PLASTICS*

General Electric Plastics (GEP) is a $5 billion global materials supplier of plastics and raw materials to many industries (e.g., automotive, computer, and medical equipment). GEP has plants all over the globe. In the past, GEP followed a pole-centric manufacturing approach wherein each product was manufactured in the geographic area (Americas, Europe, or Pacific) where it was to be delivered. When many of GEP's customers started shifting their manufacturing operations to the Pacific, a geographic imbalance was created between GEP's capacity and demand in the form of overcapacity in the Americas and undercapacity in the Pacific.

Recognizing that a pole-centric approach was no longer effective, GEP adopted a global approach to its manufacturing operations. Initial work focused on the high-performance polymers (HPP) division. Using a linear programming model, GEP was able to determine the optimal production quantities at each HPP plant to maximize the total contribution margin for the division. The model included demand constraints, manufacturing capacity constraints, and constraints that modeled the flow of materials produced at resin plants to the finishing plants and on to warehouses in three geographical regions (Americas, Europe, and Pacific). The mathematical model for a one-year problem has 3100 variables and 1100 constraints, and can be solved in less than 10 seconds. The new system proved successful at the HPP division, and other GE Plastics divisions are adapting it for their supply chain planning.

*Based on R. Tyagi, P. Kalish, and K. Akbay, "GE Plastics Optimizes the Two-Echelon Global Fulfillment Network at Its High-Performance Polymers Division," *Interfaces* (September/October 2004): 359–366.

3.4   LIMITATIONS OF CLASSICAL SENSITIVITY ANALYSIS

As we have seen, classical sensitivity analysis obtained from computer output can provide useful information on the sensitivity of the solution to changes in the model input data. However, classical sensitivity analysis provided by most computer packages does have its limitations. In this section we discuss three such limitations: simultaneous changes in input data, changes in constraint coefficients, and nonintuitive dual values. We give examples of these three cases and discuss how to effectively deal with these through re-solving the model with changes. In fact, in our experience, it is rarely the case that one solves a model once and makes a recommendaiton. More often than not, a series of models are solved using a variety of input data sets before a final plan is adopted. With improved algorithms and more powerful computers, solving multiple runs of a model is extremely cost and time effective.

Simultaneous Changes

The sensitivity analysis information in computer output is based on the assumption that only one coefficient changes; it is assumed that all other coefficients will remain as stated in the original problem. Thus, the range analysis for the objective function coefficients and the constraint right-hand sides is only applicable for changes in a single coefficient. In many cases, however, we are interested in what would happen if two or more coefficients are changed simultaneously.

Let us consider again the modified Par, Inc., problem, whose solution appears in Figure 3.5. Suppose that after we have solved the problem, we find a new supplier and can purchase the leather required for these bags at a lower cost. Leather is an important component of each of the three types of bags, but is used in different amounts in each type. After factoring in the new cost of leather, the profit margin per bag is found to be $10.30 for a standard bag, $11.40 for a deluxe bag and $12.97 for a lightweight bag. Does the current plan from Figure 3.5 remain optimal? We can easily answer this question by simply re-solving the model using the new profit margins as the objective function coefficients. That is, we use as our objective function: Maximize $10.3S + 11.4D + 12.97L$ with the same set of constraints as in the original model. The solution to this problem appears in Figure 3.7. The new optimal profit is $8718.13. All three types of bags should be produced.

FIGURE 3.7   THE SOLUTION FOR THE MODIFIED PAR, INC., PROBLEM WITH REVISED OBJECTIVE FUNCTION COEFFICIENTS

```
Optimal Objective Value =          8718.12973

        Variable                Value              Reduced Cost
    ------------------      ----------------      ----------------

           S                  403.78378              0.00000
           D                  222.81081              0.00000
           L                  155.67568              0.00000

       Constraint           Slack/Surplus            Dual Value
    ------------------      ----------------      ----------------

           1                    0.00000              3.08919
           2                   56.75676              0.00000
           3                    0.00000              6.56351
           4                    0.00000             15.74054

                          Objective        Allowable        Allowable
        Variable          Coefficient       Increase         Decrease
    ------------        ------------      -----------      -----------

           S              10.30000         2.08000          2.28600
           D              11.40000         4.26053          1.27000
           L              12.97000         1.03909          1.82000

                             RHS          Allowable        Allowable
       Constraint           Value          Increase         Decrease
    ------------        ------------      -----------      -----------

           1              630.00000        52.36364         91.60000
           2              600.00000         Infinite        56.75676
           3              708.00000       144.63158        128.00000
           4              135.00000        16.15385         18.00000
```

Suppose we had not re-solved the model with the new objective function coefficients. We would have used the solution from the original model, the solution found in Figure 3.5. Our profit would have therefore been $10.3(280) + $11.40(0) + $12.97(428) = $8435.16. By re-solving the model with the new information and using the revised plan in Figure 3.7, we have increased total profit by $8718.13 − $8435.16 = $282.97.

Changes in Constraint Coefficients

Classical sensitivity analysis provides no information about changes resulting from a change in the coefficient of a variable in a constraint. To illustrate such a case and how we may deal with it, let us again consider the Modified Par, Inc., problem discussed in Section 3.3.

Suppose we are considering the adoption of a new technology that will allow us to more efficiently finish standard bags. This technology is dedicated to standard bags and would decrease the finishing time on a standard bag from its current value of 1 to ½ of an hour. The technology would not impact the finishing time of deluxe or lightweight bags. The finishing constraint under the new sceanario is:

$$\tfrac{1}{2}S + \tfrac{2}{3}D + 1L \le 708 \quad \text{Finishing with new technology}$$

Even though this is a single change in a coefficient in the model, there is no way to tell from classical sensitivity analysis what impact the change in the coefficient of S will have on the solution. Instead, we must simply change the coefficient and rerun the model. The solution appears in Figure 3.8. Note that the optimal number of standard bags has increased from 280 to 521.1 and the optimal number of lightweight bags decreased from 428 to 331.6. It remains optimal to produce no deluxe bags. Most importantly, with the new technology, the optimal profit increased from $8299.80 to $9471.32, an increase of $1171.52. Using this information with the cost of the new technology will provide an estimate for mangement as to how long it will take to pay off the new technology based on the increase in profits.

Nonintuitive Dual Values

Constraints with variables naturally on both the left-hand and right-hand sides often lead to dual values that have a nonintuitve explantion. To illustrate such a case and how we may deal with it, let us reconsider the Modified Par, Inc., problem discussed in Section 3.3.

Suppose that after reviewing the solution shown in Figure 3.5, management states that they will not consider any solution that does not include the production of some deluxe bags. Management then decides to add the requirement that the number of deluxe bags produced must be at least 30% of the number of standard bags produced. Writing this requirement using the decision variables S and D, we obtain

$$D \ge 0.3S$$

This new constraint is constraint 5 in the modified Par, Inc., linear program. Re-solving the problem with the new constraint 5 yields the optimal solution shown in Figure 3.9.

Let us consider the interpretation of the dual value for constraint 5, the requirement that the number of deluxe bags produced must be at least 30% of the number of standard bags produced. The dual value of −1.38 indicates that a one-unit increase in the right-hand side of the constraint will lower profits by $1.38. Thus, what the dual value of −1.38 is really

FIGURE 3.8   THE SOLUTION FOR THE MODIFIED PAR, INC., PROBLEM WITH NEW
STANDARD BAG FINISHING TECHNOLOGY

```
Optimal Objective Value =          9471.31579

      Variable              Value              Reduced Cost
   ---------------      ---------------      ---------------
        S                  521.05263              0.00000
        D                    0.00000             -6.40789
        L                  331.57895              0.00000

     Constraint          Slack/Surplus           Dual Value
   ---------------      ---------------      ---------------
         1                   0.00000             12.78947
         2                   7.89474              0.00000
         3                 115.89474              0.00000
         4                   0.00000             10.47368

                    Objective         Allowable         Allowable
     Variable      Coefficient         Increase          Decrease
   -----------    -------------      ------------      ------------
        S           10.00000            1.24375           4.86000
        D            9.00000            6.40789          Infinite
        L           12.85000           12.15000           1.42143

                       RHS            Allowable         Allowable
    Constraint         Value           Increase          Decrease
   -----------    -------------      ------------      ------------
         1          630.00000          30.00000         198.00000
         2          600.00000          Infinite           7.89474
         3          708.00000          Infinite         115.89474
         4          135.00000           2.50000          45.00000
```

telling us is what will happen to the value of the optimal solution if the constraint is changed to

$$D \geq 0.3S + 1$$

The interpretation of the dual value of −1.38 is correctly stated as follows: If we are forced to produce one deluxe bag over and above the minimum 30% requirement, total profits will decrease by $1.38. Conversely, if we relax the minimum 30% requirement by one bag ($D \geq 0.3S − 1$), total profits will increase by $1.38.

We might instead be more interested in what happens when the percentage of 30% is increased to 31%. Note that dual value does *not* tell us what will happen in this case. Also, because 0.30 is the coefficient of a variable in a constraint rather than an objective function coefficient or right-hand side, no range analysis is given. Note that this is the case just discussed in the previous section. Because there is no way to get this information directly from classical sensitivity analysis, to answer such a question, we need to re-solve the problem

FIGURE 3.9   THE SOLUTION FOR THE MODIFIED PAR, INC., PROBLEM WITH THE DELUXE BAG REQUIREMENT

```
Optimal Objective Value =          8183.88000

        Variable               Value              Reduced Cost
     --------------       --------------        --------------
            S                336.00000                 0.00000
            D                100.80000                 0.00000
            L                304.80000                 0.00000

       Constraint         Slack/Surplus             Dual Value
     --------------       --------------        --------------
            1                 50.16000                 0.00000
            2                 43.20000                 0.00000
            3                  0.00000                 7.41000
            4                  0.00000                21.76000
            5                  0.00000                -1.38000

                        Objective          Allowable         Allowable
        Variable       Coefficient          Increase          Decrease
     -----------     -------------       -----------       -----------
            S            10.00000           2.07000           3.70500
            D             9.00000           1.15000          12.35000
            L            12.85000           5.29286           0.94091

                            RHS            Allowable         Allowable
       Constraint          Value           Increase          Decrease
     -----------     -------------       -----------       -----------
            1           630.00000          Infinite          50.16000
            2           600.00000          Infinite          43.20000
            3           708.00000          57.00000         168.00000
            4           135.00000          12.00000          31.75000
            5             0.00000         101.67568          84.00000
```

using the constraint $D \geq 0.31S$. To test the sensitivity of the solution to changes in the percentage required we can re-solve the model replacing 0.30 with any percentage of interest.

To get a feel for how the required percentage impacts total profit, we solved versions of the Par, Inc., model with the required percentage varying from 5% to 100% in increments of 5%. This resulted in 20 different versions of the model to be solved. The impact of changing this percentage on the total profit is shown in Figure 3.10, and results are shown in Table 3.1.

What have we learned from this analysis? Notice from Figure 3.10 that the slope of the graph becomes steeper for values larger than 55%. This indicates that there is a shift in the rate of deterioration in profit starting at 55%. Hence, we see that percentages less than or equal to 55% result in modest loss of profit. More pronounced loss of profit results from percentages larger than 55%. So, management now knows that 30% is a reasonable requirement from a profit point of view and that extending the requirement beyond 55% will lead to a more significant loss of profit. From Table 3.1, as we increase the percentage required, fewer lightweight bags are produced.

FIGURE 3.10 PROFIT FOR VARIOUS VALUES OF REQUIRED PERCENTAGE FOR
DELUXE BAGS AS A PERECENTAGE OF STANDARD BAGS

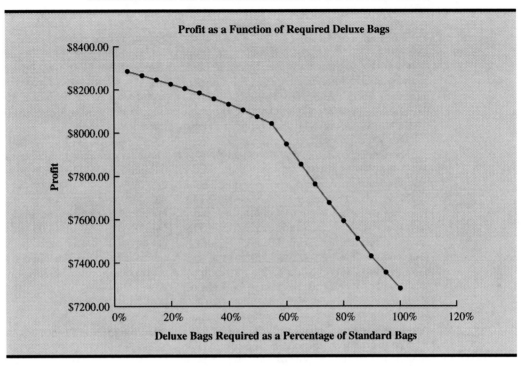

TABLE 3.1 SOLUTIONS VARIOUS VALUES OF REQUIRED PERCENTAGE FOR DELUXE
BAGS AS A PERCENTAGE OF STANDARD BAGS

Percent	Profit	Standard	Deluxe	Lightweight
5%	$8283.24	287.9999	14.4000	410.4000
10%	$8265.71	296.4704	29.6470	391.7648
15%	$8247.11	305.4543	45.8181	372.0002
20%	$8227.35	314.9996	62.9999	351.0002
25%	$8206.31	325.1608	81.2902	328.6455
30%	$8183.88	335.9993	100.7998	304.8005
35%	$8159.89	347.5854	121.6549	279.3110
40%	$8134.20	359.9990	143.9996	252.0008
45%	$8106.60	373.3321	167.9994	222.6677
50%	$8076.87	387.6908	193.8454	191.0783
55%	$8044.77	403.1982	221.7590	156.9617
60%	$7948.80	396.0000	237.6000	144.0000
65%	$7854.27	388.2353	252.3529	132.3529
70%	$7763.37	380.7692	266.5385	121.1538
75%	$7675.90	373.5849	280.1887	110.3774
80%	$7591.67	366.6667	293.3333	100.0000
85%	$7510.50	360.0000	306.0000	90.0000
90%	$7432.23	353.5714	318.2143	80.3571
95%	$7356.71	347.3684	330.0000	71.0526
100%	$7283.79	341.3793	341.3793	62.0690

MANAGEMENT SCIENCE IN ACTION

ESTIMATION OF FOOD NUTRIENT VALUES*

The Nutrition Coordinating Center (NCC) of the University of Minnesota maintains a food-composition database that is used by nutritionists and researchers throughout the world. Nutrient information provided by NCC is used to estimate the nutrient intake of individuals, to plan menus, research links between diet and disease, and meet regulatory requirements.

Nutrient intake calculations require data on an enormous number of food nutrient values. NCC's food composition database contains information on 93 different nutrients for each food product. With many new brand-name products introduced each year, NCC has the significant task of maintaining an accurate and timely database. The task is made more difficult by the fact that new brand-name products only provide data on a relatively small number of nutrients. Because of the high cost of chemically analyzing the new products, NCC uses a linear programming model to help estimate thousands of nutrient values per year.

The decision variables in the linear programming model are the amounts of each ingredient in a food product. The objective is to minimize the differences between the estimated nutrient values and the known nutrient values for the food product. Constraints are that ingredients must be in descending order by weight, ingredients must be within nutritionist-specified bounds, and the differences between the calculated nutrient values and the known nutrient values must be within specified tolerances.

In practice, an NCC nutritionist employs the linear programming model to derive estimates of the amounts of each ingredient in a new food product. Given these estimates, the nutritionist refines the estimates based on his or her knowledge of the product formulation and the food composition. Once the amounts of each ingredient are obtained, the amounts of each nutrient in the food product can be calculated. With approximately 1000 products evaluated each year, the time and cost savings provided by using linear programming to help estimate the nutrient values are significant.

*Based on Brian J. Westrich, Michael A. Altmann, and Sandra J. Potthoff, "Minnesota's Nutrition Coordinating Center Uses Mathematical Optimization to Estimate Food Nutrient Values," *Interfaces* (September/October 1998): 86–99.

3.5   THE ELECTRONIC COMMUNICATIONS PROBLEM

The Electronic Communications problem introduced in this section is a maximization problem involving four decision variables, two less-than-or-equal-to constraints, one equality constraint, and one greater-than-or-equal-to constraint. Our objective is to provide a summary of the process of formulating a mathematical model, using software to obtain an optimal solution, and interpreting the solution and sensitivity report information. In the next chapter we will continue to illustrate how linear programming can be applied by showing additional examples from the areas of marketing, finance, and production management. Your ability to formulate, solve, and interpret the solution to problems like the Electronic Communications problem is critical to understanding how more complex problems can be modeled using linear programming.

Electronic Communications manufactures portable radio systems that can be used for two-way communications. The company's new product, which has a range of up to 25 miles, is particularly suitable for use in a variety of business and personal applications. The distribution channels for the new radio are as follows:

1. Marine equipment distributors
2. Business equipment distributors
3. National chain of retail stores
4. Direct mail

TABLE 3.2 PROFIT, ADVERTISING COST, AND PERSONAL SALES TIME DATA
FOR THE ELECTRONIC COMMUNICATIONS PROBLEM

Distribution Channel	Profit per Unit Sold ($)	Advertising Cost per Unit Sold ($)	Personal Sales Effort per Unit Sold (hours)
Marine distributors	90	10	2
Business distributors	84	8	3
National retail stores	70	9	3
Direct mail	60	15	None

Because of differing distribution and promotional costs, the profitability of the product will vary with the distribution channel. In addition, the advertising cost and the personal sales effort required will vary with the distribution channels. Table 3.2 summarizes the contribution to profit, advertising cost, and personal sales effort data pertaining to the Electronic Communications problem. The firm set the advertising budget at $5000, and a maximum of 1800 hours of salesforce time is available for allocation to the sales effort. Management also decided to produce exactly 600 units for the current production period. Finally, an ongoing contract with the national chain of retail stores requires that at least 150 units be distributed through this distribution channel.

Electronic Communications is now faced with the problem of establishing a strategy that will provide for the distribution of the radios in such a way that overall profitability of the new radio production will be maximized. Decisions must be made as to how many units should be allocated to each of the four distribution channels, as well as how to allocate the advertising budget and salesforce effort to each of the four distribution channels.

Problem Formulation

We will now write the objective function and the constraints for the Electronic Communications problem. For the objective function, we can write

Objective function: Maximize profit

Four constraints are necessary for this problem. They are necessary because of (1) a limited advertising budget, (2) limited salesforce availability, (3) a production requirement, and (4) a retail stores distribution requirement.

Constraint 1: Advertising expenditures ≤ Budget
Constraint 2: Sales time used ≤ Time available
Constraint 3: Radios produced = Management requirement
Constraint 4: Retail distribution ≥ Contract requirement

These expressions provide descriptions of the objective function and the constraints. We are now ready to define the decision variables that will represent the decisions the manager must make.

For the Electronic Communications problem, we introduce the following four decision variables:

M = the number of units produced for the marine equipment distribution channel
B = the number of units produced for the business equipment distribution channel
R = the number of units produced for the national retail chain distribution channel
D = the number of units produced for the direct mail distribution channel

Using the data in Table 3.2, the objective function for maximizing the total contribution to profit associated with the radios can be written as follows:

$$\text{Max } 90M + 84B + 70R + 60D$$

Let us now develop a mathematical statement of the constraints for the problem. Because the advertising budget is set at $5000, the constraint that limits the amount of advertising expenditure can be written as follows:

$$10M + 8B + 9R + 15D \leq 5000$$

Similarly, because the sales time is limited to 1800 hours, we obtain the constraint

$$2M + 3B + 3R \leq 1800$$

Management's decision to produce exactly 600 units during the current production period is expressed as

$$M + B + R + D = 600$$

Finally, to account for the fact that the number of units distributed by the national chain of retail stores must be at least 150, we add the constraint

$$R \geq 150$$

Combining all of the constraints with the nonnegativity requirements enables us to write the complete linear programming model for the Electronic Communications problem as follows:

$$
\begin{array}{lrcrcrcrcll}
\text{Max} & 90M &+& 84B &+& 70R &+& 60D & & & \\
\text{s.t.} & & & & & & & & & & \\
& 10M &+& 8B &+& 9R &+& 15D &\leq& 5000 & \text{Advertising budget} \\
& 2M &+& 3B &+& 3R & & &\leq& 1800 & \text{Salesforce availability} \\
& M &+& B &+& R &+& D &=& 600 & \text{Production level} \\
& & & & & R & & &\geq& 150 & \text{Retail stores requirement} \\
& \multicolumn{11}{l}{M, B, R, D \geq 0} \\
\end{array}
$$

Computer Solution and Interpretation

This problem can be solved using either Excel Solver or LINGO. A portion of the standard solution output for the Electronic Communications problem is shown in Figure 3.11. The Objective Function Value section shows that the optimal solution to the problem will provide a maximum profit of $48,450. The optimal values of the decision variables are given by $M = 25$, $B = 425$, $R = 150$, and $D = 0$.

FIGURE 3.11   A PORTION OF THE COMPUTER OUTPUT FOR THE ELECTRONIC
COMMUNICATIONS PROBLEM

WEB file

Electronic

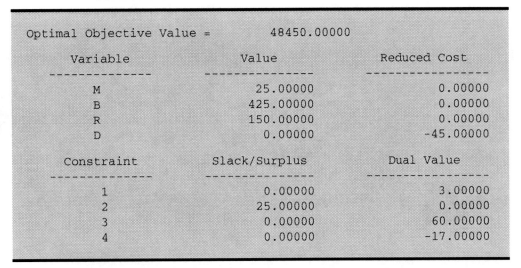

Optimal Objective Value =	48450.00000	
Variable	Value	Reduced Cost
M	25.00000	0.00000
B	425.00000	0.00000
R	150.00000	0.00000
D	0.00000	-45.00000
Constraint	Slack/Surplus	Dual Value
1	0.00000	3.00000
2	25.00000	0.00000
3	0.00000	60.00000
4	0.00000	-17.00000

Thus, the optimal strategy for Electronic Communications is to concentrate on the business equipment distribution channel with $B = 425$ units. In addition, the firm should allocate 25 units to the marine distribution channel ($M = 25$) and meet its 150-unit commitment to the national retail chain store distribution channel ($R = 150$). With $D = 0$, the optimal solution indicates that the firm should not use the direct mail distribution channel.

Now consider the information contained in the Reduced Cost column. Recall that the reduced cost of a variable is the dual value of the corresponding nonnegativity constraint. As the computer output shows, the first three reduced costs are zero because the corresponding decision variables already have positive values in the optimal solution. However, the reduced cost of –45 for decision variable D tells us that profit will decrease by $45 for every unit produced for the direct mail channel. Stated another way, the profit for the new radios distributed via the direct mail channel would have to increase from its current value of $60 per unit, by $45 per unit, to at least $60 + $45 = $105 per unit before it would be profitable to use the direct mail distribution channel.

The computer output information for the slack/surplus variables and the dual values is restated in Figure 3.12.

The advertising budget constraint has a slack of zero, indicating that the entire budget of $5000 has been used. The corresponding dual value of 3 tells us that an additional dollar added to the advertising budget will increase the objective function (increase the profit) by $3. Thus, the possibility of increasing the advertising budget should be seriously considered by the firm. The slack of 25 hours for the salesforce availability constraint shows that the allocated 1800 hours of sales time are adequate to distribute the radios produced and that 25 hours of sales time will remain unused. Because the production level constraint is an equality constraint, the zero slack/surplus shown on the output is expected. However, the dual value of 60 associated with this constraint shows that if the firm were to consider increasing the production level for the radios, the value of the objective function, or profit, would improve at the rate of $60 per radio produced. Finally, the surplus of zero associated with the retail store distribution channel commitment is a result of this constraint being binding. The negative dual value indicates that increasing the commitment from 150 to 151 units will actually decrease the profit by $17.

FIGURE 3.12   OBJECTIVE COEFFICIENT AND RIGHT-HAND-SIDE RANGES FOR THE ELECTRONIC COMMUNICATIONS PROBLEM

WEB file

Electronic

```
Optimal Objective Value =        48450.00000

      Variable                Value            Reduced Cost
   ------------          ---------------       ----------------
         M                  25.00000              0.00000
         B                 425.00000              0.00000
         R                 150.00000              0.00000
         D                   0.00000            -45.00000

     Constraint           Slack/Surplus          Dual Value
   ------------          ---------------       ----------------
         1                   0.00000              3.00000
         2                  25.00000              0.00000
         3                   0.00000             60.00000
         4                   0.00000            -17.00000

                       Objective        Allowable         Allowable
     Variable         Coefficient        Increase          Decrease
   ----------       -------------      ----------        ----------
         M             90.00000          Infinite          6.00000
         B             84.00000          6.00000          34.00000
         R             70.00000         17.00000          Infinite
         D             60.00000         45.00000          Infinite

                          RHS           Allowable         Allowable
     Constraint          Value           Increase          Decrease
   ----------       -------------      ----------        ----------
         1           5000.00000        850.00000          50.00000
         2           1800.00000         Infinite          25.00000
         3            600.00000          3.57143          85.00000
         4            150.00000         50.00000         150.00000
```

Thus, Electronic Communications may want to consider reducing its commitment to the retail store distribution channel. A *decrease* in the commitment will actually improve profit at the rate of $17 per unit.

We now consider the additional sensitivity analysis information provided by the computer output shown in Figure 3.12. The allowable increases and decreases for the objective function coefficients are as follows:

Objective Coefficient	Allowable Increase	Allowable Decrease
90.00000	Infinite	6.00000
84.00000	6.00000	34.00000
70.00000	17.00000	Infinite
60.00000	45.00000	Infinite

The current solution or strategy remains optimal, provided that the objective function coefficients do not increase or decrease by more than the allowed amount. Consider the allowable increase and decrease of the direct mail distribution channel coefficient. This information is consistent with the earlier observation for the Reduced Costs portion of the output. In both instances, we see that the per-unit profit would have to increase by $45 to $105 before the direct mail distribution channel could be in the optimal solution with a positive value.

Finally, the sensitivity analysis information on right-hand-side ranges, as shown in Figure 3.12, provides the allowable increase and decrease for the right-hand-side values.

RHS Value	Allowable Increase	Allowable Decrease
5000.00000	850.00000	50.00000
1800.00000	Infinite	25.00000
600.00000	3.57143	85.00000
150.00000	50.00000	150.00000

Try Problems 12 and 13 to test your ability at interpreting the computer output for problems involving more than two decision variables.

Several interpretations of these ranges are possible. In particular, recall that the dual value for the advertising budget enabled us to conclude that each $1 increase in the budget would increase the profit by $3. The current advertising budget is $5000. The allowable increase in the advertising budget is $850 and this implies that there is value in increasing the budget up to an advertising budget of $5850. Increases above this level would not necessarily be beneficial. Also note that the dual value of −17 for the retail stores requirement suggested the desirability of reducing this commitment. The allowable decrease for this constraint is 150, and this implies that the commitment could be reduced to zero and the value of the reduction would be at the rate of $17 per unit.

Again, the *sensitivity analysis* or *postoptimality analysis* provided by computer software packages for linear programming problems considers only *one change at a time,* with all other coefficients of the problem remaining as originally specified. As mentioned earlier, simultaneous changes are best handled by re-solving the problem.

Finally, recall that the complete solution to the Electronic Communications problem requested information not only on the number of units to be distributed over each channel, but also on the allocation of the advertising budget and the salesforce effort to each distribution channel. For the optimal solution of $M = 25$, $B = 425$, $R = 150$, and $D = 0$, we can simply evaluate each term in a given constraint to determine how much of the constraint resource is allocated to each distribution channel. For example, the advertising budget constraint of

$$10M + 8B + 9R + 15D \leq 5000$$

shows that $10M = 10(25) = \$250$, $8B = 8(425) = \$3400$, $9R = 9(150) = \$1350$, and $15D = 15(0) = \$0$. Thus, the advertising budget allocations are, respectively, $250, $3400, $1350, and $0 for each of the four distribution channels. Making similar calculations for the salesforce constraint results in the managerial summary of the Electronic Communications optimal solution as shown in Table 3.3.

TABLE 3.3   PROFIT-MAXIMIZING STRATEGY FOR THE ELECTRONIC
COMMUNICATIONS PROBLEM

Distribution Channel	Volume	Advertising Allocation	Salesforce Allocation (hours)
Marine distributors	25	$ 250	50
Business distributors	425	3400	1275
National retail stores	150	1350	450
Direct mail	0	0	0
Totals	600	$5000	1775
Projected total profit = $48,450			

SUMMARY

We began the chapter with a discussion of sensitivity analysis: the study of how changes in the coefficients of a linear program affect the optimal solution. First, we showed how a graphical method can be used to determine how a change in one of the objective function coefficients or a change in the right-hand-side value for a constraint will affect the optimal solution to the problem. Because graphical sensitivity analysis is limited to linear programs with two decision variables, we showed how to use software to produce a sensitivity report containing the same information.

We continued our discussion of problem formulation, sensitivity analysis and its limitations, and the interpretation of the solution by introducing several modifications of the Par, Inc., problem. They involved an additional decision variable and several types of percentage, or ratio, constraints. Then, in order to provide additional practice in formulating and interpreting the solution for linear programs involving more than two decision variables, we introduced the Electronic Communications problem, a maximization problem with four decision variables, two less-than-or-equal-to constraints, one equality constraint, and one greater-than-or-equal-to constraint.

The Management Science in Action, Tea Production and Distribution in India, illustrates the diversity of problems in which linear programming can be applied and the importance of sensitivity analysis. In the next chapter we will see many more applications of linear programming.

MANAGEMENT SCIENCE IN ACTION

TEA PRODUCTION AND DISTRIBUTION IN INDIA*

In India, one of the largest tea producers in the world, approximately $1 billion of tea packets and loose tea are sold. Duncan Industries Limited (DIL), the third largest producer of tea in the Indian tea market, sells about $37.5 million of tea, almost all of which is sold in packets.

DIL has 16 tea gardens, three blending units, six packing units, and 22 depots. Tea from the gardens is sent to blending units, which then mix various grades of tea to produce blends such as Sargam, Double Diamond, and Runglee Rungliot. The blended tea is transported to packing units,

where it is placed in packets of different sizes and shapes to produce about 120 different product lines. For example, one line is Sargam tea packed in 500-gram cartons, another line is Double Diamond packed in 100-gram pouches, and so on. The tea is then shipped to the depots that supply 11,500 distributors through whom the needs of approximately 325,000 retailers are satisfied.

For the coming month, sales managers provide estimates of the demand for each line of tea at each depot. Using these estimates, a team of senior managers would determine the amounts of loose tea of each blend to ship to each packing unit, the quantity of each line of tea to be packed at each packing unit, and the amounts of packed tea of each line to be transported from each packing unit to the various depots. This process requires two to three days each month and often results in stockouts of lines in demand at specific depots.

Consequently, a linear programming model involving approximately 7000 decision variables and 1500 constraints was developed to minimize the company's freight cost while satisfying demand, supply, and all operational constraints. The model was tested on past data and showed that stockouts could be prevented at little or no additional cost. Moreover, the model was able to provide management with the ability to perform various what-if types of exercises, convincing them of the potential benefits of using management science techniques to support the decision-making process.

*Based on Nilotpal Chakravarti, "Tea Company Steeped in OR," *OR/MS Today* (April 2000).

GLOSSARY

Sensitivity analysis The study of how changes in the coefficients of a linear programming problem affect the optimal solution.

Range of optimality The range of values over which an objective function coefficient may vary without causing any change in the values of the decision variables in the optimal solution.

Objective Function Allowable Increase (Decrease) The allowable increase/decrease of an objective function coefficient is the amount the coefficient may increase (decrease) without causing any change in the values of the decision variables in the optimal solution. The allowable increase/decrease for the objective function coefficients can be used to calculate the range of optimality.

Dual value The change in the value of the objective function per unit increase in the right-hand side of a constraint.

Reduced cost The reduced cost of a variable is equal to the dual value on the nonnegativity constraint for that variable.

Range of feasibility The range of values over which the dual value is applicable.

Right-Hand-Side Allowable Increase (Decrease) The allowable increase (decrease) of the right-hand side of a constraint is the amount the right-hand side may increase (decrease) without causing any change in the dual value for that constraint. The allowable increase (decrease) for the right-hand side can be used to calculate the range of feasibility for that constraint.

Sunk cost A cost that is not affected by the decision made. It will be incurred no matter what values the decision variables assume.

Relevant cost A cost that depends upon the decision made. The amount of a relevant cost will vary depending on the values of the decision variables.

PROBLEMS

1. Consider the following linear program:

$$\text{Max} \quad 3A + 2B$$

s.t.

$$1A + 1B \leq 10$$
$$3A + 1B \leq 24$$
$$1A + 2B \leq 16$$
$$A, B \geq 0$$

a. Use the graphical solution procedure to find the optimal solution.
b. Assume that the objective function coefficient for A changes from 3 to 5. Does the optimal solution change? Use the graphical solution procedure to find the new optimal solution.
c. Assume that the objective function coefficient for A remains 3, but the objective function coefficient for B changes from 2 to 4. Does the optimal solution change? Use the graphical solution procedure to find the new optimal solution.
d. The computer solution for the linear program in part (a) provides the following objective coefficient range information:

Variable	Objective Coefficient	Allowable Increase	Allowable Decrease
A	3.00000	3.00000	1.00000
B	2.00000	1.00000	1.00000

Use this objective coefficient range information to answer parts (b) and (c).

2. Consider the linear program in Problem 1. The value of the optimal solution is 27. Suppose that the right-hand side for constraint 1 is increased from 10 to 11.
a. Use the graphical solution procedure to find the new optimal solution.
b. Use the solution to part (a) to determine the dual value for constraint 1.
c. The computer solution for the linear program in Problem 1 provides the following right-hand-side range information:

Constraint	RHS Value	Allowable Increase	Allowable Decrease
1	10.00000	1.20000	2.00000
2	24.00000	6.00000	6.00000
3	16.00000	Infinite	3.00000

What does the right-hand-side range information for constraint 1 tell you about the dual value for constraint 1?
d. The dual value for constraint 2 is 0.5. Using this dual value and the right-hand-side range information in part (c), what conclusion can be drawn about the effect of changes to the right-hand side of constraint 2?

3. Consider the following linear program:

$$\text{Min} \quad 8X + 12Y$$
$$\text{s.t.}$$
$$1X + 3Y \geq 9$$
$$2X + 2Y \geq 10$$
$$6X + 2Y \geq 18$$
$$A, B \geq 0$$

a. Use the graphical solution procedure to find the optimal solution.
b. Assume that the objective function coefficient for X changes from 8 to 6. Does the optimal solution change? Use the graphical solution procedure to find the new optimal solution.

c. Assume that the objective function coefficient for X remains 8, but the objective function coefficient for Y changes from 12 to 6. Does the optimal solution change? Use the graphical solution procedure to find the new optimal solution.

d. The computer solution for the linear program in part (a) provides the following objective coefficient range information:

Variable	Objective Coefficient	Allowable Increase	Allowable Decrease
X	8.00000	4.00000	4.00000
Y	12.00000	12.00000	4.00000

How would this objective coefficient range information help you answer parts (b) and (c) prior to re-solving the problem?

4. Consider the linear program in Problem 3. The value of the optimal solution is 48. Suppose that the right-hand side for constraint 1 is increased from 9 to 10.

a. Use the graphical solution procedure to find the new optimal solution.

b. Use the solution to part (a) to determine the dual value for constraint 1.

c. The computer solution for the linear program in Problem 3 provides the following right-hand-side range information:

Constraint	RHS Value	Allowable Increase	Allowable Decrease
1	9.00000	2.00000	4.00000
2	10.00000	8.00000	1.00000
3	18.00000	4.00000	Infinite

What does the right-hand-side range information for constraint 1 tell you about the dual value for constraint 1?

d. The dual value for constraint 2 is 3. Using this dual value and the right-hand-side range information in part (c), what conclusion can be drawn about the effect of changes to the right-hand side of constraint 2?

5. Refer to the Kelson Sporting Equipment problem (Chapter 2, Problem 24). Letting

$$R = \text{number of regular gloves}$$
$$C = \text{number of catcher's mitts}$$

leads to the following formulation:

$$\text{Max} \quad 5R + 8C$$
$$\text{s.t.}$$

$$R + \tfrac{3}{2}C \leq 900 \quad \text{Cutting and sewing}$$
$$\tfrac{1}{2}R + \tfrac{1}{3}C \leq 300 \quad \text{Finishing}$$
$$\tfrac{1}{8}R + \tfrac{1}{4}C \leq 100 \quad \text{Packaging and shipping}$$
$$R, C \geq 0$$

FIGURE 3.13   THE SOLUTION FOR THE KELSON SPORTING EQUIPMENT PROBLEM

```
Optimal Objective Value  =          3700.00000

        Variable               Value              Reduced Cost
       -----------          ------------         --------------
           R                 500.00000               0.00000
           C                 150.00000               0.00000

       Constraint          Slack/Surplus             Dual Value
      ------------         -------------           --------------
           1                 175.00000               0.00000
           2                   0.00000               3.00000
           3                   0.00000              28.00000

                        Objective         Allowable         Allowable
        Variable        Coefficient        Increase          Decrease
       -----------     ------------      ----------        ----------
           R              5.00000          7.00000           1.00000
           C              8.00000          2.00000           4.66667

                           RHS            Allowable         Allowable
       Constraint         Value            Increase          Decrease
      ------------     ------------      ----------        ----------
           1             900.00000         Infinite         175.00000
           2             300.00000        100.00000         166.66667
           3             100.00000         35.00000          25.00000
```

The computer solution is shown in Figure 3.13.
- a. What is the optimal solution, and what is the value of the total profit contribution?
- b. Which constraints are binding?
- c. What are the dual values for the resources? Interpret each.
- d. If overtime can be scheduled in one of the departments, where would you recommend doing so?

6. Refer to the computer solution of the Kelson Sporting Equipment problem in Figure 3.13 (see Problem 5).
- a. Determine the objective coefficient ranges.
- b. Interpret the ranges in part (a).
- c. Interpret the right-hand-side ranges.
- d. How much will the value of the optimal solution improve if 20 extra hours of packaging and shipping time are made available?

7. Investment Advisors, Inc., is a brokerage firm that manages stock portfolios for a number of clients. A particular portfolio consists of U shares of U.S. Oil and H shares of Huber Steel. The annual return for U.S. Oil is $3 per share and the annual return for Huber Steel is $5 per share. U.S. Oil sells for $25 per share and Huber Steel sells for $50 per share. The portfolio has $80,000 to be invested. The portfolio risk index (0.50 per share of U.S. Oil and 0.25 per share for Huber Steel) has a maximum of 700. In addition, the portfolio is limited to a maximum of 1000 shares of U.S. Oil. The linear

FIGURE 3.14   THE SOLUTION FOR THE INVESTMENT ADVISORS PROBLEM

```
Optimal Objective Value =        8400.00000

        Variable              Value            Reduced Cost
    --------------        --------------      ----------------

           U                800.00000             0.00000
           H               1200.00000             0.00000


     Constraint           Slack/Surplus          Dual Value
    --------------        --------------      ----------------

           1                  0.00000             0.09333
           2                  0.00000             1.33333
           3                200.00000             0.00000


                      Objective        Allowable       Allowable
       Variable       Coefficient      Increase        Decrease
     ----------      ------------      ----------      ----------

           U            3.00000         7.00000         0.50000
           H            5.00000         1.00000         3.50000


                         RHS           Allowable       Allowable
     Constraint         Value          Increase        Decrease
     ----------      ------------      ----------      ----------

           1        80000.00000      60000.00000     15000.00000
           2          700.00000         75.00000       300.00000
           3         1000.00000        Infinite        200.00000
```

programming formulation that will maximize the total annual return of the portfolio is as follows:

$$\text{Max} \quad 3U + 5H \qquad \text{Maximize total annual return}$$

s.t.

$$25U + 50H \le 80{,}000 \quad \text{Funds available}$$
$$0.50U + 0.25D \le 700 \quad \text{Risk maximum}$$
$$1U \le 1000 \quad \text{U.S. Oil maximum}$$
$$U, H \ge 0$$

The computer solution of this problem is shown in Figure 3.14.

a. What is the optimal solution, and what is the value of the total annual return?

b. Which constraints are binding? What is your interpretation of these constraints in terms of the problem?

c. What are the dual values for the constraints? Interpret each.

d. Would it be beneficial to increase the maximum amount invested in U.S. Oil? Why or why not?

8. Refer to Figure 3.14, which shows the computer solution of Problem 7.

a. How much would the return for U.S. Oil have to increase before it would be beneficial to increase the investment in this stock?

b. How much would the return for Huber Steel have to decrease before it would be beneficial to reduce the investment in this stock?

c. How much would the total annual return be reduced if the U.S. Oil maximum were reduced to 900 shares?

9. Recall the Tom's, Inc., problem (Chapter 2, Problem 28). Letting

$$W = \text{jars of Western Foods Salsa}$$
$$M = \text{jars of Mexico City Salsa}$$

leads to the formulation:

$$\text{Max} \quad 1W + 1.25M$$

s.t.

$5W +$	$7M \leq 4480$	Whole tomatoes
$3W +$	$1M \leq 2080$	Tomato sauce
$2W +$	$2M \leq 1600$	Tomato paste
$W, M \geq 0$		

The computer solution is shown in Figure 3.15.

a. What is the optimal solution, and what are the optimal production quantities?

b. Specify the objective function ranges.

FIGURE 3.15   THE SOLUTION FOR THE TOM'S, INC., PROBLEM

```
Optimal Objective Value =          860.00000

        Variable              Value             Reduced Cost
    ----------------      ---------------      ---------------
           W                  560.00000               0.00000
           M                  240.00000               0.00000

        Constraint         Slack/Surplus           Dual Value
    ----------------      ---------------      ---------------
           1                    0.00000               0.12500
           2                  160.00000               0.00000
           3                    0.00000               0.18750

                        Objective          Allowable          Allowable
        Variable        Coefficient         Increase           Decrease
    -----------        -----------        -----------        -----------
           W              1.00000            0.25000            0.10714
           M              1.25000            0.15000            0.25000

                           RHS             Allowable          Allowable
        Constraint        Value             Increase           Decrease
    -----------        -----------        -----------        -----------
           1            4480.00000         1120.00000          160.00000
           2            2080.00000           Infinite          160.00000
           3            1600.00000            40.00000          320.00000
```

c. What are the dual values for each constraint? Interpret each.
d. Identify each of the right-hand-side ranges.

10. Recall the Innis Investments problem (Chapter 2, Problem 39). Letting

$$S = \text{units purchased in the stock fund}$$
$$M = \text{units purchased in the money market fund}$$

leads to the following formulation:

$$\text{Min} \quad 8S + 3M$$
s.t.
$$50S + 100M \leq 1,200,000 \quad \text{Funds available}$$
$$5S + 4M \geq 60,000 \quad \text{Annual income}$$
$$M \geq 3,000 \quad \text{Units in money market}$$
$$S, M \geq 0$$

The computer solution is shown in Figure 3.16.
a. What is the optimal solution, and what is the minimum total risk?
b. Specify the objective coefficient ranges.
c. How much annual income will be earned by the portfolio?

FIGURE 3.16 THE SOLUTION FOR THE INNIS INVESTMENTS PROBLEM

Optimal Objective Value =	62000.00000	
Variable	**Value**	**Reduced Cost**
S	4000.00000	0.00000
M	10000.00000	0.00000
Constraint	**Slack/Surplus**	**Dual Value**
1	0.00000	-0.05667
2	0.00000	2.16667
3	7000.00000	0.00000

Variable	Objective Coefficient	Allowable Increase	Allowable Decrease
S	8.00000	Infinite	4.25000
M	3.00000	3.40000	Infinite

Constraint	RHS Value	Allowable Increase	Allowable Decrease
1	1200000.00000	300000.00000	420000.00000
2	60000.00000	42000.00000	12000.00000
3	3000.00000	7000.00000	Infinite

    d.   What is the rate of return for the portfolio?

    e.   What is the dual value for the funds available constraint?

    f.   What is the marginal rate of return on extra funds added to the portfolio?

11. Refer to Problem 10 and the computer solution shown in Figure 3.16.

    a.   Suppose the risk index for the stock fund (the value of C_S) increases from its current value of 8 to 12. How does the optimal solution change, if at all?

    b.   Suppose the risk index for the money market fund (the value of C_M) increases from its current value of 3 to 3.5. How does the optimal solution change, if at all?

    c.   Suppose C_S increases to 12 and C_M increases to 3.5. How does the optimal solution change, if at all?

12. Quality Air Conditioning manufactures three home air conditioners: an economy model, a standard model, and a deluxe model. The profits per unit are $63, $95, and $135, respectively. The production requirements per unit are as follows:

	Number of Fans	Number of Cooling Coils	Manufacturing Time (hours)
Economy	1	1	8
Standard	1	2	12
Deluxe	1	4	14

For the coming production period, the company has 200 fan motors, 320 cooling coils, and 2400 hours of manufacturing time available. How many economy models (E), standard models (S), and deluxe models (D) should the company produce in order to maximize profit? The linear programming model for the problem is as follows:

$$\text{Max} \quad 63E + 95S + 135D$$

s.t.

$$
\begin{aligned}
1E + 1S + 1D &\leq 200 \quad \text{Fan motors} \\
1E + 2S + 4D &\leq 320 \quad \text{Cooling coils} \\
8E + 12S + 14D &\leq 2400 \quad \text{Manufacturing time} \\
E, S, D &\geq 0
\end{aligned}
$$

The computer solution is shown in Figure 3.17.

    a.   What is the optimal solution, and what is the value of the objective function?

    b.   Which constraints are binding?

    c.   Which constraint shows extra capacity? How much?

    d.   If the profit for the deluxe model were increased to $150 per unit, would the optimal solution change? Use the information in Figure 3.17 to answer this question.

13. Refer to the computer solution of Problem 12 in Figure 3.17.

    a.   Identify the range of optimality for each objective function coefficient.

    b.   Suppose the profit for the economy model is increased by $6 per unit, the profit for the standard model is decreased by $2 per unit, and the profit for the deluxe model is increased by $4 per unit. What will the new optimal solution be?

    c.   Identify the range of feasibility for the right-hand-side values.

    d.   If the number of fan motors available for production is increased by 100, will the dual value for that constraint change? Explain.

FIGURE 3.17   THE SOLUTION FOR THE QUALITY AIR CONDITIONING PROBLEM

```
Optimal Objective Value =        16440.00000

        Variable              Value            Reduced Cost
     --------------      ---------------     ------------------
          E                  80.00000              0.00000
          S                 120.00000              0.00000
          D                   0.00000            -24.00000


      Constraint          Slack/Surplus          Dual Value
     --------------      ---------------     ------------------
          1                   0.00000             31.00000
          2                   0.00000             32.00000
          3                 320.00000              0.00000


                        Objective           Allowable          Allowable
        Variable        Coefficient         Increase           Decrease
     -----------       ------------       -----------        -----------
          E               63.00000          12.00000          15.50000
          S               95.00000          31.00000           8.00000
          D              135.00000          24.00000          Infinite


                          RHS               Allowable          Allowable
      Constraint          Value             Increase           Decrease
     -----------       ------------       -----------        -----------
          1              200.00000          80.00000          40.00000
          2              320.00000          80.00000         120.00000
          3             2400.00000          Infinite         320.00000
```

14. Digital Controls, Inc. (DCI), manufactures two models of a radar gun used by police to monitor the speed of automobiles. Model A has an accuracy of plus or minus 1 mile per hour, whereas the smaller model B has an accuracy of plus or minus 3 miles per hour. For the next week, the company has orders for 100 units of model A and 150 units of model B. Although DCI purchases all the electronic components used in both models, the plastic cases for both models are manufactured at a DCI plant in Newark, New Jersey. Each model A case requires 4 minutes of injection-molding time and 6 minutes of assembly time. Each model B case requires 3 minutes of injection-molding time and 8 minutes of assembly time. For next week, the Newark plant has 600 minutes of injection-molding time available and 1080 minutes of assembly time available. The manufacturing cost is $10 per case for model A and $6 per case for model B. Depending upon demand and the time available at the Newark plant, DCI occasionally purchases cases for one or both models from an outside supplier in order to fill customer orders that could not be filled otherwise. The purchase cost is $14 for each model A case and $9 for each model B case. Management wants to develop a minimum cost plan that will determine how many cases of each model should be produced at the Newark plant and how many cases of each model

should be purchased. The following decision variables were used to formulate a linear programming model for this problem:

$$AM = \text{number of cases of model A manufactured}$$
$$BM = \text{number of cases of model B manufactured}$$
$$AP = \text{number of cases of model A purchased}$$
$$BP = \text{number of cases of model B purchased}$$

The linear programming model that can be used to solve this problem is as follows:

Min $10AM + 6BM + 14AP + 9BP$
s.t.

$1AM +$		$+ 1AP +$		$=$	100	Demand for model A
	$1BM +$		$1BP =$		150	Demand for model B
$4AM +$	$3BM$			$\leq$	600	Injection molding time
$6AM +$	$8BM$			$\leq$	1080	Assembly time

$$AM, BM, AP, BP \geq 0$$

The computer solution is shown in Figure 3.18.

a. What is the optimal solution and what is the optimal value of the objective function?
b. Which constraints are binding?
c. What are the dual values? Interpret each.
d. If you could change the right-hand side of one constraint by one unit, which one would you choose? Why?

15. Refer to the computer solution to Problem 14 in Figure 3.18.
a. Interpret the ranges of optimality for the objective function coefficients.
b. Suppose that the manufacturing cost increases to $11.20 per case for model A. What is the new optimal solution?
c. Suppose that the manufacturing cost increases to $11.20 per case for model A and the manufacturing cost for model B decreases to $5 per unit. Would the optimal solution change?

16. Tucker Inc. produces high-quality suits and sport coats for men. Each suit requires 1.2 hours of cutting time and 0.7 hours of sewing time, uses 6 yards of material, and provides a profit contribution of $190. Each sport coat requires 0.8 hours of cutting time and 0.6 hours of sewing time, uses 4 yards of material, and provides a profit contribution of $150. For the coming week, 200 hours of cutting time, 180 hours of sewing time, and 1200 yards of fabric are available. Additional cutting and sewing time can be obtained by scheduling overtime for these operations. Each hour of overtime for the cutting operation increases the hourly cost by $15, and each hour of overtime for the sewing operation increases the hourly cost by $10. A maximum of 100 hours of overtime can be scheduled. Marketing requirements specify a minimum production of 100 suits and 75 sport coats. Let

$$S = \text{number of suits produced}$$
$$SC = \text{number of sport coats produced}$$
$$D1 = \text{hours of overtime for the cutting operation}$$
$$D2 = \text{hours of overtime for the sewing operation}$$

FIGURE 3.18   THE SOLUTION FOR THE DIGITAL CONTROLS, INC., PROBLEM

```
Optimal Objective Value =           2170.00000

        Variable                 Value              Reduced Cost
    ---------------        ---------------        ---------------
           AB                 100.00000                0.00000
           BM                  60.00000                0.00000
           AP                   0.00000                1.75000
           BP                  90.00000                0.00000


      Constraint          Slack/Surplus             Dual Value
    ---------------        ---------------        ---------------
            1                   0.00000               12.25000
            2                   0.00000                9.00000
            3                  20.00000                0.00000
            4                   0.00000               -0.37500


                      Objective          Allowable          Allowable
        Variable      Coefficient        Increase           Decrease
    ------------    -------------      -----------        -----------
           AB          10.00000          1.75000            Infinite
           BM           6.00000          3.00000            2.33333
           AP          14.00000          Infinite           1.75000
           BP           9.00000          2.33333            3.00000


                         RHS             Allowable          Allowable
      Constraint        Value            Increase           Decrease
    ------------    -------------      -----------        -----------
            1         100.00000         11.42857           100.00000
            2         150.00000         Infinite            90.00000
            3         600.00000         Infinite            20.00000
            4        1080.00000         53.33333           480.00000
```

The computer solution is shown in Figure 3.19.

a. What is the optimal solution, and what is the total profit? What is the plan for the use of overtime?

b. A price increase for suits is being considered that would result in a profit contribution of $210 per suit. If this price increase is undertaken, how will the optimal solution change?

c. Discuss the need for additional material during the coming week. If a rush order for material can be placed at the usual price plus an extra $8 per yard for handling, would you recommend the company consider placing a rush order for material? What is the maximum price Tucker would be willing to pay for an additional yard of material? How many additional yards of material should Tucker consider ordering?

d. Suppose the minimum production requirement for suits is lowered to 75. Would this change help or hurt profit? Explain.

FIGURE 3.19   THE SOLUTION FOR THE TUCKER INC. PROBLEM

Optimal Objective Value =   40900.00000

Variable	Value	Reduced Cost
S	100.00000	0.00000
SC	150.00000	0.00000
D1	40.00000	0.00000
D2	0.00000	-10.00000

Constraint	Slack/Surplus	Dual Value
1	0.00000	15.00000
2	20.00000	0.00000
3	0.00000	34.50000
4	60.00000	0.00000
5	0.00000	-35.00000
6	75.00000	0.00000

Variable	Objective Coefficient	Allowable Increase	Allowable Decrease
S	190.00000	35.00000	Infinite
SC	150.00000	Infinite	23.33333
D1	-15.00000	15.00000	172.50000
D2	-10.00000	10.00000	Infinite

Constraint	RHS Value	Allowable Increase	Allowable Decrease
1	200.00000	40.00000	60.00000
2	180.00000	Infinite	20.00000
3	1200.00000	133.33333	200.00000
4	100.00000	Infinite	60.00000
5	100.00000	50.00000	100.00000
6	75.00000	75.00000	Infinite

17. The Porsche Club of America sponsors driver education events that provide high-performance driving instruction on actual race tracks. Because safety is a primary consideration at such events, many owners elect to install roll bars in their cars. Deegan Industries manufactures two types of roll bars for Porsches. Model DRB is bolted to the car using existing holes in the car's frame. Model DRW is a heavier roll bar that must be welded to the car's frame. Model DRB requires 20 pounds of a special high alloy steel, 40 minutes of manufacturing time, and 60 minutes of assembly time. Model DRW requires 25 pounds of the special high alloy steel, 100 minutes of manufacturing time, and 40 minutes of assembly time. Deegan's steel supplier indicated that at most 40,000 pounds of the high-alloy steel will be available next quarter. In addition, Deegan estimates that 2000 hours of manufacturing time and 1600 hours of assembly time will be available next quarter. The profit

contributions are $200 per unit for model DRB and $280 per unit for model DRW. The linear programming model for this problem is as follows:

$$\text{Max} \quad 200DRB + 280DRW$$

s.t.

$$20DRB + 25DRW \leq 40,000 \quad \text{Steel available}$$
$$40DRB + 100DRW \leq 120,000 \quad \text{Manufacturing minutes}$$
$$60DRB + 40DRW \leq 96,000 \quad \text{Assembly minutes}$$
$$DRB, DRW \geq 0$$

The computer solution is shown in Figure 3.20.

a. What are the optimal solution and the total profit contribution?

b. Another supplier offered to provide Deegan Industries with an additional 500 pounds of the steel alloy at $2 per pound. Should Deegan purchase the additional pounds of the steel alloy? Explain.

c. Deegan is considering using overtime to increase the available assembly time. What would you advise Deegan to do regarding this option? Explain.

d. Because of increased competition, Deegan is considering reducing the price of model DRB such that the new contribution to profit is $175 per unit. How would this change in price affect the optimal solution? Explain.

e. If the available manufacturing time is increased by 500 hours, will the dual value for the manufacturing time constraint change? Explain.

FIGURE 3.20   THE SOLUTION FOR THE DEEGAN INDUSTRIES PROBLEM

```
Optimal Objective Value =        424000.00000

        Variable              Value            Reduced Cost
    --------------       --------------      ----------------
         DRB               1000.00000             0.00000
         DRW                800.00000             0.00000

       Constraint         Slack/Surplus          Dual Value
    --------------       --------------      ----------------
           1                  0.00000             8.80000
           2                  0.00000             0.60000
           3               4000.00000             0.00000

                      Objective         Allowable         Allowable
        Variable      Coefficient       Increase          Decrease
      ----------     ------------      ----------        ----------
         DRB          200.00000         24.00000          88.00000
         DRW          280.00000        220.00000          30.00000

                         RHS            Allowable         Allowable
       Constraint       Value           Increase          Decrease
      ----------     ------------      ----------        ----------
           1         40000.00000        909.09091       10000.00000
           2        120000.00000      40000.00000        5714.28571
           3         96000.00000         Infinite        4000.00000
```

18. Davison Electronics manufactures two LCD television monitors, identified as model A and model B. Each model has its lowest possible production cost when produced on Davison's new production line. However, the new production line does not have the capacity to handle the total production of both models. As a result, at least some of the production must be routed to a higher-cost, old production line. The following table shows the minimum production requirements for next month, the production line capacities in units per month, and the production cost per unit for each production line:

Model	Production Cost per Unit		Minimum Production Requirements
	New Line	Old Line	
A	$30	$50	50,000
B	$25	$40	70,000
Production Line Capacity	80,000	60,000	

Let

$$AN = \text{Units of model A produced on the new production line}$$
$$AO = \text{Units of model A produced on the old production line}$$
$$BN = \text{Units of model B produced on the new production line}$$
$$BO = \text{Units of model B produced on the old production line}$$

Davison's objective is to determine the minimum cost production plan. The computer solution is shown in Figure 3.21.

a. Formulate the linear programming model for this problem using the following four constraints:

Constraint 1: Minimum production for model A
Constraint 2: Minimum production for model B
Constraint 3: Capacity of the new production line
Constraint 4: Capacity of the old production line

b. Using computer solution in Figure 3.21, what is the optimal solution, and what is the total production cost associated with this solution?

c. Which constraints are binding? Explain.

d. The production manager noted that the only constraint with a positive dual value is the constraint on the capacity of the new production line. The manager's interpretation of the dual value was that a one-unit increase in the right-hand side of this constraint would actually increase the total production cost by $15 per unit. Do you agree with this interpretation? Would an increase in capacity for the new production line be desirable? Explain.

e. Would you recommend increasing the capacity of the old production line? Explain.

f. The production cost for model A on the old production line is $50 per unit. How much would this cost have to change to make it worthwhile to produce model A on the old production line? Explain.

g. Suppose that the minimum production requirement for model B is reduced from 70,000 units to 60,000 units. What effect would this change have on the total production cost? Explain.

FIGURE 3.21 THE SOLUTION FOR THE DAVISON INDUSTRIES PROBLEM

```
Optimal Objective Value =            3850000.00000

          Variable                Value              Reduced Cost
      --------------        ---------------        ----------------

            AN                50000.00000                0.00000
            AO                    0.00000                5.00000
            BN                30000.00000                0.00000
            BO                40000.00000                0.00000


          Constraint          Slack/Surplus             Dual Value
      --------------        ---------------        ----------------

             1                    0.00000               45.00000
             2                    0.00000               40.00000
             3                    0.00000              -15.00000
             4                20000.00000                0.00000


                          Objective          Allowable          Allowable
          Variable        Coefficient        Increase           Decrease
      ----------        ------------        ----------        ----------

            AN              30.00000            5.00000           Infinite
            AO              50.00000            Infinite          5.00000
            BN              25.00000           15.00000           5.00000
            BO              40.00000            5.00000          15.00000


                             RHS              Allowable          Allowable
          Constraint        Value            Increase           Decrease
      ----------        ------------        ----------        ----------

             1            50000.00000        20000.00000        40000.00000
             2            70000.00000        20000.00000        40000.00000
             3            80000.00000        40000.00000        20000.00000
             4            60000.00000            Infinite        20000.00000
```

Problems 19–32 require formulation and computer solution.

19. Better Products, Inc., manufactures three products on two machines. In a typical week, 40 hours are available on each machine. The profit contribution and production time in hours per unit are as follows:

Category	Product 1	Product 2	Product 3
Profit/unit	$30	$50	$20
Machine 1 time/unit	0.5	2.0	0.75
Machine 2 time/unit	1.0	1.0	0.5

Two operators are required for machine 1; thus, 2 hours of labor must be scheduled for each hour of machine 1 time. Only one operator is required for machine 2. A maximum of 100 labor-hours is available for assignment to the machines during the coming week.

Other production requirements are that product 1 cannot account for more than 50% of the units produced and that product 3 must account for at least 20% of the units produced.

a. How many units of each product should be produced to maximize the total profit contribution? What is the projected weekly profit associated with your solution?

b. How many hours of production time will be scheduled on each machine?

c. What is the value of an additional hour of labor?

d. Assume that labor capacity can be increased to 120 hours. Would you be interested in using the additional 20 hours available for this resource? Develop the optimal product mix assuming the extra hours are made available.

20. Adirondack Savings Bank (ASB) has $1 million in new funds that must be allocated to home loans, personal loans, and automobile loans. The annual rates of return for the three types of loans are 7% for home loans, 12% for personal loans, and 9% for automobile loans. The bank's planning committee has decided that at least 40% of the new funds must be allocated to home loans. In addition, the planning committee has specified that the amount allocated to personal loans cannot exceed 60% of the amount allocated to automobile loans.

a. Formulate a linear programming model that can be used to determine the amount of funds ASB should allocate to each type of loan in order to maximize the total annual return for the new funds.

b. How much should be allocated to each type of loan? What is the total annual return? What is the annual percentage return?

c. If the interest rate on home loans increased to 9%, would the amount allocated to each type of loan change? Explain.

d. Suppose the total amount of new funds available was increased by $10,000. What effect would this have on the total annual return? Explain.

e. Assume that ASB has the original $1 million in new funds available and that the planning committee has agreed to relax the requirement that at least 40% of the new funds must be allocated to home loans by 1%. How much would the annual return change? How much would the annual percentage return change?

21. Round Tree Manor is a hotel that provides two types of rooms with three rental classes: Super Saver, Deluxe, and Business. The profit per night for each type of room and rental class is as follows:

		Rental Class		
		Super Saver	**Deluxe**	**Business**
Room	**Type I**	$30	$35	—
	Type II	$20	$30	$40

Type I rooms do not have Internet access and are not available for the Business rental class.

Round Tree's management makes a forecast of the demand by rental class for each night in the future. A linear programming model developed to maximize profit is used to determine how many reservations to accept for each rental class. The demand forecast for a particular night is 130 rentals in the Super Saver class, 60 rentals in the Deluxe class, and 50 rentals in the Business class. Round Tree has 100 Type I rooms and 120 Type II rooms.

a. Use linear programming to determine how many reservations to accept in each rental class and how the reservations should be allocated to room types. Is the demand by any rental class not satisfied? Explain.

b. How many reservations can be accommodated in each rental class?

c. Management is considering offering a free breakfast to anyone upgrading from a Super Saver reservation to Deluxe class. If the cost of the breakfast to Round Tree is $5, should this incentive be offered?

d. With a little work, an unused office area could be converted to a rental room. If the conversion cost is the same for both types of rooms, would you recommend converting the office to a Type I or a Type II room? Why?

e. Could the linear programming model be modified to plan for the allocation of rental demand for the next night? What information would be needed and how would the model change?

22. Industrial Designs has been awarded a contract to design a label for a new wine produced by Lake View Winery. The company estimates that 150 hours will be required to complete the project. The firm's three graphics designers available for assignment to this project are Lisa, a senior designer and team leader; David, a senior designer; and Sarah, a junior designer. Because Lisa has worked on several projects for Lake View Winery, management specified that Lisa must be assigned at least 40% of the total number of hours assigned to the two senior designers. To provide label-designing experience for Sarah, Sarah must be assigned at least 15% of the total project time. However, the number of hours assigned to Sarah must not exceed 25% of the total number of hours assigned to the two senior designers. Due to other project commitments, Lisa has a maximum of 50 hours available to work on this project. Hourly wage rates are $30 for Lisa, $25 for David, and $18 for Sarah.

a. Formulate a linear program that can be used to determine the number of hours each graphic designer should be assigned to the project in order to minimize total cost.

b. How many hours should each graphic designer be assigned to the project? What is the total cost?

c. Suppose Lisa could be assigned more than 50 hours. What effect would this have on the optimal solution? Explain.

d. If Sarah were not required to work a minimum number of hours on this project, would the optimal solution change? Explain.

23. Vollmer Manufacturing makes three components for sale to refrigeration companies. The components are processed on two machines: a shaper and a grinder. The times (in minutes) required on each machine are as follows:

Component	Machine	
	Shaper	**Grinder**
1	6	4
2	4	5
3	4	2

The shaper is available for 120 hours, and the grinder is available for 110 hours. No more than 200 units of component 3 can be sold, but up to 1000 units of each of the other components can be sold. In fact, the company already has orders for 600 units of component 1 that must be satisfied. The profit contributions for components 1, 2, and 3 are $8, $6, and $9, respectively.

a. Formulate and solve for the recommended production quantities.

b. What are the objective coefficient ranges for the three components? Interpret these ranges for company management.

c. What are the right-hand-side ranges? Interpret these ranges for company management.

d. If more time could be made available on the grinder, how much would it be worth?

e. If more units of component 3 can be sold by reducing the sales price by $4, should the company reduce the price?

24. National Insurance Associates carries an investment portfolio of stocks, bonds, and other investment alternatives. Currently $200,000 of funds are available and must be considered for new investment opportunities. The four stock options National is considering and the relevant financial data are as follows:

	Stock			
	A	**B**	**C**	**D**
Price per share	$100	$50	$80	$40
Annual rate of return	0.12	0.08	0.06	0.10
Risk measure per dollar invested	0.10	0.07	0.05	0.08

The risk measure indicates the relative uncertainty associated with the stock in terms of its realizing the projected annual return; higher values indicate greater risk. The risk measures are provided by the firm's top financial advisor.

National's top management has stipulated the following investment guidelines: The annual rate of return for the portfolio must be at least 9% and no one stock can account for more than 50% of the total dollar investment.

a. Use linear programming to develop an investment portfolio that minimizes risk.

b. If the firm ignores risk and uses a maximum return-on-investment strategy, what is the investment portfolio?

c. What is the dollar difference between the portfolios in parts (a) and (b)? Why might the company prefer the solution developed in part (a)?

25. Georgia Cabinets manufactures kitchen cabinets that are sold to local dealers throughout the Southeast. Because of a large backlog of orders for oak and cherry cabinets, the company decided to contract with three smaller cabinetmakers to do the final finishing operation. For the three cabinetmakers, the number of hours required to complete all the oak cabinets, the number of hours required to complete all the cherry cabinets, the number of hours available for the final finishing operation, and the cost per hour to perform the work are shown here.

	Cabinetmaker 1	Cabinetmaker 2	Cabinetmaker 3
Hours required to complete all the oak cabinets	50	42	30
Hours required to complete all the cherry cabinets	60	48	35
Hours available	40	30	35
Cost per hour	$36	$42	$55

For example, Cabinetmaker 1 estimates it will take 50 hours to complete all the oak cabinets and 60 hours to complete all the cherry cabinets. However, Cabinetmaker 1 only has 40 hours available for the final finishing operation. Thus, Cabinetmaker 1 can only complete $40/50 = 0.80$, or 80%, of the oak cabinets if it worked only on oak cabinets. Similarly, Cabinetmaker 1 can only complete $40/60 = 0.67$, or 67%, of the cherry cabinets if it worked only on cherry cabinets.

a. Formulate a linear programming model that can be used to determine the percentage of the oak cabinets and the percentage of the cherry cabinets that should be given to each of the three cabinetmakers in order to minimize the total cost of completing both projects.

b. Solve the model formulated in part (a). What percentage of the oak cabinets and what percentage of the cherry cabinets should be assigned to each cabinetmaker? What is the total cost of completing both projects?

c. If Cabinetmaker 1 has additional hours available, would the optimal solution change? Explain.

d. If Cabinetmaker 2 has additional hours available, would the optimal solution change? Explain.

e. Suppose Cabinetmaker 2 reduced its cost to $38 per hour. What effect would this change have on the optimal solution? Explain.

26. Benson Electronics manufactures three components used to produce cell telephones and other communication devices. In a given production period, demand for the three components may exceed Benson's manufacturing capacity. In this case, the company meets demand by purchasing the components from another manufacturer at an increased cost per unit. Benson's manufacturing cost per unit and purchasing cost per unit for the three components are as follows:

Source	Component 1	Component 2	Component 3
Manufacture	$4.50	$5.00	$2.75
Purchase	$6.50	$8.80	$7.00

Manufacturing times in minutes per unit for Benson's three departments are as follows:

Department	Component 1	Component 2	Component 3
Production	2	3	4
Assembly	1	1.5	3
Testing & Packaging	1.5	2	5

For instance, each unit of component 1 that Benson manufactures requires 2 minutes of production time, 1 minute of assembly time, and 1.5 minutes of testing and packaging time. For the next production period, Benson has capacities of 360 hours in the production department, 250 hours in the assembly department, and 300 hours in the testing and packaging department.

a. Formulate a linear programming model that can be used to determine how many units of each component to manufacture and how many units of each component to purchase. Assume that component demands that must be satisfied are 6000 units for component 1, 4000 units for component 2, and 3500 units for component 3. The objective is to minimize the total manufacturing and purchasing costs.

b. What is the optimal solution? How many units of each component should be manufactured and how many units of each component should be purchased?

c. Which departments are limiting Benson's manufacturing quantities? Use the dual value to determine the value of an *extra hour* in each of these departments.

d. Suppose that Benson had to obtain one additional unit of component 2. Discuss what the dual value for the component 2 constraint tells us about the cost to obtain the additional unit.

27. Golf Shafts, Inc. (GSI), produces graphite shafts for several manufacturers of golf clubs. Two GSI manufacturing facilities, one located in San Diego and the other in Tampa, have the capability to produce shafts in varying degrees of stiffness, ranging from regular models used primarily by average golfers to extra stiff models used primarily by low-handicap and professional golfers. GSI just received a contract for the production of 200,000 regular shafts and 75,000 stiff shafts. Because both plants are currently producing shafts for previous orders, neither plant has sufficient capacity by itself to fill the new order. The San Diego plant can produce up to a total of 120,000 shafts, and the Tampa plant can produce up to a total of 180,000 shafts. Because of equipment differences at each of the plants and differing labor costs, the per-unit production costs vary as shown here:

	San Diego Cost	Tampa Cost
Regular shaft	$5.25	$4.95
Stiff shaft	$5.45	$5.70

a. Formulate a linear programming model to determine how GSI should schedule production for the new order in order to minimize the total production cost.
b. Solve the model that you developed in part (a).
c. Suppose that some of the previous orders at the Tampa plant could be rescheduled in order to free up additional capacity for the new order. Would this option be worthwhile? Explain.
d. Suppose that the cost to produce a stiff shaft in Tampa had been incorrectly computed, and that the correct cost is $5.30 per shaft. What effect, if any, would the correct cost have on the optimal solution developed in part (b)? What effect would it have on total production cost?

28. The Pfeiffer Company manages approximately $15 million for clients. For each client, Pfeiffer chooses a mix of three investment vehicles: a growth stock fund, an income fund, and a money market fund. Each client has different investment objectives and different tolerances for risk. To accommodate these differences, Pfeiffer places limits on the percentage of each portfolio that may be invested in the three funds and assigns a portfolio risk index to each client.

Here's how the system works for Dennis Hartmann, one of Pfeiffer's clients. Based on an evaluation of Hartmann's risk tolerance, Pfeiffer has assigned Hartmann's portfolio a risk index of 0.05. Furthermore, to maintain diversity, the fraction of Hartmann's portfolio invested in the growth and income funds must be at least 10% for each, and at least 20% must be in the money market fund.

The risk ratings for the growth, income, and money market funds are 0.10, 0.05, and 0.01, respectively. A portfolio risk index is computed as a weighted average of the risk ratings for the three funds where the weights are the fraction of the portfolio invested in each of the funds. Hartmann has given Pfeiffer $300,000 to manage. Pfeiffer is currently forecasting a yield of 20% on the growth fund, 10% on the income fund, and 6% on the money market fund.

a. Develop a linear programming model to select the best mix of investments for Hartmann's portfolio.
b. Solve the model you developed in part (a).
c. How much may the yields on the three funds vary before it will be necessary for Pfeiffer to modify Hartmann's portfolio?
d. If Hartmann were more risk tolerant, how much of a yield increase could he expect? For instance, what if his portfolio risk index is increased to 0.06?
e. If Pfeiffer revised the yield estimate for the growth fund downward to 0.10, how would you recommend modifying Hartmann's portfolio?

f. What information must Pfeiffer maintain on each client in order to use this system to manage client portfolios?

g. On a weekly basis Pfeiffer revises the yield estimates for the three funds. Suppose Pfeiffer has 50 clients. Describe how you would envision Pfeiffer making weekly modifications in each client's portfolio and allocating the total funds managed among the three investment funds.

29. La Jolla Beverage Products is considering producing a wine cooler that would be a blend of a white wine, a rosé wine, and fruit juice. To meet taste specifications, the wine cooler must consist of at least 50% white wine, at least 20% and no more than 30% rosé, and exactly 20% fruit juice. La Jolla purchases the wine from local wineries and the fruit juice from a processing plant in San Francisco. For the current production period, 10,000 gallons of white wine and 8000 gallons of rosé wine can be purchased; an unlimited amount of fruit juice can be ordered. The costs for the wine are $1.00 per gallon for the white and $1.50 per gallon for the rosé; the fruit juice can be purchased for $0.50 per gallon. La Jolla Beverage Products can sell all of the wine cooler they can produce for $2.50 per gallon.

a. Is the cost of the wine and fruit juice a sunk cost or a relevant cost in this situation? Explain.

b. Formulate a linear program to determine the blend of the three ingredients that will maximize the total profit contribution. Solve the linear program to determine the number of gallons of each ingredient La Jolla should purchase and the total profit contribution they will realize from this blend.

c. If La Jolla could obtain additional amounts of the white wine, should they do so? If so, how much should they be willing to pay for each additional gallon, and how many additional gallons would they want to purchase?

d. If La Jolla Beverage Products could obtain additional amounts of the rosé wine, should they do so? If so, how much should they be willing to pay for each additional gallon, and how many additional gallons would they want to purchase?

e. Interpret the dual value for the constraint corresponding to the requirement that the wine cooler must contain at least 50% white wine. What is your advice to management given this dual value?

f. Interpret the dual value for the constraint corresponding to the requirement that the wine cooler must contain exactly 20% fruit juice. What is your advice to management given this dual value?

30. The program manager for Channel 10 would like to determine the best way to allocate the time for the 11:00–11:30 evening news broadcast. Specifically, she would like to determine the number of minutes of broadcast time to devote to local news, national news, weather, and sports. Over the 30-minute broadcast, 10 minutes are set aside for advertising. The station's broadcast policy states that at least 15% of the time available should be devoted to local news coverage; the time devoted to local news or national news must be at least 50% of the total broadcast time; the time devoted to the weather segment must be less than or equal to the time devoted to the sports segment; the time devoted to the sports segment should be no longer than the total time spent on the local and national news; and at least 20% of the time should be devoted to the weather segment. The production costs per minute are $300 for local news, $200 for national news, $100 for weather, and $100 for sports.

a. Formulate and solve a linear program that can determine how the 20 available minutes should be used to minimize the total cost of producing the program.

b. Interpret the dual value for the constraint corresponding to the available time. What advice would you give the station manager given this dual value?

c. Interpret the dual value for the constraint corresponding to the requirement that at least 15% of the available time should be devoted to local coverage. What advice would you give the station manager given this dual value?

    d. Interpret the dual value for the constraint corresponding to the requirement that the time devoted to the local and the national news must be at least 50% of the total broadcast time. What advice would you give the station manager given this dual value?

    e. Interpret the dual value for the constraint corresponding to the requirement that the time devoted to the weather segment must be less than or equal to the time devoted to the sports segment. What advice would you give the station manager given this dual value?

31. Gulf Coast Electronics is ready to award contracts for printing their annual report. For the past several years, the four-color annual report has been printed by Johnson Printing and Lakeside Litho. A new firm, Benson Printing, inquired into the possibility of doing a portion of the printing. The quality and service level provided by Lakeside Litho has been extremely high; in fact, only 0.5% of their reports have had to be discarded because of quality problems. Johnson Printing has also had a high quality level historically, producing an average of only 1% unacceptable reports. Because Gulf Coast Electronics has had no experience with Benson Printing, they estimated their defective rate to be 10%. Gulf Coast would like to determine how many reports should be printed by each firm to obtain 75,000 acceptable-quality reports. To ensure that Benson Printing will receive some of the contract, management specified that the number of reports awarded to Benson Printing must be at least 10% of the volume given to Johnson Printing. In addition, the total volume assigned to Benson Printing, Johnson Printing, and Lakeside Litho should not exceed 30,000, 50,000, and 50,000 copies, respectively. Because of the long-term relationship with Lakeside Litho, management also specified that at least 30,000 reports should be awarded to Lakeside Litho. The cost per copy is $2.45 for Benson Printing, $2.50 for Johnson Printing, and $2.75 for Lakeside Litho.

    a. Formulate and solve a linear program for determining how many copies should be assigned to each printing firm to minimize the total cost of obtaining 75,000 acceptable-quality reports.

    b. Suppose that the quality level for Benson Printing is much better than estimated. What effect, if any, would this quality level have?

    c. Suppose that management is willing to reconsider their requirement that Lakeside Litho be awarded at least 30,000 reports. What effect, if any, would this consideration have?

32. PhotoTech, Inc., a manufacturer of rechargeable batteries for digital cameras, signed a contract with a digital photography company to produce three different lithium-ion battery packs for a new line of digital cameras. The contract calls for the following:

Battery Pack	Production Quantity
PT-100	200,000
PT-200	100,000
PT-300	150,000

PhotoTech can manufacture the battery packs at manufacturing plants located in the Philippines and Mexico. The unit cost of the battery packs differs at the two plants because of differences in production equipment and wage rates. The unit costs for each battery pack at each manufacturing plant are as follows:

| | Plant | |
Product	Philippines	Mexico
PT-100	$0.95	$0.98
PT-200	$0.98	$1.06
PT-300	$1.34	$1.15

The PT-100 and PT-200 battery packs are produced using similar production equipment available at both plants. However, each plant has a limited capacity for the total number of PT-100 and PT-200 battery packs produced. The combined PT-100 and PT-200 production capacities are 175,000 units at the Philippines plant and 160,000 units at the Mexico plant. The PT-300 production capacities are 75,000 units at the Philippines plant and 100,000 units at the Mexico plant. The cost of shipping from the Philippines plant is $0.18 per unit, and the cost of shipping from the Mexico plant is $0.10 per unit.

a. Develop a linear program that PhotoTech can use to determine how many units of each battery pack to produce at each plant in order to minimize the total production and shipping cost associated with the new contract.

b. Solve the linear program developed in part (a) to determine the optimal production plan.

c. Use sensitivity analysis to determine how much the production and/or shipping cost per unit would have to change in order to produce additional units of the PT-100 in the Philippines plant.

d. Use sensitivity analysis to determine how much the production and/or shipping cost per unit would have to change in order to produce additional units of the PT-200 in the Mexico plant.

Case Problem 1   PRODUCT MIX

TJ's, Inc., makes three nut mixes for sale to grocery chains located in the Southeast. The three mixes, referred to as the Regular Mix, the Deluxe Mix, and the Holiday Mix, are made by mixing different percentages of five types of nuts.

In preparation for the fall season, TJ's has just purchased the following shipments of nuts at the prices shown:

Type of Nut	Shipment Amount (pounds)	Cost per Shipment ($)
Almond	6000	7500
Brazil	7500	7125
Filbert	7500	6750
Pecan	6000	7200
Walnut	7500	7875

The Regular Mix consists of 15% almonds, 25% Brazil nuts, 25% filberts, 10% pecans, and 25% walnuts. The Deluxe Mix consists of 20% of each type of nut, and the Holiday Mix consists of 25% almonds, 15% Brazil nuts, 15% filberts, 25% pecans, and 20% walnuts.

TJ's accountant analyzed the cost of packaging materials, sales price per pound, and so forth, and determined that the profit contribution per pound is $1.65 for the Regular Mix, $2.00 for the Deluxe Mix, and $2.25 for the Holiday Mix. These figures do not include the cost of specific types of nuts in the different mixes because that cost can vary greatly in the commodity markets.

Customer orders already received are summarized here:

Type of Mix	Orders (pounds)
Regular	10,000
Deluxe	3,000
Holiday	5,000

Because demand is running high, it is expected that TJ's will receive many more orders than can be satisfied.

TJ's is committed to using the available nuts to maximize profit over the fall season; nuts not used will be given to a local charity. Even if it is not profitable to do so, TJ's president indicated that the orders already received must be satisfied.

Managerial Report

Perform an analysis of TJ's product-mix problem, and prepare a report for TJ's president that summarizes your findings. Be sure to include information and analysis on the following:

1. The cost per pound of the nuts included in the Regular, Deluxe, and Holiday mixes
2. The optimal product mix and the total profit contribution
3. Recommendations regarding how the total profit contribution can be increased if additional quantities of nuts can be purchased
4. A recommendation as to whether TJ's should purchase an additional 1000 pounds of almonds for $1000 from a supplier who overbought
5. Recommendations on how profit contribution could be increased (if at all) if TJ's does not satisfy all existing orders

Case Problem 2   INVESTMENT STRATEGY

J. D. Williams, Inc., is an investment advisory firm that manages more than $120 million in funds for its numerous clients. The company uses an asset allocation model that recommends the portion of each client's portfolio to be invested in a growth stock fund, an income fund, and a money market fund. To maintain diversity in each client's portfolio, the firm places limits on the percentage of each portfolio that may be invested in each of the three funds. General guidelines indicate that the amount invested in the growth fund must be between 20% and 40% of the total portfolio value. Similar percentages for the other two funds stipulate that between 20% and 50% of the total portfolio value must be in the income fund, and at least 30% of the total portfolio value must be in the money market fund.

In addition, the company attempts to assess the risk tolerance of each client and adjust the portfolio to meet the needs of the individual investor. For example, Williams just contracted with a new client who has $800,000 to invest. Based on an evaluation of the client's risk tolerance, Williams assigned a maximum risk index of 0.05 for the client. The firm's risk indicators show the risk of the growth fund at 0.10, the income fund at 0.07, and the money market fund at 0.01. An overall portfolio risk index is computed as a weighted average of the risk rating for the three funds where the weights are the fraction of the client's portfolio invested in each of the funds.

Additionally, Williams is currently forecasting annual yields of 18% for the growth fund, 12.5% for the income fund, and 7.5% for the money market fund. Based on the information provided, how should the new client be advised to allocate the $800,000 among the growth, income, and money market funds? Develop a linear programming model that will provide the maximum yield for the portfolio. Use your model to develop a managerial report.

Managerial Report

1. Recommend how much of the $800,000 should be invested in each of the three funds. What is the annual yield you anticipate for the investment recommendation?
2. Assume that the client's risk index could be increased to 0.055. How much would the yield increase and how would the investment recommendation change?

3. Refer again to the original situation where the client's risk index was assessed to be 0.05. How would your investment recommendation change if the annual yield for the growth fund were revised downward to 16% or even to 14%?
4. Assume that the client expressed some concern about having too much money in the growth fund. How would the original recommendation change if the amount invested in the growth fund is not allowed to exceed the amount invested in the income fund?
5. The asset allocation model you developed may be useful in modifying the portfolios for all of the firm's clients whenever the anticipated yields for the three funds are periodically revised. What is your recommendation as to whether use of this model is possible?

Case Problem 3   TRUCK LEASING STRATEGY

Reep Construction recently won a contract for the excavation and site preparation of a new rest area on the Pennsylvania Turnpike. In preparing his bid for the job, Bob Reep, founder and president of Reep Construction, estimated that it would take four months to perform the work and that 10, 12, 14, and 8 trucks would be needed in months 1 through 4, respectively.

The firm currently has 20 trucks of the type needed to perform the work on the new project. These trucks were obtained last year when Bob signed a long-term lease with PennState Leasing. Although most of these trucks are currently being used on existing jobs, Bob estimates that one truck will be available for use on the new project in month 1, two trucks will be available in month 2, three trucks will be available in month 3, and one truck will be available in month 4. Thus, to complete the project, Bob will have to lease additional trucks.

The long-term leasing contract with PennState has a monthly cost of $600 per truck. Reep Construction pays its truck drivers $20 an hour, and daily fuel costs are approximately $100 per truck. All maintenance costs are paid by PennState Leasing. For planning purposes, Bob estimates that each truck used on the new project will be operating eight hours a day, five days a week for approximately four weeks each month.

Bob does not believe that current business conditions justify committing the firm to additional long-term leases. In discussing the short-term leasing possibilities with PennState Leasing, Bob learned that he can obtain short-term leases of 1–4 months. Short-term leases differ from long-term leases in that the short-term leasing plans include the cost of both a truck and a driver. Maintenance costs for short-term leases also are paid by PennState Leasing. The following costs for each of the four months cover the lease of a truck and driver:

Length of Lease	Cost per Month ($)
1	4000
2	3700
3	3225
4	3040

Bob Reep would like to acquire a lease that would minimize the cost of meeting the monthly trucking requirements for his new project, but he also takes great pride in the fact that his company has never laid off employees. Bob is committed to maintaining his no-layoff policy; that is, he will use his own drivers even if costs are higher.

Managerial Report

Perform an analysis of Reep Construction's leasing problem and prepare a report for Bob Reep that summarizes your findings. Be sure to include information on and analysis of the following items:

1. The optimal leasing plan
2. The costs associated with the optimal leasing plan
3. The cost for Reep Construction to maintain its current policy of no layoffs

Appendix 3.1   SENSITIVITY ANALYSIS WITH EXCEL

In Appendix 2.2 we showed how Excel Solver can be used to solve a linear program by using it to solve the Par, Inc., problem. Let us now see how it can be used to provide sensitivity analysis.

When Solver finds the optimal solution to a linear program, the **Solver Results** dialog box (see Figure 3.22) will appear on the screen. If only the solution is desired, you simply click **OK**. To obtain the optimal solution and the sensitivity analysis output, you must select **Sensitivity** in the **Reports** box before clicking **OK;** the sensitivity report is created on another worksheet in the same Excel workbook. Using this procedure for the Par problem, we obtained the optimal solution shown in Figure 3.23 and the sensitivity report shown in Figure 3.24.

FIGURE 3.22   EXCEL SOLVER RESULTS DIALOG BOX

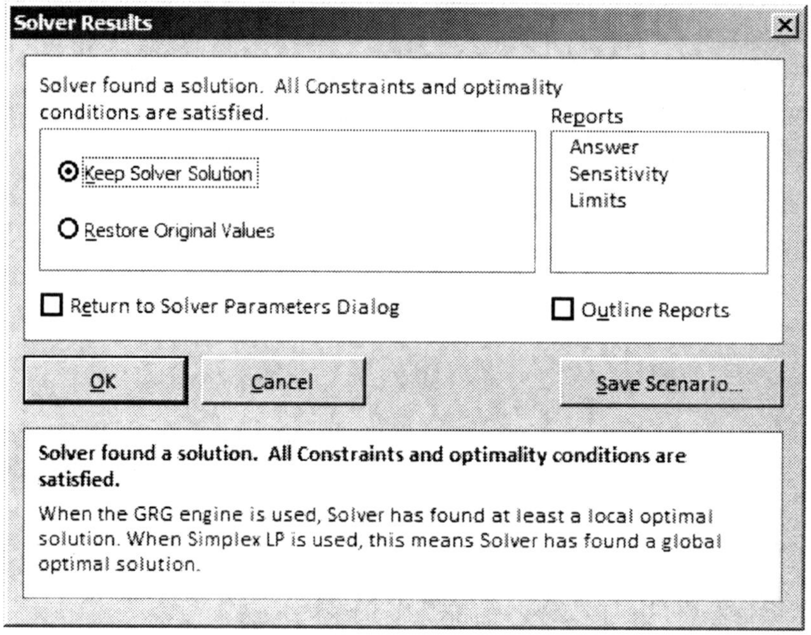

[1]In Excel, if the value of a variable in an optimal solution is equal to the upper bound of the variable, then reduced cost will be the dual value of this upper bound constraint.

FIGURE 3.23   EXCEL SOLUTION FOR THE PAR, INC., PROBLEM

WEB file

Par

	A	B	C	D
1	Par, Inc.			
2				
3		**Production Time**		
4	**Operation**	**Standard**	**Deluxe**	**Time Available**
5	Cutting and Dyeing	0.7	1	630
6	Sewing	0.5	0.83333	600
7	Finishing	1	0.66667	708
8	Inspection and packaging	0.1	0.25	135
9	**Profit Per Bag**	10	9	
10				
11				
12	**Model**			
13				
14		**Decision Variables**		
15		**Standard**	**Deluxe**	
16	**Bags Produced**	539.99842	252.00110	
17				
18	**Maximize Total Profit**	7668		
19				
20	**Constraints**	**Hours Used (LHS)**		**Hours Available (RHS)**
21	Cutting and Dyeing	630	<=	630
22	Sewing	479.99929	<=	600
23	Finishing	708	<=	708
24	Inspection and Packaging	117.00012	<=	135

FIGURE 3.24   EXCEL SENSITIVITY REPORT FOR THE PAR, INC., PROBLEM

Variable Cells

Cell	Name	Final Value	Reduced Cost	Objective Coefficient	Allowable Increase	Allowable Decrease
$B$16	Bags Produced Standard	540	0	10	3.5	3.7
$C$16	Bags Produced Deluxe	252	0	9	5.285714286	2.333333333

Constraints

Cell	Name	Final Value	Shadow Price	Constraint R.H. Side	Allowable Increase	Allowable Decrease
$B$21	Cutting and Dyeing Hours Used (LHS)	630	4.375	630	52.36363636	134.4
$B$22	Sewing Hours Used (LHS)	480	0	600	1E+30	120
$B$23	Finishing Hours Used (LHS)	708	6.9375	708	192	128
$B$24	Inspection and Packaging Hours Used (LHS)	117	0	135	1E+30	18

Interpretation of Excel Sensitivity Report

In the Adjustable Cells section of the Sensitivity Report, the column labeled Final Value contains the optimal values of the decision variables. For the Par, Inc., problem the optimal solution is 540 standard bags and 252 deluxe bags. Next, let us consider the values in the Reduced Cost column.[1] For the Par, Inc., problem the reduced costs for both decision variables are zero; they are at their optimal values.

To the right of the Reduced Cost column in Figure 3.24, we find three columns labeled Objective Coefficient, Allowable Increase, and Allowable Decrease. Note that for the standard bag decision variable, the objective function coefficient value is 10, the allowable increase is 3.5, and the allowable decrease is 3.7. Adding 3.5 to and subtracting 3.7 from the current coefficient of 10 provides the range of optimality for C_S.

$$6.3 \leq C_S \leq 13.5$$

Similarly, the range of optimality for C_D is

$$6.67 \leq C_D \leq 14.29$$

Next, consider the information in the Constraints section of the report. The entries in the Final Value column are the number of hours needed in each department to produce the optimal production quantities of 540 standard bags and 252 deluxe bags. Thus, at the optimal solution, 630 hours of cutting and dyeing time, 480 hours of sewing time, 708 hours of finishing time, and 117 hours of inspection and packaging time are required. The values in the Constraint R.H. Side column are just the original right-hand-side values: 630 hours of cutting and dyeing time, 600 hours of sewing time, 708 hours of finishing time, and 135 hours of inspection and packaging time. Note that for the Par, Inc., problem, the values of the slack variables for each constraint are simply the differences between the entries in the Constraint R.H. Side column and the corresponding entries in the Final Value column.

The sensitivity analysis interpretations provided in this appendix are based on the assumption that only one objective function coefficient or only one right-hand-side change occurs at a time.

The entries in the Shadow Price column provide the *shadow price* for each constraint. The shadow price is another, often-used term for the dual value. The last two columns of the Sensitivity Report contain the range of feasibility information for the constraint right-hand sides. For example, consider the cutting and dyeing constraint with an allowable increase value of 52.4 and an allowable decrease value of 134.4. The values in the Allowable Increase and Allowable Decrease columns indicate that the shadow price of $4.375 is valid for increases up to 52.4 hours and decreases to 134.4 hours. Thus, the shadow price of $4.375 is applicable for increases up to 630 + 52.4 = 682.4 and decreases down to 630 − 134.4 = 495.6 hours.

In summary, the range of feasibility information provides the limits where the shadow prices are applicable. For changes outside the range, the problem must be re-solved to find the new optimal solution and the new shadow price.

Appendix 3.2   SENSITIVITY ANALYSIS WITH LINGO

In Appendix 2.1 we showed how LINGO can be used to solve a linear program by using it to solve the Par, Inc., problem. A copy of the Solution Report is shown in Figure 3.25. As we discussed previously, the value of the objective function is 7668, the optimal solution is $S = 540$ and $D = 252$, and the values of the slack variables corresponding to the four constraints (rows 2–5) are 0, 120, 0, and 18. Now let us consider the information in the Reduced Cost column and the Dual Price column.

FIGURE 3.25   PAR, INC., SOLUTION REPORT USING LINGO

```
Global optimal solution found.
    Objective value:                7668.000
    Total solver iterations:             2

            Variable            Value          Reduced Cost
            --------         ----------        ------------
               S             540.0000             0.000000
               D             252.0000             0.000000

              Row         Slack or Surplus       Dual Price
            --------         ----------        ------------
               1            7668.000             1.000000
               2            0.000000             4.375000
               3            120.0000             0.000000
               4            0.000000             6.937500
               5            18.00000             0.000000
```

LINGO always takes the absolute value of the reduced cost.

For the Par, Inc., problem, the reduced costs for both decision variables are zero because both variables are at a positive value. LINGO reports a **dual price** rather than a dual value. For a maximization problem, the dual value and dual price are identical. For a minimization problem, the dual price is equal to the negative of the dual value. There are historical reasons for this oddity that are beyond the scope of the book. When interpreting the LINGO output for a minimization problem, multiply the dual prices by –1, treat the resulting number as the dual value, and interpret the number as described in Section 3.2. The nonzero dual prices of 4.374957 for constraint 1 (cutting and dyeing constraint in row 2) and 6.937530 for constraint 3 (finishing constraint in row 4) tell us that an additional hour of cutting and dyeing time improves (increases) the value of the optimal solution by $4.37 and an additional hour of finishing time improves (increases) the value of the optimal solution by $6.94.

Next, let us consider how LINGO can be used to compute the range of optimality for each objective function coefficient and the range of feasibility for each of the dual prices. By default, range computations are not enabled in LINGO. To enable range computations, perform the following steps:

Step 1. Choose the **LINGO** menu
Step 2. Select **Options**
Step 3. When the LINGO Options dialog box appears:
Select the **General Solver** tab
Choose **Prices and Ranges** in the **Dual Computations** box
Click **Apply**
Click **OK**

You will now have to re-solve the Par, Inc., problem in order for LINGO to perform the range computations. After re-solving the problem, close or minimize the Solution Report window. To display the range information, select the Range command from the LINGO menu. LINGO displays the range information in a new window titled Range Report. The

FIGURE 3.26   PAR, INC., SENSITIVITY REPORT USING LINGO

```
Ranges in which the basis is unchanged:

                     OBJECTIVE COEFFICIENT RANGES

                   Current         Allowable        Allowable
     Variable      Coefficient     Increase         Decrease
    ------------   -------------   -------------    -------------
        S          10.00000         3.500000         3.700000
        D           9.000000        5.285714         2.333333

                     RIGHTHAND SIDE RANGES

                   Current         Allowable        Allowable
      Row          RHS             Increase         Decrease
    ------------   -------------   -------------    -------------
        2          630.0000         52.36364        134.4000
        3          600.0000         INFINITY        120.0000
        4          708.0000        192.0000         128.0000
        5          135.0000         INFINITY         18.00000
```

output that appears in the Range Report window for the Par, Inc., problem is shown in Figure 3.26.

We will use the information in the Objective Coefficient Ranges section of the range report to compute the range of optimality for the objective function coefficients. For example, the current objective function coefficient for S is 10. Note that the corresponding allowable increase is 3.5 and the corresponding allowable decrease is 3.700000. Thus, the range of optimality for C_S, the objective function coefficient for S, is $10 - 3.700000 = 6.300000$ to $10 + 3.5 = 13.5$. After rounding, the range of optimality for C_S is $6.30 \leq C_S \leq 13.50$. Similarly, with an allowable increase of 5.285714 and an allowable decrease of 2.333300, the range of optimality for C_D is $6.67 \leq C_S \leq 14.29$.

To compute the range of feasibility for each dual price, we will use the information in the Right-Hand-Side Ranges section of the range report. For example, the current right-hand-side value for the cutting and dyeing constraint (row 2) is 630, the allowable increase is 52.36316, and the allowable decrease is 134.40000. Because the dual price for this constraint is 4.375 (shown in the LINGO solution report), we can conclude that additional hours will increase the objective function by $4.37 per hour. From the range information given, we see that after rounding the dual price of $4.37 is valid for increases up to $630 + 52.36 = 682.4$ and decreases to $630 - 134.4 = 495.6$. Thus, the range of feasibility for the cutting and dyeing constraint is 495.6 to 682.4. The ranges of feasibility for the other constraints can be determined in a similar manner.

CHAPTER 4

Linear Programming Applications in Marketing, Finance, and Operations Management

CONTENTS

Linear programming has proven to be one of the most successful quantitative approaches to decision making. Applications have been reported in almost every industry. These applications include production scheduling, media selection, financial planning, capital budgeting, transportation, distribution system design, product mix, staffing, and blending.

The wide variety of Management Science in Actions presented in Chapters 2 and 3 illustrated the use of linear programming as a flexible problem-solving tool. The Management Science in Action, A Marketing Planning Model at Marathon Oil Company, provides another example of the use of linear programming by showing how Marathon uses a large-scale linear programming model to solve a wide variety of planning problems. Later in the chapter other Management Science in Action features illustrate how GE Capital uses linear programming for optimal lease structuring; how Jeppesen Sanderson uses linear programming to optimize production of flight manuals; and how the Kellogg Company uses a large-scale linear programming model to integrate production, distribution, and inventory planning.

In this chapter we present a variety of applications from the traditional business areas of marketing, finance, and operations management. Modeling, computer solution, and interpretation of output are emphasized. A mathematical model is developed for each problem studied, and solutions are presented for most of the applications. In the chapter appendix we illustrate the use of Excel Solver by solving a financial planning problem.

MANAGEMENT SCIENCE IN ACTION

A MARKETING PLANNING MODEL AT MARATHON OIL COMPANY*

Marathon Oil Company has four refineries within the United States, operates 50 light products terminals, and has product demand at more than 95 locations. The Supply and Transportation Division faces the problem of determining which refinery should supply which terminal and, at the same time, determining which products should be transported via pipeline, barge, or tanker to minimize cost. Product demand must be satisfied, and the supply capability of each refinery must not be exceeded. To help solve this difficult problem, Marathon Oil developed a marketing planning model.

The marketing planning model is a large-scale linear programming model that takes into account sales not only at Marathon product terminals but also at all exchange locations. An exchange contract is an agreement with other oil product marketers that involves exchanging or trading Marathon's products for theirs at different locations. All pipelines, barges, and tankers within Marathon's marketing area are also represented in the linear programming model.

The objective of the model is to minimize the cost of meeting a given demand structure, taking into account sales price, pipeline tariffs, exchange contract costs, product demand, terminal operating costs, refining costs, and product purchases.

The marketing planning model is used to solve a wide variety of planning problems that vary from evaluating gasoline blending economics to analyzing the economics of a new terminal or pipeline. With daily sales of about 10 million gallons of refined light product, a savings of even one-thousandth of a cent per gallon can result in significant long-term savings. At the same time, what may appear to be a savings in one area, such as refining or transportation, may actually add to overall costs when the effects are fully realized throughout the system. The marketing planning model allows a simultaneous examination of this total effect.

*Based on information provided by Robert W. Wernert at Marathon Oil Company, Findlay, Ohio.

4.1   MARKETING APPLICATIONS

Applications of linear programming in marketing are numerous. In this section we discuss applications in media selection and marketing research.

Media Selection

In Section 2.1 we provided some general guidelines for modeling linear programming problems. You may want to review Section 2.1 before proceeding with the linear programming applications in this chapter.

Media selection applications of linear programming are designed to help marketing managers allocate a fixed advertising budget to various advertising media. Potential media include newspapers, magazines, radio, television, and direct mail. In these applications, the objective is to maximize reach, frequency, and quality of exposure. Restrictions on the allowable allocation usually arise during consideration of company policy, contract requirements, and media availability. In the application that follows, we illustrate how a media selection problem might be formulated and solved using a linear programming model.

Relax-and-Enjoy Lake Development Corporation is developing a lakeside community at a privately owned lake. The primary market for the lakeside lots and homes includes all middle- and upper-income families within approximately 100 miles of the development. Relax-and-Enjoy employed the advertising firm of Boone, Phillips, and Jackson (BP&J) to design the promotional campaign.

After considering possible advertising media and the market to be covered, BP&J recommended that the first month's advertising be restricted to five media. At the end of the month, BP&J will then reevaluate its strategy based on the month's results. BP&J collected data on the number of potential customers reached, the cost per advertisement, the maximum number of times each medium is available, and the exposure quality rating for each of the five media. The quality rating is measured in terms of an exposure quality unit, a measure of the relative value of one advertisement in each of the media. This measure, based on BP&J's experience in the advertising business, takes into account factors such as audience demographics (age, income, and education of the audience reached), image presented, and quality of the advertisement. The information collected is presented in Table 4.1.

Relax-and-Enjoy provided BP&J with an advertising budget of $30,000 for the first month's campaign. In addition, Relax-and-Enjoy imposed the following restrictions on how BP&J may allocate these funds: At least 10 television commercials must be used, at least 50,000 potential customers must be reached, and no more than $18,000 may be spent on television advertisements. What advertising media selection plan should be recommended?

TABLE 4.1 ADVERTISING MEDIA ALTERNATIVES FOR THE RELAX-AND-ENJOY LAKE DEVELOPMENT CORPORATION

Advertising Media	Number of Potential Customers Reached	Cost ($) per Advertisement	Maximum Times Available per Month*	Exposure Quality Units
1. Daytime TV (1 min), station WKLA	1000	1500	15	65
2. Evening TV (30 sec), station WKLA	2000	3000	10	90
3. Daily newspaper (full page), *The Morning Journal*	1500	400	25	40
4. Sunday newspaper magazine (½ page color), *The Sunday Press*	2500	1000	4	60
5. Radio, 8:00 A.M. or 5:00 P.M. news (30 sec), station KNOP	300	100	30	20

*The maximum number of times the medium is available is either the maximum number of times the advertising medium occurs (e.g., four Sundays per month) or the maximum number of times BP&J recommends that the medium be used.

The decision to be made is how many times to use each medium. We begin by defining the decision variables:

$$DTV = \text{number of times daytime TV is used}$$
$$ETV = \text{number of times evening TV is used}$$
$$DN = \text{number of times daily newspaper is used}$$
$$SN = \text{number of times Sunday newspaper is used}$$
$$R = \text{number of times radio is used}$$

The data on quality of exposure in Table 4.1 show that each daytime TV (DTV) advertisement is rated at 65 exposure quality units. Thus, an advertising plan with DTV advertisements will provide a total of $65DTV$ exposure quality units. Continuing with the data in Table 4.1, we find evening TV (ETV) rated at 90 exposure quality units, daily newspaper (DN) rated at 40 exposure quality units, Sunday newspaper (SN) rated at 60 exposure quality units, and radio (R) rated at 20 exposure quality units. With the objective of maximizing the total exposure quality units for the overall media selection plan, the objective function becomes

Care must be taken to ensure the linear programming model accurately reflects the real problem. Always review your formulation thoroughly before attempting to solve the model.

$$\text{Max} \quad 65DTV + 90ETV + 40DN + 60SN + 20R \qquad \text{Exposure quality}$$

We now formulate the constraints for the model from the information given:

$$
\begin{array}{rcll}
DTV & \leq & 15 & \left.\rule{0pt}{48pt}\right\} \text{Availability of media} \\
ETV & \leq & 10 & \\
DN & \leq & 25 & \\
SN & \leq & 4 & \\
R & \leq & 30 & \\
1500DTV + 3000ETV + 400DN + 1000SN + 100R & \leq & 30{,}000 & \text{Budget} \\
DTV + ETV & \geq & 10 & \left.\rule{0pt}{20pt}\right\} \text{Television restrictions} \\
1500DTV + 3000ETV & \leq & 18{,}000 & \\
1000DTV + 2000ETV + 1500DN + 2500SN + 300R & \geq & 50{,}000 & \text{Customers reached} \\
DTV, ETV, DN, SN, R & \geq & 0 &
\end{array}
$$

Problem 1 provides practice at formulating a similar media selection model.

The optimal solution to this five-variable, nine-constraint linear programming model is shown in Figure 4.1; a summary is presented in Table 4.2.

The optimal solution calls for advertisements to be distributed among daytime TV, daily newspaper, Sunday newspaper, and radio. The maximum number of exposure quality units is 2370, and the total number of customers reached is 61,500. The Reduced Costs column in Figure 4.1 indicates that the number of exposure quality units for evening TV would have to increase by at least 65 before this media alternative could appear in the optimal solution. Note that the budget constraint (constraint 6) has a dual value of 0.060. Therefore, a $1.00 increase in the advertising budget will lead to an increase of 0.06 exposure quality units. The dual value of –25.000 for constraint 7 indicates that increasing the number of television commercials by 1 will decrease the exposure quality of the advertising plan by 25 units. Alternatively, decreasing the number of television commercials by 1 will increase the exposure quality of the advertising plan by 25 units. Thus,

FIGURE 4.1 THE SOLUTION FOR THE RELAX-AND-ENJOY LAKE DEVELOPMENT
CORPORATION PROBLEM

```
Optimal Objective Value =        2370.00000

        Variable              Value           Reduced Cost
     ---------------      ---------------      ---------------
           DTV               10.00000              0.00000
           ETV                0.00000            -65.00000
           DN                25.00000              0.00000
           SN                 2.00000              0.00000
           R                 30.00000              0.00000

        Constraint         Slack/Surplus          Dual Value
     ---------------      ---------------      ---------------
            1                 5.00000              0.00000
            2                10.00000              0.00000
            3                 0.00000             16.00000
            4                 2.00000              0.00000
            5                 0.00000             14.00000
            6                 0.00000              0.06000
            7                 0.00000            -25.00000
            8              3000.00000              0.00000
            9             11500.00000              0.00000
```

Relax

Media Availability

Budget

Television Restrictions

Audience Coverage

TABLE 4.2 ADVERTISING PLAN FOR THE RELAX-AND-ENJOY LAKE
DEVELOPMENT CORPORATION

Media	Frequency	Budget
Daytime TV	10	$15,000
Daily newspaper	25	10,000
Sunday newspaper	2	2,000
Radio	30	3,000
		$30,000

Exposure quality units = 2370
Total customers reached = 61,500

Relax-and-Enjoy should consider reducing the requirement of having at least 10 television commercials.

A possible shortcoming of this model is that, even if the exposure quality measure were not subject to error, it offers no guarantee that maximization of total exposure quality will lead to maximization of profit or of sales (a common surrogate for profit). However, this issue is not a shortcoming of linear programming; rather, it is a shortcoming of the use of exposure quality as a criterion. If we could directly measure the effect of an advertisement on profit, we could use total profit as the objective to be maximized.

NOTES AND COMMENTS

1. The media selection model required subjective evaluations of the exposure quality for the media alternatives. Marketing managers may have substantial data concerning exposure quality, but the final coefficients used in the objective function may also include considerations based primarily on managerial judgment. Judgment is an acceptable way of obtaining input for a linear programming model.

2. The media selection model presented in this section uses exposure quality as the objective function and places a constraint on the number of customers reached. An alternative formulation of this problem would be to use the number of customers reached as the objective function and add a constraint indicating the minimum total exposure quality required for the media plan.

Marketing Research

An organization conducts marketing research to learn about consumer characteristics, attitudes, and preferences. Marketing research firms that specialize in providing such information often do the actual research for client organizations. Typical services offered by a marketing research firm include designing the study, conducting market surveys, analyzing the data collected, and providing summary reports and recommendations for the client. In the research design phase, targets or quotas may be established for the number and types of respondents to be surveyed. The marketing research firm's objective is to conduct the survey so as to meet the client's needs at a minimum cost.

Market Survey, Inc. (MSI), specializes in evaluating consumer reaction to new products, services, and advertising campaigns. A client firm requested MSI's assistance in ascertaining consumer reaction to a recently marketed household product. During meetings with the client, MSI agreed to conduct door-to-door personal interviews to obtain responses from households with children and households without children. In addition, MSI agreed to conduct both day and evening interviews. Specifically, the client's contract called for MSI to conduct 1000 interviews under the following quota guidelines.

1. Interview at least 400 households with children.
2. Interview at least 400 households without children.
3. The total number of households interviewed during the evening must be at least as great as the number of households interviewed during the day.
4. At least 40% of the interviews for households with children must be conducted during the evening.
5. At least 60% of the interviews for households without children must be conducted during the evening.

Because the interviews for households with children take additional interviewer time and because evening interviewers are paid more than daytime interviewers, the cost varies with the type of interview. Based on previous research studies, estimates of the interview costs are as follows:

Household	Interview Cost	
	Day	Evening
Children	$20	$25
No children	$18	$20

What is the household, time-of-day interview plan that will satisfy the contract requirements at a minimum total interviewing cost?

In formulating the linear programming model for the MSI problem, we utilize the following decision-variable notation:

DC = the number of daytime interviews of households with children

EC = the number of evening interviews of households with children

DNC = the number of daytime interviews of households without children

ENC = the number of evening interviews of households without children

We begin the linear programming model formulation by using the cost-per-interview data to develop the objective function:

$$\text{Min} \quad 20DC + 25EC + 18DNC + 20ENC$$

The constraint requiring a total of 1000 interviews is

$$DC + EC + DNC + ENC = 1000$$

The five specifications concerning the types of interviews are as follows.

* Households with children:

$$DC + EC \geq 400$$

* Households without children:

$$DNC + ENC \geq 400$$

* At least as many evening interviews as day interviews:

$$EC + ENC \geq DC + DNC$$

* At least 40% of interviews of households with children during the evening:

$$EC \geq 0.4(DC + EC)$$

* At least 60% of interviews of households without children during the evening:

$$ENC \geq 0.6(DNC + ENC)$$

When we add the nonnegativity requirements, the four-variable and six-constraint linear programming model becomes

Min $\quad 20DC + 25EC + 18DNC + 20ENC$

s.t.

$DC +$	$EC +$	$DNC +$	$ENC = 1000$	Total interviews
$DC +$	EC		$\geq \ 400$	Households with children
		$DNC +$	$ENC \geq \ 400$	Households without children
	$EC + ENC \geq DC + DNC$			Evening interviews
	$EC \geq 0.4(DC + EC)$			Evening interviews in households with children
	$ENC \geq 0.6(DNC + ENC)$			Evening interviews in households without children

$DC, EC, DNC, ENC \geq 0$

The optimal solution to this linear program is shown in Figure 4.2. The solution reveals that the minimum cost of $20,320 occurs with the following interview schedule.

| Household | Number of Interviews | | |
	Day	Evening	Totals
Children	240	160	400
No children	240	360	600
Totals	480	520	1000

Hence, 480 interviews will be scheduled during the day and 520 during the evening. Households with children will be covered by 400 interviews, and households without children will be covered by 600 interviews.

Selected sensitivity analysis information from Figure 4.2 shows a dual value of 19.200 for constraint 1. In other words, the value of the optimal solution will increase by $19.20 if the number of interviews is increased from 1000 to 1001. Thus, $19.20 is the incremental cost of obtaining additional interviews. It also is the savings that could be realized by reducing the number of interviews from 1000 to 999.

The surplus variable, with a value of 200.000, for constraint 3 shows that 200 more households without children will be interviewed than required. Similarly, the surplus variable, with a value of 40.000, for constraint 4 shows that the number of evening interviews exceeds the number of daytime interviews by 40. The zero values for the surplus variables in constraints 5 and 6 indicate that the more expensive evening interviews are being held at a minimum. Indeed, the dual value of 5.000 for constraint 5 indicates that if one more household (with children) than the minimum requirement must be interviewed during the evening, the total interviewing cost will go up by $5.00. Similarly, constraint 6 shows that requiring one more household (without children) to be interviewed during the evening will increase costs by $2.00.

FIGURE 4.2   THE SOLUTION FOR THE MARKET SURVEY PROBLEM

Market

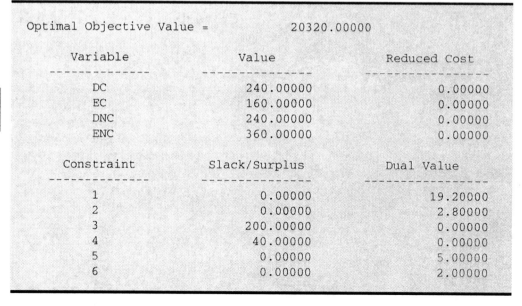

```
Optimal Objective Value =            20320.00000

        Variable              Value            Reduced Cost
        --------              -----            ------------
            DC              240.00000              0.00000
            EC              160.00000              0.00000
           DNC              240.00000              0.00000
           ENC              360.00000              0.00000

      Constraint         Slack/Surplus           Dual Value
      ----------         -------------           ----------
            1                0.00000              19.20000
            2                0.00000               2.80000
            3              200.00000               0.00000
            4               40.00000               0.00000
            5                0.00000               5.00000
            6                0.00000               2.00000
```

4.2 FINANCIAL APPLICATIONS

In finance, linear programming can be applied in problem situations involving capital budgeting, make-or-buy decisions, asset allocation, portfolio selection, financial planning, and many more. In this section, we describe a portfolio selection problem and a problem involving funding of an early retirement program.

Portfolio Selection

Portfolio selection problems involve situations in which a financial manager must select specific investments—for example, stocks and bonds—from a variety of investment alternatives. Managers of mutual funds, credit unions, insurance companies, and banks frequently encounter this type of problem. The objective function for portfolio selection problems usually is maximization of expected return or minimization of risk. The constraints usually take the form of restrictions on the type of permissible investments, state laws, company policy, maximum permissible risk, and so on. Problems of this type have been formulated and solved using a variety of mathematical programming techniques. In this section we formulate and solve a portfolio selection problem as a linear program.

Consider the case of Welte Mutual Funds, Inc., located in New York City. Welte just obtained $100,000 by converting industrial bonds to cash and is now looking for other investment opportunities for these funds. Based on Welte's current investments, the firm's top financial analyst recommends that all new investments be made in the oil industry, steel industry, or in government bonds. Specifically, the analyst identified five investment opportunities and projected their annual rates of return. The investments and rates of return are shown in Table 4.3.

Management of Welte imposed the following investment guidelines.

1. Neither industry (oil or steel) should receive more than $50,000.
2. Government bonds should be at least 25% of the steel industry investments.
3. The investment in Pacific Oil, the high-return but high-risk investment, cannot be more than 60% of the total oil industry investment.

What portfolio recommendations—investments and amounts—should be made for the available $100,000? Given the objective of maximizing projected return subject to the budgetary and managerially imposed constraints, we can answer this question by formulating and solving a linear programming model of the problem. The solution will provide investment recommendations for the management of Welte Mutual Funds.

TABLE 4.3 INVESTMENT OPPORTUNITIES FOR WELTE MUTUAL FUNDS

Investment	Projected Rate of Return (%)
Atlantic Oil	7.3
Pacific Oil	10.3
Midwest Steel	6.4
Huber Steel	7.5
Government bonds	4.5

Let

$$A = \text{dollars invested in Atlantic Oil}$$
$$P = \text{dollars invested in Pacific Oil}$$
$$M = \text{dollars invested in Midwest Steel}$$
$$H = \text{dollars invested in Huber Steel}$$
$$G = \text{dollars invested in government bonds}$$

Using the projected rates of return shown in Table 4.3, we write the objective function for maximizing the total return for the portfolio as

$$\text{Max} \quad 0.073A + 0.103P + 0.064M + 0.075H + 0.045G$$

The constraint specifying investment of the available $100,000 is

$$A + P + M + H + G = 100,000$$

The requirements that neither the oil nor the steel industry should receive more than $50,000 are

$$A + P \leq 50,000$$
$$M + H \leq 50,000$$

The requirement that government bonds be at least 25% of the steel industry investment is expressed as

$$G \geq 0.25(M + H)$$

Finally, the constraint that Pacific Oil cannot be more than 60% of the total oil industry investment is

$$P \leq 0.60(A + P)$$

By adding the nonnegativity restrictions, we obtain the complete linear programming model for the Welte Mutual Funds investment problem:

Max $0.073A + 0.103P + 0.064M + 0.075H + 0.045G$
s.t.

$A +$	$P +$	$M +$	$H +$	G	$=$	$100,000$	Available funds
$A +$	P				$\leq$	$50,000$	Oil industry maximum
		$M +$	H		$\leq$	$50,000$	Steel industry maximum
	$G \geq 0.25\,(M + H)$						Government bonds minimum
	$P \leq 0.60\,(A + P)$						Pacific Oil restriction

$$A, P, M, H, G \geq 0$$

The optimal solution to this linear program is shown in Figure 4.3. Table 4.4 shows how the funds are divided among the securities. Note that the optimal solution indicates that the portfolio should be diversified among all the investment opportunities except

FIGURE 4.3   THE SOLUTION FOR THE WELTE MUTUAL FUNDS PROBLEM

WEB file

Welte

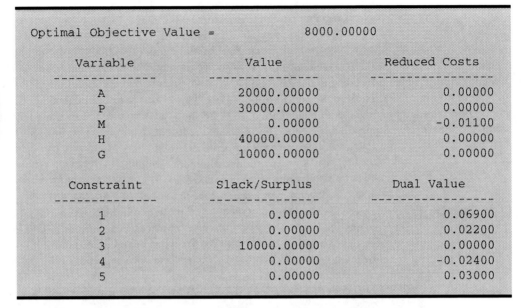

```
Optimal Objective Value =              8000.00000

           Variable              Value          Reduced Costs
        -------------       ---------------     ----------------
              A               20000.00000             0.00000
              P               30000.00000             0.00000
              M                   0.00000            -0.01100
              H               40000.00000             0.00000
              G               10000.00000             0.00000

          Constraint         Slack/Surplus         Dual Value
        -------------       ---------------     ----------------
              1                   0.00000             0.06900
              2                   0.00000             0.02200
              3               10000.00000             0.00000
              4                   0.00000            -0.02400
              5                   0.00000             0.03000
```

Midwest Steel. The projected annual return for this portfolio is $8000, which is an overall return of 8%.

The optimal solution shows the dual value for constraint 3 is zero. The reason is that the steel industry maximum isn't a binding constraint; increases in the steel industry limit of $50,000 will not improve the value of the optimal solution. Indeed, the slack variable for this constraint shows that the current steel industry investment is $10,000 below its limit of $50,000. The dual values for the other constraints are nonzero, indicating that these constraints are binding.

The dual value for the available funds constraint provides information on the rate of return from additional investment funds.

The dual value of 0.069 for constraint 1 shows that the value of the optimal solution can be increased by 0.069 if one more dollar can be made available for the portfolio investment. If more funds can be obtained at a cost of less than 6.9%, management should consider obtaining them. However, if a return in excess of 6.9% can be obtained by investing funds elsewhere (other than in these five securities), management should question the wisdom of investing the entire $100,000 in this portfolio.

Similar interpretations can be given to the other dual values. Note that the dual value for constraint 4 is negative at –0.024. This result indicates that increasing the value on the

TABLE 4.4   OPTIMAL PORTFOLIO SELECTION FOR WELTE MUTUAL FUNDS

Investment	Amount	Expected Annual Return
Atlantic Oil	$ 20,000	$1460
Pacific Oil	30,000	3090
Huber Steel	40,000	3000
Government bonds	10,000	450
Totals	$100,000	$8000

Expected annual return of $8000
Overall rate of return = 8%

right-hand side of the constraint by one unit can be expected to decrease the objective function value of the optimal solution by 0.024. In terms of the optimal portfolio, then, if Welte invests one more dollar in government bonds (beyond the minimum requirement), the total return will decrease by $0.024. To see why this decrease occurs, note again from the dual value for constraint 1 that the marginal return on the funds invested in the portfolio is 6.9% (the average return is 8%). The rate of return on government bonds is 4.5%. Thus, the cost of investing one more dollar in government bonds is the difference between the marginal return on the portfolio and the marginal return on government bonds: 6.9% − 4.5% = 2.4%.

Practice formulating a variation of the Welte problem by working Problem 9.

Note that the optimal solution shows that Midwest Steel should not be included in the portfolio ($M = 0$). The associated reduced cost for M of −0.011 tells us that the objective function coefficient for Midwest Steel would have to increase by 0.011 before considering the Midwest Steel investment alternative would be advisable. With such an increase the Midwest Steel return would be $0.064 + 0.011 = 0.075$, making this investment just as desirable as the currently used Huber Steel investment alternative.

Finally, a simple modification of the Welte linear programming model permits determining the fraction of available funds invested in each security. That is, we divide each of the right-hand-side values by 100,000. Then the optimal values for the variables will give the fraction of funds that should be invested in each security for a portfolio of any size.

NOTES AND COMMENTS

1. The optimal solution to the Welte Mutual Funds problem indicates that $20,000 is to be spent on the Atlantic Oil stock. If Atlantic Oil sells for $75 per share, we would have to purchase exactly 266⅔ shares in order to spend exactly $20,000. The difficulty of purchasing fractional shares can be handled by purchasing the largest possible integer number of shares with the allotted funds (e.g., 266 shares of Atlantic Oil). This approach guarantees that the budget constraint will not be violated. This approach, of course, introduces the possibility that the solution will no longer be optimal, but the danger is slight if a large number of securities are involved. In cases where the analyst believes that the decision variables *must* have integer values, the problem must be formulated as an integer linear programming model. Integer linear programming is the topic of Chapter 7.

2. Financial portfolio theory stresses obtaining a proper balance between risk and return. In the Welte problem, we explicitly considered return in the objective function. Risk is controlled by choosing constraints that ensure diversity among oil and steel stocks and a balance between government bonds and the steel industry investment.

Financial Planning

Linear programming has been used for a variety of financial planning applications. The Management Science in Action, Optimal Lease Structuring at GE Capital, describes how linear programming is used to optimize the structure of a leveraged lease.

MANAGEMENT SCIENCE IN ACTION

OPTIMAL LEASE STRUCTURING AT GE CAPITAL*

GE Capital is a $70 billion subsidiary of General Electric. As one of the nation's largest and most diverse financial services companies, GE Capital arranges leases in both domestic and international markets, including leases for telecommunications; data processing; construction; and fleets of cars, trucks, and commercial aircraft. To help allocate and schedule the rental and debt payments of a leveraged lease, GE Capital analysts developed an optimization model, which is available as an optional component of the company's lease analysis proprietary software.

Leveraged leases are designed to provide financing for assets with economic lives of at least five years, which require large capital outlays. A leveraged lease represents an agreement among the lessor (the owner of the asset), the lessee (the user of the asset), and the lender who provides a nonrecourse loan of 50% to 80% of the lessor's purchase price. In a nonrecourse loan, the lenders cannot turn to the lessor for repayment in the event of default. As the lessor in such arrangements, GE Capital is able to claim ownership and realize income tax benefits such as depreciation and interest deductions. These deductions usually produce tax losses during the early years of the lease, which reduces the total tax liability. Approximately 85% of all financial leases in the United States are leveraged leases.

In its simplest form, the leveraged lease structuring problem can be formulated as a linear program. The linear program models the after-tax cash flow for the lessor, taking into consideration rental receipts, borrowing and repaying of the loan, and income taxes. Constraints are formulated to ensure compliance with IRS guidelines and to enable customizing of leases to meet lessee and lessor requirements. The objective function can be entered in a custom fashion or selected from a predefined list. Typically, the objective is to minimize the lessee's cost, expressed as the net present value of rental payments, or to maximize the lessor's after-tax yield.

GE Capital developed an optimization approach that could be applied to single-investor lease structuring. In a study with the department most involved with these transactions, the optimization approach yielded substantial benefits. The approach helped GE Capital win some single-investor transactions ranging in size from $1 million to $20 million.

*Based on C. J. Litty, "Optimal Lease Structuring at GE Capital," *Interfaces* (May/June 1994): 34–45.

Hewlitt Corporation established an early retirement program as part of its corporate restructuring. At the close of the voluntary sign-up period, 68 employees had elected early retirement. As a result of these early retirements, the company incurs the following obligations over the next eight years:

Year	1	2	3	4	5	6	7	8
Cash Requirement	430	210	222	231	240	195	225	255

The cash requirements (in thousands of dollars) are due at the beginning of each year.

The corporate treasurer must determine how much money must be set aside today to meet the eight yearly financial obligations as they come due. The financing plan for the retirement program includes investments in government bonds as well as savings. The investments in government bonds are limited to three choices:

Bond	Price	Rate (%)	Years to Maturity
1	$1150	8.875	5
2	1000	5.500	6
3	1350	11.750	7

The government bonds have a par value of $1000, which means that even with different prices each bond pays $1000 at maturity. The rates shown are based on the par value. For purposes of planning, the treasurer assumed that any funds not invested in bonds will be placed in savings and earn interest at an annual rate of 4%.

We define the decision variables as follows:

F = total dollars required to meet the retirement plan's eight-year obligation
B_1 = units of bond 1 purchased at the beginning of year 1
B_2 = units of bond 2 purchased at the beginning of year 1
B_3 = units of bond 3 purchased at the beginning of year 1
S_i = amount placed in savings at the beginning of year i for $i = 1, \ldots, 8$

The objective function is to minimize the total dollars needed to meet the retirement plan's eight-year obligation, or

$$\text{Min} \quad F$$

A key feature of this type of financial planning problem is that a constraint must be formulated for each year of the planning horizon. In general, each constraint takes the form:

$$\begin{pmatrix} \text{Funds available at} \\ \text{the beginning of the year} \end{pmatrix} - \begin{pmatrix} \text{Funds invested in bonds} \\ \text{and placed in savings} \end{pmatrix} = \begin{pmatrix} \text{Cash obligation for} \\ \text{the current year} \end{pmatrix}$$

The funds available at the beginning of year 1 are given by F. With a current price of \$1150 for bond 1 and investments expressed in thousands of dollars, the total investment for B_1 units of bond 1 would be $1.15B_1$. Similarly, the total investment in bonds 2 and 3 would be $1B_2$ and $1.35B_3$, respectively. The investment in savings for year 1 is S_1. Using these results and the first-year obligation of 430, we obtain the constraint for year 1:

$$F - 1.15B_1 - 1B_2 - 1.35B_3 - S_1 = 430 \quad \text{Year 1}$$

We do not consider future investments in bonds because the future price of bonds depends on interest rates and cannot be known in advance.

Investments in bonds can take place only in this first year, and the bonds will be held until maturity.

The funds available at the beginning of year 2 include the investment returns of 8.875% on the par value of bond 1, 5.5% on the par value of bond 2, 11.75% on the par value of bond 3, and 4% on savings. The new amount to be invested in savings for year 2 is S_2. With an obligation of 210, the constraint for year 2 is

$$0.08875B_1 + 0.055B_2 + 0.1175B_3 + 1.04S_1 - S_2 = 210 \quad \text{Year 2}$$

Similarly, the constraints for years 3 to 8 are

$$0.08875B_1 + 0.055B_2 + 0.1175B_3 + 1.04S_2 - S_3 = 222 \quad \text{Year 3}$$
$$0.08875B_1 + 0.055B_2 + 0.1175B_3 + 1.04S_3 - S_4 = 231 \quad \text{Year 4}$$
$$0.08875B_1 + 0.055B_2 + 0.1175B_3 + 1.04S_4 - S_5 = 240 \quad \text{Year 5}$$
$$1.08875B_1 + 0.055B_2 + 0.1175B_3 + 1.04S_5 - S_6 = 195 \quad \text{Year 6}$$
$$1.055B_2 + 0.1175B_3 + 1.04S_6 - S_7 = 225 \quad \text{Year 7}$$
$$1.1175B_3 + 1.04S_7 - S_8 = 255 \quad \text{Year 8}$$

Note that the constraint for year 6 shows that funds available from bond 1 are $1.08875B_1$. The coefficient of 1.08875 reflects the fact that bond 1 matures at the end of year 5. As a result, the par value plus the interest from bond 1 during year 5 is available at the beginning of year 6. Also, because bond 1 matures in year 5 and becomes available for use at the beginning of year 6, the variable B_1 does not appear in the constraints for years 7 and 8. Note the similar interpretation for bond 2, which matures at the end of year 6 and has the par value plus interest available at the beginning of year 7. In addition, bond 3 matures at the end of year 7 and has the par value plus interest available at the beginning of year 8.

Finally, note that a variable S_8 appears in the constraint for year 8. The retirement fund obligation will be completed at the beginning of year 8, so we anticipate that S_8 will be zero and no funds will be put into savings. However, the formulation includes S_8 in the event that the bond income plus interest from the savings in year 7 exceed the 255 cash requirement for year 8. Thus, S_8 is a surplus variable that shows any funds remaining after the eight-year cash requirements have been satisfied.

The optimal solution to this 12-variable, 8-constraint linear program is shown in Figure 4.4. With an objective function value of 1728.79385, the total investment required to meet the retirement plan's eight-year obligation is $1,728,794. Using the current prices of $1150, $1000, and $1350 for each of the bonds, respectively, we can summarize the initial investments in the three bonds as follows:

Bond	Units Purchased	Investment Amount
1	$B_1 = 144.988$	$1150(144.988) = \$166,736$
2	$B_2 = 187.856$	$1000(187.856) = \$187,856$
3	$B_3 = 228.188$	$1350(228.188) = \$308,054$

FIGURE 4.4 THE SOLUTION FOR THE HEWLITT CORPORATION CASH
REQUIREMENTS PROBLEM

WEB **file**

Hewlitt

```
Optimal Objective Value =              1728.79385

        Variable              Value              Reduced Cost
      -------------        -------------        -------------
           F              1728.79385                0.00000
           B1              144.98815                0.00000
           B2              187.85585                0.00000
           B3              228.18792                0.00000
           S1              636.14794                0.00000
           S2              501.60571                0.00000
           S3              349.68179                0.00000
           S4              182.68091                0.00000
           S5                0.00000                0.06403
           S6                0.00000                0.01261
           S7                0.00000                0.02132
           S8                0.00000                0.67084


       Constraint         Slack/Surplus           Dual Value
      -------------        -------------        -------------
            1                 0.00000                1.00000
            2                 0.00000                0.96154
            3                 0.00000                0.92456
            4                 0.00000                0.88900
            5                 0.00000                0.85480
            6                 0.00000                0.76036
            7                 0.00000                0.71899
            8                 0.00000                0.67084
```

The solution also shows that $636,148 (see S_1) will be placed in savings at the beginning of the first year. By starting with $1,728,794, the company can make the specified bond and savings investments and have enough left over to meet the retirement program's first-year cash requirement of $430,000.

The optimal solution in Figure 4.4 shows that the decision variables S_1, S_2, S_3, and S_4 all are greater than zero, indicating investments in savings are required in each of the first four years. However, interest from the bonds plus the bond maturity incomes will be sufficient to cover the retirement program's cash requirements in years 5 through 8.

In this application, the dual value can be thought of as the present value of each dollar in the cash requirement. For example, each dollar that must be paid in year 8 has a present value of $0.67084.

The dual values have an interesting interpretation in this application. Each right-hand-side value corresponds to the payment that must be made in that year. Note that the dual values are positive, indicating that increasing the required payment in any year by $1,000 would *increase* the total funds required for the retirement program's obligation by $1,000 times the dual value. Also note that the dual values show that increases in required payments in the early years have the largest impact. This makes sense in that there is little time to build up investment income in the early years versus the subsequent years. This suggests that if Hewlitt faces increases in required payments it would benefit by deferring those increases to later years if possible.

NOTES AND COMMENTS

1. The optimal solution for the Hewlitt Corporation problem shows fractional numbers of government bonds at 144.988, 187.856, and 228.188 units, respectively. However, fractional bond units usually are not available. If we were conservative and rounded up to 145, 188, and 229 units, respectively, the total funds required for the eight-year retirement program obligation would be approximately $1254 more than the total funds indicated by the objective function. Because of the magnitude of the funds involved, rounding up probably would provide a workable solution. If an optimal integer solution were required, the methods of integer linear programming covered in Chapter 7 would have to be used.

2. We implicitly assumed that interest from the government bonds is paid annually. Investments such as treasury notes actually provide interest payments every six months. In such cases, the model can be reformulated with six-month periods, with interest and/or cash payments occurring every six months.

4.3   OPERATIONS MANAGEMENT APPLICATIONS

Linear programming applications developed for production and operations management include scheduling, staffing, inventory control, and capacity planning. In this section we describe examples with make-or-buy decisions, production scheduling, and workforce assignments.

A Make-or-Buy Decision

We illustrate the use of a linear programming model to determine how much of each of several component parts a company should manufacture and how much it should purchase from an outside supplier. Such a decision is referred to as a make-or-buy decision.

The Janders Company markets various business and engineering products. Currently, Janders is preparing to introduce two new calculators: one for the business market called the Financial Manager and one for the engineering market called the Technician. Each calculator has three components: a base, an electronic cartridge, and a faceplate or top. The same base is used for both calculators, but the cartridges and tops are different. All components can be manufactured by the company or purchased from outside suppliers. The manufacturing costs and purchase prices for the components are summarized in Table 4.5.

TABLE 4.5 MANUFACTURING COSTS AND PURCHASE PRICES FOR JANDERS CALCULATOR COMPONENTS

| | Cost per Unit | |
Component	Manufacture (regular time)	Purchase
Base	$0.50	$0.60
Financial cartridge	$3.75	$4.00
Technician cartridge	$3.30	$3.90
Financial top	$0.60	$0.65
Technician top	$0.75	$0.78

Company forecasters indicate that 3000 Financial Manager calculators and 2000 Technician calculators will be needed. However, manufacturing capacity is limited. The company has 200 hours of regular manufacturing time and 50 hours of overtime that can be scheduled for the calculators. Overtime involves a premium at the additional cost of $9 per hour. Table 4.6 shows manufacturing times (in minutes) for the components.

The problem for Janders is to determine how many units of each component to manufacture and how many units of each component to purchase. We define the decision variables as follows:

BM = number of bases manufactured

BP = number of bases purchased

FCM = number of Financial cartridges manufactured

FCP = number of Financial cartridges purchased

TCM = number of Technician cartridges manufactured

TCP = number of Technician cartridges purchased

FTM = number of Financial tops manufactured

FTP = number of Financial tops purchased

TTM = number of Technician tops manufactured

TTP = number of Technician tops purchased

One additional decision variable is needed to determine the hours of overtime that must be scheduled:

OT = number of hours of overtime to be scheduled

TABLE 4.6 MANUFACTURING TIMES IN MINUTES PER UNIT FOR JANDERS CALCULATOR COMPONENTS

Component	Manufacturing Time
Base	1.0
Financial cartridge	3.0
Technician cartridge	2.5
Financial top	1.0
Technician top	1.5

The objective function is to minimize the total cost, including manufacturing costs, purchase costs, and overtime costs. Using the cost-per-unit data in Table 4.5 and the overtime premium cost rate of $9 per hour, we write the objective function as

$$\text{Min} \quad 0.5BM + 0.6BP + 3.75FCM + 4FCP + 3.3TCM + 3.9TCP + 0.6FTM$$
$$+ 0.65FTP + 0.75TTM + 0.78TTP + 9OT$$

The first five constraints specify the number of each component needed to satisfy the demand for 3000 Financial Manager calculators and 2000 Technician calculators. A total of 5000 base components are needed, with the number of other components depending on the demand for the particular calculator. The five demand constraints are

$$
\begin{array}{ll}
BM + BP = 5000 & \text{Bases} \\
FCM + FCP = 3000 & \text{Financial cartridges} \\
TCM + TCP = 2000 & \text{Technician cartridges} \\
FTM + FTP = 3000 & \text{Financial tops} \\
TTM + TTP = 2000 & \text{Technician tops}
\end{array}
$$

Two constraints are needed to guarantee that manufacturing capacities for regular time and overtime cannot be exceeded. The first constraint limits overtime capacity to 50 hours, or

$$OT \leq 50$$

The same units of measure must be used for both the left-hand side and right-hand side of the constraint. In this case, minutes are used.

The second constraint states that the total manufacturing time required for all components must be less than or equal to the total manufacturing capacity, including regular time plus overtime. The manufacturing times for the components are expressed in minutes, so we state the total manufacturing capacity constraint in minutes, with the 200 hours of regular time capacity becoming $60(200) = 12,000$ minutes. The actual overtime required is unknown at this point, so we write the overtime as $60OT$ minutes. Using the manufacturing times from Table 4.6, we have

$$BM + 3FCM + 2.5TCM + FTM + 1.5TTM \leq 12,000 + 60OT$$

The complete formulation of the Janders make-or-buy problem with all decision variables greater than or equal to zero is

$$\text{Min} \quad 0.5BM + 0.6BP + 3.75FCM + 4FCP + 3.3TCM + 3.9TCP$$
$$+ 0.6FTM + 0.65FTP + 0.75TTM + 0.78TTP + 9OT$$

$$
\begin{array}{rll}
\text{s.t.} & & \\
BM + BP = 5000 & & \text{Bases} \\
FCM + FCP = 3000 & & \text{Financial cartridges} \\
TCM + TCP = 2000 & & \text{Technician cartridges} \\
FTM + FTP = 3000 & & \text{Financial tops} \\
TTM + TTP = 2000 & & \text{Technician tops} \\
OT \leq 50 & & \text{Overtime hours} \\
BM + 3FCM + 2.5TCM + FTM + 1.5TTM \leq 12,000 + 60OT & & \text{Manufacturing capacity}
\end{array}
$$

The optimal solution to this 11-variable, 7-constraint linear program is shown in Figure 4.5. The optimal solution indicates that all 5000 bases (*BM*), 667 Financial Manager cartridges (*FCM*), and 2000 Technician cartridges (*TCM*) should be manufactured. The remaining 2333 Financial Manager cartridges (*FCP*), all the Financial Manager tops (*FTP*),

FIGURE 4.5   THE SOLUTION FOR THE JANDERS MAKE-OR-BUY PROBLEM

Optimal Objective Value =   24443.33333

Variable	Value	Reduced Cost
BM	5000.00000	0.00000
BP	0.00000	0.01667
FCM	666.66667	0.00000
FCP	2333.33333	0.00000
TCM	2000.00000	0.00000
TCP	0.00000	0.39167
FTM	0.00000	0.03333
FTP	3000.00000	0.00000
TTM	0.00000	0.09500
TTP	2000.00000	0.00000
OT	0.00000	4.00000

Constraint	Slack/Surplus	Dual Value
1	0.00000	0.58333
2	0.00000	4.00000
3	0.00000	3.50833
4	0.00000	0.65000
5	0.00000	0.78000
6	50.00000	0.00000
7	0.00000	-0.08333

Variable	Objective Coefficient	Allowable Increase	Allowable Decrease
BM	0.50000	0.01667	Infinite
BP	0.60000	Infinite	0.01667
FCM	3.75000	0.10000	0.05000
FCP	4.00000	0.05000	0.10000
TCM	3.30000	0.39167	Infinite
TCP	3.90000	Infinite	0.39167
FTM	0.60000	Infinite	0.03333
FTP	0.65000	0.03333	Infinite
TTM	0.75000	Infinite	0.09500
TTP	0.78000	0.09500	Infinite
OT	9.00000	Infinite	4.00000

Constraint	RHS Value	Allowable Increase	Allowable Decrease
1	5000.00000	2000.00000	5000.00000
2	3000.00000	Infinite	2333.33333
3	2000.00000	800.00000	2000.00000
4	3000.00000	Infinite	3000.00000
5	2000.00000	Infinite	2000.00000
6	50.00000	Infinite	50.00000
7	12000.00000	7000.00000	2000.00000

WEB file

Janders

and all Technician tops (*TTP*) should be purchased. No overtime manufacturing is necessary, and the total cost associated with the optimal make-or-buy plan is $24,443.33.

Sensitivity analysis provides some additional information about the unused overtime capacity. The Reduced Costs column shows that the overtime (*OT*) premium would have to decrease by $4 per hour before overtime production should be considered. That is, if the overtime premium is $9 − $4 = $5 or less, Janders may want to replace some of the purchased components with components manufactured on overtime.

The dual value for the manufacturing capacity constraint 7 is −0.083. This value indicates that an additional hour of manufacturing capacity is worth $0.083 per minute or ($0.083)(60) = $5 per hour. The right-hand-side range for constraint 7 shows that this conclusion is valid until the amount of regular time increases to 19,000 minutes, or 316.7 hours.

Sensitivity analysis also indicates that a change in prices charged by the outside suppliers can affect the optimal solution. For instance, the objective coefficient range for *BP* is 0.583 (0.600 – 0.017) to no upper limit. If the purchase price for bases remains at $0.583 or more, the number of bases purchased (*BP*) will remain at zero. However, if the purchase price drops below $0.583, Janders should begin to purchase rather than manufacture the base component. Similar sensitivity analysis conclusions about the purchase price ranges can be drawn for the other components.

NOTES AND COMMENTS

The proper interpretation of the dual value for manufacturing capacity (constraint 7) in the Janders problem is that an additional hour of manufacturing capacity is worth ($0.083)(60) = $5 per hour. Thus, the company should be willing to pay a premium of $5 per hour over and above the current regular time cost per hour, which is already included in the manufacturing cost of the product. Thus, if the regular time cost is $18 per hour, Janders should be willing to pay up to $18 + $5 = $23 per hour to obtain additional labor capacity.

Production Scheduling

One of the most important applications of linear programming deals with multiperiod planning such as production scheduling. The solution to a production scheduling problem enables the manager to establish an efficient low-cost production schedule for one or more products over several time periods (weeks or months). Essentially, a production scheduling problem can be viewed as a product-mix problem for each of several periods in the future. The manager must determine the production levels that will allow the company to meet product demand requirements, given limitations on production capacity, labor capacity, and storage space, while minimizing total production costs.

One advantage of using linear programming for production scheduling problems is that they recur. A production schedule must be established for the current month, then again for the next month, for the month after that, and so on. When looking at the problem each month, the production manager will find that, although demand for the products has changed, production times, production capacities, storage space limitations, and so on are roughly the same. Thus, the production manager is basically re-solving the same problem handled in previous months, and a general linear programming model of the production scheduling procedure may be applied frequently. Once the model has been formulated, the manager can simply supply the data—demand, capacities, and so on—for the given production period and use the linear programming model repeatedly to develop the production schedule. The Management Science in Action, *Optimizing Production of Flight Manuals at*

TABLE 4.7   THREE-MONTH DEMAND SCHEDULE FOR BOLLINGER
ELECTRONICS COMPANY

Component	April	May	June
322A	1000	3000	5000
802B	1000	500	3000

Jeppesen Sanderson, Inc., describes how linear programming is used to minimize the cost of producing weekly revisions to flight manuals.

Let us consider the case of the Bollinger Electronics Company, which produces two different electronic components for a major airplane engine manufacturer. The airplane engine manufacturer notifies the Bollinger sales office each quarter of its monthly requirements for components for each of the next three months. The monthly requirements for the components may vary considerably, depending on the type of engine the airplane engine manufacturer is producing. The order shown in Table 4.7 has just been received for the next three-month period.

After the order is processed, a demand statement is sent to the production control department. The production control department must then develop a three-month production plan for the components. In arriving at the desired schedule, the production manager will want to identify the following:

1. Total production cost
2. Inventory holding cost
3. Change-in-production-level costs

In the remainder of this section, we show how to formulate a linear programming model of the production and inventory process for Bollinger Electronics to minimize the total cost.

MANAGEMENT SCIENCE IN ACTION

OPTIMIZING PRODUCTION OF FLIGHT MANUALS AT JEPPESEN SANDERSON, INC.*

Jeppesen Sanderson, Inc., manufactures and distributes flight manuals that contain safety information to more than 300,000 pilots and 4000 airlines. Every week Jeppesen mails between 5 and 30 million pages of chart revisions to 200,000 customers worldwide, and the company receives about 1500 new orders each week. In the late 1990s, its customer service deteriorated as its existing production and supporting systems failed to keep up with this level of activity. To meet customer service goals, Jeppesen turned to optimization-based decision support tools for production planning.

Jeppesen developed a large-scale linear program called Scheduler to minimize the cost of producing the weekly revisions. Model constraints included capacity constraints and numerous internal business rules. The model includes 250,000

variables, and 40,000 to 50,000 constraints. Immediately after introducing the model, Jeppesen established a new record for the number of consecutive weeks with 100% on-time revisions. Scheduler decreased tardiness of revisions from approximately 9% to 3% and dramatically improved customer satisfaction. Even more importantly, Scheduler provided a model of the production system for Jeppesen to use in strategic economic analysis. Overall, the use of optimization techniques at Jeppesen resulted in cost reductions of nearly 10% and a 24% increase in profit.

*Based on E. Katok, W. Tarantino, and R. Tiedman, "Improving Performance and Flexibility at Jeppesen: The World's Leading Aviation-Information Company," *Interfaces* (January/February 2001): 7–29.

To develop the model, we let x_{im} denote the production volume in units for product i in month m. Here $i = 1, 2$, and $m = 1, 2, 3$; $i = 1$ refers to component 322A, $i = 2$ refers to component 802B, $m = 1$ refers to April, $m = 2$ refers to May, and $m = 3$ refers to June. The purpose of the double subscript is to provide a more descriptive notation. We could simply use x_6 to represent the number of units of product 2 produced in month 3, but x_{23} is more descriptive, identifying directly the product and month represented by the variable.

If component 322A costs \$20 per unit produced and component 802B costs \$10 per unit produced, the total production cost part of the objective function is

$$\text{Total production cost} = 20x_{11} + 20x_{12} + 20x_{13} + 10x_{21} + 10x_{22} + 10x_{23}$$

Because the production cost per unit is the same each month, we don't need to include the production costs in the objective function; that is, regardless of the production schedule selected, the total production cost will remain the same. In other words, production costs are not relevant costs for the production scheduling decision under consideration. In cases in which the production cost per unit is expected to change each month, the variable production costs per unit per month must be included in the objective function. The solution for the Bollinger Electronics problem will be the same regardless of whether these costs are included; therefore, we included them so that the value of the linear programming objective function will include all the costs associated with the problem.

To incorporate the relevant inventory holding costs into the model, we let s_{im} denote the inventory level for product i at the end of month m. Bollinger determined that on a monthly basis inventory holding costs are 1.5% of the cost of the product; that is, $(0.015)(\$20) = \$0.30$ per unit for component 322A and $(0.015)(\$10) = \$0.15$ per unit for component 802B. A common assumption made in using the linear programming approach to production scheduling is that monthly ending inventories are an acceptable approximation to the average inventory levels throughout the month. Making this assumption, we write the inventory holding cost portion of the objective function as

$$\text{Inventory holding cost} = 0.30s_{11} + 0.30s_{12} + 0.30s_{13} + 0.15s_{21} + 0.15s_{22} + 0.15s_{23}$$

To incorporate the costs of fluctuations in production levels from month to month, we need to define two additional variables:

I_m = increase in the total production level necessary during month m

D_m = decrease in the total production level necessary during month m

After estimating the effects of employee layoffs, turnovers, reassignment training costs, and other costs associated with fluctuating production levels, Bollinger estimates that the cost associated with increasing the production level for any month is \$0.50 per unit increase. A similar cost associated with decreasing the production level for any month is \$0.20 per unit. Thus, we write the third portion of the objective function as

$$\text{Change-in-production-level costs} = 0.50I_1 + 0.50I_2 + 0.50I_3$$
$$+ 0.20D_1 + 0.20D_2 + 0.20D_3$$

Note that the cost associated with changes in production level is a function of the change in the total number of units produced in month m compared to the total number of units produced in month $m - 1$. In other production scheduling applications, fluctuations in production level might be measured in terms of machine hours or labor-hours required rather than in terms of the total number of units produced.

Combining all three costs, the complete objective function becomes

$$\text{Min} \quad 20x_{11} + 20x_{12} + 20x_{13} + 10x_{21} + 10x_{22} + 10x_{23} + 0.30s_{11}$$
$$+ 0.30s_{12} + 0.30s_{13} + 0.15s_{21} + 0.15s_{22} + 0.15s_{23} + 0.50I_1$$
$$+ 0.50I_2 + 0.50I_3 + 0.20D_1 + 0.20D_2 + 0.20D_3$$

We now consider the constraints. First, we must guarantee that the schedule meets customer demand. Because the units shipped can come from the current month's production or from inventory carried over from previous months, the demand requirement takes the form

$$\left(\begin{array}{c} \text{Ending} \\ \text{inventory} \\ \text{from previous} \\ \text{month} \end{array} \right) + \left(\begin{array}{c} \text{Current} \\ \text{production} \end{array} \right) - \left(\begin{array}{c} \text{Ending} \\ \text{inventory} \\ \text{for this} \\ \text{month} \end{array} \right) = \left(\begin{array}{c} \text{This month's} \\ \text{demand} \end{array} \right)$$

Suppose that the inventories at the beginning of the three-month scheduling period were 500 units for component 322A and 200 units for component 802B. The demand for both products in the first month (April) was 1000 units, so the constraints for meeting demand in the first month become

$$500 + x_{11} - s_{11} = 1000$$
$$200 + x_{21} - s_{21} = 1000$$

Moving the constants to the right-hand side, we have

$$x_{11} - s_{11} = 500$$
$$x_{21} - s_{21} = 800$$

Similarly, we need demand constraints for both products in the second and third months. We write them as follows:

Month 2

$$s_{11} + x_{12} - s_{12} = 3000$$
$$s_{21} + x_{22} - s_{22} = 500$$

Month 3

$$s_{12} + x_{13} - s_{13} = 5000$$
$$s_{22} + x_{23} - s_{23} = 3000$$

If the company specifies a minimum inventory level at the end of the three-month period of at least 400 units of component 322A and at least 200 units of component 802B, we can add the constraints

$$s_{13} \geq 400$$
$$s_{23} \geq 200$$

TABLE 4.8   MACHINE, LABOR, AND STORAGE CAPACITIES
FOR BOLLINGER ELECTRONICS

Month	Machine Capacity (hours)	Labor Capacity (hours)	Storage Capacity (square feet)
April	400	300	10,000
May	500	300	10,000
June	600	300	10,000

TABLE 4.9   MACHINE, LABOR, AND STORAGE REQUIREMENTS FOR COMPONENTS
322A AND 802B

Component	Machine (hours/unit)	Labor (hours/unit)	Storage (square feet/unit)
322A	0.10	0.05	2
802B	0.08	0.07	3

Suppose that we have the additional information on machine, labor, and storage capacity shown in Table 4.8. Machine, labor, and storage space requirements are given in Table 4.9. To reflect these limitations, the following constraints are necessary:

Machine Capacity

$$0.10x_{11} + 0.08x_{21} \leq 400 \quad \text{Month 1}$$
$$0.10x_{12} + 0.08x_{22} \leq 500 \quad \text{Month 2}$$
$$0.10x_{13} + 0.08x_{23} \leq 600 \quad \text{Month 3}$$

Labor Capacity

$$0.05x_{11} + 0.07x_{21} \leq 300 \quad \text{Month 1}$$
$$0.05x_{12} + 0.07x_{22} \leq 300 \quad \text{Month 2}$$
$$0.05x_{13} + 0.07x_{23} \leq 300 \quad \text{Month 3}$$

Storage Capacity

$$2s_{11} + 3s_{21} \leq 10,000 \quad \text{Month 1}$$
$$2s_{12} + 3s_{22} \leq 10,000 \quad \text{Month 2}$$
$$2s_{13} + 3s_{23} \leq 10,000 \quad \text{Month 3}$$

One final set of constraints must be added to guarantee that I_m and D_m will reflect the increase or decrease in the total production level for month m. Suppose that the production levels for March, the month before the start of the current production scheduling period, had been 1500 units of component 322A and 1000 units of component 802B for a total production level of $1500 + 1000 = 2500$ units. We can find the amount of the change in production for April from the relationship

$$\text{April production} - \text{March production} = \text{Change}$$

Using the April production variables, x_{11} and x_{21}, and the March production of 2500 units, we have

$$(x_{11} + x_{21}) - 2500 = \text{Change}$$

Note that the change can be positive or negative. A positive change reflects an increase in the total production level, and a negative change reflects a decrease in the total production level. We can use the increase in production for April, I_1, and the decrease in production for April, D_1, to specify the constraint for the change in total production for the month of April:

$$(x_{11} + x_{21}) - 2500 = I_1 - D_1$$

Of course, we cannot have an increase in production and a decrease in production during the same one-month period; thus, either I_1 or D_1 will be zero. If April requires 3000 units of production, $I_1 = 500$ and $D_1 = 0$. If April requires 2200 units of production, $I_1 = 0$ and $D_1 = 300$. This approach of denoting the change in production level as the difference between two nonnegative variables, I_1 and D_1, permits both positive and negative changes in the total production level. If a single variable (say, c_m) had been used to represent the change in production level, only positive changes would be possible because of the non-negativity requirement.

Using the same approach in May and June (always subtracting the previous month's total production from the current month's total production), we obtain the constraints for the second and third months of the production scheduling period:

$$(x_{12} + x_{22}) - (x_{11} + x_{21}) = I_2 - D_2$$
$$(x_{13} + x_{23}) - (x_{12} + x_{22}) = I_3 - D_3$$

Linear programming models for production scheduling are often very large. Thousands of decision variables and constraints are necessary when the problem involves numerous products, machines, and time periods. Data collection for large-scale models can be more time-consuming than either the formulation of the model or the development of the computer solution.

The initially rather small, two-product, three-month scheduling problem has now developed into an 18-variable, 20-constraint linear programming problem. Note that in this problem we were concerned only with one type of machine process, one type of labor, and one type of storage area. Actual production scheduling problems usually involve several machine types, several labor grades, and/or several storage areas, requiring large-scale linear programs. For instance, a problem involving 100 products over a 12-month period could have more than 1000 variables and constraints.

Figure 4.6 shows the optimal solution to the Bollinger Electronics production scheduling problem. Table 4.10 contains a portion of the managerial report based on the optimal solution.

Consider the monthly variation in the production and inventory schedule shown in Table 4.10. Recall that the inventory cost for component 802B is one-half the inventory cost for component 322A. Therefore, as might be expected, component 802B is produced heavily in the first month (April) and then held in inventory for the demand that will occur in future months. Component 322A tends to be produced when needed, and only small amounts are carried in inventory.

FIGURE 4.6   THE SOLUTION FOR THE BOLLINGER ELECTRONICS PROBLEM

Bollinger

```
Optimal Objective Value =          225295.00000

       Variable                Value            Reduced Cost
    ---------------      ---------------      ---------------
          X11               500.00000              0.00000
          X12              3200.00000              0.00000
          X13              5200.00000              0.00000
          S11                 0.00000              0.17222
          S12               200.00000              0.00000
          S12               400.00000              0.00000
          X21              2500.00000              0.00000
          X22              2000.00000              0.00000
          X23                 0.00000              0.12778
          S21              1700.00000              0.00000
          S22              3200.00000              0.00000
          S23               200.00000              0.00000
          I1                500.00000              0.00000
          I2               2200.00000              0.00000
          I3                  0.00000              0.07222
          D1                  0.00000              0.70000
          D2                  0.00000              0.70000
          D3                  0.00000              0.62778

      Constraint           Slack/Surplus           Dual Value
    ---------------      ---------------      ---------------
           1                  0.00000             20.00000
           2                  0.00000             10.00000
           3                  0.00000             20.12778
           4                  0.00000             10.15000
           5                  0.00000             20.42778
           6                  0.00000             10.30000
           7                  0.00000             20.72778
           8                  0.00000             10.45000
           9                150.00000              0.00000
          10                 20.00000              0.00000
          11                 80.00000              0.00000
          12                100.00000              0.00000
          13                  0.00000             -1.11111
          14                 40.00000              0.00000
          15               4900.00000              0.00000
          16                  0.00000              0.00000
          17               8600.00000              0.00000
          18                  0.00000             -0.50000
          19                  0.00000             -0.50000
          20                  0.00000             -0.42778
```

TABLE 4.10 MINIMUM COST PRODUCTION SCHEDULE INFORMATION FOR THE BOLLINGER ELECTRONICS PROBLEM

Activity	April	May	June
Production			
Component 322A	500	3200	5200
Component 802B	2500	2000	0
Totals	3000	5200	5200
Ending inventory			
Component 322A	0	200	400
Component 802B	1700	3200	200
Machine usage			
Scheduled hours	250	480	520
Slack capacity hours	150	20	80
Labor usage			
Scheduled hours	200	300	260
Slack capacity hours	100	0	40
Storage usage			
Scheduled storage	5100	10,000	1400
Slack capacity	4900	0	8600
Total production, inventory, and production-smoothing cost = $225,295			

The costs of increasing and decreasing the total production volume tend to smooth the monthly variations. In fact, the minimum-cost schedule calls for a 500-unit increase in total production in April and a 2200-unit increase in total production in May. The May production level of 5200 units is then maintained during June.

The machine usage section of the report shows ample machine capacity in all three months. However, labor capacity is at full utilization (slack = 0 for constraint 13 in Figure 4.6) in the month of May. The dual value shows that an additional hour of labor capacity in May will decrease total cost by approximately $1.11.

A linear programming model of a two-product, three-month production system can provide valuable information in terms of identifying a minimum-cost production schedule. In larger production systems, where the number of variables and constraints is too large to track manually, linear programming models can provide a significant advantage in developing cost-saving production schedules. The Management Science in Action, Optimizing Production, Inventory, and Distribution at the Kellogg Company, illustrates the use of a large-scale multiperiod linear program for production planning and distribution.

Workforce Assignment

Workforce assignment problems frequently occur when production managers must make decisions involving staffing requirements for a given planning period. Workforce assignments often have some flexibility, and at least some personnel can be assigned to more than one department or work center. Such is the case when employees have been cross-trained on two or more jobs or, for instance, when sales personnel can be transferred between stores. In the following application, we show how linear programming

OPTIMIZING PRODUCTION, INVENTORY, AND DISTRIBUTION AT THE KELLOGG COMPANY*

The Kellogg Company is the largest cereal producer in the world and a leading producer of convenience foods, such as Kellogg's Pop-Tarts and Nutri-Grain cereal bars. Kellogg produces more than 40 different cereals at plants in 19 countries, on six continents. The company markets its products in more than 160 countries and employs more than 15,600 people in its worldwide organization. In the cereal business alone, Kellogg coordinates the production of about 80 products using a total of approximately 90 production lines and 180 packaging lines.

Kellogg has a long history of using linear programming for production planning and distribution. The Kellogg Planning System (KPS) is a large-scale, multiperiod linear program. The operational version of KPS makes production, packaging, inventory, and distribution decisions on a weekly basis. The primary objective of the system is to minimize the total cost of meeting estimated demand; constraints involve processing line capacities, packaging line capacities, and satisfying safety stock requirements.

A tactical version of KPS helps to establish plant budgets and make capacity-expansion and consolidation decisions on a monthly basis. The tactical version was recently used to guide a consolidation of production capacity that resulted in projected savings of $35 to $40 million per year. Because of the success Kellogg has had using KPS in their North American operations, the company is now introducing KPS into Latin America, and is studying the development of a global KPS model.

*Based on G. Brown, J. Keegan, B. Vigus, and K. Wood, "The Kellogg Company Optimizes Production, Inventory, and Distribution," *Interfaces* (November/December 2001): 1–15.

---

can be used to determine not only an optimal product mix, but also an optimal workforce assignment.

McCormick Manufacturing Company produces two products with contributions to profit per unit of $10 and $9, respectively. The labor requirements per unit produced and the total hours of labor available from personnel assigned to each of four departments are shown in Table 4.11. Assuming that the number of hours available in each department is fixed, we can formulate McCormick's problem as a standard product-mix linear program with the following decision variables:

$$P_1 = \text{units of product 1}$$
$$P_2 = \text{units of product 2}$$

TABLE 4.11   DEPARTMENTAL LABOR-HOURS PER UNIT AND TOTAL HOURS AVAILABLE FOR THE McCORMICK MANUFACTURING COMPANY

	Labor-Hours per Unit		
Department	Product 1	Product 2	Total Hours Available
1	0.65	0.95	6500
2	0.45	0.85	6000
3	1.00	0.70	7000
4	0.15	0.30	1400

The linear program is

$$\text{Max} \quad 10P_1 + 9P_2$$

s.t.

$$0.65P_1 + 0.95P_2 \leq 6500$$
$$0.45P_1 + 0.85P_2 \leq 6000$$
$$1.00P_1 + 0.70P_2 \leq 7000$$
$$0.15P_1 + 0.30P_2 \leq 1400$$
$$P_1, P_2 \geq 0$$

The optimal solution to the linear programming model is shown in Figure 4.7. After rounding, it calls for 5744 units of product 1, 1795 units of product 2, and a total profit of $73,590. With this optimal solution, departments 3 and 4 are operating at capacity, and departments 1 and 2 have a slack of approximately 1062 and 1890 hours, respectively. We would anticipate that the product mix would change and that the total profit would increase if the workforce assignment could be revised so that the slack, or unused hours, in departments 1 and 2 could be transferred to the departments currently working at capacity. However, the production manager may be uncertain as to how the workforce should be reallocated among the four departments. Let us expand the linear programming model to include decision variables that will help determine the optimal workforce assignment in addition to the profit-maximizing product mix.

Suppose that McCormick has a cross-training program that enables some employees to be transferred between departments. By taking advantage of the cross-training skills, a limited number of employees and labor-hours may be transferred from one department to another. For example, suppose that the cross-training permits transfers as shown in Table 4.12. Row 1 of this table shows that some employees assigned to department 1 have cross-training skills that permit them to be transferred to department 2 or 3. The right-hand column shows that, for the current production planning period, a maximum of 400 hours can be transferred from department 1. Similar cross-training transfer capabilities and capacities are shown for departments 2, 3, and 4.

FIGURE 4.7 THE SOLUTION FOR THE McCORMICK MANUFACTURING COMPANY PROBLEM WITH NO WORKFORCE TRANSFERS PERMITTED

WEB file

McCormick

Optimal Objective Value =	73589.74359	
Variable	**Value**	**Reduced Cost**
1	5743.58974	0.00000
2	1794.87179	0.00000
Constraint	**Slack/Surplus**	**Dual Value**
1	1061.53846	0.00000
2	1889.74359	0.00000
3	0.00000	8.46154
4	0.00000	10.25641

TABLE 4.12   CROSS-TRAINING ABILITY AND CAPACITY INFORMATION

From Department	Cross-Training Transfers Permitted to Department				Maximum Hours Transferable
	1	2	3	4	
1	—	yes	yes	—	400
2	—	—	yes	yes	800
3	—	—	—	yes	100
4	yes	yes	—	—	200

When workforce assignments are flexible, we do not automatically know how many hours of labor should be assigned to or be transferred from each department. We need to add decision variables to the linear programming model to account for such changes.

b_i = the labor-hours allocated to department i for i = 1, 2, 3, and 4

t_{ij} = the labor-hours transferred from department i to department j

The right-hand sides are now treated as decision variables.

With the addition of decision variables b_1, b_2, b_3, and b_4, we write the capacity restrictions for the four departments as follows:

$$0.65P_1 + 0.95P_2 \leq b_1$$
$$0.45P_1 + 0.85P_2 \leq b_2$$
$$1.00P_1 + 0.70P_2 \leq b_3$$
$$0.15P_1 + 0.30P_2 \leq b_4$$

The labor-hours ultimately allocated to each department must be determined by a series of labor balance equations, or constraints, that include the number of hours initially assigned to each department plus the number of hours transferred into the department minus the number of hours transferred out of the department. Using department 1 as an example, we determine the workforce allocation as follows:

$$b_1 = \left(\begin{array}{c} \text{Hours} \\ \text{initially in} \\ \text{department 1} \end{array}\right) + \left(\begin{array}{c} \text{Hours} \\ \text{transferred into} \\ \text{department 1} \end{array}\right) - \left(\begin{array}{c} \text{Hours} \\ \text{transferred out of} \\ \text{department 1} \end{array}\right)$$

Table 4.11 shows 6500 hours initially assigned to department 1. We use the transfer decision variables t_{i1} to denote transfers into department 1 and t_{1j} to denote transfers from department 1. Table 4.12 shows that the cross-training capabilities involving department 1 are restricted to transfers from department 4 (variable t_{41}) and transfers to either department 2 or department 3 (variables t_{12} and t_{13}). Thus, we can express the total workforce allocation for department 1 as

$$b_1 = 6500 + t_{41} - t_{12} - t_{13}$$

Moving the decision variables for the workforce transfers to the left-hand side, we have the labor balance equation or constraint

$$b_1 - t_{41} + t_{12} + t_{13} = 6500$$

This form of constraint will be needed for each of the four departments. Thus, the following labor balance constraints for departments 2, 3, and 4 would be added to the model.

$$b_2 - t_{12} - t_{42} + t_{23} + t_{24} = 6000$$
$$b_3 - t_{13} - t_{23} + t_{34} \qquad = 7000$$
$$b_4 - t_{24} - t_{34} + t_{41} + t_{42} = 1400$$

Finally, Table 4.12 shows the number of hours that may be transferred from each department is limited, indicating that a transfer capacity constraint must be added for each of the four departments. The additional constraints are

$$t_{12} + t_{13} \leq 400$$
$$t_{23} + t_{24} \leq 800$$
$$t_{34} \qquad \leq 100$$
$$t_{41} + t_{42} \leq 200$$

The complete linear programming model has two product decision variables (P_1 and P_2), four department workforce assignment variables (b_1, b_2, b_3, and b_4), seven transfer variables (t_{12}, t_{13}, t_{23}, t_{24}, t_{34}, t_{41}, and t_{42}), and 12 constraints. Figure 4.8 shows the optimal solution to this linear program.

Variations in the workforce assignment model could be used in situations such as allocating raw material resources to products, allocating machine time to products, and allocating salesforce time to stores or sales territories.

McCormick's profit can be increased by $\$84,011 - \$73,590 = \$10,421$ by taking advantage of cross-training and workforce transfers. The optimal product mix of 6825 units of product 1 and 1751 units of product 2 can be achieved if $t_{13} = 400$ hours are transferred from department 1 to department 3; $t_{23} = 651$ hours are transferred from department 2 to department 3; and $t_{24} = 149$ hours are transferred from department 2 to department 4. The resulting workforce assignments for departments 1 through 4 would provide 6100, 5200, 8051, and 1549 hours, respectively.

If a manager has the flexibility to assign personnel to different departments, reduced workforce idle time, improved workforce utilization, and improved profit should result. The linear programming model in this section automatically assigns employees and labor-hours to the departments in the most profitable manner.

Blending Problems

Blending problems arise whenever a manager must decide how to blend two or more resources to produce one or more products. In these situations, the resources contain one or more essential ingredients that must be blended into final products that will contain specific percentages of each. In most of these applications, then, management must decide how much of each resource to purchase to satisfy product specifications and product demands at minimum cost.

Blending problems occur frequently in the petroleum industry (e.g., blending crude oil to produce different octane gasolines), chemical industry (e.g., blending chemicals to produce fertilizers and weed killers), and food industry (e.g., blending ingredients to produce soft drinks and soups). In this section we illustrate how to apply linear programming to a blending problem in the petroleum industry.

The Grand Strand Oil Company produces regular and premium gasoline for independent service stations in the southeastern United States. The Grand Strand refinery manufactures the gasoline products by blending three petroleum components. The gasolines are sold at different prices, and the petroleum components have different costs. The firm wants

FIGURE 4.8   THE SOLUTION FOR THE McCORMICK MANUFACTURING COMPANY PROBLEM

WEB file

McCormick

```
Optimal Objective Value =           84011.29945

          Variable                  Value              Reduced Cost
        ------------            ----------------       -------------

            P1                   6824.85900               0.00000
            P2                   1751.41200               0.00000
            B1                   6100.00000               0.00000
            B2                   5200.00000               0.00000
            B3                   8050.84700               0.00000
            B4                   1549.15300               0.00000
           T41                      0.00000               7.45763
           T12                      0.00000               8.24859
           T13                    400.00000               0.00000
           T42                      0.00000               8.24859
           T23                    650.84750               0.00000
           T24                    149.15250               0.00000
           T34                      0.00000               0.00000


          Constraint            Slack/Surplus           Dual Value
        ------------            ----------------       -------------

             1                      0.00000               0.79096
             2                    640.11300               0.00000
             3                      0.00000               8.24859
             4                      0.00000               8.24859
             5                      0.00000               0.79096
             6                      0.00000               0.00000
             7                      0.00000               8.24859
             8                      0.00000               8.24859
             9                      0.00000               7.45763
            10                      0.00000               8.24859
            11                    100.00000               0.00000
            12                    200.00000               0.00000
```

to determine how to mix or blend the three components into the two gasoline products and maximize profits.

Data available show that regular gasoline can be sold for \$2.90 per gallon and premium gasoline for \$3.00 per gallon. For the current production planning period, Grand Strand can obtain the three petroleum components at the cost per gallon and in the quantities shown in Table 4.13.

Product specifications for the regular and premium gasolines restrict the amounts of each component that can be used in each gasoline product. Table 4.14 lists the product specifications. Current commitments to distributors require Grand Strand to produce at least 10,000 gallons of regular gasoline.

The Grand Strand blending problem is to determine how many gallons of each component should be used in the regular gasoline blend and how many should be used in the

TABLE 4.13 PETROLEUM COST AND SUPPLY FOR THE GRAND STRAND
BLENDING PROBLEM

Petroleum Component	Cost/Gallon	Maximum Available
1	$2.50	5,000 gallons
2	$2.60	10,000 gallons
3	$2.84	10,000 gallons

TABLE 4.14 PRODUCT SPECIFICATIONS FOR THE GRAND STRAND
BLENDING PROBLEM

Product	Specifications
Regular gasoline	At most 30% component 1
	At least 40% component 2
	At most 20% component 3
Premium gasoline	At least 25% component 1
	At most 45% component 2
	At least 30% component 3

premium gasoline blend. The optimal blending solution should maximize the firm's profit, subject to the constraints on the available petroleum supplies shown in Table 4.13, the product specifications shown in Table 4.14, and the required 10,000 gallons of regular gasoline.

We define the decision variables as

$$x_{ij} = \text{gallons of component } i \text{ used in gasoline } j,$$
$$\text{where } i = 1, 2, \text{ or } 3 \text{ for components } 1, 2, \text{ or } 3,$$
$$\text{and } j = r \text{ if regular or } j = p \text{ if premium}$$

The six decision variables are

$$x_{1r} = \text{gallons of component 1 in regular gasoline}$$
$$x_{2r} = \text{gallons of component 2 in regular gasoline}$$
$$x_{3r} = \text{gallons of component 3 in regular gasoline}$$
$$x_{1p} = \text{gallons of component 1 in premium gasoline}$$
$$x_{2p} = \text{gallons of component 2 in premium gasoline}$$
$$x_{3p} = \text{gallons of component 3 in premium gasoline}$$

The total number of gallons of each type of gasoline produced is the sum of the number of gallons produced using each of the three petroleum components.

Total Gallons Produced

$$\text{Regular gasoline} = x_{1r} + x_{2r} + x_{3r}$$
$$\text{Premium gasoline} = x_{1p} + x_{2p} + x_{3p}$$

The total gallons of each petroleum component are computed in a similar fashion.

Total Petroleum Component Use

$$\text{Component } 1 = x_{1r} + x_{1p}$$
$$\text{Component } 2 = x_{2r} + x_{2p}$$
$$\text{Component } 3 = x_{3r} + x_{3p}$$

We develop the objective function of maximizing the profit contribution by identifying the difference between the total revenue from both gasolines and the total cost of the three petroleum components. By multiplying the \$2.90 per gallon price by the total gallons of regular gasoline, the \$3.00 per gallon price by the total gallons of premium gasoline, and the component cost per gallon figures in Table 4.13 by the total gallons of each component used, we obtain the objective function:

$$\text{Max} \quad 2.90(x_{1r} + x_{2r} + x_{3r}) + 3.00(x_{1p} + x_{2p} + x_{3p})$$
$$- 2.50(x_{1r} + x_{1p}) - 2.60(x_{2r} + x_{2p}) - 2.84(x_{3r} + x_{3p})$$

When we combine terms, the objective function becomes

$$\text{Max} \quad 0.40x_{1r} + 0.30x_{2r} + 0.06x_{3r} + 0.50x_{1p} + 0.40x_{2p} + 0.16x_{3p}$$

The limitations on the availability of the three petroleum components are

$$\begin{aligned} x_{1r} + x_{1p} &\leq 5{,}000 \quad \text{Component 1} \\ x_{2r} + x_{2p} &\leq 10{,}000 \quad \text{Component 2} \\ x_{3r} + x_{3p} &\leq 10{,}000 \quad \text{Component 3} \end{aligned}$$

Six constraints are now required to meet the product specifications stated in Table 4.14. The first specification states that component 1 can account for no more than 30% of the total gallons of regular gasoline produced. That is,

$$x_{1r} \leq 0.30(x_{1r} + x_{2r} + x_{3r})$$

The second product specification listed in Table 4.14 becomes

$$x_{2r} \geq 0.40(x_{1r} + x_{2r} + x_{3r})$$

Similarly, we write the four remaining blending specifications listed in Table 4.14 as

$$\begin{aligned} x_{3r} &\leq 0.20(x_{1r} + x_{2r} + x_{3r}) \\ x_{1p} &\geq 0.25(x_{1p} + x_{2p} + x_{3p}) \\ x_{2p} &\leq 0.45(x_{1p} + x_{2p} + x_{3p}) \\ x_{3p} &\geq 0.30(x_{1p} + x_{2p} + x_{3p}) \end{aligned}$$

The constraint for at least 10,000 gallons of regular gasoline is

$$x_{1r} + x_{2r} + x_{3r} \geq 10{,}000$$

The complete linear programming model with six decision variables and 10 constraints is

Max $0.40x_{1r} + 0.30x_{2r} + 0.06x_{3r} + 0.50x_{1p} + 0.40x_{2p} + 0.16x_{3p}$

s.t.

$$
\begin{array}{llll}
x_{1r} & + x_{1p} & \le 5{,}000 \\
x_{2r} & + x_{2p} & \le 10{,}000 \\
x_{3r} & + x_{3p} \le 10{,}000 \\
x_{1r} & \le 0.30(x_{1r} + x_{2r} + x_{3r}) \\
x_{2r} & \ge 0.40(x_{1r} + x_{2r} + x_{3r}) \\
x_{3r} & \le 0.20(x_{1r} + x_{2r} + x_{3r}) \\
& x_{1p} \ge 0.25(x_{1p} + x_{2p} + x_{3p}) \\
& x_{2p} \le 0.45(x_{1p} + x_{2p} + x_{3p}) \\
& x_{3p} \ge 0.30(x_{1p} + x_{2p} + x_{3p}) \\
\end{array}
$$

$$x_{1r} + x_{2r} + x_{2r} \ge 10{,}000$$

$$x_{1r}, x_{2r}, x_{3r}, x_{1p}, x_{2p}, x_{3p} \ge 0$$

Try Problem 15 as another example of a blending model.

The optimal solution to the Grand Strand blending problem is shown in Figure 4.9. The optimal solution, which provides a profit of $7100, is summarized in Table 4.15. The optimal blending strategy shows that 10,000 gallons of regular gasoline should be produced. The regular gasoline will be manufactured as a blend of 1250 gallons of component 1, 6750 gallons of component 2, and 2000 gallons of component 3. The 15,000 gallons of premium gasoline will be manufactured as a blend of 3750 gallons of component 1, 3250 gallons of component 2, and 8000 gallons of component 3.

FIGURE 4.9   THE SOLUTION FOR THE GRAND STRAND BLENDING PROBLEM

WEB file
Grand

```
Optimal Objective Value =              7100.00000

        Variable              Value              Reduced Cost
     --------------       --------------       ------------------
           X1R              1250.00000             0.00000
           X2R              6750.00000             0.00000
           X3R              2000.00000             0.00000
           X1P              3750.00000             0.00000
           X2P              3250.00000             0.00000
           X3P              8000.00000             0.00000

       Constraint         Slack/Surplus            Dual Value
     --------------       --------------       ------------------
            1                 0.00000               0.50000
            2                 0.00000               0.40000
            3                 0.00000               0.16000
            4              1750.00000               0.00000
            5              2750.00000               0.00000
            6                 0.00000               0.00000
            7                 0.00000               0.00000
            8              3500.00000               0.00000
            9              3500.00000               0.00000
           10                 0.00000              -0.10000
```

TABLE 4.15   GRAND STRAND GASOLINE BLENDING SOLUTION

| Gasoline | Gallons of Component (percentage) | | | Total |
	Component 1	Component 2	Component 3	
Regular	1250 (12.5%)	6750 (67.5%)	2000 (20%)	10,000
Premium	3750 (25%)	3250 (21⅔%)	8000 (53⅓%)	15,000

The interpretation of the slack and surplus variables associated with the product specification constraints (constraints 4–9) in Figure 4.9 needs some clarification. If the constraint is a $\leq$ constraint, the value of the slack variable can be interpreted as the gallons of component use below the maximum amount of the component use specified by the constraint. For example, the slack of 1750.000 for constraint 4 shows that component 1 use is 1750 gallons below the maximum amount of component 1 that could have been used in the production of 10,000 gallons of regular gasoline. If the product specification constraint is a $\geq$ constraint, a surplus variable shows the gallons of component use above the minimum amount of component use specified by the blending constraint. For example, the surplus of 2750.000 for constraint 5 shows that component 2 use is 2750 gallons above the minimum amount of component 2 that must be used in the production of 10,000 gallons of regular gasoline.

NOTES AND COMMENTS

A convenient way to define the decision variables in a blending problem is to use a matrix in which the rows correspond to the raw materials and the columns correspond to the final products. For example, in the Grand Strand blending problem, we define the decision variables as follows:

This approach has two advantages: (1) it provides a systematic way to define the decision variables for any blending problem; and (2) it provides a visual image of the decision variables in terms of how they are related to the raw materials, products, and each other.

| | | Final Products | |
		Regular Gasoline	Premium Gasoline
Raw Materials	Component 1	x_{1r}	x_{1p}
	Component 2	x_{2r}	x_{2p}
	Component 3	x_{3r}	x_{3p}

SUMMARY

In this chapter we presented a broad range of applications that demonstrate how to use linear programming to assist in the decision-making process. We formulated and solved problems from marketing, finance, and operations management, and interpreted the computer output.

Many of the illustrations presented in this chapter are scaled-down versions of actual situations in which linear programming has been applied. In real-world applications, the problem may not be so concisely stated, the data for the problem may not be as readily available, and the problem most likely will involve numerous decision variables and/or constraints. However, a thorough study of the applications in this chapter is a good place to begin in applying linear programming to real problems.

PROBLEMS

Note: The following problems have been designed to give you an understanding and appreciation of the broad range of problems that can be formulated as linear programs. You should be able to formulate a linear programming model for each of the problems. However, you will need access to a linear programming computer package to develop the solutions and make the requested interpretations.

1. The Westchester Chamber of Commerce periodically sponsors public service seminars and programs. Currently, promotional plans are under way for this year's program. Advertising alternatives include television, radio, and newspaper. Audience estimates, costs, and maximum media usage limitations are as shown.

Constraint	Television	Radio	Newspaper
Audience per advertisement	100,000	18,000	40,000
Cost per advertisement	$2000	$300	$600
Maximum media usage	10	20	10

To ensure a balanced use of advertising media, radio advertisements must not exceed 50% of the total number of advertisements authorized. In addition, television should account for at least 10% of the total number of advertisements authorized.

a. If the promotional budget is limited to $18,200, how many commercial messages should be run on each medium to maximize total audience contact? What is the allocation of the budget among the three media, and what is the total audience reached?

b. By how much would audience contact increase if an extra $100 were allocated to the promotional budget?

2. The management of Hartman Company is trying to determine the amount of each of two products to produce over the coming planning period. The following information concerns labor availability, labor utilization, and product profitability.

Department	Product (hours/unit)		Labor-Hours Available
	1	2	
A	1.00	0.35	100
B	0.30	0.20	36
C	0.20	0.50	50
Profit contribution/unit	$30.00	$15.00	

a. Develop a linear programming model of the Hartman Company problem. Solve the model to determine the optimal production quantities of products 1 and 2.

b. In computing the profit contribution per unit, management doesn't deduct labor costs because they are considered fixed for the upcoming planning period. However, suppose that overtime can be scheduled in some of the departments. Which departments would you recommend scheduling for overtime? How much would you be willing to pay per hour of overtime in each department?

c. Suppose that 10, 6, and 8 hours of overtime may be scheduled in departments A, B, and C, respectively. The cost per hour of overtime is $18 in department A, $22.50 in department B, and $12 in department C. Formulate a linear programming model that

can be used to determine the optimal production quantities if overtime is made available. What are the optimal production quantities, and what is the revised total contribution to profit? How much overtime do you recommend using in each department?
What is the increase in the total contribution to profit if overtime is used?

3. The employee credit union at State University is planning the allocation of funds for the
coming year. The credit union makes four types of loans to its members. In addition, the
credit union invests in risk-free securities to stabilize income. The various revenue-
producing investments together with annual rates of return are as follows:

Type of Loan/Investment	Annual Rate of Return (%)
Automobile loans	8
Furniture loans	10
Other secured loans	11
Signature loans	12
Risk-free securities	9

The credit union will have $2 million available for investment during the coming year.
State laws and credit union policies impose the following restrictions on the composition
of the loans and investments.

* Risk-free securities may not exceed 30% of the total funds available for investment.
* Signature loans may not exceed 10% of the funds invested in all loans (automobile,
  furniture, other secured, and signature loans).
* Furniture loans plus other secured loans may not exceed the automobile loans.
* Other secured loans plus signature loans may not exceed the funds invested in risk-
  free securities.

How should the $2 million be allocated to each of the loan/investment alternatives to max-
imize total annual return? What is the projected total annual return?

4. Hilltop Coffee manufactures a coffee product by blending three types of coffee beans. The
cost per pound and the available pounds of each bean are as follows:

Bean	Cost per Pound	Available Pounds
1	$0.50	500
2	$0.70	600
3	$0.45	400

Consumer tests with coffee products were used to provide ratings on a scale of 0–100,
with higher ratings indicating higher quality. Product quality standards for the blended
coffee require a consumer rating for aroma to be at least 75 and a consumer rating for taste
to be at least 80. The individual ratings of the aroma and taste for coffee made from 100%
of each bean are as follows.

Bean	Aroma Rating	Taste Rating
1	75	86
2	85	88
3	60	75

Assume that the aroma and taste attributes of the coffee blend will be a weighted average of the attributes of the beans used in the blend.

   a. What is the minimum-cost blend that will meet the quality standards and provide 1000 pounds of the blended coffee product?

   b. What is the cost per pound for the coffee blend?

   c. Determine the aroma and taste ratings for the coffee blend.

   d. If additional coffee were to be produced, what would be the expected cost per pound?

5. Ajax Fuels, Inc., is developing a new additive for airplane fuels. The additive is a mixture of three ingredients: A, B, and C. For proper performance, the total amount of additive (amount of A + amount of B + amount of C) must be at least 10 ounces per gallon of fuel. However, because of safety reasons, the amount of additive must not exceed 15 ounces per gallon of fuel. The mix or blend of the three ingredients is critical. At least 1 ounce of ingredient A must be used for every ounce of ingredient B. The amount of ingredient C must be at least one-half the amount of ingredient A. If the costs per ounce for ingredients A, B, and C are $0.10, $0.03, and $0.09, respectively, find the minimum-cost mixture of A, B, and C for each gallon of airplane fuel.

6. G. Kunz and Sons, Inc., manufactures two products used in the heavy equipment industry. Both products require manufacturing operations in two departments. The following are the production time (in hours) and profit contribution figures for the two products.

Product	Profit per Unit	Labor-Hours	
		Dept. A	Dept. B
1	$25	6	12
2	$20	8	10

For the coming production period, Kunz has available a total of 900 hours of labor that can be allocated to either of the two departments. Find the production plan and labor allocation (hours assigned in each department) that will maximize the total contribution to profit.

7. As part of the settlement for a class action lawsuit, Hoxworth Corporation must provide sufficient cash to make the following annual payments (in thousands of dollars).

Year	1	2	3	4	5	6
Payment	190	215	240	285	315	460

The annual payments must be made at the beginning of each year. The judge will approve an amount that, along with earnings on its investment, will cover the annual payments. Investment of the funds will be limited to savings (at 4% annually) and government securities, at prices and rates currently quoted in *The Wall Street Journal*.

   Hoxworth wants to develop a plan for making the annual payments by investing in the following securities (par value = $1000). Funds not invested in these securities will be placed in savings.

Security	Current Price	Rate (%)	Years to Maturity
1	$1055	6.750	3
2	$1000	5.125	4

Assume that interest is paid annually. The plan will be submitted to the judge and, if approved, Hoxworth will be required to pay a trustee the amount that will be required to fund the plan.

a. Use linear programming to find the minimum cash settlement necessary to fund the annual payments.

b. Use the dual value to determine how much more Hoxworth should be willing to pay now to reduce the payment at the beginning of year 6 to $400,000.

c. Use the dual value to determine how much more Hoxworth should be willing to pay to reduce the year 1 payment to $150,000.

d. Suppose that the annual payments are to be made at the end of each year. Reformulate the model to accommodate this change. How much would Hoxworth save if this change could be negotiated?

8. The Clark County Sheriff's Department schedules police officers for 8-hour shifts. The beginning times for the shifts are 8:00 A.M., noon, 4:00 P.M., 8:00 P.M., midnight, and 4:00 A.M. An officer beginning a shift at one of these times works for the next 8 hours. During normal weekday operations, the number of officers needed varies depending on the time of day. The department staffing guidelines require the following minimum number of officers on duty:

Time of Day	Minimum Officers on Duty
8:00 A.M.–Noon	5
Noon–4:00 P.M.	6
4:00 P.M.–8:00 P.M.	10
8:00 P.M.–Midnight	7
Midnight–4:00 A.M.	4
4:00 A.M.–8:00 A.M.	6

Determine the number of police officers that should be scheduled to begin the 8-hour shifts at each of the six times (8:00 A.M., noon, 4:00 P.M., 8:00 P.M., midnight, and 4:00 A.M.) to minimize the total number of officers required. (*Hint:* Let x_1 = the number of officers beginning work at 8:00 A.M., x_2 = the number of officers beginning work at noon, and so on.)

9. Reconsider the Welte Mutual Funds problem from Section 4.2. Define your decision variables as the fraction of funds invested in each security. Also, modify the constraints limiting investments in the oil and steel industries as follows: No more than 50% of the total funds invested in stock (oil and steel) may be invested in the oil industry, and no more than 50% of the funds invested in stock (oil and steel) may be invested in the steel industry.

a. Solve the revised linear programming model. What fraction of the portfolio should be invested in each type of security?

b. How much should be invested in each type of security?

c. What are the total earnings for the portfolio?

d. What is the marginal rate of return on the portfolio? That is, how much more could be earned by investing one more dollar in the portfolio?

10. An investment advisor at Shore Financial Services wants to develop a model that can be used to allocate investment funds among four alternatives: stocks, bonds, mutual funds, and cash. For the coming investment period, the company developed estimates of the annual rate of return and the associated risk for each alternative. Risk is measured using an index between 0 and 1, with higher risk values denoting more volatility and thus more uncertainty.

Investment	Annual Rate of Return (%)	Risk
Stocks	10	0.8
Bonds	3	0.2
Mutual funds	4	0.3
Cash	1	0.0

Because cash is held in a money market fund, the annual return is lower, but it carries essentially no risk. The objective is to determine the portion of funds allocated to each investment alternative in order to maximize the total annual return for the portfolio subject to the risk level the client is willing to tolerate.

Total risk is the sum of the risk for all investment alternatives. For instance, if 40% of a client's funds are invested in stocks, 30% in bonds, 20% in mutual funds, and 10% in cash, the total risk for the portfolio would be $0.40(0.8) + 0.30(0.2) + 0.20(0.3) + 0.10(0.0) = 0.44$. An investment advisor will meet with each client to discuss the client's investment objectives and to determine a maximum total risk value for the client. A maximum total risk value of less than 0.3 would be assigned to a conservative investor; a maximum total risk value of between 0.3 and 0.5 would be assigned to a moderate tolerance to risk; and a maximum total risk value greater than 0.5 would be assigned to a more aggressive investor.

Shore Financial Services specified additional guidelines that must be applied to all clients. The guidelines are as follows:

- No more than 75% of the total investment may be in stocks.
- The amount invested in mutual funds must be at least as much as invested in bonds.
- The amount of cash must be at least 10%, but no more than 30% of the total investment funds.

a. Suppose the maximum risk value for a particular client is 0.4. What is the optimal allocation of investment funds among stocks, bonds, mutual funds, and cash? What is the annual rate of return and the total risk for the optimal portfolio?

b. Suppose the maximum risk value for a more conservative client is 0.18. What is the optimal allocation of investment funds for this client? What is the annual rate of return and the total risk for the optimal portfolio?

c. Another more aggressive client has a maximum risk value of 0.7. What is the optimal allocation of investment funds for this client? What is the annual rate of return and the total risk for the optimal portfolio?

d. Refer to the solution for the more aggressive client in part (c). Would this client be interested in having the investment advisor increase the maximum percentage allowed in stocks or decrease the requirement that the amount of cash must be at least 10% of the funds invested? Explain.

e. What is the advantage of defining the decision variables as is done in this model rather than stating the amount to be invested and expressing the decision variables directly in dollar amounts?

11. Edwards Manufacturing Company purchases two component parts from three different suppliers. The suppliers have limited capacity, and no one supplier can meet all the company's needs. In addition, the suppliers charge different prices for the components. Component price data (in price per unit) are as follows:

Component	Supplier		
	1	2	3
1	$12	$13	$14
2	$10	$11	$10

Each supplier has a limited capacity in terms of the total number of components it can supply. However, as long as Edwards provides sufficient advance orders, each supplier can devote its capacity to component 1, component 2, or any combination of the two components, if the total number of units ordered is within its capacity. Supplier capacities are as follows:

Supplier	1	2	3
Capacity	600	1000	800

If the Edwards production plan for the next period includes 1000 units of component 1 and 800 units of component 2, what purchases do you recommend? That is, how many units of each component should be ordered from each supplier? What is the total purchase cost for the components?

12. The Atlantic Seafood Company (ASC) is a buyer and distributor of seafood products that are sold to restaurants and specialty seafood outlets throughout the Northeast. ASC has a frozen storage facility in New York City that serves as the primary distribution point for all products. One of the ASC products is frozen large black tiger shrimp, which are sized at 16–20 pieces per pound. Each Saturday ASC can purchase more tiger shrimp or sell the tiger shrimp at the existing New York City warehouse market price. The ASC goal is to buy tiger shrimp at a low weekly price and sell it later at a higher price. ASC currently has 20,000 pounds of tiger shrimp in storage. Space is available to store a maximum of 100,000 pounds of tiger shrimp each week. In addition, ASC developed the following estimates of tiger shrimp prices for the next four weeks:

Week	Price/lb.
1	$6.00
2	$6.20
3	$6.65
4	$5.55

ASC would like to determine the optimal buying-storing-selling strategy for the next four weeks. The cost to store a pound of shrimp for one week is $0.15, and to account for unforeseen changes in supply or demand, management also indicated that 25,000 pounds of tiger shrimp must be in storage at the end of week 4. Determine the optimal buying-storing-selling strategy for ASC. What is the projected four-week profit?

13. Romans Food Market, located in Saratoga, New York, carries a variety of specialty foods from around the world. Two of the store's leading products use the Romans Food Market name: Romans Regular Coffee and Romans DeCaf Coffee. These coffees are blends of Brazilian Natural and Colombian Mild coffee beans, which are purchased from a distributor located in New York City. Because Romans purchases large quantities, the coffee beans may be purchased on an as-needed basis for a price 10% higher than the market price the distributor pays for the beans. The current market price is $0.47 per pound for Brazilian Natural and $0.62 per pound for Colombian Mild. The compositions of each coffee blend are as follows:

Bean	Blend	
	Regular	DeCaf
Brazilian Natural	75%	40%
Colombian Mild	25%	60%

Romans sells the Regular blend for $3.60 per pound and the DeCaf blend for $4.40 per pound. Romans would like to place an order for the Brazilian and Colombian coffee beans that will enable the production of 1000 pounds of Romans Regular coffee and 500 pounds of Romans DeCaf coffee. The production cost is $0.80 per pound for the Regular blend. Because of the extra steps required to produce DeCaf, the production cost for the DeCaf blend is $1.05 per pound. Packaging costs for both products are $0.25 per pound. Formulate a linear programming model that can be used to determine the pounds of Brazilian Natural and Colombian Mild that will maximize the total contribution to profit. What is the optimal solution and what is the contribution to profit?

14. The production manager for the Classic Boat Corporation must determine how many units of the Classic 21 model to produce over the next four quarters. The company has a beginning inventory of 100 Classic 21 boats, and demand for the four quarters is 2000 units in quarter 1, 4000 units in quarter 2, 3000 units in quarter 3, and 1500 units in quarter 4. The firm has limited production capacity in each quarter. That is, up to 4000 units can be produced in quarter 1, 3000 units in quarter 2, 2000 units in quarter 3, and 4000 units in quarter 4. Each boat held in inventory in quarters 1 and 2 incurs an inventory holding cost of $250 per unit; the holding cost for quarters 3 and 4 is $300 per unit. The production costs for the first quarter are $10,000 per unit; these costs are expected to increase by 10% each quarter because of increases in labor and material costs. Management specified that the ending inventory for quarter 4 must be at least 500 boats.

   a. Formulate a linear programming model that can be used to determine the production schedule that will minimize the total cost of meeting demand in each quarter subject to the production capacities in each quarter and also to the required ending inventory in quarter 4.

   b. Solve the linear program formulated in part (a). Then develop a table that will show for each quarter the number of units to manufacture, the ending inventory, and the costs incurred.

   c. Interpret each of the dual values corresponding to the constraints developed to meet demand in each quarter. Based on these dual values, what advice would you give the production manager?

   d. Interpret each of the dual values corresponding to the production capacity in each quarter. Based on each of these dual values, what advice would you give the production manager?

 15. Seastrand Oil Company produces two grades of gasoline: regular and high octane. Both gasolines are produced by blending two types of crude oil. Although both types of crude oil contain the two important ingredients required to produce both gasolines, the percentage of important ingredients in each type of crude oil differs, as does the cost per gallon. The percentage of ingredients A and B in each type of crude oil and the cost per gallon are shown.

Crude Oil	Cost	Ingredient A	Ingredient B	
1	$0.10	20%	60%	Crude oil 1 is 60% ingredient B
2	$0.15	50%	30%	

Each gallon of regular gasoline must contain at least 40% of ingredient A, whereas each gallon of high octane can contain at most 50% of ingredient B. Daily demand for regular and high-octane gasoline is 800,000 and 500,000 gallons, respectively. How many gallons of each type of crude oil should be used in the two gasolines to satisfy daily demand at a minimum cost?

16. The Ferguson Paper Company produces rolls of paper for use in adding machines, desk calculators, and cash registers. The rolls, which are 200 feet long, are produced in widths of $1\frac{1}{2}$, $2\frac{1}{2}$, and $3\frac{1}{2}$ inches. The production process provides 200-foot rolls in 10-inch widths only. The firm must therefore cut the rolls to the desired final product sizes. The seven cutting alternatives and the amount of waste generated by each are as follows:

Cutting Alternative	Number of Rolls			Waste (inches)
	$1\frac{1}{2}$ in.	$2\frac{1}{2}$ in.	$3\frac{1}{2}$ in.	
1	6	0	0	1
2	0	4	0	0
3	2	0	2	0
4	0	1	2	$\frac{1}{2}$
5	1	3	0	1
6	1	2	1	0
7	4	0	1	$\frac{1}{2}$

The minimum requirements for the three products are

Roll Width (inches)	$1\frac{1}{2}$	$2\frac{1}{2}$	$3\frac{1}{2}$
Units	1000	2000	4000

a. If the company wants to minimize the number of 10-inch rolls that must be manufactured, how many 10-inch rolls will be processed on each cutting alternative? How many rolls are required, and what is the total waste (inches)?

b. If the company wants to minimize the waste generated, how many 10-inch rolls will be processed on each cutting alternative? How many rolls are required, and what is the total waste (inches)?

c. What are the differences in parts (a) and (b) to this problem? In this case, which objective do you prefer? Explain. What types of situations would make the other objective more desirable?

17. Frandec Company manufactures, assembles, and rebuilds material handling equipment used in warehouses and distribution centers. One product, called a Liftmaster, is assembled from four components: a frame, a motor, two supports, and a metal strap. Frandec's production schedule calls for 5000 Liftmasters to be made next month. Frandec purchases the motors from an outside supplier, but the frames, supports, and straps may be either manufactured by the company or purchased from an outside supplier. Manufacturing and purchase costs per unit are shown.

Component	Manufacturing Cost	Purchase Cost
Frame	$38.00	$51.00
Support	$11.50	$15.00
Strap	$ 6.50	$ 7.50

Three departments are involved in the production of these components. The time (in minutes per unit) required to process each component in each department and the available capacity (in hours) for the three departments are as follows:

| | | Department | |
Component	Cutting	Milling	Shaping
Frame	3.5	2.2	3.1
Support	1.3	1.7	2.6
Strap	0.8	—	1.7
Capacity (hours)	350	420	680

a. Formulate and solve a linear programming model for this make-or-buy application. How many of each component should be manufactured and how many should be purchased?

b. What is the total cost of the manufacturing and purchasing plan?

c. How many hours of production time are used in each department?

d. How much should Frandec be willing to pay for an additional hour of time in the shaping department?

e. Another manufacturer has offered to sell frames to Frandec for $45 each. Could Frandec improve its position by pursuing this opportunity? Why or why not?

18. The Two-Rivers Oil Company near Pittsburgh transports gasoline to its distributors by truck. The company recently contracted to supply gasoline distributors in southern Ohio, and it has $600,000 available to spend on the necessary expansion of its fleet of gasoline tank trucks. Three models of gasoline tank trucks are available.

Truck Model	Capacity (gallons)	Purchase Cost	Monthly Operating Cost, Including Depreciation
Super Tanker	5000	$67,000	$550
Regular Line	2500	$55,000	$425
Econo-Tanker	1000	$46,000	$350

The company estimates that the monthly demand for the region will be 550,000 gallons of gasoline. Because of the size and speed differences of the trucks, the number of deliveries or round trips possible per month for each truck model will vary. Trip capacities are estimated at 15 trips per month for the Super Tanker, 20 trips per month for the Regular Line, and 25 trips per month for the Econo-Tanker. Based on maintenance and driver availability, the firm does not want to add more than 15 new vehicles to its fleet. In addition, the company has decided to purchase at least three of the new Econo-Tankers for use on short-run, low-demand routes. As a final constraint, the company does not want more than half the new models to be Super Tankers.

a. If the company wishes to satisfy the gasoline demand with a minimum monthly operating expense, how many models of each truck should be purchased?

b. If the company did not require at least three Econo-Tankers and did not limit the number of Super Tankers to at most half the new models, how many models of each truck should be purchased?

19. The Silver Star Bicycle Company will be manufacturing both men's and women's models for its Easy-Pedal 10-speed bicycles during the next two months. Management wants to develop a production schedule indicating how many bicycles of each model should be produced in each month. Current demand forecasts call for 150 men's and 125 women's

models to be shipped during the first month and 200 men's and 150 women's models to be shipped during the second month. Additional data are shown:

Model	Production Costs	Labor Requirements (hours) Manufacturing	Assembly	Current Inventory
Men's	$120	2.0	1.5	20
Women's	$ 90	1.6	1.0	30

Last month the company used a total of 1000 hours of labor. The company's labor relations policy will not allow the combined total hours of labor (manufacturing plus assembly) to increase or decrease by more than 100 hours from month to month. In addition, the company charges monthly inventory at the rate of 2% of the production cost based on the inventory levels at the end of the month. The company would like to have at least 25 units of each model in inventory at the end of the two months.

a. Establish a production schedule that minimizes production and inventory costs and satisfies the labor-smoothing, demand, and inventory requirements. What inventories will be maintained and what are the monthly labor requirements?

b. If the company changed the constraints so that monthly labor increases and decreases could not exceed 50 hours, what would happen to the production schedule? How much will the cost increase? What would you recommend?

20. Filtron Corporation produces filtration containers used in water treatment systems. Although business has been growing, the demand each month varies considerably. As a result, the company utilizes a mix of part-time and full-time employees to meet production demands. Although this approach provides Filtron with great flexibility, it has resulted in increased costs and morale problems among employees. For instance, if Filtron needs to increase production from one month to the next, additional part-time employees have to be hired and trained, and costs go up. If Filtron has to decrease production, the workforce has to be reduced and Filtron incurs additional costs in terms of unemployment benefits and decreased morale. Best estimates are that increasing the number of units produced from one month to the next will increase production costs by $1.25 per unit, and that decreasing the number of units produced will increase production costs by $1.00 per unit. In February Filtron produced 10,000 filtration containers but only sold 7500 units; 2500 units are currently in inventory. The sales forecasts for March, April, and May are for 12,000 units, 8000 units, and 15,000 units, respectively. In addition, Filtron has the capacity to store up to 3000 filtration containers at the end of any month. Management would like to determine the number of units to be produced in March, April, and May that will minimize the total cost of the monthly production increases and decreases.

21. Greenville Cabinets received a contract to produce speaker cabinets for a major speaker manufacturer. The contract calls for the production of 3300 bookshelf speakers and 4100 floor speakers over the next two months, with the following delivery schedule:

Model	Month 1	Month 2
Bookshelf	2100	1200
Floor	1500	2600

Greenville estimates that the production time for each bookshelf model is 0.7 hour and the production time for each floor model is 1 hour. The raw material costs are $10 for each bookshelf model and $12 for each floor model. Labor costs are $22 per hour using regular production time and $33 using overtime. Greenville has up to 2400 hours of regular production time available each month and up to 1000 additional hours of overtime available each month. If production for either cabinet exceeds demand in month 1, the cabinets can be stored at a cost of $5 per cabinet. For each product, determine the number of units that should be manufactured each month on regular time and on overtime to minimize total production and storage costs.

22. TriCity Manufacturing (TCM) makes Styrofoam cups, plates, and sandwich and meal containers. Next week's schedule calls for the production of 80,000 small sandwich containers, 80,000 large sandwich containers, and 65,000 meal containers. To make these containers, Styrofoam sheets are melted and formed into final products using three machines: M1, M2, and M3. Machine M1 can process Styrofoam sheets with a maximum width of 12 inches. The width capacity of machine M2 is 16 inches, and the width capacity of machine M3 is 20 inches. The small sandwich containers require 10-inch-wide Styrofoam sheets; thus, these containers can be produced on each of the three machines. The large sandwich containers require 12-inch-wide sheets; thus, these containers can also be produced on each of the three machines. However, the meal containers require 16-inch-wide Styrofoam sheets, so the meal containers cannot be produced on machine M1. Waste is incurred in the production of all three containers because Styrofoam is lost in the heating and forming process as well as in the final trimming of the product. The amount of waste generated varies depending upon the container produced and the machine used. The following table shows the waste in square inches for each machine and product combination. The waste material is recycled for future use.

Machine	Small Sandwich	Large Sandwich	Meal
M1	20	15	—
M2	24	28	18
M3	32	35	36

Production rates also depend upon the container produced and the machine used. The following table shows the production rates in units per minute for each machine and product combination. Machine capacities are limited for the next week. Time available is 35 hours for machine M1, 35 hours for machine M2, and 40 hours for machine M3.

Machine	Small Sandwich	Large Sandwich	Meal
M1	30	25	—
M2	45	40	30
M3	60	52	44

a. Costs associated with reprocessing the waste material have been increasing. Thus, TCM would like to minimize the amount of waste generated in meeting next week's production schedule. Formulate a linear programming model that can be used to determine the best production schedule.

b. Solve the linear program formulated in part (a) to determine the production schedule. How much waste is generated? Which machines, if any, have idle capacity?

23. EZ-Windows, Inc., manufactures replacement windows for the home remodeling business. In January, the company produced 15,000 windows and ended the month with 9000 windows in inventory. EZ-Windows' management team would like to develop a production schedule for the next three months. A smooth production schedule is obviously desirable because it maintains the current workforce and provides a similar month-to-month operation. However, given the sales forecasts, the production capacities, and the storage capabilities as shown, the management team does not think a smooth production schedule with the same production quantity each month possible.

	February	March	April
Sales forecast	15,000	16,500	20,000
Production capacity	14,000	14,000	18,000
Storage capacity	6,000	6,000	6,000

The company's cost accounting department estimates that increasing production by one window from one month to the next will increase total costs by $1.00 for each unit increase in the production level. In addition, decreasing production by one unit from one month to the next will increase total costs by $0.65 for each unit decrease in the production level. Ignoring production and inventory carrying costs, formulate and solve a linear programming model that will minimize the cost of changing production levels while still satisfying the monthly sales forecasts.

24. Morton Financial must decide on the percentage of available funds to commit to each of two investments, referred to as A and B, over the next four periods. The following table shows the amount of new funds available for each of the four periods, as well as the cash expenditure required for each investment (negative values) or the cash income from the investment (positive values). The data shown (in thousands of dollars) reflect the amount of expenditure or income if 100% of the funds available in any period are invested in either A or B. For example, if Morton decides to invest 100% of the funds available in any period in investment A, it will incur cash expenditures of $1000 in period 1, $800 in period 2, $200 in period 3, and income of $200 in period 4. Note, however, if Morton made the decision to invest 80% in investment A, the cash expenditures or income would be 80% of the values shown.

Period	New Investment Funds Available	Investment	
		A	B
1	1500	−1000	−800
2	400	−800	−500
3	500	−200	−300
4	100	200	300

The amount of funds available in any period is the sum of the new investment funds for the period, the new loan funds, the savings from the previous period, the cash income from investment A, and the cash income from investment B. The funds available in any period can be used to pay the loan and interest from the previous period, placed in savings, used to pay the cash expenditures for investment A, or used to pay the cash expenditures for investment B.

Assume an interest rate of 10% per period for savings and an interest rate of 18% per period on borrowed funds. Let

$$S(t) = \text{the savings for period } t$$
$$L(t) = \text{the new loan funds for period } t$$

Then, in any period t, the savings income from the previous period is $1.1S(t-1)$, and the loan and interest expenditure from the previous period is $1.18L(t-1)$.

At the end of period 4, investment A is expected to have a cash value of $3200 (assuming a 100% investment in A), and investment B is expected to have a cash value of $2500 (assuming a 100% investment in B). Additional income and expenses at the end of period 4 will be income from savings in period 4 less the repayment of the period 4 loan plus interest.

Suppose that the decision variables are defined as

$$x_1 = \text{the proportion of investment A undertaken}$$
$$x_2 = \text{the proportion of investment B undertaken}$$

For example, if $x_1 = 0.5$, $500 would be invested in investment A during the first period, and all remaining cash flows and ending investment A values would be multiplied by 0.5. The same holds for investment B. The model must include constraints $x_1 \leq 1$ and $x_2 \leq 1$ to make sure that no more than 100% of the investments can be undertaken.

If no more than $200 can be borrowed in any period, determine the proportions of investments A and B and the amount of savings and borrowing in each period that will maximize the cash value for the firm at the end of the four periods.

25. Western Family Steakhouse offers a variety of low-cost meals and quick service. Other than management, the steakhouse operates with two full-time employees who work 8 hours per day. The rest of the employees are part-time employees who are scheduled for 4-hour shifts during peak meal times. On Saturdays the steakhouse is open from 11:00 A.M. to 10:00 P.M. Management wants to develop a schedule for part-time employees that will minimize labor costs and still provide excellent customer service. The average wage rate for the part-time employees is $7.60 per hour. The total number of full-time and part-time employees needed varies with the time of day as shown.

Time	Total Number of Employees Needed
11:00 A.M.–Noon	9
Noon–1:00 P.M.	9
1:00 P.M.–2:00 P.M.	9
2:00 P.M.–3:00 P.M.	3
3:00 P.M.–4:00 P.M.	3
4:00 P.M.–5:00 P.M.	3
5:00 P.M.–6:00 P.M.	6
6:00 P.M.–7:00 P.M.	12
7:00 P.M.–8:00 P.M.	12
8:00 P.M.–9:00 P.M.	7
9:00 P.M.–10:00 P.M.	7

One full-time employee comes on duty at 11:00 A.M., works 4 hours, takes an hour off, and returns for another 4 hours. The other full-time employee comes to work at 1:00 P.M. and works the same 4-hours-on, 1-hour-off, 4-hours-on pattern.

a. Develop a minimum-cost schedule for part-time employees.
b. What is the total payroll for the part-time employees? How many part-time shifts are needed? Use the surplus variables to comment on the desirability of scheduling at least some of the part-time employees for 3-hour shifts.
c. Assume that part-time employees can be assigned either a 3-hour or a 4-hour shift. Develop a minimum-cost schedule for the part-time employees. How many part-time shifts are needed, and what is the cost savings compared to the previous schedule?

Case Problem 1   PLANNING AN ADVERTISING CAMPAIGN

The Flamingo Grill is an upscale restaurant located in St. Petersburg, Florida. To help plan an advertising campaign for the coming season, Flamingo's management team hired the advertising firm of Haskell & Johnson (HJ). The management team requested HJ's recommendation concerning how the advertising budget should be distributed across television, radio, and newspaper advertisements. The budget has been set at $279,000.

In a meeting with Flamingo's management team, HJ consultants provided the following information about the industry exposure effectiveness rating per ad, their estimate of the number of potential new customers reached per ad, and the cost for each ad.

Advertising Media	Exposure Rating per Ad	New Customers per Ad	Cost per Ad
Television	90	4000	$10,000
Radio	25	2000	$ 3,000
Newspaper	10	1000	$ 1,000

The exposure rating is viewed as a measure of the value of the ad to both existing customers and potential new customers. It is a function of such things as image, message recall, visual and audio appeal, and so on. As expected, the more expensive television advertisement has the highest exposure effectiveness rating along with the greatest potential for reaching new customers.

At this point, the HJ consultants pointed out that the data concerning exposure and reach were only applicable to the first few ads in each medium. For television, HJ stated that the exposure rating of 90 and the 4000 new customers reached per ad were reliable for the first 10 television ads. After 10 ads, the benefit is expected to decline. For planning purposes, HJ recommended reducing the exposure rating to 55 and the estimate of the potential new customers reached to 1500 for any television ads beyond 10. For radio ads, the preceding data are reliable up to a maximum of 15 ads. Beyond 15 ads, the exposure rating declines to 20 and the number of new customers reached declines to 1200 per ad. Similarly, for newspaper ads, the preceding data are reliable up to a maximum of 20; the exposure rating declines to 5 and the potential number of new customers reached declines to 800 for additional ads.

Flamingo's management team accepted maximizing the total exposure rating, across all media, as the objective of the advertising campaign. Because of management's concern with attracting new customers, management stated that the advertising campaign must reach at least 100,000 new customers. To balance the advertising campaign and make use of all advertising media, Flamingo's management team also adopted the following guidelines.

- Use at least twice as many radio advertisements as television advertisements.
- Use no more than 20 television advertisements.

- The television budget should be at least $140,000.
- The radio advertising budget is restricted to a maximum of $99,000.
- The newspaper budget is to be at least $30,000.

HJ agreed to work with these guidelines and provide a recommendation as to how the $279,000 advertising budget should be allocated among television, radio, and newspaper advertising.

Managerial Report

Develop a model that can be used to determine the advertising budget allocation for the Flamingo Grill. Include a discussion of the following in your report.

1. A schedule showing the recommended number of television, radio, and newspaper advertisements and the budget allocation for each medium. Show the total exposure and indicate the total number of potential new customers reached.
2. How would the total exposure change if an additional $10,000 were added to the advertising budget?
3. A discussion of the ranges for the objective function coefficients. What do the ranges indicate about how sensitive the recommended solution is to HJ's exposure rating coefficients?
4. After reviewing HJ's recommendation, the Flamingo's management team asked how the recommendation would change if the objective of the advertising campaign was to maximize the number of potential new customers reached. Develop the media schedule under this objective.
5. Compare the recommendations from parts 1 and 4. What is your recommendation for the Flamingo Grill's advertising campaign?

Case Problem 2   PHOENIX COMPUTER

Phoenix Computer manufactures and sells personal computers directly to customers. Orders are accepted by phone and through the company's website. Phoenix will be introducing several new laptop models over the next few months and management recognizes a need to develop technical support personnel to specialize in the new laptop systems. One option being considered is to hire new employees and put them through a three-month training program. Another option is to put current customer service specialists through a two-month training program on the new laptop models. Phoenix estimates that the need for laptop specialists will grow from 0 to 100 during the months of May through September as follows: May—20; June—30; July—85; August—85; and September—100. After September, Phoenix expects that maintaining a staff of 100 laptop specialists will be sufficient.

The annual salary for a new employee is estimated to be $27,000 whether the person is hired to enter the training program or to replace a current employee who is entering the training program. The annual salary for the current Phoenix employees who are being considered for the training program is approximately $36,000. The cost of the three-month training program is $1500 per person, and the cost of the two-month training program is $1000 per person. Note that the length of the training program means that a lag will occur between the time when a new person is hired and the time a new laptop specialist is available. The number of current employees who will be available for training is limited. Phoenix estimates that the following numbers can be made available in the coming months: March—15; April—20; May—0; June—5; and July—10. The training center has the capacity to start new three-month and two-month training classes each month; however, the total number of students (new and current employees) that begin training each month cannot exceed 25.

Phoenix needs to determine the number of new hires that should begin the three-month training program each month and the number of current employees that should begin the two-month training program each month. The objective is to satisfy staffing needs during May through September at the lowest possible total cost; that is, minimize the incremental salary cost and the total training cost.

It is currently January, and Phoenix Computer would like to develop a plan for hiring new employees and determining the mix of new hires and current employees to place in the training program.

Managerial Report

Perform an analysis of the Phoenix Computer problem and prepare a report that summarizes your findings. Be sure to include information on and analysis of the following items:

1. The incremental salary and training cost associated with hiring a new employee and training him/her to be a laptop specialist.
2. The incremental salary and training cost associated with putting a current employee through the training program. (Don't forget that a replacement must be hired when the current employee enters the program.)
3. Recommendations regarding the hiring and training plan that will minimize the salary and training costs over the February through August period as well as answers to these questions: What is the total cost of providing technical support for the new laptop models? How much higher will monthly payroll costs be in September than in January?

Case Problem 3   TEXTILE MILL SCHEDULING

The Scottsville Textile Mill* produces five different fabrics. Each fabric can be woven on one or more of the mill's 38 looms. The sales department's forecast of demand for the next month is shown in Table 4.16, along with data on the selling price per yard, variable cost per yard, and purchase price per yard. The mill operates 24 hours a day and is scheduled for 30 days during the coming month.

TABLE 4.16   MONTHLY DEMAND, SELLING PRICE, VARIABLE COST, AND PURCHASE PRICE DATA FOR SCOTTSVILLE TEXTILE MILL FABRICS

Fabric	Demand (yards)	Selling Price ($/yard)	Variable Cost ($/yard)	Purchase Price ($/yard)
1	16,500	0.99	0.66	0.80
2	22,000	0.86	0.55	0.70
3	62,000	1.10	0.49	0.60
4	7,500	1.24	0.51	0.70
5	62,000	0.70	0.50	0.70

*This case is based on the Calhoun Textile Mill Case by Jeffrey D. Camm, P. M. Dearing, and Suresh K. Tadisnia, 1987.

TABLE 4.17   LOOM PRODUCTION RATES FOR THE SCOTTSVILLE TEXTILE MILL

| | Loom Rate (yards/hour) | |
Fabric	Dobbie	Regular
1	4.63	—
2	4.63	—
3	5.23	5.23
4	5.23	5.23
5	4.17	4.17

Note: Fabrics 1 and 2 can be manufactured only on the dobbie loom.

The mill has two types of looms: dobbie and regular. The dobbie looms are more versatile and can be used for all five fabrics. The regular looms can produce only three of the fabrics. The mill has a total of 38 looms: 8 are dobbie and 30 are regular. The rate of production for each fabric on each type of loom is given in Table 4.17. The time required to change over from producing one fabric to another is negligible and does not have to be considered.

The Scottsville Textile Mill satisfies all demand with either its own fabric or fabric purchased from another mill. Fabrics that cannot be woven at the Scottsville Mill because of limited loom capacity will be purchased from another mill. The purchase price of each fabric is also shown in Table 4.16.

Managerial Report

Develop a model that can be used to schedule production for the Scottsville Textile Mill, and at the same time, determine how many yards of each fabric must be purchased from another mill. Include a discussion and analysis of the following items in your report:

1. The final production schedule and loom assignments for each fabric.
2. The projected total contribution to profit.
3. A discussion of the value of additional loom time. (The mill is considering purchasing a ninth dobbie loom. What is your estimate of the monthly profit contribution of this additional loom?)
4. A discussion of the objective coefficients' ranges.
5. A discussion of how the objective of minimizing total costs would provide a different model than the objective of maximizing total profit contribution. (How would the interpretation of the objective coefficients' ranges differ for these two models?)

Case Problem 4   WORKFORCE SCHEDULING

Davis Instruments has two manufacturing plants located in Atlanta, Georgia. Product demand varies considerably from month to month, causing Davis extreme difficulty in workforce scheduling. Recently Davis started hiring temporary workers supplied by WorkForce Unlimited, a company that specializes in providing temporary employees for firms in the greater Atlanta area. WorkForce Unlimited offered to provide temporary employees under three contract options that differ in terms of the length of employment and the cost. The three options are summarized:

Option	Length of Employment	Cost
1	One month	$2000
2	Two months	$4800
3	Three months	$7500

The longer contract periods are more expensive because WorkForce Unlimited experiences greater difficulty finding temporary workers who are willing to commit to longer work assignments.

Over the next six months, Davis projects the following needs for additional employees:

Month	January	February	March	April	May	June
Employees Needed	10	23	19	26	20	14

Each month, Davis can hire as many temporary employees as needed under each of the three options. For instance, if Davis hires five employees in January under Option 2, WorkForce Unlimited will supply Davis with five temporary workers who will work two months: January and February. For these workers, Davis will have to pay 5($4800) = $24,000. Because of some merger negotiations under way, Davis does not want to commit to any contractual obligations for temporary employees that extend beyond June.

Davis's quality control program requires each temporary employee to receive training at the time of hire. The training program is required even if the person worked for Davis Instruments in the past. Davis estimates that the cost of training is $875 each time a temporary employee is hired. Thus, if a temporary employee is hired for one month, Davis will incur a training cost of $875, but will incur no additional training cost if the employee is on a two- or three-month contract.

Managerial Report

Develop a model that can be used to determine the number of temporary employees Davis should hire each month under each contract plan in order to meet the projected needs at a minimum total cost. Include the following items in your report:

1. A schedule that shows the number of temporary employees that Davis should hire each month for each contract option.
2. A summary table that shows the number of temporary employees that Davis should hire under each contract option, the associated contract cost for each option, and the associated training cost for each option. Provide summary totals showing the total number of temporary employees hired, total contract costs, and total training costs.
3. If the cost to train each temporary employee could be reduced to $700 per month, what effect would this change have on the hiring plan? Explain. Discuss the implications that this effect on the hiring plan has for identifying methods for reducing training costs. How much of a reduction in training costs would be required to change the hiring plan based on a training cost of $875 per temporary employee?

4. Suppose that Davis hired 10 full-time employees at the beginning of January in order to satisfy part of the labor requirements over the next six months. If Davis can hire full-time employees for $16.50 per hour, including fringe benefits, what effect would it have on total labor and training costs over the six-month period as compared to hiring only temporary employees? Assume that full-time and temporary employees both work approximately 160 hours per month. Provide a recommendation regarding the decision to hire additional full-time employees.

Case Problem 5   DUKE ENERGY COAL ALLOCATION*

Duke Energy manufactures and distributes electricity to customers in the United States and Latin America. Duke recently purchased Cinergy Corporation, which has generating facilities and energy customers in Indiana, Kentucky, and Ohio. For these customers Cinergy has been spending $725 to $750 million each year for the fuel needed to operate its coal-fired and gas-fired power plants; 92% to 95% of the fuel used is coal. In this region, Duke Energy uses 10 coal-burning generating plants: five located inland and five located on the Ohio River. Some plants have more than one generating unit. Duke Energy uses 28–29 million tons of coal per year at a cost of approximately $2 million every day in this region.

The company purchases coal using fixed-tonnage or variable-tonnage contracts from mines in Indiana (49%), West Virginia (20%), Ohio (12%), Kentucky (11%), Illinois (5%), and Pennsylvania (3%). The company must purchase all of the coal contracted for on fixed-tonnage contracts, but on variable-tonnage contracts it can purchase varying amounts up to the limit specified in the contract. The coal is shipped from the mines to Duke Energy's generating facilities in Ohio, Kentucky, and Indiana. The cost of coal varies from $19 to $35 per ton and transportation/delivery charges range from $1.50 to $5.00 per ton.

A model is used to determine the megawatt-hours (mWh) of electricity that each generating unit is expected to produce and to provide a measure of each generating unit's efficiency, referred to as the heat rate. The heat rate is the total BTUs required to produce 1 kilowatt-hour (kWh) of electrical power.

Coal Allocation Model

Duke Energy uses a linear programming model, called the coal allocation model, to allocate coal to its generating facilities. The objective of the coal allocation model is to determine the lowest-cost method for purchasing and distributing coal to the generating units. The supply/availability of the coal is determined by the contracts with the various mines, and the demand for coal at the generating units is determined indirectly by the megawatt-hours of electricity each unit must produce.

The cost to process coal, called the add-on cost, depends upon the characteristics of the coal (moisture content, ash content, BTU content, sulfur content, and grindability) and the efficiency of the generating unit. The add-on cost plus the transportation cost are added to the purchase cost of the coal to determine the total cost to purchase and use the coal.

---

*The authors are indebted to Thomas Mason and David Bossee of Duke Energy Corporation, formerly Cinergy Corp., for their contribution to this case problem.

Current Problem

Duke Energy signed three fixed-tonnage contracts and four variable-tonnage contracts. The company would like to determine the least-cost way to allocate the coal available through these contracts to five generating units. The relevant data for the three fixed-tonnage contracts are as follows:

Supplier	Number of Tons Contracted For	Cost ($/ton)	BTUs/lb
RAG	350,000	22	13,000
Peabody Coal Sales	300,000	26	13,300
American Coal Sales	275,000	22	12,600

For example, the contract signed with RAG requires Duke Energy to purchase 350,000 tons of coal at a price of $22 per ton; each pound of this particular coal provides 13,000 BTUs.

The data for the four variable-tonnage contracts follow:

Supplier	Number of Tons Available	Cost ($/ton)	BTUs/lb
Consol, Inc.	200,000	32	12,250
Cyprus Amax	175,000	35	12,000
Addington Mining	200,000	31	12,000
Waterloo	180,000	33	11,300

For example, the contract with Consol, Inc., enables Duke Energy to purchase up to 200,000 tons of coal at a cost of $32 per ton; each pound of this coal provides 12,250 BTUs.

The number of megawatt-hours of electricity that each generating unit must produce and the heat rate provided are as follows:

Generating Unit	Electricity Produced (mWh)	Heat Rate (BTUs per kWh)
Miami Fort Unit 5	550,000	10,500
Miami Fort Unit 7	500,000	10,200
Beckjord Unit 1	650,000	10,100
East Bend Unit 2	750,000	10,000
Zimmer Unit 1	1,100,000	10,000

For example, Miami Fort Unit 5 must produce 550,000 megawatt-hours of electricity, and 10,500 BTUs are needed to produce each kilowatt-hour.

The transportation cost and the add-on cost in dollars per ton are shown here:

| | Transportation Cost ($/ton) | | | | |
Supplier	Miami Fort Unit 5	Miami Fort Unit 7	Beckjord Unit 1	East Bend Unit 2	Zimmer Unit 1
RAG	5.00	5.00	4.75	5.00	4.75
Peabody	3.75	3.75	3.50	3.75	3.50
American	3.00	3.00	2.75	3.00	2.75
Consol	3.25	3.25	2.85	3.25	2.85
Cyprus	5.00	5.00	4.75	5.00	4.75
Addington	2.25	2.25	2.00	2.25	2.00
Waterloo	2.00	2.00	1.60	2.00	1.60

| | Add-On Cost ($/ton) | | | | |
Supplier	Miami Fort Unit 5	Miami Fort Unit 7	Beckjord Unit 1	East Bend Unit 2	Zimmer Unit 1
RAG	10.00	10.00	10.00	5.00	6.00
Peabody	10.00	10.00	11.00	6.00	7.00
American	13.00	13.00	15.00	9.00	9.00
Consol	10.00	10.00	11.00	7.00	7.00
Cyprus	10.00	10.00	10.00	5.00	6.00
Addington	5.00	5.00	6.00	4.00	4.00
Waterloo	11.00	11.00	11.00	7.00	9.00

Managerial Report

Prepare a report that summarizes your recommendations regarding Duke Energy's coal allocation problem. Be sure to include information and analysis for the following issues:

1. Determine how much coal to purchase from each of the mining companies and how it should be allocated to the generating units. What is the cost to purchase, deliver, and process the coal?
2. Compute the average cost of coal in cents per million BTUs for each generating unit (a measure of the cost of fuel for the generating units).
3. Compute the average number of BTUs per pound of coal received at each generating unit (a measure of the energy efficiency of the coal received at each unit).
4. Suppose that Duke Energy can purchase an additional 80,000 tons of coal from American Coal Sales as an "all or nothing deal" for $30 per ton. Should Duke Energy purchase the additional 80,000 tons of coal?
5. Suppose that Duke Energy learns that the energy content of the coal from Cyprus Amax is actually 13,000 BTUs per pound. Should Duke Energy revise its procurement plan?
6. Duke Energy has learned from its trading group that Duke Energy can sell 50,000 megawatt-hours of electricity over the grid (to other electricity suppliers) at a price of $30 per megawatt-hour. Should Duke Energy sell the electricity? If so, which generating units should produce the additional electricity?

Appendix 4.1   EXCEL SOLUTION OF HEWLITT CORPORATION FINANCIAL PLANNING PROBLEM

In Appendix 2.2 we showed how Excel could be used to solve the Par, Inc., linear programming problem. To illustrate the use of Excel in solving a more complex linear programming problem, we show the solution to the Hewlitt Corporation financial planning problem presented in Section 4.2.

The spreadsheet formulation and solution of the Hewlitt Corporation problem are shown in Figure 4.10. As described in Appendix 2.2, our practice is to put the data required for the problem in the top part of the worksheet and build the model in the bottom part of the worksheet. The model consists of a set of cells for the decision variables, a cell for the objective function, a set of cells for the left-hand-side functions, and a set of cells for the right-hand sides of the constraints. The cells for each of these model components are screened; the cells for the decision variables are also enclosed by a boldface line. Descriptive labels are used to make the spreadsheet easy to read.

Formulation

The data and descriptive labels are contained in cells A1:G12. The screened cells in the bottom portion of the spreadsheet contain the key elements of the model required by the Excel Solver.

FIGURE 4.10   EXCEL SOLUTION FOR THE HEWLITT CORPORATION PROBLEM

	A	B	C	D	E	F	G	H	I	J	K	L
1	Hewlitt Corporation Cash Requirements											
2												
3		Cash										
4	Year	Rqmt.				Bond						
5	1	430			1	2	3					
6	2	210	Price ($1000)		1.15	1	1.35					
7	3	222		Rate	0.08875	0.055	0.1175					
8	4	231	Years to Maturity		5	6	7					
9	5	240										
10	6	195	Annual Savings Multiple			1.04						
11	7	225										
12	8	255										
13												
14	Model											
15												
16	F	B1	B2	B3	S1	S2	S3	S4	S5	S6	S7	S8
17	1728.794	144.988	187.856	228.188	636.148	501.606	349.682	182.681	0	0	0	0
18												
19					Cash Flow		Net Cash		Cash			
20	Min Funds	1728.7939		Constraints	In	Out	Flow		Rqmt.			
21				Year 1	1728.794	1298.794	430	=	430			
22				Year 2	711.6057	501.6057	210	=	210			
23				Year 3	571.6818	349.6818	222	=	222			
24				Year 4	413.6809	182.6809	231	=	231			
25				Year 5	240	0	240	=	240			
26				Year 6	195	0	195	=	195			
27				Year 7	225	0	225	=	225			
28				Year 8	255	0	255	=	255			

Decision Variables   Cells A17:L17 are reserved for the decision variables. The optimal values (rounded to three places), are shown to be $F = 1728.794$, $B_1 = 144.988$, $B_2 = 187.856$, $B_3 = 228.188$, $S_1 = 636.148$, $S_2 = 501.606$, $S_3 = 349.682$, $S_4 = 182.681$, and $S_5 = S_6 = S_7 = S_8 = 0$.

Objective Function   The formula $=A17$ has been placed into cell B20 to reflect the total funds required. It is simply the value of the decision variable, F. The total funds required by the optimal solution is shown to be $1,728,794.

Left-Hand Sides   The left-hand sides for the eight constraints represent the annual net cash flow. They are placed into cells G21:G28.
Cell $G21 = E21 - F21$ (Copy to G22:G28)

For this problem, some of the left-hand-side cells reference other cells that contain formulas. These referenced cells provide Hewlitt's cash flow in and cash flow out for each of the eight years.* The cells and their formulas are as follows:

Cell $E21 = A17$

Cell $E22 = SUMPRODUCT(\$E\$7:\$G\$7,\$B\$17:\$D\$17)+\$F\$10*E17$

Cell $E23 = SUMPRODUCT(\$E\$7:\$G\$7,\$B\$17:\$D\$17)+\$F\$10*F17$

Cell $E24 = SUMPRODUCT(\$E\$7:\$G\$7,\$B\$17:\$D\$17)+\$F\$10*G17$

Cell $E25 = SUMPRODUCT(\$E\$7:\$G\$7,\$B\$17:\$D\$17)+\$F\$10*H17$

Cell $E26 = (1+E7)*B17+F7*C17+G7*D17+F10*I17$

Cell $E27 = (1+F7)*C17+G7*D17+F10*J17$

Cell $E28 = (1+G7)*D17+F10*K17$

Cell $F21 = SUMPRODUCT(E6:G6,B17:D17)+E17$

Cell $F22 = F17$

Cell $F23 = G17$

Cell $F24 = H17$

Cell $F25 = I17$

Cell $F26 = J17$

Cell $F27 = K17$

Cell $F28 = L17$

Right-Hand Sides   The right-hand sides for the eight constraints represent the annual cash requirements. They are placed into cells I21:I28.
Cell $I21 = B5$ (Copy to I22:I28)

Excel Solution

We are now ready to use the information in the worksheet to determine the optimal solution to the Hewlitt Corporation problem. The following steps describe how to use Excel to obtain the optimal solution.

---

*The cash flow in is the sum of the positive terms in each constraint equation in the mathematical model, and the cash flow out is the sum of the negative terms in each constraint equation.

FIGURE 4.11   SOLVER PARAMETERS DIALOG BOX FOR THE HEWLITT
CORPORATION PROBLEM

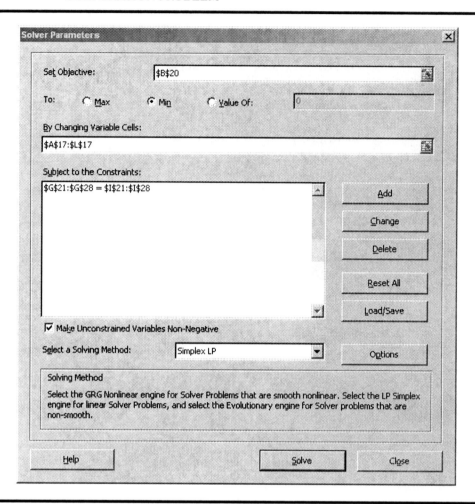

Step 1. Select the **Data** tab
Step 2. Select **Solver** from the **Analysis** group
Step 3. When the **Solver Parameters** dialog box appears (see Figure 4.11):
    Enter B20 in the **Set Objective** box
    Select the **To: Min** option
    Enter A17:L17 in the **By Changing Variable Cells** box
Step 4. Choose **Add**
    When the **Add Constraint** dialog box appears:
    Enter G21:G28 in the left-hand box of the **Cell Reference** area
    Select = from the middle drop-down button
    Enter I21:I28 in the **Constraint** area
    Click **OK**
Step 5. When the **Solver Parameters** dialog box reappears (see Figure 4.11):
    Select **Make Unconstrained Variables Non-Negative**

Step 6. Select the **Select a Solving Method** drop-down button
Select **Simplex LP**
Step 7. Choose **Solve**
Step 8. When the **Solver Results** dialog box appears:
Select **Keep Solver Solution**
Select **Sensitivity** in the **Reports** box
Click **OK**

The Solver Parameters dialog box is shown in Figure 4.11. The optimal solution is shown in Figure 4.10; the accompanying sensitivity report is shown in Figure 4.12.

Discussion

Figures 4.10 and 4.12 contain essentially the same information as that provided in Figure 4.4. Recall that the Excel sensitivity report uses the term *shadow price* to describe the *change* in value of the solution per unit increase in the right-hand side of a constraint. This is the same as the Dual Value in Figure 4.4.

FIGURE 4.12   EXCEL'S SENSITIVITY REPORT FOR THE HEWLITT CORPORATION PROBLEM

Variable Cells

Cell	Name	Final Value	Reduced Cost	Objective Coefficient	Allowable Increase	Allowable Decrease
$A$17	F	1728.793855	0	1	1E + 30	1
$B$17	B1	144.9881496	0	0	0.067026339	0.013026775
$C$17	B2	187.8558478	0	0	0.012795531	0.020273774
$D$17	B3	228.1879195	0	0	0.022906851	0.749663022
$E$17	S1	636.1479438	0	0	0.109559907	0.05507386
$F$17	S2	501.605712	0	0	0.143307365	0.056948823
$G$17	S3	349.681791	0	0	0.210854199	0.059039182
$H$17	S4	182.680913	0	0	0.413598622	0.061382404
$I$17	S5	0	0.064025159	0	1E + 30	0.064025159
$J$17	S6	0	0.012613604	0	1E + 30	0.012613604
$K$17	S7	0	0.021318233	0	1E + 30	0.021318233
$L$17	S8	0	0.670839393	0	1E + 30	0.670839393

Constraints

Cell	Name	Final Value	Shadow Price	Constraint R.H. Side	Allowable Increase	Allowable Decrease
$G$21	Year 1 Flow	430	1	430	1E + 30	1728.793855
$G$22	Year 2 Flow	210	0.961538462	210	1E + 30	661.5938616
$G$23	Year 3 Flow	222	0.924556213	222	1E + 30	521.6699405
$G$24	Year 4 Flow	231	0.888996359	231	1E + 30	363.6690626
$G$25	Year 5 Flow	240	0.854804191	240	1E + 30	189.9881496
$G$26	Year 6 Flow	195	0.760364454	195	2149.927647	157.8558478
$G$27	Year 7 Flow	225	0.718991202	225	3027.962172	198.1879195
$G$28	Year 8 Flow	255	0.670839393	255	1583.881915	255

CHAPTER 15

Time Series Analysis and Forecasting

CONTENTS

A forecast is simply a prediction of what will happen in the future. Managers must learn to accept the fact that regardless of the technique used, they will not be able to develop perfect forecasts.

The purpose of this chapter is to provide an introduction to time series analysis and forecasting. Suppose we are asked to provide quarterly forecasts of sales for one of our company's products over the coming one-year period. Production schedules, raw material purchasing, inventory policies, and sales quotas will all be affected by the quarterly forecasts we provide. Consequently, poor forecasts may result in poor planning and increased costs for the company. How should we go about providing the quarterly sales forecasts? Good judgment, intuition, and an awareness of the state of the economy may give us a rough idea or "feeling" of what is likely to happen in the future, but converting that feeling into a number that can be used as next year's sales forecast is difficult.

Forecasting methods can be classified as qualitative or quantitative. Qualitative methods generally involve the use of expert judgment to develop forecasts. Such methods are appropriate when historical data on the variable being forecast are either not applicable or unavailable. Quantitative forecasting methods can be used when (1) past information about the variable being forecast is available, (2) the information can be quantified, and (3) it is reasonable to assume that the pattern of the past will continue into the future. We will focus exclusively on quantitative forecasting methods in this chapter.

If the historical data are restricted to past values of the variable to be forecast, the forecasting procedure is called a time series method and the historical data are referred to as a time series. The objective of time series analysis is to discover a pattern in the historical data or time series and then extrapolate the pattern into the future; the forecast is based solely on past values of the variable and/or on past forecast errors.

In Section 15.1 we discuss the various kinds of time series that a forecaster might be faced with in practice. These include a constant or horizontal pattern, trends, seasonal patterns, both a trend and a seasonal pattern, and cyclical patterns. In order to build a quantitative forecasting model, it is necessary to have a measurement of forecast accuracy. Different measurements, and their respective advantages and disadvantages, are discussed in Section 15.2. In Section 15.3 we consider the simplest case, which is a horizontal or constant pattern. For this pattern, we develop the classical moving average and exponential smoothing models. We show how the best parameters can be selected using an optimization model, which provides a good application of the optimization tools developed in Chapters 2 through 8. Many time series have a trend, and taking this trend into account is important. In Section 15.4 we give optimization models for finding the best model parameters when a trend is present. Finally, in Section 15.5 we show how to incorporate both a trend and seasonality into a forecasting model.

MANAGEMENT SCIENCE IN ACTION

FORECASTING ENERGY NEEDS IN THE UTILITY INDUSTRY*

Duke Energy is a diversified energy company with a portfolio of natural gas and electric businesses and an affiliated real estate company. In 2006, Duke Energy merged with Cinergy of Cincinnati, Ohio, to create one of North America's largest energy companies, with assets totaling more than $70 billion. As a result of this merger the Cincinnati Gas & Electric Company became part of Duke Energy. Today, Duke Energy services over 5.5 million retail electric and gas customers in North Carolina, South Carolina, Ohio, Kentucky, Indiana, and Ontario, Canada.

Forecasting in the utility industry offers some unique perspectives. Because electricity cannot take the form of finished goods or in-process inventories, this product must be generated to meet the instantaneous requirements of the customers. Electrical shortages are not just lost sales, but "brownouts" or "blackouts." This situation places an unusual burden on the utility forecaster. On the positive side, the demand for energy and the sale of energy are more predictable than for many other products. Also, unlike the situation in a multiproduct firm, a great amount of forecasting effort and expertise can be concentrated on the two products: gas and electricity.

The largest observed electric demand for any given period, such as an hour, a day, a month, or a year, is defined as the peak load. The forecast of the annual electric peak load guides the timing decision for constructing future generating units, and the financial impact of this decision is great. Obviously, a timing decision that leads to having the unit available no sooner than necessary is crucial.

The energy forecasts are important in other ways also. For example, purchases of coal as fuel for the generating units are based on the forecast levels of energy needed. The revenue from the electric operations of the company is determined from forecasted sales, which in turn enters into the planning of rate changes and external financing. These planning and decision-making processes are among the most important managerial activities in the company. It is imperative that the decision makers have the best forecast information available to assist them in arriving at these decisions.

*Based on information provided by Dr. Richard Evans of Cincinnati Gas & Electric Company, Cincinnati, Ohio.

15.1   TIME SERIES PATTERNS

A time series is a sequence of observations on a variable measured at successive points in time or over successive periods of time. The measurements may be taken every hour, day, week, month, or year, or at any other regular interval.[1] The pattern of the data is an important factor in understanding how the time series has behaved in the past. If such behavior can be expected to continue in the future, we can use it to guide us in selecting an appropriate forecasting method.

To identify the underlying pattern in the data, a useful first step is to construct a time series plot. A time series plot is a graphical presentation of the relationship between time and the time series variable; time is on the horizontal axis and the time series values are shown on the vertical axis. Let us review some of the common types of data patterns that can be identified when examining a time series plot.

Horizontal Pattern

A horizontal pattern exists when the data fluctuate around a constant mean. To illustrate a time series with a horizontal pattern, consider the 12 weeks of data in Table 15.1. These data show the number of gallons of gasoline sold by a gasoline distributor in Bennington, Vermont, over the past 12 weeks. The average value or mean for this time series is 19.25, or 19,250 gallons per week. Figure 15.1 shows a time series plot for these data. Note how the data fluctuate around the sample mean of 19,250 gallons. Although random variability is present, we would say that these data follow a horizontal pattern.

The term stationary time series[2] is used to denote a time series whose statistical properties are independent of time. In particular this means that

1. The process generating the data has a constant mean.
2. The variability of the time series is constant over time.

---

[1]We limit our discussion to time series in which the values of the series are recorded at equal intervals. Cases in which the observations are made at unequal intervals are beyond the scope of this text.
[2]For a formal definition of stationarity see Box, G. E. P., G. M. Jenkins, and G. C. Reinsell (1994), *Time Series Analysis: Forecasting and Control*, 3rd ed., Prentice-Hall, p. 23.

TABLE 15.1   GASOLINE SALES TIME SERIES

Gasoline

Week	Sales (1000s of gallons)
1	17
2	21
3	19
4	23
5	18
6	16
7	20
8	18
9	22
10	20
11	15
12	22

A time series plot for a stationary time series will always exhibit a horizontal pattern. But simply observing a horizontal pattern is not sufficient evidence to conclude that the time series is stationary. More advanced texts on forecasting discuss procedures for determining whether a time series is stationary and provide methods for transforming a time series that is not stationary into a stationary series.

FIGURE 15.1   GASOLINE SALES TIME SERIES PLOT

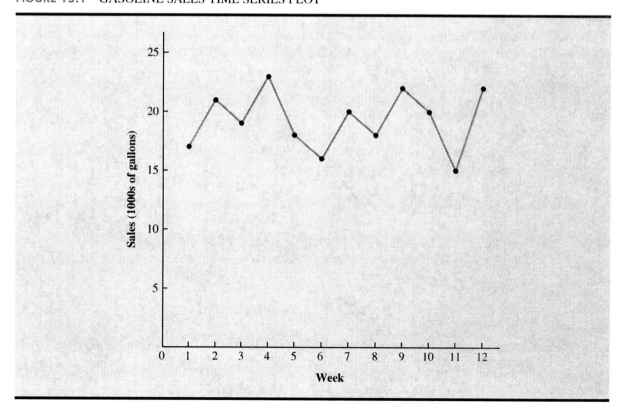

Changes in business conditions can often result in a time series that has a horizontal pattern shifting to a new level. For instance, suppose the gasoline distributor signs a contract with the Vermont Sate Police to provide gasoline for state police cars located in southern Vermont. With this new contract, the distributor expects to see a major increase in weekly sales starting in week 13. Table 15.2 shows the number of gallons of gasoline sold for the original time series and the 10 weeks after signing the new contract. Figure 15.2 shows the corresponding time series plot. Note the increased level of the time series beginning in week 13. This change in the level of the time series makes it more difficult to choose an appropriate forecasting method. Selecting a forecasting method that adapts well to changes in the level of a time series is an important consideration in many practical applications.

Trend Pattern

Although time series data generally exhibit random fluctuations, a time series may also show gradual shifts or movements to relatively higher or lower values over a longer period of time. If a time series plot exhibits this type of behavior, we say that a trend pattern exists. Trend is usually the result of long-term factors such as population increases or decreases, changing demographic characteristics of the population, technology, and/or consumer preferences.

GasolineRevised

TABLE 15.2   GASOLINE SALES TIME SERIES AFTER OBTAINING THE
CONTRACT WITH THE VERMONT STATE POLICE

Week	Sales (1000s of gallons)
1	17
2	21
3	19
4	23
5	18
6	16
7	20
8	18
9	22
10	20
11	15
12	22
13	31
14	34
15	31
16	33
17	28
18	32
19	30
20	29
21	34
22	33

FIGURE 15.2   GASOLINE SALES TIME SERIES PLOT AFTER OBTAINING THE CONTRACT WITH THE VERMONT STATE POLICE

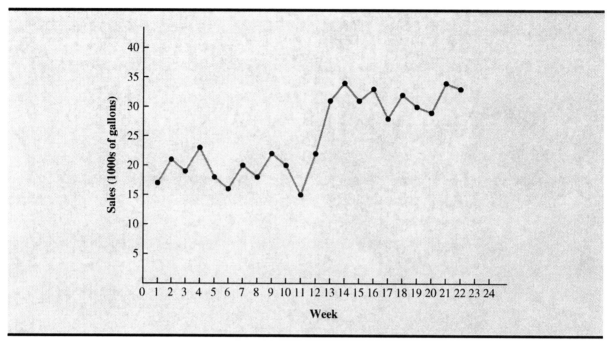

To illustrate a time series with a trend pattern, consider the time series of bicycle sales for a particular manufacturer over the past 10 years, as shown in Table 15.3 and Figure 15.3. Note that 21,600 bicycles were sold in year 1, 22,900 were sold in year 2, and so on. In year 10, the most recent year, 31,400 bicycles were sold. Visual inspection of the time series plot shows some up and down movement over the past 10 years, but the time series seems to also have a systematically increasing or upward trend.

The trend for the bicycle sales time series appears to be linear and increasing over time, but sometimes a trend can be described better by other types of patterns. For instance, the

TABLE 15.3   BICYCLE SALES TIME SERIES

Bicycle

Year	Sales (1000s)
1	21.6
2	22.9
3	25.5
4	21.9
5	23.9
6	27.5
7	31.5
8	29.7
9	28.6
10	31.4

FIGURE 15.3 BICYCLE SALES TIME SERIES PLOT

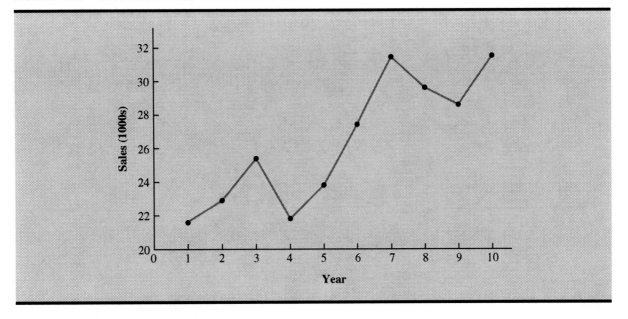

data in Table 15.4 and the corresponding time series plot in Figure 15.4 show the sales revenue for a cholesterol drug since the company won FDA approval for it 10 years ago. The time series increases in a nonlinear fashion; that is, the rate of change of revenue does not increase by a constant amount from one year to the next. In fact the revenue appears to be growing in an exponential fashion. Exponential relationships such as this are appropriate when the percentage change from one period to the next is relatively constant.

Seasonal Pattern

The trend of a time series can be identified by analyzing multiyear movements in historical data. Seasonal patterns are recognized by seeing the same repeating patterns over successive periods of time. For example, a manufacturer of swimming pools expects low sales

TABLE 15.4 CHOLESTEROL REVENUE TIME SERIES ($ MILLIONS)

WEB file

Cholesterol

Year	Revenue
1	23.1
2	21.3
3	27.4
4	34.6
5	33.8
6	43.2
7	59.5
8	64.4
9	74.2
10	99.3

FIGURE 15.4   CHOLESTEROL REVENUE TIMES SERIES PLOT ($ MILLIONS)

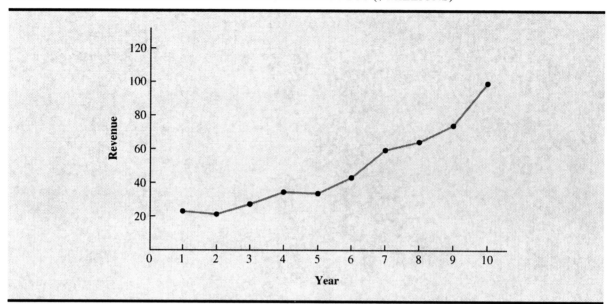

activity in the fall and winter months, with peak sales in the spring and summer months. Manufacturers of snow removal equipment and heavy clothing, however, expect just the opposite yearly pattern. Not surprisingly, the pattern for a time series plot that exhibits a repeating pattern over a one-year period due to seasonal influences is called a seasonal pattern. Although we generally think of seasonal movement in a time series as occurring within one year, time series data can also exhibit seasonal patterns of less than one year in duration. For example, daily traffic volume shows within-the-day "seasonal" behavior, with peak levels occurring during rush hours, moderate flow during the rest of the day and early evening, and light flow from midnight to early morning.

As an example of a seasonal pattern, consider the number of umbrellas sold at a clothing store over the past five years. Table 15.5 shows the time series and Figure 15.5 shows the corresponding time series plot. The time series plot does not indicate any long-term trend in sales. In fact, unless you look carefully at the data, you might conclude that the data follow a horizontal pattern. But closer inspection of the time series plot reveals a regular pattern in the data. That is, the first and third quarters have moderate sales, the second quarter has the highest sales, and the fourth quarter tends to have the lowest sales volume. Thus, we would conclude that a quarterly seasonal pattern is present.

Trend and Seasonal Pattern

Some time series include a combination of a trend and seasonal pattern. For instance, the data in Table 15.6 and the corresponding time series plot in Figure 15.6 show television set sales for a particular manufacturer over the past four years. Clearly, an increasing trend is present. But Figure 15.6 also indicates that sales are lowest in the second quarter of each year and increase in quarters 3 and 4. Thus, we conclude that a seasonal pattern also exists for television set sales. In such cases we need to use a forecasting method that has the capability to deal with both trend and seasonality.

TABLE 15.5   UMBRELLA SALES TIME SERIES

Umbrella

Year	Quarter	Sales
1	1	125
	2	153
	3	106
	4	88
2	1	118
	2	161
	3	133
	4	102
3	1	138
	2	144
	3	113
	4	80
4	1	109
	2	137
	3	125
	4	109
5	1	130
	2	165
	3	128
	4	96

FIGURE 15.5   UMBRELLA SALES TIME SERIES PLOT

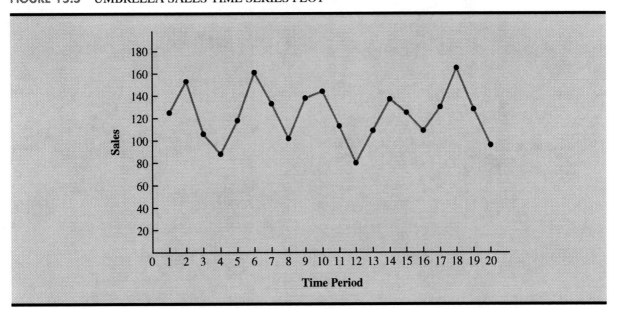

TABLE 15.6   QUARTERLY TELEVISION SET SALES TIME SERIES

TVSales

Year	Quarter	Sales (1000s)
1	1	4.8
	2	4.1
	3	6.0
	4	6.5
2	1	5.8
	2	5.2
	3	6.8
	4	7.4
3	1	6.0
	2	5.6
	3	7.5
	4	7.8
4	1	6.3
	2	5.9
	3	8.0
	4	8.4

FIGURE 15.6   QUARTERLY TELEVISION SET SALES TIME SERIES PLOT

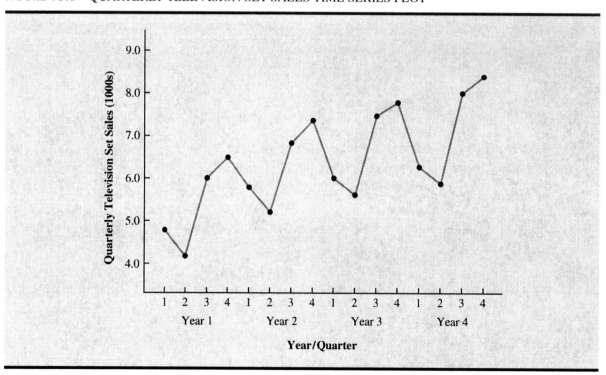

Cyclical Pattern

A cyclical pattern exists if the time series plot shows an alternating sequence of points below and above the trend line lasting more than one year. Many economic time series exhibit cyclical behavior with regular runs of observations below and above the trend line. Often, the cyclical component of a time series is due to multiyear business cycles. For example, periods of moderate inflation followed by periods of rapid inflation can lead to time series that alternate below and above a generally increasing trend line (e.g., a time series for housing costs). Business cycles are extremely difficult, if not impossible, to forecast. As a result, cyclical effects are often combined with long-term trend effects and referred to as trend-cycle effects. In this chapter we do not deal with cyclical effects that may be present in the time series.

Selecting a Forecasting Method

The underlying pattern in the time series is an important factor in selecting a forecasting method. Thus, a time series plot should be one of the first things developed when trying to determine which forecasting method to use. If we see a horizontal pattern, then we need to select a method appropriate for this type of pattern. Similarly, if we observe a trend in the data, then we need to use a forecasting method that has the capability to handle trends effectively. The next two sections illustrate methods that can be used in situations where the underlying pattern is horizontal; in other words, no trend or seasonal effects are present. We then consider methods appropriate when trend and or seasonality are present in the data.

15.2   FORECAST ACCURACY

In this section we begin by developing forecasts for the gasoline time series shown in Table 15.1, using the simplest of all the forecasting methods, an approach that uses the most recent week's sales volume as the forecast for the next week. For instance, the distributor sold 17 thousand gallons of gasoline in week 1; this value is used as the forecast for week 2. Next, we use 21, the actual value of sales in week 2, as the forecast for week 3, and so on. The forecasts obtained for the historical data using this method are shown in Table 15.7 in the column labeled Forecast. Because of its simplicity, this method is often referred to as a naïve forecasting method.

How accurate are the forecasts obtained using this naïve forecasting method? To answer this question, we will introduce several measures of forecast accuracy. These measures are used to determine how well a particular forecasting method is able to reproduce the time series data that are already available. By selecting the method that has the best accuracy for the data already known, we hope to increase the likelihood that we will obtain better forecasts for future time periods.

The key concept associated with measuring forecast accuracy is forecast error, defined as follows:

$$\text{Forecast Error} = \text{Actual Value} - \text{Forecast}$$

For instance, because the distributor actually sold 21 thousand gallons of gasoline in week 2 and the forecast, using the sales volume in week 1, was 17 thousand gallons, the forecast error in week 2 is

$$\text{Forecast Error in week 2} = 21 - 17 = 4$$

TABLE 15.7   COMPUTING FORECASTS AND MEASURES OF FORECAST ACCURACY
USING THE MOST RECENT VALUE AS THE FORECAST FOR THE
NEXT PERIOD

Week	Time Series Value	Forecast	Forecast Error	Absolute Value of Forecast Error	Squared Forecast Error	Percentage Error	Absolute Value of Percentage Error
1	17						
2	21	17	4	4	16	19.05	19.05
3	19	21	−2	2	4	−10.53	10.53
4	23	19	4	4	16	17.39	17.39
5	18	23	−5	5	25	−27.78	27.78
6	16	18	−2	2	4	−12.50	12.50
7	20	16	4	4	16	20.00	20.00
8	18	20	−2	2	4	−11.11	11.11
9	22	18	4	4	16	18.18	18.18
10	20	22	−2	2	4	−10.00	10.00
11	15	20	−5	5	25	−33.33	33.33
12	22	15	7	7	49	31.82	31.82
		Totals	5	41	179	1.19	211.69

The fact that the forecast error is positive indicates that in week 2 the forecasting method underestimated the actual value of sales. Next, we use 21, the actual value of sales in week 2, as the forecast for week 3. Because the actual value of sales in week 3 is 19, the forecast error for week 3 is 19 − 21 = −2. In this case the negative forecast error indicates that in week 3 the forecast overestimated the actual value. Thus, the forecast error may be positive or negative, depending on whether the forecast is too low or too high. A complete summary of the forecast errors for this naïve forecasting method is shown in Table 15.7 in the column labeled Forecast Error.

A simple measure of forecast accuracy is the mean or average of the forecast errors. Table 15.7 shows that the sum of the forecast errors for the gasoline sales time series is 5; thus, the mean or average error is 5/11 = 0.45. Note that although the gasoline time series consists of 12 values, to compute the mean error we divided the sum of the forecast errors by 11 because there are only 11 forecast errors. Because the mean forecast error is positive, the method is under-forecasting; in other words, the observed values tend to be greater than the forecasted values. Because positive and negative forecast errors tend to offset one another, the mean error is likely to be small; thus, the mean error is not a very useful measure of forecast accuracy.

The mean absolute error, denoted MAE, is a measure of forecast accuracy that avoids the problem of positive and negative forecast errors offsetting one another. As you might expect given its name, MAE is the average of the absolute values of the forecast errors. Table 15.7 shows that the sum of the absolute values of the forecast errors is 41; thus

$$\text{MAE} = \text{average of the absolute value of forecast errors} = \frac{41}{11} = 3.73$$

Another measure that avoids the problem of positive and negative errors offsetting each other is obtained by computing the average of the squared forecast errors. This measure of forecast accuracy, referred to as the mean squared error, is denoted MSE. From Table 15.7, the sum of the squared errors is 179; hence,

$$\text{MSE} = \text{average of the sum of squared forecast errors} = \frac{179}{11} = 16.27$$

The size of MAE and MSE depend upon the scale of the data. As a result it is difficult to make comparisons for different time intervals, such as comparing a method of forecasting monthly gasoline sales to a method of forecasting weekly sales, or to make comparisons across different time series. To make comparisons like these, we need to work with relative or percentage error measures. The mean absolute percentage error, denoted MAPE, is such a measure. To compute MAPE, we must first compute the percentage error for each forecast. For example, the percentage error corresponding to the forecast of 17 in week 2 is computed by dividing the forecast error in week 2 by the actual value in week 2 and multiplying the result by 100. For week 2 the percentage error is computed as follows:

$$\text{Percentage error for week 2} = \frac{4}{21}(100) = 19.05\%$$

Thus, the forecast error for week 2 is 19.05% of the observed value in week 2. A complete summary of the percentage errors is shown in Table 15.7 in the column labeled Percentage Error. In the next column, we show the absolute value of the percentage error.

Table 15.7 shows that the sum of the absolute values of the percentage errors is 211.69; thus

$$\text{MAPE} = \text{average of the absolute value of percentage}$$
$$\text{forecast errors} = \frac{211.69}{11} = 19.24\%$$

Summarizing, using the naïve (most recent observation) forecasting method, we obtained the following measures of forecast accuracy:

$$\text{MAE} = 3.73$$
$$\text{MSE} = 16.27$$
$$\text{MAPE} = 19.24\%$$

These measures of forecast accuracy simply measure how well the forecasting method is able to forecast historical values of the time series. Now, suppose we want to forecast sales for a future time period, such as week 13. In this case the forecast for week 13 is 22, the actual value of the time series in week 12. Is this an accurate estimate of sales for week 13? Unfortunately, there is no way to address the issue of accuracy associated with forecasts for future time periods. However, if we select a forecasting method that works well for the historical data and we think that the historical pattern will continue into the future, we should obtain results that will ultimately be shown to be good.

Before closing this section, let us consider another method for forecasting the gasoline sales time series in Table 15.1. Suppose we use the average of all the historical data available as the forecast for the next period. We begin by developing a forecast for week 2. Because there is only one historical value available prior to week 2, the forecast for week 2 is just the time series value in week 1; thus, the forecast for week 2 is 17 thousand gallons of gasoline. To compute the forecast for week 3, we take the average of the sales values in weeks 1 and 2. Thus,

$$\text{Forecast for week 3} = \frac{17 + 21}{2} = 19$$

Similarly, the forecast for week 4 is

$$\text{Forecast for week 4} = \frac{17 + 21 + 19}{3} = 19$$

The forecasts obtained using this method for the gasoline time series are shown in Table 15.8 in the column labeled Forecast. Using the results shown in Table 15.8, we obtained the following values of MAE, MSE, and MAPE:

$$\text{MAE} = \frac{26.81}{11} = 2.44$$

$$\text{MSE} = \frac{89.07}{11} = 8.10$$

$$\text{MAPE} = \frac{141.34}{11} = 12.85\%$$

We can now compare the accuracy of the two forecasting methods we have considered in this section by comparing the values of MAE, MSE, and MAPE for each method.

	Naïve Method	**Average of Past Values**
MAE	3.73	2.44
MSE	16.27	8.10
MAPE	19.24%	12.85%

For every measure, the average of past values provides more accurate forecasts than using the most recent observation as the forecast for the next period. In general, if the underlying time series is stationary, the average of all the historical data will always provide the best results.

TABLE 15.8   COMPUTING FORECASTS AND MEASURES OF FORECAST ACCURACY USING THE AVERAGE OF ALL THE HISTORICAL DATA AS THE FORECAST FOR THE NEXT PERIOD

Week	Time Series Value	Forecast	Forecast Error	Absolute Value of Forecast Error	Squared Forecast Error	Percentage Error	Absolute Value of Percentage Error
1	17						
2	21	17.00	4.00	4.00	16.00	19.05	19.05
3	19	19.00	0.00	0.00	0.00	0.00	0.00
4	23	19.00	4.00	4.00	16.00	17.39	17.39
5	18	20.00	−2.00	2.00	4.00	−11.11	11.11
6	16	19.60	−3.60	3.60	12.96	−22.50	22.50
7	20	19.00	1.00	1.00	1.00	5.00	5.00
8	18	19.14	−1.14	1.14	1.31	−6.35	6.35
9	22	19.00	3.00	3.00	9.00	13.64	13.64
10	20	19.33	0.67	0.67	0.44	3.33	3.33
11	15	19.40	−4.40	4.40	19.36	−29.33	29.33
12	22	19.00	3.00	3.00	9.00	13.64	13.64
		Totals	4.52	26.81	89.07	2.75	141.34

But suppose that the underlying time series is not stationary. In Section 15.1 we mentioned that changes in business conditions can often result in a time series that has a horizontal pattern shifting to a new level. We discussed a situation in which the gasoline distributor signed a contract with the Vermont Sate Police to provide gasoline for state police cars located in southern Vermont. Table 15.2 shows the number of gallons of gasoline sold for the original time series and the 10 weeks after signing the new contract, and Figure 15.2 shows the corresponding time series plot. Note the change in level in week 13 for the resulting time series. When a shift to a new level like this occurs, it takes a long time for the forecasting method that uses the average of all the historical data to adjust to the new level of the time series. But in this case the simple naïve method adjusts very rapidly to the change in level because it uses the most recent observation available as the forecast.

Measures of forecast accuracy are important factors in comparing different forecasting methods; but we have to be careful to not rely upon them too heavily. Good judgment and knowledge about business conditions that might affect the forecast also have to be carefully considered when selecting a method. In addition, historical forecast accuracy is not the only consideration, especially if the time series is likely to change in the future.

In the next section we will introduce more sophisticated methods for developing forecasts for a time series that exhibits a horizontal pattern. Using the measures of forecast accuracy developed here, we will be able to determine whether such methods provide more accurate forecasts than we obtained using the simple approaches illustrated in this section. The methods that we will introduce also have the advantage that they adapt well in situations where the time series changes to a new level. The ability of a forecasting method to adapt quickly to changes in level is an important consideration, especially in short-term forecasting situations.

15.3 MOVING AVERAGES AND EXPONENTIAL SMOOTHING

In this section we discuss three forecasting methods that are appropriate for a time series with a horizontal pattern: moving averages, weighted moving averages, and exponential smoothing. These methods also adapt well to changes in the level of a horizontal pattern such as what we saw with the extended gasoline sales time series (Table 15.2 and Figure 15.2). However, without modification they are not appropriate when significant trend, cyclical, or seasonal effects are present. Because the objective of each of these methods is to "smooth out" the random fluctuations in the time series, they are referred to as smoothing methods. These methods are easy to use and generally provide a high level of accuracy for short-range forecasts, such as a forecast for the next time period.

Moving Averages

The moving averages method uses the average of the most recent k data values in the time series as the forecast for the next period. Mathematically, a moving average forecast of order k is as follows:

$$F_{t+1} = \frac{\sum(\text{most recent } k \text{ data values})}{k} = \frac{Y_1 + Y_{t-1} + \cdots + Y_{t-k+1}}{k} \qquad (15.1)$$

where

$$F_{t+1} = \text{forecast of the time series for period } t + 1$$

The term *moving* is used because every time a new observation becomes available for the time series, it replaces the oldest observation in the equation and a new average is computed. As a result, the average will change, or move, as new observations become available.

To illustrate the moving averages method, let us return to the gasoline sales data in Table 15.1 and Figure 15.1. The time series plot in Figure 15.1 indicates that the gasoline sales time series has a horizontal pattern. Thus, the smoothing methods of this section are applicable.

To use moving averages to forecast a time series, we must first select the order, or number of time series values, to be included in the moving average. If only the most recent values of the time series are considered relevant, a small value of k is preferred. If more past values are considered relevant, then a larger value of k is better. As mentioned earlier, a time series with a horizontal pattern can shift to a new level over time. A moving average will adapt to the new level of the series and resume providing good forecasts in k periods. Thus, a smaller value of k will track shifts in a time series more quickly. But larger values of k will be more effective in smoothing out the random fluctuations over time. So managerial judgment based on an understanding of the behavior of a time series is helpful in choosing a good value for k.

To illustrate how moving averages can be used to forecast gasoline sales, we will use a three-week moving average ($k = 3$). We begin by computing the forecast of sales in week 4 using the average of the time series values in weeks 1–3.

$$F_4 = \text{average of weeks } 1\text{–}3 = \frac{17 + 21 + 19}{3} = 19$$

Thus, the moving average forecast of sales in week 4 is 19, or 19,000 gallons of gasoline. Because the actual value observed in week 4 is 23, the forecast error in week 4 is $23 - 19 = 4$.

Next, we compute the forecast of sales in week 5 by averaging the time series values in weeks 2–4.

$$F_5 = \text{average of weeks } 2\text{–}4 = \frac{21 + 19 + 23}{3} = 21$$

Hence, the forecast of sales in week 5 is 21 and the error associated with this forecast is $18 - 21 = -3$. A complete summary of the three-week moving average forecasts for the gasoline sales time series is provided in Table 15.9. Figure 15.7 shows the original time series plot and the three-week moving average forecasts. Note how the graph of the moving average forecasts has tended to smooth out the random fluctuations in the time series.

To forecast sales in week 13, the next time period in the future, we simply compute the average of the time series values in weeks 10, 11, and 12.

$$F_{13} = \text{average of weeks } 10\text{–}12 = \frac{20 + 15 + 22}{3} = 19$$

Thus, the forecast for week 13 is 19, or 19,000 gallons of gasoline.

Forecast Accuracy   In Section 15.2 we discussed three measures of forecast accuracy: mean absolute error (MAE), mean squared error (MSE), and mean absolute percentage error (MAPE). Using the three-week moving average calculations in Table 15.9, the values for these three measures of forecast accuracy are

TABLE 15.9 SUMMARY OF THREE-WEEK MOVING AVERAGE CALCULATIONS

Week	Time Series Value	Forecast	Forecast Error	Absolute Value of Forecast Error	Squared Forecast Error	Percentage Error	Absolute Value of Percentage Error
1	17						
2	21						
3	19						
4	23	19	4	4	16	17.39	17.39
5	18	21	−3	3	9	−16.67	16.67
6	16	20	−4	4	16	−25.00	25.00
7	20	19	1	1	1	5.00	5.00
8	18	18	0	0	0	0.00	0.00
9	22	18	4	4	16	18.18	18.18
10	20	20	0	0	0	0.00	0.00
11	15	20	−5	5	25	−33.33	33.33
12	22	19	3	3	9	13.64	13.64
		Totals	0	24	92	−20.79	129.21

FIGURE 15.7 GASOLINE SALES TIME SERIES PLOT AND THREE-WEEK MOVING AERAGE FORECASTS

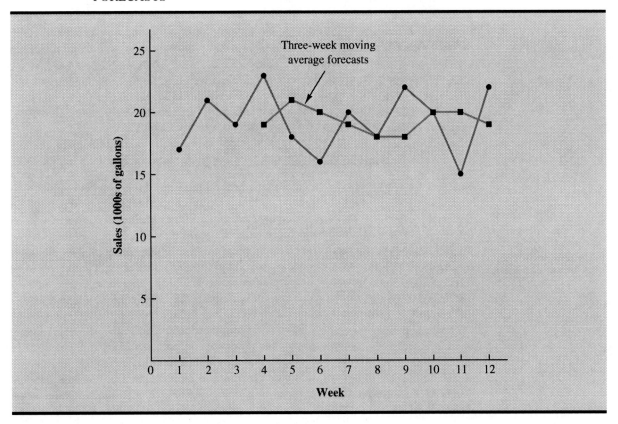

$$MAE = \frac{24}{9} = 2.67$$

$$MSE = \frac{92}{9} = 10.22$$

$$MAPE = \frac{129.21}{9} = 14.36\%$$

In situations where you need to compare forecasting methods for different time periods, such as comparing a forecast of weekly sales to a forecast of monthly sales, relative measures such as MAPE are preferred.

In Section 15.2 we showed that using the most recent observation as the forecast for the next week (a moving average of order $k = 1$) resulted in values of MAE = 3.73; MSE = 16.27; and MAPE = 19.24%. Thus, in each case the three-week moving average approach provided more accurate forecasts than simply using the most recent observation as the forecast.

To determine whether a moving average with a different order k can provide more accurate forecasts, we recommend using trial and error to determine the value of k that minimizes MSE. For the gasoline sales time series, it can be shown that the minimum value of MSE corresponds to a moving average of order $k = 6$ with MSE = 6.79. If we are willing to assume that the order of the moving average that is best for the historical data will also be best for future values of the time series, the most accurate moving average forecasts of gasoline sales can be obtained using a moving average of order $k = 6$.

Weighted Moving Averages

In the moving averages method, each observation in the moving average calculation receives the same weight. One variation, known as weighted moving averages, involves selecting a different weight for each data value and then computing a weighted average of the most recent k values as the forecast. In most cases, the most recent observation receives the most weight, and the weight decreases for older data values. Let us use the gasoline sales time series to illustrate the computation of a weighted three-week moving average. We assign a weight of $\frac{3}{6}$ to the most recent observation, a weight of $\frac{2}{6}$ to the second most recent observation, and a weight of $\frac{1}{6}$ to the third most recent observation. Using this weighted average, our forecast for week 4 is computed as follows:

Forecast for week 4 = $\frac{1}{6}(17) + \frac{2}{6}(21) + \frac{3}{6}(19) = 19.33$

Note that for the weighted moving average method the sum of the weights is equal to 1.

A moving average forecast of order $k = 3$ is just a special case of the weighted moving averages method in which each weight is equal to $\frac{1}{3}$.

Forecast Accuracy   To use the weighted moving averages method, we must first select the number of data values to be included in the weighted moving average and then choose weights for each of the data values. In general, if we believe that the recent past is a better predictor of the future than the distant past, larger weights should be given to the more recent observations. However, when the time series is highly variable, selecting approximately equal weights for the data values may be best. The only requirements in selecting the weights are that they be nonnegative and that their sum must equal 1. To determine whether one particular combination of number of data values and weights provides a more accurate forecast than another combination, we recommend using MSE as the measure of forecast accuracy. That is, if we assume that the combination that is best for the past will also be best for the future, we would use the combination of the number of data values and weights that minimized MSE for the historical time series to forecast the next value in the time series.

Exponential Smoothing

There are a number of exponential smoothing procedures. Because it has a single smoothing constant α, the method presented here is often referred to as single exponential smoothing.

Exponential smoothing also uses a weighted average of past time series values as a forecast; it is a special case of the weighted moving averages method in which we select only one weight—the weight for the most recent observation. The weights for the other data values are computed automatically and become smaller as the observations move farther into the past. The exponential smoothing model follows:

$$F_{t+1} = \alpha Y_t + (1 - \alpha)F_t \qquad (15.2)$$

where

$$F_{t+1} = \text{forecast of the time series for period } t + 1$$
$$Y_t = \text{actual value of the time series in period } t$$
$$F_t = \text{forecast of the time series for period } t$$
$$\alpha = \text{smoothing constant } (0 \leq \alpha \leq 1)$$

Equation (15.2) shows that the forecast for period $t + 1$ is a weighted average of the actual value in period t and the forecast for period t. The weight given to the actual value in period t is the smoothing constant α and the weight given to the forecast in period t is $1 - \alpha$. It turns out that the exponential smoothing forecast for any period is actually a weighted average of *all the previous actual values* of the time series. Let us illustrate by working with a time series involving only three periods of data: Y_1, Y_2, and Y_3.

To initiate the calculations, we let F_1 equal the actual value of the time series in period 1; that is, $F_1 = Y_1$. Hence, the forecast for period 2 is

$$F_2 = \alpha Y_1 + (1 - \alpha)F_1$$
$$= \alpha Y_1 + (1 - \alpha)Y_1$$
$$= Y_1$$

We see that the exponential smoothing forecast for period 2 is equal to the actual value of the time series in period 1.

The forecast for period 3 is

$$F_3 = \alpha Y_2 + (1-\alpha)F_2 = \alpha Y_2 + (1-\alpha)Y_1$$

Finally, substituting this expression for F_3 into the expression for F_4, we obtain

$$F_4 = \alpha Y_3 + (1-\alpha)F_3$$
$$= \alpha Y_3 + (1-\alpha)[\alpha Y_2 + (1-\alpha)Y_1]$$
$$= \alpha Y_3 + \alpha(1-\alpha)Y_2 + (1-\alpha)^2 Y_1$$

The term exponential smoothing comes from the exponential nature of the weighting scheme for the historical values.

We now see that F_4 is a weighted average of the first three time series values. The sum of the coefficients, or weights, for Y_1, Y_2, and Y_3 equals 1. A similar argument can be made to show that, in general, any forecast F_{t+1} is a weighted average of all the previous time series values.

Despite the fact that exponential smoothing provides a forecast that is a weighted average of all past observations, all past data do not need to be saved to compute the forecast for the next period. In fact, Equation (15.2) shows that once the value for the smoothing constant α is selected, only two pieces of information are needed to compute the forecast: Y_t, the actual value of the time series in period t; and F_t, the forecast for period t.

To illustrate the exponential smoothing approach to forecasting, let us again consider the gasoline sales time series in Table 15.1 and Figure 15.2. As indicated previously, to start the calculations we set the exponential smoothing forecast for period 2 equal to the actual value of the time series in period 1. Thus, with $Y_1 = 17$, we set $F_2 = 17$ to initiate the computations. Referring to the time series data in Table 15.1, we find an actual time series value in period 2 of $Y_2 = 21$. Thus, period 2 has a forecast error of $21 - 17 = 4$.

Continuing with the exponential smoothing computations using a smoothing constant of $\alpha = 0.2$, we obtain the following forecast for period 3:

$$F_3 = 0.2Y_2 + 0.8F_2 = 0.2(21) + 0.8(17) = 17.8$$

Once the actual time series value in period 3, $Y_3 = 19$, is known, we can generate a forecast for period 4 as follows:

$$F_4 = 0.2Y_3 + 0.8F_3 = 0.2(19) + 0.8(17.8) = 18.04$$

Continuing the exponential smoothing calculations, we obtain the weekly forecast values shown in Table 15.10. Note that we have not shown an exponential smoothing forecast or a forecast error for week 1 because no forecast was made. For week 12, we have $Y_{12} = 22$ and $F_{12} = 18.48$. We can use this information to generate a forecast for week 13.

$$F_{13} = 0.2Y_{12} + 0.8F_{12} = 0.2(22) + 0.8(18.48) = 19.18$$

Thus, the exponential smoothing forecast of the amount sold in week 13 is 19.18, or 19,180 gallons of gasoline. With this forecast, the firm can make plans and decisions accordingly.

TABLE 15.10   SUMMARY OF THE EXPONENTIAL SMOOTHING FORECASTS AND FORECAST ERRORS FOR THE GASOLINE SALES TIME SERIES WITH SMOOTHING CONSTANT $\alpha = 0.2$

Week	Time Series Value	Forecast	Forecast Error	Squared Forecast Error
1	17			
2	21	17.00	4.00	16.00
3	19	17.80	1.20	1.44
4	23	18.04	4.96	24.60
5	18	19.03	−1.03	1.06
6	16	18.83	−2.83	8.01
7	20	18.26	1.74	3.03
8	18	18.61	−0.61	0.37
9	22	18.49	3.51	12.32
10	20	19.19	0.81	0.66
11	15	19.35	−4.35	18.92
12	22	18.48	3.52	12.39
		Totals	10.92	98.80

FIGURE 15.8 ACTUAL AND FORECAST GASOLINE TIME SERIES WITH SMOOTHING CONSTANT $\alpha = 0.2$

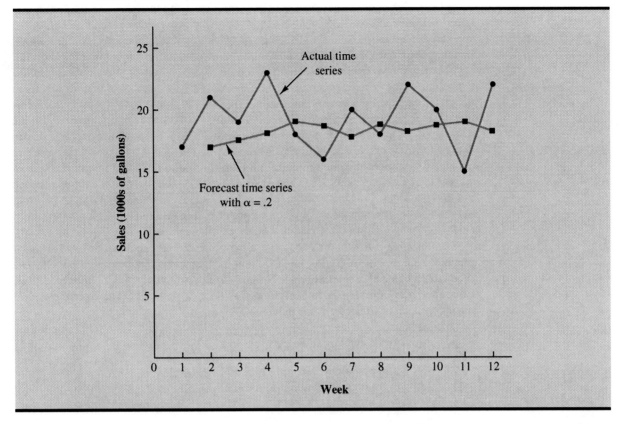

Figure 15.8 shows the time series plot of the actual and forecast time series values. Note in particular how the forecasts "smooth out" the irregular or random fluctuations in the time series.

Forecast Accuracy In the preceding exponential smoothing calculations, we used a smoothing constant of $\alpha = 0.2$. Although any value of α between 0 and 1 is acceptable, some values will yield better forecasts than others. Insight into choosing a good value for α can be obtained by rewriting the basic exponential smoothing model as follows:

$$F_{t+1} = \alpha Y_t + (1 - \alpha)F_t$$
$$F_{t+1} = \alpha Y_t + F_t - \alpha F_t$$
$$F_{t+1} = F_t + \alpha(Y_t - F_t) \qquad (15.3)$$

Thus, the new forecast F_{t+1} is equal to the previous forecast F_t plus an adjustment, which is the smoothing constant α times the most recent forecast error, $Y_t - F_t$. That is, the forecast in period $t + 1$ is obtained by adjusting the forecast in period t by a fraction of the forecast error. If the time series contains substantial random variability, a small value of the smoothing constant is preferred. The reason for this choice is that if much of the forecast error is due to random variability, we do not want to overreact and adjust the forecasts too quickly. For a time series with relatively little random variability, forecast errors are more likely to represent a change in the level of the series. Thus, larger values of the smoothing constant provide the advantage of quickly adjusting the forecasts; this allows the forecasts to react more quickly to changing conditions.

The criterion we will use to determine a desirable value for the smoothing constant α is the same as the criterion we proposed for determining the number of periods of data to include in the moving averages calculation. That is, we choose the value of α that minimizes the mean squared error (MSE). A summary of the MSE calculations for the exponential smoothing forecast of gasoline sales with $\alpha = 0.2$ is shown in Table 15.10. Note that there is one less squared error term than the number of time periods because we had no past values with which to make a forecast for period 1. The value of the sum of squared forecast errors is 98.80; hence MSE = 98.80/11 = 8.98. Would a different value of α provide better results in terms of a lower MSE value? Determining the value of α that minimizes MSE is a nonlinear optimization problem, as discussed in Chapter 8 (see Problem 8.12). These types of optimization models are often referred to as *curve-fitting* models.

The objective is to minimize the sum of the squared error (note that this is equivalent to minimizing MSE), subject to the smoothing parameter requirement, $0 \leq \alpha \leq 1$. The smoothing parameter α is treated as a variable in the optimization model. In addition, we define a set of variables F_t, the forecast for period t, for $t = 1, \ldots, 12$. The objective of minimizing the sum of squared error is then

$$
\begin{aligned}
\text{Minimize } \{ & (21 - F_2)^2 + (19 - F_3)^2 + (23 - F_4)^2 + (18 - F_5)^2 + (16 - F_6)^2 \\
& + (20 - F_7)^2 + (18 - F_8)^2 + (22 - F_9)^2 + (20 - F_{10})^2 \\
& + (15 - F_{11})^2 + (22 - F_{12})^2 \}
\end{aligned}
$$

The first set of constraints defines the forecasts as a function of observed and forecasted values as defined by equation (15.2). Recall that we set the forecast in period 1 to the observed time series value in period 1:

$$
\begin{aligned}
F_1 &= 17 \\
F_2 &= \alpha 17 + (1-\alpha)F_1 \\
F_3 &= \alpha 21 + (1-\alpha)F_2 \\
F_4 &= \alpha 19 + (1-\alpha)F_3 \\
F_5 &= \alpha 23 + (1-\alpha)F_4 \\
F_6 &= \alpha 18 + (1-\alpha)F_5 \\
F_7 &= \alpha 16 + (1-\alpha)F_6 \\
F_8 &= \alpha 20 + (1-\alpha)F_7 \\
F_9 &= \alpha 18 + (1-\alpha)F_8 \\
F_{10} &= \alpha 22 + (1-\alpha)F_9 \\
F_{11} &= \alpha 20 + (1-\alpha)F_{10} \\
F_{12} &= \alpha 15 + (1-\alpha)F_{11}
\end{aligned}
$$

Finally, the value of α is restricted to

$$
0 \leq \alpha \leq 1
$$

The complete nonlinear curve-fitting optimization model is:

$$\text{Minimize } \{(21 - F_2)^2 + (19 - F_3)^2 + (23 - F_4)^2 + (18 - F_5)^2 + (16 - F_6)^2$$
$$+ (20 - F_7)^2 + (18 - F_8)^2 + (22 - F_9)^2 + (20 - F_{10})^2$$
$$+ (15 - F_{11})^2 + (22 - F_{12})^2\}$$

s.t.

$$F_1 = 17$$
$$F_2 = \alpha 17 + (1-\alpha)F_1$$
$$F_3 = \alpha 21 + (1-\alpha)F_2$$
$$F_4 = \alpha 19 + (1-\alpha)F_3$$
$$F_5 = \alpha 23 + (1-\alpha)F_4$$
$$F_6 = \alpha 18 + (1-\alpha)F_5$$
$$F_7 = \alpha 16 + (1-\alpha)F_6$$
$$F_8 = \alpha 20 + (1-\alpha)F_7$$
$$F_9 = \alpha 18 + (1-\alpha)F_8$$
$$F_{10} = \alpha 22 + (1-\alpha)F_9$$
$$F_{11} = \alpha 20 + (1-\alpha)F_{10}$$
$$F_{12} = \alpha 15 + (1-\alpha)F_{11}$$
$$0 \leq \alpha \leq 1$$

Gasoline_ES

We may use Excel Solver or LINGO to solve for the best value of α. The optimal value of $\alpha = 0.17439$ with a sum of squared error of 98.56 and an MSE of 98.56/11 = 8.96. So, our initial value of $\alpha = .2$ is very close to the best we can do to minimize MSE. It will not always be the case that our guess will be so close to optimal, so we recommend you solve the nonlinear optimization for the best value of α.

The general optimization problem for exponential smoothing with n time periods and observed values Y_t is

$$\text{Min} \sum_{t=2}^{n} (Y_t - F_t)^2 \qquad\qquad (15.4)$$

s.t.

$$F_t = \alpha Y_{t-1} + (1 - \alpha)F_{t-1} \qquad t = 2, 3, \ldots, n \qquad (15.5)$$

$$F_1 = Y_1 \qquad\qquad (15.6)$$

$$0 \leq \alpha \leq 1 \qquad\qquad (15.7)$$

The objective function (equation 15.4) is to minimize the sum of the squared errors. As in Table 15.10, we have errors (observed data – forecast) only for time periods 2 through n, and we initialize F_1 to Y_1. The optimal value of α can be used in the exponential smoothing model to provide forecasts for the future. At a later date, after new time series observations are obtained, we may analyze the newly collected time series data to determine whether the smoothing constant should be revised to provide better forecasting results. Revised forecasts may be obtained by solving the model in (15.4)–(15.7), including any new observations.

NOTES AND COMMENTS

1. Spreadsheet packages are an effective tool for implementing exponential smoothing. With the time series data and the forecasting formulas in a spreadsheet as shown in Table 15.10, you can solve the nonlinear model described by equations (15.4)–(15.7) using Solver. Notice that in equation set (15.5) each forecast variable F_t is defined in terms of the smoothing parameter α and the previous periods forecast variable. Thus, these are what we have called definitional variables. In the Solver spreadsheet model, only α needs to be declared a decision variable. The forecast variables F_t are simply calculatons in the spreadsheet. We give details for doing this for the gasoline data in Appendix 15.1.

2. We presented the moving average and exponential smoothing methods in the context of a stationary time series. These methods can also be used to forecast a nonstationary time series which shifts in level, but exhibits no trend or seasonality. Moving averages with small values of k adapt more quickly than moving averages with larger values of k. Exponential smoothing models with smoothing constants closer to one adapt more quickly than models with smaller values of the smoothing constant.

15.4   TREND PROJECTION

We present two forecasting methods in this section that are appropriate for a time series exhibiting a trend pattern. First, we show how curve fitting may be used to forecast a time series with a linear trend. Second, we show how curve fitting can also be used to forecast time series with a curvilinear or nonlinear trend.

Linear Trend

In Section 15.1 we used the bicycle sales time series in Table 15.3 and Figure 15.3 to illustrate a time series with a trend pattern. Let us now use this time series to illustrate how curve fitting can be used to forecast a time series with a linear trend. The data for the bicycle time series are repeated in Table 15.11 and Figure 15.9.

Although the time series plot in Figure 15.9 shows some up and down movement over the past 10 years, we might agree that the linear trend line shown in Figure 15.10 provides

TABLE 15.11   BICYCLE SALES TIME SERIES

Bicycle

Year	Sales (1000s)
1	21.6
2	22.9
3	25.5
4	21.9
5	23.9
6	27.5
7	31.5
8	29.7
9	28.6
10	31.4

FIGURE 15.9 BICYCLE SALES TIME SERIES PLOT

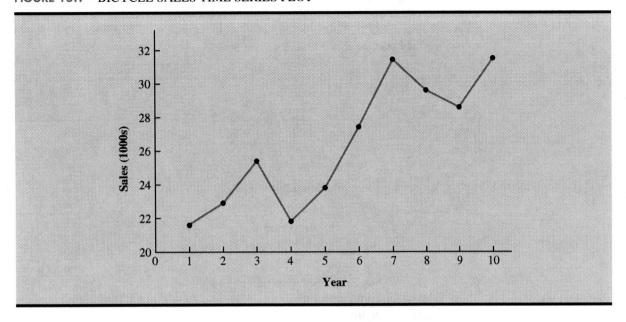

a reasonable approximation of the long-run movement in the series. We can use curve fitting to develop such a linear trend line for the bicycle sales time series.

Curve fitting can be used to find a best-fitting line to a set of data that exhibits a linear trend. The criterion used to determine the best-fitting line is one we used in the previous section. Curve fitting minimizes the sum of squared error between the observed and fitted time series data where the model is a trend line. We build a nonlinear optimization model

FIGURE 15.10 TREND REPRESENTED BY A LINEAR FUNCTION FOR THE BICYCLE SALES TIME SERIES

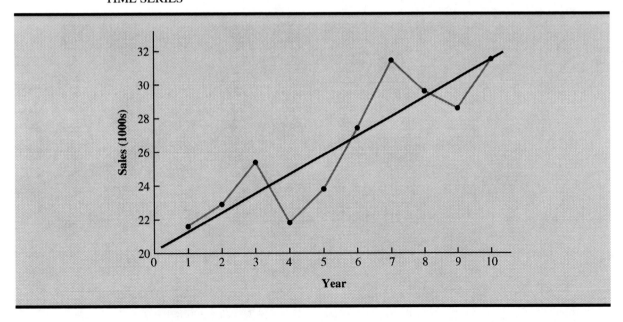

that is similar to the model we used to find the best value of α for exponential smoothing. In the case of a straight line $y = a + mx$, our objective is to find the best values of parameters a and m, so that the line provides forecasts that minimize sum of squared error. For estimating the linear trend in a time series, we will use the following notation for a line:

$$T_t = b_0 + b_1 t \qquad (15.8)$$

where

$$T_t = \text{linear trend forecast in period } t$$
$$b_0 = \text{the intercept of the linear trend line}$$
$$b_1 = \text{the slope of the linear trend line}$$
$$t = \text{the time period}$$

In equation (15.8), the time variable begins at $t = 1$ corresponding to the first time series observation (year 1 for the bicycle sales time series) and continues until $t = n$ corresponding to the most recent time series observation (year 10 for the bicycle sales time series). Thus, for the bicycle sales time series $t = 1$ corresponds to the oldest time series value and $t = 10$ corresponds to the most recent year.

Let us formulate the curve-fitting model that will give us the best values of b_0 and b_1 in equation (15.8) for the bicycle sales data. The objective is to minimize the sum of squared error between the observed values of the time series given in Table 15.11 and the forecasted values for each period:

$$\text{Min } \{(21.6 - T_1)^2 + (22.9 - T_2)^2 + (22.5 - T_3)^2 + (21.9 - T_4)^2 + (23.9 - T_5)^2$$
$$(27.5 - T_6)^2 + (31.5 - T_7)^2 + (29.7 - T_8)^2 + (28.6 - T_9)^2 + (31.4 - T_{10})^2\}$$

The only constraints then are to define the forecasts as a linear function of parameters b_0 and b_1 as described by equation (15.8):

$$T_1 = b_0 + b_1 1$$
$$T_2 = b_0 + b_1 2$$
$$T_3 = b_0 + b_1 3$$
$$T_4 = b_0 + b_1 4$$
$$T_5 = b_0 + b_1 5$$
$$T_6 = b_0 + b_1 6$$
$$T_7 = b_0 + b_1 7$$
$$T_8 = b_0 + b_1 8$$
$$T_9 = b_0 + b_1 9$$
$$T_{10} = b_0 + b_1 10$$

The entire nonlinear curve-fitting optimization model is:

$$\text{Min } \{(21.6 - T_1)^2 + (22.9 - T_2)^2 + (22.5 - T_3)^2 + (21.9 - T_4)^2 + (23.9 - T_5)^2$$
$$(27.5 - T_6)^2 + (31.5 - T_7)^2 + (29.7 - T_8)^2 + (28.6 - T_9)^2 + (31.4 - T_{10})^2\}$$

s.t.

$$T_1 = b_0 + b_1 1$$
$$T_2 = b_0 + b_1 2$$
$$T_3 = b_0 + b_1 3$$
$$T_4 = b_0 + b_1 4$$
$$T_5 = b_0 + b_1 5$$
$$T_6 = b_0 + b_1 6$$
$$T_7 = b_0 + b_1 7$$
$$T_8 = b_0 + b_1 8$$
$$T_9 = b_0 + b_1 9$$
$$T_{10} = b_0 + b_1 10$$

Bicycle_Linear

Note that b_0, b_1, and T_t are decision variables and that none are restricted to be nonnegative.

The solution to this problem may be obtained using Excel Solver or LINGO. The solution is $b_0 = 20.4$ and $b_1 = 1.1$ with a sum of squared error of 30.7. Therefore, the trend equation is

$$T_t = 20.4 + 1.1t$$

The slope of 1.1 indicates that over the past 10 years the firm experienced an average growth in sales of about 1100 units per year. If we assume that the past 10-year trend in sales is a good indicator of the future, this trend equation can be used to develop forecasts for future time periods. For example, substituting $t = 11$ into the equation yields next year's trend projection or forecast, T_{11}.

$$T_{11} = 20.4 + 1.1(11) = 32.5$$

Thus, using trend projection, we would forecast sales of 32,500 bicycles for year 11.

Table 15.12 shows the computation of the minimized sum of squared errors for the bicycle sales time series. As previously noted, minimizing sum of squared error also minimizes the commonly used measure of accuracy, mean squared error (MSE). For the bicycle sales time series

$$\text{MSE} = \frac{\sum_{t=1}^{n}(Y_t - F_t)^2}{n} = \frac{30.7}{10} = 3.07$$

We may write a general optimization curve-fitting model for linear trend curve fitting for a time series with n data points. Let Y_t = the observed value of the time series in period t. The general model is

$$\text{Min} \sum_{t=1}^{n}(Y_t - T_t)^2 \qquad\qquad (15.9)$$

s.t.

$$T_t = b_0 + b_1 t \qquad t = 1,2,3 \dots n \qquad\qquad (15.10)$$

TABLE 15.12　SUMMARY OF THE LINEAR TREND FORECASTS AND FORECAST ERRORS FOR THE BICYCLE SALES TIME SERIES

Week	Sales (1000s) Y_t	Forecast T_t	Forecast Error	Squared Forecast Error
1	21.6	21.5	0.1	0.01
2	22.9	22.6	0.3	0.09
3	25.5	23.7	1.8	3.24
4	21.9	24.8	−2.9	8.41
5	23.9	25.9	−2.0	4.00
6	27.5	27.0	0.5	0.25
7	31.5	28.1	3.4	11.56
8	29.7	29.2	0.5	0.25
9	28.6	30.3	−1.7	2.89
10	31.4	31.4	0.0	0.00
			Total	30.70

The decision variables in this optimization model are b_0 the intercept and b_1 the slope of the line. The variables T_t, the fitted forecast for period t, are definitional variables, as discussed in Chapter 5. Note that none of these are restricted to be nonnegative. This model will have $n + 2$ decision variables and n constraints, one for each data point in the time series.

NOTES AND COMMENTS

1. The optimization model given by equations (15.9) and (15.10) is easily generalized for other types of models. Given the objective is to minimize the sum of squared errors, to test a different forecasting model, you only need to change the form of equation (15.10). We will see an example of this in the forthcoming seciton on nonlinear trend. Examples of both LINGO and Excel Solver models are provided in the appendices to this chapter.

2. Statistical packages such as Minitab and SAS, as well as Excel have routines to perform curve fitting under the label regression analysis. Regression analysis solves the curve-fitting problem of minimizing the sum of squared error, but also under certain assumptions, allows the analyst to make statistical statements about the parameters and the forecasts.

Nonlinear Trend

The use of a linear function to model trend is common. However, as we discussed previously, sometimes time series have a curvilinear or nonlinear trend. As an example, consider the annual revenue in millions of dollars for a cholesterol drug for the first ten years of sales. Table 15.13 shows the time series and Figure 15.11 shows the corresponding time series plot. For instance, revenue in year 1 was $23.1 million; revenue in year 2 was $21.3 million; and so on. The time series plot indicates an overall increasing or upward trend. But, unlike the bicycle sales time series, a linear trend does not appear to be appropriate. Instead, a curvilinear function appears to be needed to model the long-term trend.

TABLE 15.13   CHOLESTEROL REVENUE TIME SERIES ($ MILLIONS)

Cholesterol

Year	Revenue ($ millions)
1	23.1
2	21.3
3	27.4
4	34.6
5	33.8
6	43.2
7	59.5
8	64.4
9	74.2
10	99.3

Quadratic Trend Equation   A variety of nonlinear functions can be used to develop an estimate of the trend for the cholesterol time series. For instance, consider the following quadratic trend equation:

$$T_t = b_0 + b_1 t + b_2 t^2 \qquad (15.11)$$

For the cholesterol time series, $t = 1$ corresponds to year 1, $t = 2$ corresponds to year 2, and so on.

Let us construct the optimization model to find the values of b_0, b_1, and b_2 that minimize the sum of squared errors. Note that we need the value of t and the value of t^2 for each period.

FIGURE 15.11   CHOLESTEROL REVENUE TIMES SERIES PLOT ($ MILLIONS)

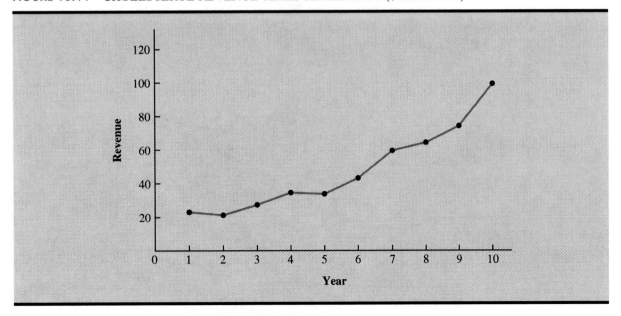

The model to find the best values of b_0, b_1, and b_2 so that the sum of squared error is minimized is as follows:

$$\text{Min } \{(23.1 - T_1)^2 + (21.3 - T_2)^2 + (27.4 - T_3)^2 + (34.6 - T_4)^2 + (33.8 - T_5)^2$$
$$(43.2 - T_6)^2 + (59.5 - T_7)^2 + (64.4 - T_8)^2 + (74.2 - T_9)^2 + (99.3 - T_{10})^2\}$$

s.t.

$$T_1 = b_0 + b_1 1 + b_2 1$$
$$T_2 = b_0 + b_1 2 + b_2 4$$
$$T_3 = b_0 + b_1 3 + b_2 9$$
$$T_4 = b_0 + b_1 4 + b_2 16$$
$$T_5 = b_0 + b_1 5 + b_2 25$$
$$T_6 = b_0 + b_1 6 + b_2 36$$
$$T_7 = b_0 + b_1 7 + b_2 49$$
$$T_8 = b_0 + b_1 8 + b_2 64$$
$$T_9 = b_0 + b_1 9 + b_2 81$$
$$T_{10} = b_0 + b_1 10 + b_2 100$$

WEB file

Cholesterol_Quad

This model may be solved with Excel Solver or LINGO. The optimal values from this optimization are $b_0 = 24.182$, $b_1 = -2.11$, and $b_2 = 0.922$ with a sum of squared errors of 110.65 and an MSE $= 110.65/10 = 11.065$. The fitted curve is therefore

$$T_t = 24.182 - 2.11 \, t + 0.922 \, t^2$$

Figure 15.12 shows the observed data along with this curve.

FIGURE 15.12   TIME SERIES QUADRATIC TREND FOR THE CHOLESTEROL SALES TIME SERIES

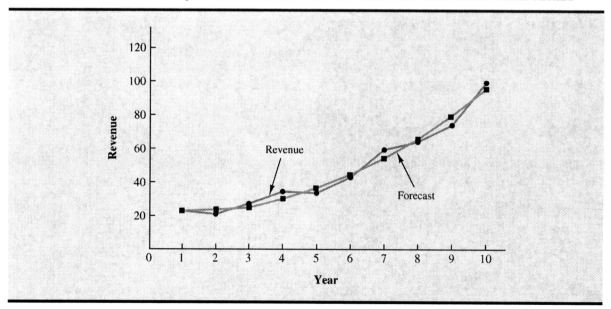

Exponential Trend Equation Another alternative that can be used to model the nonlinear pattern exhibited by the cholesterol time series is to fit an exponential model to the data. For instance, consider the following exponential growth trend equation:

$$T_t = b_0 (b_1)^t \qquad (15.12)$$

Like equation (15.11), this model is a nonlinear function of period t. As with the quadratic case, we can update equation (15.12) to yield the values of b_0 and b_1 that minimize the sum of squared errors. For the cholesterol sales data, minimizing the sum of squared errors yields the following curve-fitting model:

$$\text{Min } \{(23.1 - T_1)^2 + (21.3 - T_2)^2 + (27.4 - T_3)^2 + (34.6 - T_4)^2 + (33.8 - T_5)^2$$
$$(43.2 - T_6)^2 + (59.5 - T_7)^2 + (64.4 - T_8)^2 + (74.2 - T_9)^2 + (99.3 - T_{10})^2\}$$

s.t.

Cholesterol_Exp

$$T_1 = b_0 \, b_1{}^1$$
$$T_2 = b_0 \, b_1{}^2$$
$$T_3 = b_0 \, b_1{}^3$$
$$T_4 = b_0 \, b_1{}^4$$
$$T_5 = b_0 \, b_1{}^5$$
$$T_6 = b_0 \, b_1{}^6$$
$$T_7 = b_0 \, b_1{}^7$$
$$T_8 = b_0 \, b_1{}^8$$
$$T_9 = b_0 \, b_1{}^9$$
$$T_{10} = b_0 \, b_1{}^{10}$$

This may be solved with LINGO or Excel Solver. The optimal values are $b_0 = 15.42$ and $b_1 = 1.2$ with a sum of squared errors of 123.12 and an MSE = 123.12/10 = 12.312. Based on MSE, the quadratic model provides a better fit than the exponential model.

NOTES AND COMMENTS

The exponential model (15.12) is nonlinear and the curve-fitting optimization based on it can be difficult to solve. We suggest using a number of different starting values to ensure that the solution found is a global optimum. Also, we found it helpful to bound b_0 and b_1 away from zero (add constraints $b_0 \geq 0.01$ and $b_1 \geq 0.01$).

15.5 SEASONALITY

In this section we show how to develop forecasts for a time series that has a seasonal pattern. To the extent that seasonality exists, we need to incorporate it into our forecasting models to ensure accurate forecasts. We begin the section by considering a seasonal time series with no trend and then discuss how to model seasonality with trend.

Seasonality Without Trend

As an example, consider the number of umbrellas sold at a clothing store over the past five years. Table 15.14 shows the time series and Figure 15.13 shows the corresponding time series plot. The time series plot does not indicate any long-term trend in sales. In fact, unless you look carefully at the data, you might conclude that the data follow a horizontal pattern and that single exponential smoothing could be used to forecast sales. However, closer inspection of the time series plot reveals a pattern in the data. That is, the first and third quarters have moderate sales, the second quarter has the highest sales, and the fourth quarter tends to be the lowest quarter in terms of sales volume. Thus, we would conclude that a quarterly seasonal pattern is present.

We can model a time series with a seasonal pattern by treating the season as a *categorical variable*. Categorical variables are data used to categorize observations of data. When a categorical variable has k levels, $k - 1$ dummy or 0-1 variables are required. So, if there are four seasons, we need three dummy variables. For instance, in the umbrella sales time series the quarter each observation corresponds to is treated as a season; it is a categorical variable with four levels: Quarter 1, Quarter 2, Quarter 3, and Quarter 4. Thus, to model the seasonal effects in the umbrella time series we need $4 - 1 = 3$ dummy variables. The three dummy variables can be coded as follows:

$$\text{Qtr1} = \begin{cases} 1 \text{ if Quarter 1} \\ 0 \text{ otherwise} \end{cases} \quad \text{Qtr2} = \begin{cases} 1 \text{ if Quarter 2} \\ 0 \text{ otherwise} \end{cases} \quad \text{Qtr3} = \begin{cases} 1 \text{ if Quarter 3} \\ 0 \text{ otherwise} \end{cases}$$

Using F_t to denote the forecasted value of sales for period t, the general form of the equation relating the number of umbrellas sold to the quarter the sale takes place follows:

$$F_t = b_0 + b_1 \text{Qtr1}_t + b_2 \text{Qtr2}_t + b_3 \text{Qtr3}_t$$

TABLE 15.14   UMBRELLA SALES TIME SERIES

Umbrella

Year	Quarter	Sales
1	1	125
	2	153
	3	106
	4	88
2	1	118
	2	161
	3	133
	4	102
3	1	138
	2	144
	3	113
	4	80
4	1	109
	2	137
	3	125
	4	109
5	1	130
	2	165
	3	128
	4	96

FIGURE 15.13   UMBRELLA SALES TIME SERIES PLOT

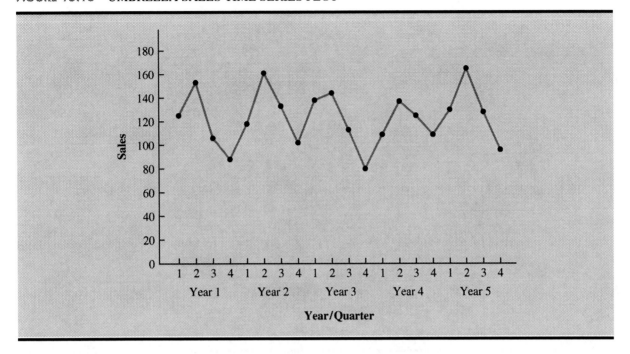

Table 15.15 is the umbrella sales time series with the coded values of the dummy variables shown. We may use an optimization model to find the values of b_0, b_1, b_2, and b_3 that minimize the sum of squared error. The model is as follows:

$$\text{Min } \{(125 - F_1)^2 + (153 - F_2)^2 + (106 - F_3)^2 \cdots + (96 - F_{20})^2\}$$

s.t.

$$F_1 = b_0 + 1b_1 + 0b_2 + 0b_3$$
$$F_2 = b_0 + 0b_1 + 1b_2 + 0b_3$$
$$F_3 = b_0 + 0b_1 + 0b_2 + 1b_3$$
$$F_4 = b_0 + 0b_1 + 0b_2 + 0b_3$$
$$\vdots$$
$$F_{17} = b_0 + 1b_1 + 0b_2 + 0b_3$$
$$F_{18} = b_0 + 0b_1 + 1b_2 + 0b_3$$
$$F_{19} = b_0 + 0b_1 + 0b_2 + 1b_3$$
$$F_{20} = b_0 + 0b_1 + 0b_2 + 0b_3$$

WEB file

Umbrella_Seas

Note that we have numbered the observations in Table 15.15 as periods 1–20. For example, year 3, quarter 3 is observation 11.

This model may be solved with LINGO or Excel Solver. Using the data in Table 15.15 and the above optimization model, we obtained the following equation:

$$F_t = 95.0 + 29.0 \, \text{Qtr1}_t + 57.0 \, \text{Qtr2}_t + 26.0 \, \text{Qtr3}_t \qquad (15.13)$$

TABLE 15.15   UMBRELLA SALES TIME SERIES WITH DUMMY VARIABLES

Period	Year	Quarter	Qtr1	Qtr2	Qtr3	Sales
1	1	1	1	0	0	125
2		2	0	1	0	153
3		3	0	0	1	106
4		4	0	0	0	88
5	2	1	1	0	0	118
6		2	0	1	0	161
7		3	0	0	1	133
8		4	0	0	0	102
9	3	1	1	0	0	138
10		2	0	1	0	144
11		3	0	0	1	113
12		4	0	0	0	80
13	4	1	1	0	0	109
14		2	0	1	0	137
15		3	0	0	1	125
16		4	0	0	0	109
17	5	1	1	0	0	130
18		2	0	1	0	165
19		3	0	0	1	128
20		4	0	0	0	96

We can use equation (15.13) to forecast quarterly sales for next year.

$$\text{Quarter 1: Sales} = 95.0 + 29.0(1) + 57.0(0) + 26.0(0) = 124$$
$$\text{Quarter 2: Sales} = 95.0 + 29.0(0) + 57.0(1) + 26.0(0) = 152$$
$$\text{Quarter 3: Sales} = 95.0 + 29.0(0) + 57.0(0) + 26.0(1) = 121$$
$$\text{Quarter 4: Sales} = 95.0 + 29.0(0) + 57.0(1) + 26.0(0) = 95$$

It is interesting to note that we could have obtained the quarterly forecasts for next year by simply computing the average number of umbrellas sold in each quarter, as shown in the following table:

Year	Quarter 1	Quarter 2	Quarter 3	Quarter 4
1	125	153	106	88
2	118	161	133	102
3	138	144	113	80
4	109	137	125	109
5	130	165	128	96
Average	124	152	121	95

Nonetheless, for more complex types of problem situations, such as dealing with a time series that has both trend and seasonal effects, this simple averaging approach will not work.

TABLE 15.16   TELEVISION SET SALES TIME SERIES

Year	Quarter	Sales (1000s)
1	1	4.8
	2	4.1
	3	6.0
	4	6.5
2	1	5.8
	2	5.2
	3	6.8
	4	7.4
3	1	6.0
	2	5.6
	3	7.5
	4	7.8
4	1	6.3
	2	5.9
	3	8.0
	4	8.4

WEB file

TVSales

Seasonality and Trend

We now extend the curve-fitting approach to include situations where the time series contains both a seasonal effect and a linear trend, by showing how to forecast the quarterly television set sales time series introduced in Section 15.1. The data for the television set time series are shown in Table 15.16. The time series plot in Figure 15.14 indicates that sales are lowest in the second quarter of each year and increase in quarters 3 and 4. Thus, we conclude that a seasonal pattern exists for television set sales. But the time series also has an upward linear trend that will need to be accounted for in order to develop accurate forecasts of quarterly sales. This is easily done by combining the dummy variable approach for handling seasonality with the approach we discussed in Section 15.3 for handling linear trend.

The general form of the equation for modeling both the quarterly seasonal effects and the linear trend in the television set time series is

$$F_t = b_0 + b_1 \, \text{Qtr1}_t + b_2 \, \text{Qtr2}_t + b_3 \, \text{Qtr3}_t + b_4 t$$

where

F_t = forecast of sales in period t

Qtr1_t = 1 if time period t corresponds to the first quarter of the year; 0 otherwise

Qtr2_t = 1 if time period t corresponds to the second quarter of the year; 0 otherwise

Qtr3_t = 1 if period t corresponds to the third quarter of the year; 0 otherwise

t = time period

WEB file

TVSales_Seas_Trend

Table 15.17 is the revised television set sales time series that includes the coded values of the dummy variables and the time period t. Using the data in Table 15.17 with the sum

FIGURE 15.14   TELEVISION SET SALES TIME SERIES PLOT

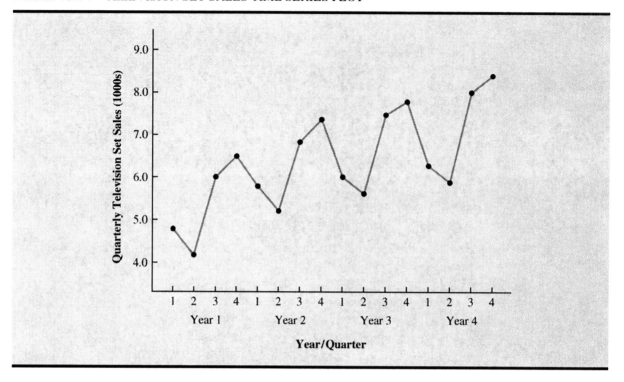

TABLE 15.17   TELEVISION SET SALES TIME SERIES WITH DUMMY VARIABLES
AND TIME PERIOD

Period	Year	Quarter	Qtr1	Qtr2	Qtr3	Period	Sales (1000s)
1	1	1	1	0	0	1	4.8
2		2	0	1	0	2	4.1
3		3	0	0	1	3	6.0
4		4	0	0	0	4	6.5
5	2	1	1	0	0	5	5.8
6		2	0	1	0	6	5.2
7		3	0	0	1	7	6.8
8		4	0	0	0	8	7.4
9	3	1	1	0	0	9	6.0
10		2	0	1	0	10	5.6
11		3	0	0	1	11	7.5
12		4	0	0	0	12	7.8
13	4	1	1	0	0	13	6.3
14		2	0	1	0	14	5.9
15		3	0	0	1	15	8.0
16		4	0	0	0	16	8.4

of squared error minimization model with the seasonal and trend components, we obtain the following equation:

$$F_t = 6.07 - 1.36\,\text{Qtr}1_t - 2.03\,\text{Qtr}2_t - 0.304\,\text{Qtr}3_t + 0.146\,t \qquad (15.14)$$

We can now use equation (15.14) to forecast quarterly sales for next year. Next year is year 5 for the television set sales time series; that is, time periods 17, 18, 19, and 20.

Forecast for Time Period 17 (quarter 1 in year 5)

$$F_{17} = 6.07 - 1.36(1) - 2.03(0) - 0.304(0) + 0.146(17) = 7.19$$

Forecast for Time Period 18 (quarter 2 in year 5)

$$F_{18} = 6.07 - 1.36(0) - 2.03(1) - 0.304(0) + 0.146(18) = 6.67$$

Forecast for Time Period 19 (quarter 3 in year 5)

$$F_{19} = 6.07 - 1.36(0) - 2.03(0) - 0.304(1) + 0.146(19) = 8.54$$

Forecast for Time Period 20 (quarter 4 in year 5)

$$F_{20} = 6.07 - 1.36(0) - 2.03(0) - 0.304(0) + 0.146(20) = 8.99$$

Thus, accounting for the seasonal effects and the linear trend in television set sales, the estimates of quarterly sales in year 5 are 7190, 6670, 8540, and 8990.

The dummy variables in the equation actually provide four equations, one for each quarter. For instance, if time period t corresponds to quarter 1, the estimate of quarterly sales is

Quarter 1: Sales $= 6.07 - 1.36(1) - 2.03(0) - 0.304(0) + 0.146t = 4.71 + 0.146t$

Similarly, if time period t corresponds to quarters 2, 3, and 4, the estimates of quarterly sales are

Quarter 2: Sales $= 6.07 - 1.36(0) - 2.03(1) - 0.304(0) + 0.146t = 4.04 + 0.146t$

Quarter 3: Sales $= 6.07 - 1.36(0) - 2.03(0) - 0.304(1) + 0.146t = 5.77 + 0.146t$

Quarter 4: Sales $= 6.07 - 1.36(0) - 2.03(0) - 0.304(0) + 0.146t = 6.07 + 0.146t$

The slope of the trend line for each quarterly forecast equation is 0.146, indicating a growth in sales of about 146 sets per quarter. The only difference in the four equations is that they have different intercepts.

Models Based on Monthly Data

In the preceding television set sales example, we showed how dummy variables can be used to account for the quarterly seasonal effects in the time series. Because there were four levels for the categorical variable season, three dummy variables were required. However, many businesses use monthly rather than quarterly forecasts. For monthly data, season is a categorical variable with 12 levels and thus $12 - 1 = 11$ dummy variables are required. For example, the 11 dummy variables could be coded as follows:

$$\text{Month1} = \begin{cases} 1 \text{ if January} \\ 0 \text{ otherwise} \end{cases}$$

$$\text{Month2} = \begin{cases} 1 \text{ if February} \\ 0 \text{ otherwise} \end{cases}$$

.

.

.

$$\text{Month11} = \begin{cases} 1 \text{ if November} \\ 0 \text{ otherwise} \end{cases}$$

Whenever a categorical variable such as season has k levels, k – 1 dummy variables are required.

Other than this change, the approach for handling seasonality remains the same.

SUMMARY

This chapter provided an introduction to the basic methods of time series analysis and forecasting. First, we showed that the underlying pattern in the time series can often be identified by constructing a time series plot. Several types of data patterns can be distinguished, including a horizontal pattern, a trend pattern, and a seasonal pattern. The forecasting methods we have discussed are based on which of these patterns are present in the time series.

For a time series with a horizontal pattern, we showed how moving averages and exponential smoothing can be used to develop a forecast. The moving averages method consists of computing an average of past data values and then using that average as the forecast for the next period. In the exponential smoothing method, a weighted average of past time series values is used to compute a forecast. These methods also adapt well when a horizontal pattern shifts to a different level but maintains a horizontal pattern at the new level.

An important factor in determining what forecasting method to use involves the accuracy of the method. We discussed three measures of forecast accuracy: mean absolute error (MAE), mean squared error (MSE), and mean absolute percentage error (MAPE). Each of these measures is designed to determine how well a particular forecasting method is able to reproduce the time series data that are already available. By selecting a method that has the best accuracy for the data already known, we hope to increase the likelihood that we will obtain better forecasts for future time periods.

For time series that have only a long-term linear trend, we showed how curve fitting can be used to make trend projections. For a time series with a curvilinear or nonlinear trend, we showed how curve-fitting optimization can be used to fit a quadratic trend equation or an exponential trend equation to the data.

For a time series with a seasonal trend, we showed how the use of dummy variables can be used to develop an equation with seasonal effects. We then extended the approach to include situations where the time series contains both a seasonal and a linear trend effect by showing how to combine the dummy variable approach for handling seasonality with the approach for handling linear trend.

GLOSSARY

Time series A sequence of observations on a variable measured at successive points in time or over successive periods of time.

Time series plot A graphical presentation of the relationship between time and the time series variable. Time is shown on the horizontal axis and the time series values are shown on the verical axis.

Stationary time series A time series whose statistical properties are independent of time. For a stationary time series the process generating the data has a constant mean and the variability of the time series is constant over time.

Trend pattern A trend pattern exists if the time series plot shows gradual shifts or movements to relatively higher or lower values over a longer period of time.

Seasonal pattern A seasonal pattern exists if the time series plot exhibits a repeating pattern over successive periods. The successive periods are often one-year intervals, which is where the name seasonal pattern comes from.

Cyclical pattern A cyclical pattern exists if the time series plot shows an alternating sequence of points below and above the trend line lasting more than one year.

Forecast error The difference between the actual time series value and the forecast.

Mean absolute error (MAE) The average of the absolute values of the forecast errors.

Mean squared error (MSE) The average of the sum of squared forecast errors.

Mean absolute percentage error (MAPE) The average of the absolute values of the percentage forecast errors.

Moving averages A forecasting method that uses the average of the most recent k data values in the time series as the forecast for the next period.

Weighted moving averages A forecasting method that involves selecting a different weight for the most recent k data values values in the time series and then computing a weighted average of the values. The sum of the weights must equal 1.

Exponential smoothing A forecasting method that uses a weighted average of past time series values as the forecast; it is a special case of the weighted moving averages method in which we select only one weight—the weight for the most recent observation.

Smoothing constant A parameter of the exponential smoothing model that provides the weight given to the most recent time series value in the calculation of the forecast value.

PROBLEMS

1. Consider the following time series data:

Week	1	2	3	4	5	6
Value	18	13	16	11	17	14

Using the naïve method (most recent value) as the forecast for the next week, compute the following measures of forecast accuracy:
a. Mean absolute error
b. Mean squared error

c. Mean absolute percentage error

d. What is the forecast for week 7?

2. Refer to the time series data in Problem 1. Using the average of all the historical data as a forecast for the next period, compute the following measures of forecast accuracy:

a. Mean absolute error

b. Mean squared error

c. Mean absolute percentage error

d. What is the forecast for week 7?

3. Problems 1 and 2 used different forecasting methods. Which method appears to provide the more accurate forecasts for the historical data? Explain.

4. Consider the following time series data:

Month	1	2	3	4	5	6	7
Value	24	13	20	12	19	23	15

a. Compute MSE using the most recent value as the forecast for the next period. What is the forecast for month 8?

b. Compute MSE using the average of all the data available as the forecast for the next period. What is the forecast for month 8?

c. Which method appears to provide the better forecast?

5. Consider the following time series data:

Week	1	2	3	4	5	6
Value	18	13	16	11	17	14

a. Construct a time series plot. What type of pattern exists in the data?

b. Develop a three-week moving average for this time series. Compute MSE and a forecast for week 7.

c. Use $\alpha = 0.2$ to compute the exponential smoothing values for the time series. Compute MSE and a forecast for week 7.

d. Compare the three-week moving average forecast with the exponential smoothing forecast using $\alpha = 0.2$. Which appears to provide the better forecast based on MSE? Explain.

e. Use Excel Solver or LINGO to find the value of α that minimizes MSE. (*Hint:* Minimize the sum of squared error.)

6. Consider the following time series data:

Month	1	2	3	4	5	6	7
Value	24	13	20	12	19	23	15

a. Construct a time series plot. What type of pattern exists in the data?

b. Develop a three-week moving average for this time series. Compute MSE and a forecast for week 8.

c. Use $\alpha = 0.2$ to compute the exponential smoothing values for the time series. Compute MSE and a forecast for week 8.

    d. Compare the three-week moving average forecast with the exponential smoothing forecast using $\alpha = 0.2$. Which appears to provide the better forecast based on MSE?

    e. Use Excel Solver or LINGO to find the value of α that minimizes MSE. (*Hint:* Minimize the sum of squared error.)

7. Refer to the gasoline sales time series data in Table 15.1.

Gasoline

    a. Compute four-week and five-week moving averages for the time series.

    b. Compute the MSE for the four-week and five-week moving average forecasts.

    c. What appears to be the best number of weeks of past data (three, four, or five) to use in the moving average computation? Recall that MSE for the three-week moving average is 10.22.

8. Refer again to the gasoline sales time series data in Table 15.1.

Gasoline

    a. Using a weight of $\frac{1}{2}$ for the most recent observation, $\frac{1}{3}$ for the second most recent, and $\frac{1}{6}$ for third most recent, compute a three-week weighted moving average for the time series.

    b. Compute the MSE for the weighted moving average in part (a). Do you prefer this weighted moving average to the unweighted moving average? Remember that the MSE for the unweighted moving average is 10.22.

    c. Suppose you are allowed to choose any weights as long as they sum to 1. Could you always find a set of weights that would make the MSE at least as small as for a weighted moving average than for an unweighted moving average? Why or why not?

9. With the gasoline time series data from Table 15.1, show the exponential smoothing forecasts using $\alpha = 0.1$.

Gasoline

    a. Applying the MSE measure of forecast accuracy, would you prefer a smoothing constant of $\alpha = 0.1$ or $\alpha = 0.2$ for the gasoline sales time series?

    b. Are the results the same if you apply MAE as the measure of accuracy?

    c. What are the results if MAPE is used?

10. With a smoothing constant of $\alpha = 0.2$, equation (15.5) shows that the forecast for week 13 of the gasoline sales data from Table 15.1 is given by $F_{13} = 0.2Y_{12} + 0.8F_{12}$. However, the forecast for week 12 is given by $F_{12} = 0.2Y_{11} + 0.8F_{11}$. Thus, we could combine these two results to show that the forecast for week 13 can be written

$$F_{13} = 0.2Y_{12} + 0.8(0.2Y_{11} + 0.8F_{11}) = 0.2Y_{12} + 0.16Y_{11} + 0.64F_{11}$$

    a. Making use of the fact that $F_{11} = 0.2Y_{10} + 0.8F_{10}$ (and similarly for F_{10} and F_9), continue to expand the expression for F_{13} until it is written in terms of the past data values $Y_{12}, Y_{11}, Y_{10}, Y_9, Y_8$, and the forecast for period 8.

    b. Refer to the coefficients or weights for the past values $Y_{12}, Y_{11}, Y_{10}, Y_9, Y_8$; what observation can you make about how exponential smoothing weights past data values in arriving at new forecasts? Compare this weighting pattern with the weighting pattern of the moving averages method.

11. For the Hawkins Company, the monthly percentages of all shipments received on time over the past 12 months are 80, 82, 84, 83, 83, 84, 85, 84, 82, 83, 84, and 83.

    a. Construct a time series plot. What type of pattern exists in the data?

    b. Compare a three-month moving average forecast with an exponential smoothing forecast for $\alpha = 0.2$. Which provides the better forecasts using MSE as the measure of model accuracy?

    c. What is the forecast for next month?

12. Corporate triple A bond interest rates for 12 consecutive months follow:

    9.5   9.3   9.4   9.6   9.8   9.7   9.8   10.5   9.9   9.7   9.6   9.6

a. Construct a time series plot. What type of pattern exists in the data?
b. Develop three-month and four-month moving averages for this time series. Does the three-month or four-month moving average provide the better forecasts based on MSE? Explain.
c. What is the moving average forecast for the next month?

13. The values of Alabama building contracts (in millions of dollars) for a 12-month period follow:

240   350   230   260   280   320   220   310   240   310   240   230

a. Construct a time series plot. What type of pattern exists in the data?
b. Compare a three-month moving average forecast with an exponential smoothing forecast. Use $\alpha = 0.2$. Which provides the better forecasts based on MSE?
c. What is the forecast for the next month?

14. The following time series shows the sales of a particular product over the past 12 months:

Month	Sales	Month	Sales
1	105	7	145
2	135	8	140
3	120	9	100
4	105	10	80
5	90	11	100
6	120	12	110

a. Construct a time series plot. What type of pattern exists in the data?
b. Use $\alpha = 0.3$ to compute the exponential smoothing values for the time series.
c. Use Excel Solver or LINGO to find the value of α that minimizes MSE. (*Hint*: Minimize the sum of squared error.)

15. Ten weeks of data on the Commodity Futures Index are 7.35, 7.40, 7.55, 7.56, 7.60, 7.52, 7.52, 7.70, 7.62, and 7.55.
a. Construct a time series plot. What type of pattern exists in the data?
b. Use Excel Solver or LINGO to find the value of α that minimizes MSE. (*Hint*: Minimize the sum of squared error.)

16. The Nielsen ratings (percentage of U.S. households that tuned in) for the Masters golf tournament from 1997 through 2008 follow (*Golf Magazine*, January 2009):

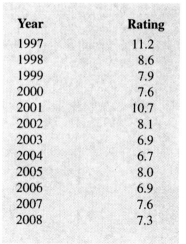

WEB file

Masters

Year	Rating
1997	11.2
1998	8.6
1999	7.9
2000	7.6
2001	10.7
2002	8.1
2003	6.9
2004	6.7
2005	8.0
2006	6.9
2007	7.6
2008	7.3

The rating of 11.2 in 1997 indicates that 11.2% of U.S. households tuned in to watch Tiger Woods win his first major golf tournament and become the first African-American to win the Masters. Tiger Woods also won the Masters in 2001 and 2005.

a. Construct a time series plot. What type of pattern exists in the data? Discuss some of the factors that may have resulted in the pattern exhibited in the time series plot for this time series.

b. Given the pattern of the time series plot developed in part (a), do you think the forecasting methods discussed in this section are appropriate to develop forecasts for this time series? Explain.

c. Would you recommend using only the Nielsen ratings for 2002–2008 to forecast the rating for 2009, or should the entire time series from 1997–2008 be used? Explain.

17. Consider the following time series:

t	1	2	3	4	5
Y_t	6	11	9	14	15

a. Construct a time series plot. What type of pattern exists in the data?

b. Use Excel Solver or LINGO to find the parameters for the line that minimizes MSE this time series.

c. What is the forecast for $t = 6$?

18. The following table reports the percentage of stocks in a portfolio for nine quarters from 2007 to 2009:

Quarter	Stock %
1st—2007	29.8
2nd—2007	31.0
3rd—2007	29.9
4th—2007	30.1
1st—2008	32.2
2nd—2008	31.5
3rd—2008	32.0
4th—2008	31.9
1st—2009	30.0

a. Construct a time series plot. What type of pattern exists in the data?

b. Use exponential smoothing to forecast this time series. Using Excel Solver or LINGO find the value of α that minimizes the sum of squared error.

c. What is the forecast of the percentage of stocks in a typical portfolio for the second quarter of 2009?

19. Consider the following time series:

t	1	2	3	4	5	6	7
Y_t	120	110	100	96	94	92	88

a. Construct a time series plot. What type of pattern exists in the data?

b. Use Excel Solver or LINGO to find the parameters for the line that minimizes MSE this time series.

c. What is the forecast for $t = 8$?

20. Consider the following time series:

t	1	2	3	4	5	6	7
Y_t	82	60	44	35	30	29	35

   a. Construct a time series plot. What type of pattern exists in the data?
   b. Using LINGO or EXCEL Solver, develop the quadratic trend equation for the time series.
   c. What is the forecast for $t = 8$?

21. Because of high tuition costs at state and private universities, enrollments at community colleges have increased dramatically in recent years. The following data show the enrollment (in thousands) for Jefferson Community College from 2001–2009:

Year	Period (t)	Enrollment (1000s)
2001	1	6.5
2002	2	8.1
2003	3	8.4
2004	4	10.2
2005	5	12.5
2006	6	13.3
2007	7	13.7
2008	8	17.2
2009	9	18.1

   a. Construct a time series plot. What type of pattern exists in the data?
   b. Use Excel Solver or LINGO to find the parameters for the line that minimizes MSE this time series.
   c. What is the forecast for 2010?

22. The Seneca Children's Fund (SCC) is a local charity that runs a summer camp for disadvantaged children. The fund's board of directors has been working very hard over recent years to decrease the amount of overhead expenses, a major factor in how charities are rated by independent agencies. The following data show the percentage of the money SCC has raised that were spent on administrative and fund-raising expenses for 2003–2009:

Year	Period (t)	Expense (%)
2003	1	13.9
2004	2	12.2
2005	3	10.5
2006	4	10.4
2007	5	11.5
2008	6	10.0
2009	7	8.5

   a. Construct a time series plot. What type of pattern exists in the data?
   b. Use Excel Solver or LINGO to find the parameters for the line that minimizes MSE this time series.
   c. Forecast the percentage of administrative expenses for 2010.
   d. If SCC can maintain their current trend in reducing administrative expenses, how long will it take them to achieve a level of 5% or less?

23. The president of a small manufacturing firm is concerned about the continual increase in manufacturing costs over the past several years. The following figures provide a time series of the cost per unit for the firm's leading product over the past eight years:

Year	Cost/Unit ($)	Year	Cost/Unit ($)
1	20.00	5	26.60
2	24.50	6	30.00
3	28.20	7	31.00
4	27.50	8	36.00

a. Construct a time series plot. What type of pattern exists in the data?
b. Use Excel Solver or LINGO to find the parameters for the line that minimizes MSE this time series.
c. What is the average cost increase that the firm has been realizing per year?
d. Compute an estimate of the cost/unit for next year.

Exchange Rate

24. FRED® (Federal Reserve Economic Data), a database of more than 3000 U.S. economic time series, contains historical data on foreign exchange rates. The following data show the foreign exchange rate for the United States and China (http://research.stlouisfed.org/fred2/). The units for Rate are the number of Chinese yuan renmimbis to one U.S. dollar.

Year	Month	Rate
2007	October	7.5019
2007	November	7.4210
2007	December	7.3682
2008	January	7.2405
2008	February	7.1644
2008	March	7.0722
2008	April	6.9997
2008	May	6.9725
2008	June	6.8993
2008	July	6.8355

a. Construct a time series plot. Does a linear trend appear to be present?
b. Use Excel Solver or LINGO to find the parameters for the line that minimizes MSE this time series.
c. Use the trend equation to forecast the exchange rate for August 2008.
d. Would you feel comfortable using the trend equation to forecast the exchange rate for December 2008?

25. Automobile unit sales at B. J. Scott Motors, Inc., provided the following 10-year time series:

Year	Sales	Year	Sales
1	400	6	260
2	390	7	300
3	320	8	320
4	340	9	340
5	270	10	370

a. Construct a time series plot. Comment on the appropriateness of a linear trend.
b. Using Excel Solver or LINGO, develop a quadratic trend equation that can be used to forecast sales.

c. Using the trend equation developed in part (b), forecast sales in year 11.
d. Suggest an alternative to using a quadratic trend equation to forecast sales. Explain.

Pasta

26. Giovanni Food Products produces and sells frozen pizzas to public schools throughout the eastern United States. Using a very aggressive marketing strategy they have been able to increase their annual revenue by approximately $10 million over the past 10 years. But, increased competition has slowed their growth rate in the past few years. The annual revenue, in millions of dollars, for the previous 10 years is shown below.

Year	Revenue
1	8.53
2	10.84
3	12.98
4	14.11
5	16.31
6	17.21
7	18.37
8	18.45
9	18.40
10	18.43

a. Construct a time series plot. Comment on the appropriateness of a linear trend.
b. Using Excel Solver or LINGO, develop a quadratic trend equation that can be used to forecast revenue.
c. Using the trend equation developed in part (b), forecast revenue in year 11.

NFL Value

27. *Forbes* magazine (www.Forbes.com) ranks NFL teams by value each year. The data below are the value of the Indianapolis Colts from 1998 to 2008.

Year	Period	Value ($ million)
1998	1	227
1999	2	305
2000	3	332
2001	4	367
2002	5	419
2003	6	547
2004	7	609
2005	8	715
2006	9	837
2007	10	911
2008	11	1076

a. Construct a time series plot. What type of pattern exists in the data?
b. Using Excel Solver or LINGO, develop the quadratic trend equation that can be used to forecast the team's value.
c. Using Excel Solver or LINGO, develop the exponential trend equation that can be used to forecast the team's value.
d. Using Excel Solver or LINGO, develop the linear trend equation that can be used to forecast the team's value.
e. Which equation would you recommend using to estimate the team's value in 2009?
f. Use the model you recommended in part (e) to forecast the value of the Colts in 2009.

28. Consider the following time series:

Quarter	Year 1	Year 2	Year 3
1	71	68	62
2	49	41	51
3	58	60	53
4	78	81	72

a. Construct a time series plot. What type of pattern exists in the data?
b. Use an Excel or LINGO model with dummy variables as follows to develop an equation to account for seasonal effects in the data. Qtr1 = 1 if Quarter 1, 0 otherwise; Qtr2 = 1 if Quarter 2, 0 otherwise; Qtr3 = 1 if Quarter 3, 0 otherwise.
c. Compute the quarterly forecasts for next year.

29. Consider the following time series data:

Quarter	Year 1	Year 2	Year 3
1	4	6	7
2	2	3	6
3	3	5	6
4	5	7	8

a. Construct a time series plot. What type of pattern exists in the data?
b. Use an Excel or LINGO model with dummy variables as follows to develop an equation to account for seasonal effects in the data. Qtr1 = 1 if Quarter 1, 0 otherwise; Qtr2 = 1 if Quarter 2, 0 otherwise; Qtr3 = 1 if Quarter 3, 0 otherwise.
c. Compute the quarterly forecasts for next year.

30. The quarterly sales data (number of copies sold) for a college textbook over the past three years follow:

Quarter	Year 1	Year 2	Year 3
1	1690	1800	1850
2	940	900	1100
3	2625	2900	2930
4	2500	2360	2615

a. Construct a time series plot. What type of pattern exists in the data?
b. Use an Excel or LINGO model with dummy variables as follows to develop an equation to account for seasonal effects in the data. Qtr1 = 1 if Quarter 1, 0 otherwise; Qtr2 = 1 if Quarter 2, 0 otherwise; Qtr3 = 1 if Quarter 3, 0 otherwise.
c. Compute the quarterly forecasts for next year.
d. Let $t = 1$ to refer to the observation in quarter 1 of year 1; $t = 2$ to refer to the observation in quarter 2 of year 1; . . . and $t = 12$ to refer to the observation in quarter 4 of year 3. Using the dummy variables defined in part (b) and t, develop an equation to account for seasonal effects and any linear trend in the time series. Based upon the seasonal effects in the data and linear trend, compute the quarterly forecasts for next year.

31. Air pollution control specialists in southern California monitor the amount of ozone, carbon dioxide, and nitrogen dioxide in the air on an hourly basis. The hourly time series data exhibit seasonality, with the levels of pollutants showing patterns that vary over the hours

in the day. On July 15, 16, and 17, the following levels of nitrogen dioxide were observed for the 12 hours from 6:00 A.M. to 6:00 P.M.

July 15:	25	28	35	50	60	60	40	35	30	25	25	20
July 16:	28	30	35	48	60	65	50	40	35	25	20	20
July 17:	35	42	45	70	72	75	60	45	40	25	25	25

a. Construct a time series plot. What type of pattern exists in the data?
b. Use an Excel or LINGO model with dummy variables as follows to develop an equation to account for seasonal effects in the data:

Hour1 = 1 if the reading was made between 6:00 A.M. and 7:00 A.M.; 0 otherwise;
Hour2 = 1 if the reading was made between 7:00 A.M. and 8:00 A.M.; 0 otherwise

.
.
.

Hour11 = 1 if the reading was made between 4:00 P.M. and 5:00 P.M., 0 otherwise. Note that when the values of the 11 dummy variables are equal to 0, the observation corresponds to the 5:00 P.M. to 6:00 P.M. hour.

c. Using the equation developed in part (b), compute estimates of the levels of nitrogen dioxide for July 18.
d. Let $t = 1$ refer to the observation in hour 1 on July 15; $t = 2$ to refer to the observation in hour 2 of July 15; . . . and $t = 36$ to refer to the observation in hour 12 of July 17. Using the dummy variables defined in part (b) and ts, develop an equation to account for seasonal effects and any linear trend in the time series. Based upon the seasonal effects in the data and the linear trend, compute estimates of the levels of nitrogen dioxide for July 18.

SouthShore

32. South Shore Construction builds permanent docks and seawalls along the southern shore of Long Island, New York. Although the firm has been in business only five years, revenue has increased from $308,000 in the first year of operation to $1,084,000 in the most recent year. The following data show the quarterly sales revenue in thousands of dollars:

Quarter	Year 1	Year 2	Year 3	Year 4	Year 5
1	20	37	75	92	176
2	100	136	155	202	282
3	175	245	326	384	445
4	13	26	48	82	181

a. Construct a time series plot. What type of pattern exists in the data?
b. Use an Excel or LINGO model with dummy variables as follows to develop an equation to account for seasonal effects in the data. Qtr1 = 1 if Quarter 1, 0 otherwise; Qtr2 = 1 if Quarter 2, 0 otherwise; Qtr3 = 1 if Quarter 3, 0 otherwise.
c. Let Period = 1 to refer to the observation in quarter 1 of year 1; Period = 2 to refer to the observation in quarter 2 of year 1; . . . and Period = 20 refer to the observation in quarter 4 of year 5. Using the dummy variables defined in part (b) and Period, develop an equation to account for seasonal effects and any linear trend in the time series. Based upon the seasonal effects in the data and linear trend, compute estimates of quarterly sales for year 6.

TABLE 15.18   FOOD AND BEVERAGE SALES FOR THE VINTAGE
RESTAURANT ($1000s)

WEB file

Vintage

Month	First Year	Second Year	Third Year
January	242	263	282
February	235	238	255
March	232	247	265
April	178	193	205
May	184	193	210
June	140	149	160
July	145	157	166
August	152	161	174
September	110	122	126
October	130	130	148
November	152	167	173
December	206	230	235

Case Problem 1   FORECASTING FOOD AND BEVERAGE SALES

The Vintage Restaurant, on Captiva Island near Fort Myers, Florida, is owned and operated by Karen Payne. The restaurant just completed its third year of operation. During that time, Karen sought to establish a reputation for the restaurant as a high-quality dining establishment that specializes in fresh seafood. Through the efforts of Karen and her staff, her restaurant has become one of the best and fastest-growing restaurants on the island.

To better plan for future growth of the restaurant, Karen needs to develop a system that will enable her to forecast food and beverage sales by month for up to one year in advance. Table 15.18 shows the value of food and beverage sales ($1000s) for the first three years of operation.

Managerial Report

Perform an analysis of the sales data for the Vintage Restaurant. Prepare a report for Karen that summarizes your findings, forecasts, and recommendations. Include the following:

1. A time series plot. Comment on the underlying pattern in the time series.
2. Using the dummy variable approach, forecast sales for January through December of the fourth year.

Assume that January sales for the fourth year turn out to be $295,000. What was your forecast error? If this error is large, Karen may be puzzled about the difference between your forecast and the actual sales value. What can you do to resolve her uncertainty in the forecasting procedure?

Case Problem 2   FORECASTING LOST SALES

The Carlson Department Store suffered heavy damage when a hurricane struck on August 31. The store was closed for four months (September through December), and Carlson is now involved in a dispute with its insurance company about the amount of lost sales during the time the store was closed. Two key issues must be resolved: (1) the

TABLE 15.19   SALES FOR CARLSON DEPARTMENT STORE ($ MILLIONS)

CarlsonSales

Month	Year 1	Year 2	Year 3	Year 4	Year 5
January		1.45	2.31	2.31	2.56
February		1.80	1.89	1.99	2.28
March		2.03	2.02	2.42	2.69
April		1.99	2.23	2.45	2.48
May		2.32	2.39	2.57	2.73
June		2.20	2.14	2.42	2.37
July		2.13	2.27	2.40	2.31
August		2.43	2.21	2.50	2.23
September	1.71	1.90	1.89	2.09	
October	1.90	2.13	2.29	2.54	
November	2.74	2.56	2.83	2.97	
December	4.20	4.16	4.04	4.35	

amount of sales Carlson would have made if the hurricane had not struck, and (2) whether Carlson is entitled to any compensation for excess sales due to increased business activity after the storm. More than $8 billion in federal disaster relief and insurance money came into the county, resulting in increased sales at department stores and numerous other businesses.

Table 15.19 gives Carlson's sales data for the 48 months preceding the storm. Table 15.20 reports total sales for the 48 months preceding the storm for all department stores in the county, as well as the total sales in the county for the four months the Carlson Department Store was closed. Carlson's managers asked you to analyze these data and develop estimates of the lost sales at the Carlson Department Store for the months of September through December. They also asked you to determine whether a case can be made for excess storm-related sales during the same period. If such a case can be made, Carlson is entitled to compensation for excess sales it would have earned in addition to ordinary sales.

TABLE 15.20   DEPARTMENT STORE SALES FOR THE COUNTY ($ MILLIONS)

CountySales

Month	Year 1	Year 2	Year 3	Year 4	Year 5
January		46.80	46.80	43.80	48.00
February		48.00	48.60	45.60	51.60
March		60.00	59.40	57.60	57.60
April		57.60	58.20	53.40	58.20
May		61.80	60.60	56.40	60.00
June		58.20	55.20	52.80	57.00
July		56.40	51.00	54.00	57.60
August		63.00	58.80	60.60	61.80
September	55.80	57.60	49.80	47.40	69.00
October	56.40	53.40	54.60	54.60	75.00
November	71.40	71.40	65.40	67.80	85.20
December	117.60	114.00	102.00	100.20	121.80

Managerial Report

Prepare a report for the managers of the Carlson Department Store that summarizes your findings, forecasts, and recommendations. Include the following:

1. An estimate of sales for Carlson Department Store had there been no hurricane
2. An estimate of countywide department store sales had there been no hurricane
3. An estimate of lost sales for the Carlson Department Store for September through December

In addition, use the countywide actual department stores sales for September through December and the estimate in part (2) to make a case for or against excess storm-related sales.

Appendix 15.1   FORECASTING WITH EXCEL DATA ANALYSIS TOOLS

In this appendix we show how Excel can be used to develop forecasts using three forecasting methods: moving averages, exponential smoothing, and trend projection. We also show how to use Excel Solver for least-squares fitting of models to data.

Moving Averages

To show how Excel can be used to develop forecasts using the moving averages method, we will develop a forecast for the gasoline sales time series in Table 15.1 and Figure 15.1. The sales data for the 12 weeks are entered into worksheet rows 2 through 13 of column B. The following steps can be used to produce a three-week moving average.

Step 1. Click the **Data** tab on the Ribbon
Step 2. In the **Analysis** group, click **Data Analysis**
Step 3. Choose **Moving Average** from the list of Analysis Tools
Click **OK**
Step 4. When the Moving Average dialog box appears:
Enter B2:B13 in the **Input Range** box
Enter 3 in the **Interval** box
Enter C2 in the **Output Range** box
Click OK

The three-week moving averages will appear in column C of the worksheet. The forecast for week 4 appears next to the sales value for week 3, and so on. Forecasts for periods of other length can be computed easily by entering a different value in the Interval box.

Exponential Smoothing

To show how Excel can be used for exponential smoothing, we again develop a forecast for the gasoline sales time series in Table 15.1 and Figure 15.1. The sales data for the 12 weeks are entered into worksheet rows 2 through 13 of column B. The following steps can be used to produce a forecast using a smoothing constant of $\alpha = .2$.

Step 1. Click the **Data** tab on the Ribbon
Step 2. In the **Analysis** group, click **Data Analysis**
Step 3. Choose **Exponential Smoothing** from the list of Analysis Tools
Click **OK**

Step 4.   When the Exponential Smoothing dialog box appears:
Enter B2:B13 in the **Input Range** box
Enter .8 in the **Damping factor** box
Enter C2 in the **Output Range** box
Click OK

The exponential smoothing forecasts will appear in column C of the worksheet. Note that the value we entered in the Damping factor box is $1 - \alpha$; forecasts for other smoothing constants can be computed easily by entering a different value for $1 - \alpha$ in the Damping factor box.

Trend Projection

To show how Excel can be used for trend projection, we develop a forecast for the bicycle sales time series in Table 15.3 and Figure 15.3. The data, with appropriate labels in row 1, are entered into worksheet rows 1 through 11 of columns A and B. The following steps can be used to produce a forecast for year 11 by trend projection.

WEB file

Bicycle

Step 1.   Select an empty cell in the worksheet
Step 2.   Select the **Formulas** tab on the Ribbon
Step 3.   In the **Function Library** group, click **Insert** Function
Step 4.   When the Insert Function dialog box appears:
Choose **Statistical** in the **Or select a category** box
Choose **Forecast** in the Select a function box
Click **OK**
Step 5.   When the Forecast Arguments dialog box appears:
Enter 11 in the **x** box
Enter B2:B11 in the **Known y's** box
Enter A2:A11 in the **Known x's** box
Click OK

The forecast for year 11, in this case 32.5, will appear in the cell selected in step 1.

Appendix 15.2   FORECASTING WITH EXCEL SOLVER

Using Excel Solver for Fitting a Model to Data— Exponential Smoothing

To show how Excel Solver can be used to find the best-fitting value for the exponential smoothing parameter α, we develop a forecast for the gasoline sales time series in Table 15.1 and Figure 15.1. We have developed a model that calculates the exponential smoothing forecasts using equation (15.2). This is shown in Figure 15.15 for the gasoline data. Cell B2 contains the current value of $\alpha = 0.2$. As shown in Figure 15.16, we calculate the forecasts using equation (15.2) in column C. Note that we set the forecast in period 2 to the observed value in period, and for subsequent periods we use equation (15.2). The forecast error for each period is calculated in column D and the squared forecast error in column E. Cell E19 contains the sum of the squared errors.

We seek the value of α that minimizes the sum of squared errors. We will build the optimization model (15.4)–(15.7), but we will not need the definitional variables, as the

FIGURE 15.15   EXPONENTIAL SMOOTHING MODEL IN EXCEL

WEB file

Gasoline_ES

	A	B	C	D	E
1					
2	Alpha	0.2			
3					
4					Squared
5		Time Series		Forecast	Forecast
6	Week	Value	Forecast	Error	Error
7	1	17			
8	2	21	17	4.00	16.00
9	3	19	17.80	1.20	1.44
10	4	23	18.04	4.96	24.60
11	5	18	19.03	−1.03	1.07
12	6	16	18.83	−2.83	7.98
13	7	20	18.26	1.74	3.03
14	8	18	18.61	−0.61	0.37
15	9	22	18.49	3.51	12.34
16	10	20	19.19	0.81	0.66
17	11	15	19.35	−4.35	18.94
18	12	22	18.48	3.52	12.38
19				Total	98.80
20					
21					

FIGURE 15.16   EXPONENTIAL SMOOTHING MODEL IN EXCEL WITH FORMULAS

	A	B	C	D	E
1					
2	Alpha	0.2			
3					
4					Squared
5		Time Series		Forecast	Forecast
6	Week	Value	Forecast	Error	Error
7	1	17			
8	2	21	=B7	=B8-C8	=D8^2
9	3	19	=$B$2*B8+(1-$B$2)*C8	=B9-C9	=D9^2
10	4	23	=$B$2*B9+(1-$B$2)*C9	=B10-C10	=D10^2
11	5	18	=$B$2*B10+(1-$B$2)*C10	=B11-C11	=D11^2
12	6	16	=$B$2*B11+(1-$B$2)*C11	=B12-C12	=D12^2
13	7	20	=$B$2*B12+(1-$B$2)*C12	=B13-C13	=D13^2
14	8	18	=$B$2*B13+(1-$B$2)*C13	=B14-C14	=D14^2
15	9	22	=$B$2*B14+(1-$B$2)*C14	=B15-C15	=D15^2
16	10	20	=$B$2*B15+(1-$B$2)*C15	=B16-C16	=D16^2
17	11	15	=$B$2*B16+(1-$B$2)*C16	=B17-C17	=D17^2
18	12	22	=$B$2*B17+(1-$B$2)*C17	=B18-C18	=D18^2
19				Total	=SUM(E8:E18)
20					

FIGURE 15.17   SOLVER DIALOG BOX FOR EXPONENTIAL SMOOTHING FOR THE GASOLINE DATA

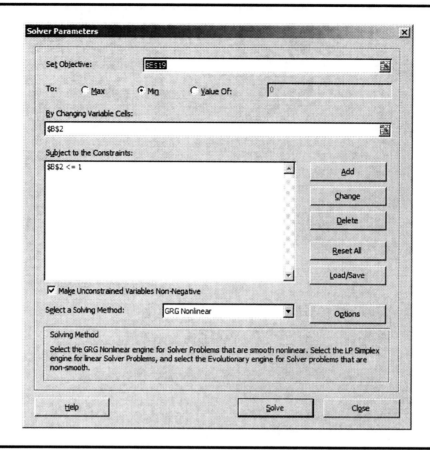

forecasts will simply be calculations in the spreadsheet (column C). The only decision variable will be α.

The following steps can be used to find the optimal value of α:

Step 1. Select the **Data** tab
Step 2. From the **Analysis** group select the **Solver** option
Step 3. In the solver dialog box, Enter E19 as the **Set Target Cell**
Choose **Min**
Enter B2 in the **Changing Variable Cells** section
Step 4. In the constraints section of the solver dialog box, click the **Add** button. The constraint dialog box appears. In the constraint dialog enter B2 in the left-hand box of the Cell Reference area
Select <=
Enter 1 in the **Constraint** box
Click **OK**
Step 5. Select the checkbox **Make Unconstrained Variables Non-Negative**
Click **OK.** The solver dialog box should appear as in Figure 15.17
Step 6. Click **Solve**
Step 7. Click **OK** to return to the spreadsheet.

The optimal value of α of 0.174388 appears in cell B2 and the minimal sum of squared errors of 98.56 is given in cell E19.

FIGURE 15.18   CHOLESTEROL DRUG REVENUE QUADRATIC MODEL
IN EXCEL

WEB file

Cholesterol_Quad

	A	B	C	D	E
1					
2		b0	5		
3		b1	1		
4		b2	1		
5					Squared
6				Forecast	Forecast
7	Year	Revenue	Forecast	Error	Error
8	1	23.10	7.00	16.10	259.21
9	2	21.30	11.00	10.30	106.09
10	3	27.40	17.00	10.40	108.16
11	4	34.60	25.00	9.60	92.16
12	5	33.80	35.00	−1.20	1.44
13	6	43.20	47.00	−3.80	14.44
14	7	59.50	61.00	−1.50	2.25
15	8	64.40	77.00	−12.60	158.76
16	9	74.20	95.00	−20.80	432.64
17	10	99.30	115.00	−15.70	246.49
18				Total	1421.64
19					
20					

FIGURE 15.19   CHOLESTEROL DRUG REVENUE QUADRATIC MODEL FORMULAS IN EXCEL

	A	B	C	D	E
1					
2		b0	5		
3		b1	1		
4		b2	1		
5					Squared
6				Forecast	Forecast
7	Year	Revenue	Forecast	Error	Error
8	1	23.1	=$C$2+$C$3*A8+$C$4*A8^2	=B8-C8	=D8^2
9	2	21.3	=$C$2+$C$3*A9+$C$4*A9^2	=B9-C9	=D9^2
10	3	27.4	=$C$2+$C$3*A10+$C$4*A10^2	=B10-C10	=D10^2
11	4	34.6	=$C$2+$C$3*A11+$C$4*A11^2	=B11-C11	=D11^2
12	5	33.8	=$C$2+$C$3*A12+$C$4*A12^2	=B12-C12	=D12^2
13	6	43.2	=$C$2+$C$3*A13+$C$4*A13^2	=B13-C13	=D13^2
14	7	59.5	=$C$2+$C$3*A14+$C$4*A14^2	=B14-C14	=D14^2
15	8	64.4	=$C$2+$C$3*A15+$C$4*A15^2	=B15-C15	=D15^2
16	9	74.2	=$C$2+$C$3*A16+$C$4*A16^2	=B16-C16	=D16^2
17	10	99.3	=$C$2+$C$3*A17+$C$4*A17^2	=B17-C17	=D17^2
18				Total	=SUM(E8:E17)
19					

FIGURE 15.20   SOLVER DIALOG BOX FOR QUADRATIC CURVE FITTING FOR THE CHOLESTEROL SALES DATA

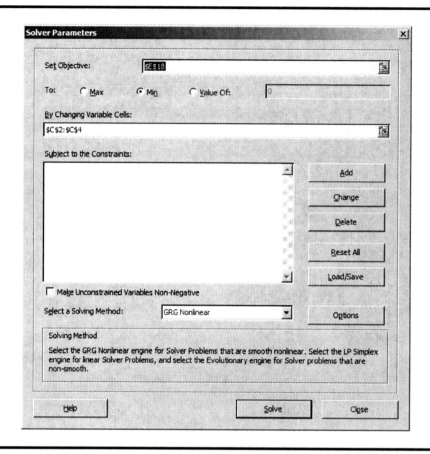

Using Excel Solver for Curve Fitting

To show how Excel Solver can be used to find the best-fitting values of the parameters of a proposed model, we use the cholesterol drug revenue data shown in Table 15.4 and Figure 15.4. The proposed model is the quadratic trend equation (15.11). We have constructed a spreadsheet model that calculates the forecasts and the sum of squared error given values for the parameters b_0, b_1, and b_2. This spreadsheet is shown in Figure 15.18.

We seek the value of α that minimizes the sum of squared errors. The decision variables are b_0, b_1, and b_2. Figure 15.19 shows the formulas used. As shown in Figure 15.19, we calculate the forecasts using equation (15.11) in column C. The forecast error for each period is calculated in column D and the squared forecast error in column E. Cell E18 contains the sum of the squared errors.

To fit a different model, (for example, equation 15.12), change the formula in cell C8 and copy to cells C9 through C17. Be sure to use absolute references for the cell locations C2, C3, and C4.

Step 1. Select the **Data** tab.
Step 2. From the **Analysis** group select the **Solver** option
Step 3. In the solver dialog box, Enter E18 as the **Set Target Cell**
Choose **Min**
Enter C2:C4 in the **Changing Variable Cells** section
The solver dialog box should appear as in **Figure 15.20**
Step 4. Click **Solve**
Step 5. Click **OK** to return to the spreadsheet

The optimal values of the decision variables are $b_0 = 24.182$, $b_1 = -2.106$, and $b_2 = 0.922$ with a minimum sum of squared error of 110.65.

Appendix 15.3 FORECASTING WITH LINGO

To show how LINGO can be used to find the best-fitting values of the parameters of a proposed model, we use the cholesterol drug revenue data shown in Table 15.4 and Figure 15.4. In the main window of LINGO, we enter the following model (be sure to end each statement with a semicolon):

```
MODEL:
TITLE Cholesterol Revenue Quadratic Least Squares Optimization;

! MINIMIZE SUM OF SQUARED ERROR ;
MIN = (23.1 − T1)^2 + (21.3 − T2)^2 + (27.4 − T3)^2 + (34.6 − T4)^2
      + (33.8 − T5)^2 + (43.2 − T6)^2 + (59.5 − T7)^2 + (64.4 − T8)^2
      + (74.2 − T9)^2 + (99.3 − T10)^2 ;

T1 = b0 + b1*1 + b2*1 ;
T2 = b0 + b1*2 + b2*4 ;
T3 = b0 + b1*3 + b2*9 ;
T4 = b0 + b1*4 + b2*16 ;
T5 = b0 + b1*5 + b2*25 ;
T6 = b0 + b1*6 + b2*36 ;
T7 = b0 + b1*7 + b2*49 ;
T8 = b0 + b1*8 + b2*64 ;
T9 = b0 + b1*9 + b2*81 ;
T10 = b0 + b1*10 + b2*100 ;

@free(b0) ;
@free(b1) ;
@free(b2) ;
@free(T1) ;
@free(T2) ;
@free(T3) ;
@free(T4) ;
@free(T5) ;
@free(T6) ;
@free(T7) ;
@free(T8) ;
@free(T9) ;
@free(T10) ;
```

To solve the model, select the Solve command from the LINGO menu or press the Solve button on the toolbar at the top of the main frame window. LINGO will begin the solution process by determining whether the model conforms to all syntax requirements. If the LINGO model doesn't pass these tests, you will be informed by an error message. If LINGO does not find any errors in the model input, it will begin to solve the model. As part of the solution process, LINGO displays a Solver Status window that allows you to monitor the progress of the solver. LINGO displays the solution in a new window titled "Solution Report." The output that appears in the Solution Report window for the fitting of the cholesterol drug revenue data is shown in Figure 15.21.

FIGURE 15.21   LINGO SOLUTION TO THE CHOLESTEROL DRUG REVENUE LEAST-SQUARES DATA
                WITH QUADRATIC MODEL

```
Local optimal solution found.
  Objective value:                           110.6479
  Infeasibilities:                        0.8009451E-09
  Total solver iterations:                      13


Model Title: Cholesterol Revenue Quadratic Least Squares Regression
Optimization

              Variable        Value        Reduced Cost
                    T1      22.99727          0.000000
                    T2      23.65606          0.000000
                    T3      26.15803          0.000000
                    T4      30.50318          0.000000
                    T5      36.69152          0.000000
                    T6      44.72303          0.000000
                    T7      54.59773          0.000000
                    T8      66.31561          0.000000
                    T9      79.87667          0.000000
                   T10      95.28091          0.000000
                    B0      24.18167          0.000000
                    B1     -2.105985          0.000000
                    B2     0.9215909          0.000000

                   Row   Slack or Surplus    Dual Price
                     1      110.6479         -1.000000
                     2      0.000000          0.2054545
                     3      0.000000         -4.712121
                     4      0.000000          2.483939
                     5      0.000000          8.193636
                     6      0.000000         -5.783030
                     7      0.000000         -3.046061
                     8      0.000000          9.804545
                     9      0.000000         -3.831212
                    10      0.000000        -11.35333
                    11      0.000000          8.038182
```

Note that the minimum sum of squared errors is 110.6479 and the optimal values of the parameters are $b_0 = 24.18167$, $b_1 = -2.105989$, and $b_2 = 0.9215909$. The best fitting curve is therefore

$$T_t = 24.18167 - 2.105989\,t + 0.9215909\,t^2$$

CHAPTER 17

Linear Programming: Simplex Method

CONTENTS

In Chapter 2 we showed how the graphical solution procedure can be used to solve linear programming problems involving two decision variables. However, most linear programming problems are too large to be solved graphically, and an algebraic solution procedure must be employed. The most widely used algebraic procedure for solving linear programming problems is called the **simplex method.**[1] Computer programs based on this method can routinely solve linear programming problems with thousands of variables and constraints. The Management Science in Action, Fleet Assignment at Delta Air Lines, describes solving a linear program involving 60,000 variables and 40,000 constraints on a daily basis.

MANAGEMENT SCIENCE IN ACTION

FLEET ASSIGNMENT AT DELTA AIR LINES*

Delta Air Lines uses linear and integer programming in its Coldstart project to solve its fleet assignment problem. The problem is to match aircraft to flight legs and fill seats with paying passengers. Airline profitability depends on being able to assign the right size of aircraft to the right leg at the right time of day. An airline seat is a perishable commodity; once a flight takes off with an empty seat the profit potential of that seat is gone forever. Primary objectives of the fleet assignment model are to minimize operating costs and lost passenger revenue. Constraints are aircraft availability, balancing arrivals and departures at airports, and maintenance requirements.

The successful implementation of the Coldstart model for assigning fleet types to flight legs shows the size of linear programs that can be solved today. The typical size of the daily Coldstart model is about 60,000 variables and 40,000 constraints. The first step in solving the fleet assignment problem is to solve the model as a linear program. The model developers report successfully solving these problems on a daily basis and contend that use of the Coldstart model will save Delta Air Lines $300 million over the next three years.

*Based on R. Subramanian, R. P. Scheff, Jr., J. D. Quillinan, D. S. Wiper, and R. E. Marsten, "Coldstart: Fleet Assignment at Delta Air Lines," *Interfaces* (January/February 1994): 104–120.

17.1   AN ALGEBRAIC OVERVIEW OF THE SIMPLEX METHOD

Let us introduce the problem we will use to demonstrate the simplex method. HighTech Industries imports electronic components that are used to assemble two different models of personal computers. One model is called the Deskpro, and the other model is called the Portable. HighTech's management is currently interested in developing a weekly production schedule for both products.

The Deskpro generates a profit contribution of $50 per unit, and the Portable generates a profit contribution of $40 per unit. For next week's production, a maximum of 150 hours of assembly time can be made available. Each unit of the Deskpro requires 3 hours of assembly time, and each unit of the Portable requires 5 hours of assembly time. In addition, HighTech currently has only 20 Portable display components in inventory; thus, no more than 20 units of the Portable may be assembled. Finally, only 300 square feet of warehouse space can be made available for new production. Assembly of each Deskpro requires 8 square feet of warehouse space; similarly, each Portable requires 5 square feet.

---

[1]Several computer codes also employ what are called interior point solution procedures. They work well on many large problems, but the simplex method is still the most widely used solution procedure.

To develop a linear programming model for the HighTech problem, we will use the following decision variables:

$$x_1 = \text{number of units of the Deskpro}$$
$$x_2 = \text{number of units of the Portable}$$

The complete mathematical model for this problem is presented here.

$$\text{Max} \quad 50x_1 + 40x_2$$

s.t.

$$3x_1 + 5x_2 \leq 150 \quad \text{Assembly time}$$
$$1x_2 \leq 20 \quad \text{Portable display}$$
$$8x_1 + 5x_2 \leq 300 \quad \text{Warehouse capacity}$$
$$x_1, x_2 \geq 0$$

Adding a slack variable to each of the constraints permits us to write the problem in standard form.

$$\text{Max} \quad 50x_1 + 40x_2 + 0s_1 + 0s_2 + 0s_3 \tag{17.1}$$

s.t.

$$3x_1 + 5x_2 + 1s_1 \qquad\qquad = 150 \tag{17.2}$$
$$1x_2 \qquad + 1s_2 \qquad = 20 \tag{17.3}$$
$$8x_1 + 5x_2 \qquad\qquad + 1s_3 = 300 \tag{17.4}$$
$$x_1, x_2, s_1, s_2, s_3 \geq 0 \tag{17.5}$$

The simplex method was developed by George Dantzig while working for the U.S. Air Force. It was first published in 1949.

Algebraic Properties of the Simplex Method

Constraint equations (17.2) to (17.4) form a system of three simultaneous linear equations with five variables. Whenever a system of simultaneous linear equations has more variables than equations, we can expect an infinite number of solutions. The simplex method can be viewed as an algebraic procedure for finding the best solution to such a system of equations. In the preceding example, the best solution is the solution to equations (17.2) to (17.4) that maximizes the objective function (17.1) and satisfies the nonnegativity conditions given by (17.5).

Determining a Basic Solution

For the HighTech Industries constraint equations, which have more variables (five) than equations (three), the simplex method finds solutions for these equations by assigning zero values to two of the variables and then solving for the values of the remaining three variables. For example, if we set $x_2 = 0$ and $s_1 = 0$, the system of constraint equations becomes

$$3x_1 \qquad\qquad = 150 \tag{17.6}$$
$$1s_2 \qquad = 20 \tag{17.7}$$
$$8x_1 \qquad + 1s_3 = 300 \tag{17.8}$$

Using equation (17.6) to solve for x_1, we have

$$3x_1 = 150$$

and hence $x_1 = 150/3 = 50$. Equation (17.7) provides $s_2 = 20$. Finally, substituting $x_1 = 50$ into equation (17.8) results in

$$8(50) + 1s_3 = 300$$

Solving for s_3, we obtain $s_3 = -100$.

Thus, we obtain the following solution to the three-equation, five-variable set of linear equations:

A basic solution is obtained by setting two of the five variables equal to zero and solving the three equations simultaneously for the values of the other three variables. Mathematically, we are guaranteed a solution only if the resulting three equations are linearly independent. Fortunately, the simplex method is designed to guarantee that a solution exists for the basic variables at each iteration.

$$
\begin{aligned}
x_1 &= 50 \\
x_2 &= 0 \\
s_1 &= 0 \\
s_2 &= 20 \\
s_3 &= -100
\end{aligned}
$$

This solution is referred to as a **basic solution** for the HighTech linear programming problem. To state a general procedure for determining a basic solution, we must consider a standard-form linear programming problem consisting of n variables and m linear equations, where n is greater than m.

Basic Solution

To determine a basic solution, set $n - m$ of the variables equal to zero, and solve the m linear constraint equations for the remaining m variables.[2]

In terms of the HighTech problem, a basic solution can be obtained by setting any two variables equal to zero and then solving the system of three linear equations for the remaining three variables. We shall refer to the $n - m$ variables set equal to zero as the **nonbasic variables** and the remaining m variables as the **basic variables.** Thus, in the preceding example, x_2 and s_1 are the nonbasic variables, and x_1, s_2, and s_3 are the basic variables.

Basic Feasible Solution

A basic solution can be either feasible or infeasible. A **basic feasible solution** is a basic solution that also satisfies the nonnegativity conditions. The basic solution found by setting x_2 and s_1 equal to zero and then solving for x_1, s_2, and s_3 is not a basic feasible solution because $s_3 = -100$. However, suppose that we had chosen to make x_1 and x_2 nonbasic variables by setting $x_1 = 0$ and $x_2 = 0$. Solving for the corresponding basic solution is easy because with $x_1 = x_2 = 0$, the three constraint equations reduce to

$$
\begin{aligned}
1s_1 \quad\quad\quad &= 150 \\
1s_2 \quad\quad &= 20 \\
1s_3 &= 300
\end{aligned}
$$

---

[2]In some cases, a unique solution cannot be found for a system of m equations and n variables. However, these cases will never be encountered when using the simplex method.

The complete solution with $x_1 = 0$ and $x_2 = 0$ is

$$x_1 = 0$$
$$x_2 = 0$$
$$s_1 = 150$$
$$s_2 = 20$$
$$s_3 = 300$$

This solution is a basic feasible solution because all of the variables satisfy the nonnegativity conditions.

The following graph shows all the constraint equations and basic solutions for the HighTech problem. Circled points ①–⑤ are basic feasible solutions; circled points ⑥–⑨ are basic solutions that are not feasible. The basic solution found by setting $x_2 = 0$ and $s_1 = 0$ corresponds to point ⑨; the basic feasible solution found by setting $x_1 = 0$ and $x_2 = 0$ corresponds to point ① in the feasible region.

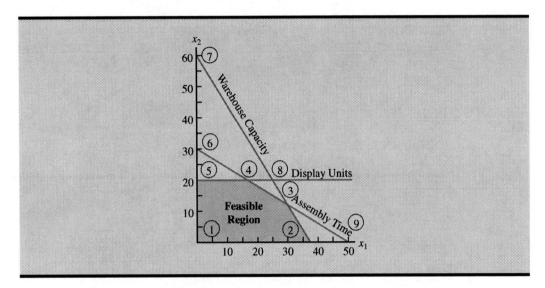

Can you find basic and basic feasible solutions to a system of equations at this point? Try Problem 1.

The graph in Figure 17.1 shows only the basic feasible solutions for the HighTech problem; note that each of these solutions is an extreme point of the feasible region. In Chapter 2 we showed that the optimal solution to a linear programming problem can be found at an extreme point. Because every extreme point corresponds to a basic feasible solution, we can now conclude that the HighTech problem does have an optimal basic feasible solution.[3] The simplex method is an iterative procedure for moving from one basic feasible solution (extreme point) to another until the optimal solution is reached.

17.2 TABLEAU FORM

A basic feasible solution to the system of m linear constraint equations and n variables is required as a starting point for the simplex method. The purpose of tableau form is to provide an initial basic feasible solution.

---

[3]We are only considering cases that have an optimal solution. That is, cases of infeasibility and unboundedness will have no optimal solution, so no optimal basic feasible solution is possible.

FIGURE 17.1   FEASIBLE REGION AND EXTREME POINTS FOR THE HIGHTECH
INDUSTRIES PROBLEM

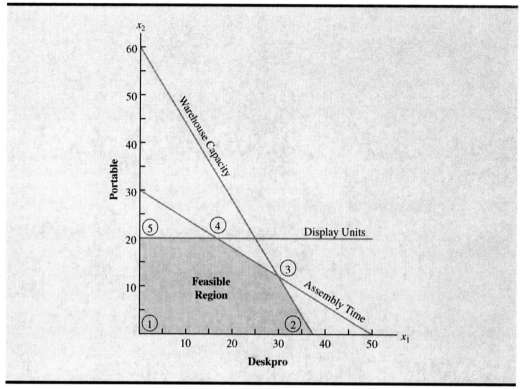

Recall that for the HighTech problem, the standard-form representation is

$$\text{Max}\quad 50x_1 + 40x_2 + 0s_1 + 0s_2 + 0s_3$$

s.t.

$$
\begin{aligned}
3x_1 +\ & 5x_2 + 1s_1 && = 150 \\
& 1x_2 && + 1s_2 && = 20 \\
8x_1 +\ & 5x_2 && + 1s_3 = 300 \\
& x_1, x_2, s_1, s_2, s_3 \geq 0
\end{aligned}
$$

When a linear programming problem with all less-than-or-equal-to constraints is written in standard form, it is easy to find a basic feasible solution. We simply set the decision
variables equal to zero and solve for the values of the slack variables. Note that this procedure sets the values of the slack variables equal to the right-hand-side values of the
constraint equations. For the HighTech problem, we obtain $x_1 = 0$, $x_2 = 0$, $s_1 = 150$,
$s_2 = 20$, and $s_3 = 300$ as the initial basic feasible solution.

If we study the standard-form representation of the HighTech constraint equations
closely, we can identify two properties that make it possible to find an initial basic feasible
solution. The first property requires that the following conditions be satisfied:

a. For each constraint equation, the coefficient of one of the m basic variables in that equation must be 1, and the coefficients for all the remaining basic variables in that equation must be 0.

b. The coefficient for each basic variable must be 1 in only one constraint equation.

When these conditions are satisfied, exactly one basic variable with a coefficient of 1 is associated with each constraint equation, and for each of the m constraint equations, it is a different basic variable. Thus, if the $n - m$ nonbasic variables are set equal to zero, the values of the basic variables are the values of the right-hand sides of the constraint equations.

For linear programs with less-than-or-equal-to constraints, the slack variables provide the initial basic feasible solution identified in tableau form.

The second property that enables us to find a basic feasible solution requires the values of the right-hand sides of the constraint equations be nonnegative. This nonnegativity ensures that the basic solution obtained by setting the basic variables equal to the values of the right-hand sides will be feasible.

If a linear programming problem satisfies these two properties, it is said to be in **tableau form.** Thus, we see that the standard-form representation of the HighTech problem is already in tableau form. In fact, standard form and tableau form for linear programs that have all less-than-or-equal-to constraints and nonnegative right-hand-side values are the same. Later in this chapter we will show how to set up the tableau form for linear programming problems where the standard form and the tableau form are not the same.

In the HighTech problem, tableau form and standard form are the same, which is true for all LPs with only less-than-or-equal-to constraints and nonnegative right-hand sides.

To summarize, the following three steps are necessary to prepare a linear programming problem for solution using the simplex method:

Step 1. Formulate the problem.
Step 2. Set up the standard form by adding slack and/or subtracting surplus variables.
Step 3. Set up the tableau form.

17.3 SETTING UP THE INITIAL SIMPLEX TABLEAU

After a linear programming problem has been converted to tableau form, we have an initial basic feasible solution that can be used to begin the simplex method. To provide a convenient means for performing the calculations required by the simplex method, we will first develop what is referred to as the initial **simplex tableau.**

Part of the initial simplex tableau is a table containing all the coefficients shown in the tableau form of a linear program. If we adopt the general notation

$$c_j = \text{objective function coefficient for variable } j$$
$$b_i = \text{right-hand-side value for constraint } i$$
$$a_{ij} = \text{coefficient associated with variable } j \text{ in constraint } i$$

we can show this portion of the initial simplex tableau as follows:

c_1	c_2	$\ldots c_n$	
a_{11}	a_{12}	$\ldots a_{1n}$	b_1
a_{21}	a_{22}	$\ldots a_{2n}$	b_2
.	.	$\ldots$	.
.	.	$\ldots$	.
a_{m1}	a_{m2}	$\ldots a_{mn}$	b_m

Thus, for the HighTech problem we obtain the following partial initial simplex tableau:

50	40	0	0	0	
3	5	1	0	0	**150**
0	1	0	1	0	**20**
8	5	0	0	1	**300**

Later we may want to refer to the objective function coefficients, all the right-hand-side values, or all the coefficients in the constraints as a group. For such groupings, we will find the following general notation helpful:

c row = row of objective function coefficients

b column = column of right-hand-side values of the constraint equations

A matrix = m rows and n columns of coefficients of the variables in the constraint equations

Using this notation, we can show these portions of the initial simplex tableau as follows:

c row	
A matrix	b column

To practice setting up the portion of the simplex tableau corresponding to the objective function and constraints at this point, try Problem 4.

To help us recall that each of the columns contains the coefficients for one of the variables, we write the variable associated with each column directly above the column. By adding the variables we obtain

x_1	x_2	s_1	s_2	s_3	
50	40	0	0	0	
3	5	1	0	0	**150**
0	1	0	1	0	**20**
8	5	0	0	1	**300**

This portion of the initial simplex tableau contains the tableau-form representation of the problem; thus, it is easy to identify the initial basic feasible solution. First, we note that for each basic variable, a corresponding column has a 1 in the only nonzero position. Such columns are known as **unit columns** or **unit vectors.** Second, a row of the tableau is associated with each basic variable. This row has a 1 in the unit column corresponding to the basic variable. The value of each basic variable is then given by the b_i value in the row associated with the basic variable. In the example, row 1 is associated with basic variable s_1 because this row has a 1 in the unit column corresponding to s_1. Thus, the value of s_1 is given by the right-hand-side value b_1: $s_1 = b_1 = 150$. In a similar fashion, $s_2 = b_2 = 20$, and $s_3 = b_3 = 300$.

To move from an initial basic feasible solution to a better basic feasible solution, the simplex method must generate a new basic feasible solution that yields a better value for the objective function. To do so requires changing the set of basic variables: we select one of the current nonbasic variables to be made basic and one of the current basic variables to be made nonbasic.

For computational convenience, we will add two new columns to the simplex tableau. One column is labeled "*Basis*" and the other column is labeled "c_B." In the **Basis** column, we list the current basic variables, and in the c_B column, we list the corresponding objective function coefficient for each of the basic variables. For the HighTech problem, this results in the following:

Basis	c_B	x_1 50	x_2 40	s_1 0	s_2 0	s_3 0	
s_1	0	3	5	1	0	0	150
s_2	0	0	1	0	1	0	20
s_3	0	8	5	0	0	1	300

Note that in the column labeled *Basis*, s_1 is listed as the first basic variable because its value is given by the right-hand-side value for the first equation. With s_2 listed second and s_3 listed third, the *Basis* column and right-hand-side values show the initial basic feasible solution has $s_1 = 150$, $s_2 = 20$, and $s_3 = 300$.

Can we improve the value of the objective function by moving to a new basic feasible solution? To find out whether it is possible, we add two rows to the bottom of the tableau. The first row, labeled z_j, represents the decrease in the value of the objective function that will result if one unit of the variable corresponding to the jth column of the A matrix is brought into the basis. The second row, labeled $c_j - z_j$, represents the net change in the value of the objective function if one unit of the variable corresponding to the jth column of the A matrix is brought into the solution. We refer to the $c_j - z_j$ row as the **net evaluation row.**

Let us first see how the entries in the z_j row are computed. Suppose that we consider increasing the value of the nonbasic variable x_1 by one unit—that is, from $x_1 = 0$ to $x_1 = 1$. In order to make this change and at the same time continue to satisfy the constraint equations, the values of some of the other variables will have to be changed. As we will show, the simplex method requires that the necessary changes be made to basic variables only. For example, in the first constraint we have

$$3x_1 + 5x_2 + 1s_1 = 150$$

The current basic variable in this constraint equation is s_1. Assuming that x_2 remains a nonbasic variable with a value of 0, if x_1 is increased in value by 1, then s_1 must be decreased by 3 for the constraint to be satisfied. Similarly, if we were to increase the value of x_1 by 1 (and keep $x_2 = 0$), we can see from the second and third equations that although s_2 would not decrease, s_3 would decrease by 8.

From analyzing all the constraint equations, we see that the coefficients in the x_1 column indicate the amount of decrease in the current basic variables when the nonbasic variable x_1 is increased from 0 to 1. In general, all the column coefficients can be interpreted this way. For instance, if we make x_2 a basic variable at a value of 1, s_1 will decrease by 5, s_2 will decrease by 1, and s_3 will decrease by 5.

Recall that the values in the c_B column of the simplex tableau are the objective function coefficients for the current basic variables. Hence, to compute the values in the z_j row (the decrease in value of the objective function when x_j is increased by one), we form the sum of the products obtained by multiplying the elements in the c_B column by the corresponding elements in the jth column of the A matrix. Doing these calculations we obtain

$$z_1 = 0(3) + 0(0) + 0(8) = 0$$
$$z_2 = 0(5) + 0(1) + 0(5) = 0$$
$$z_3 = 0(1) + 0(0) + 0(0) = 0$$
$$z_4 = 0(0) + 0(1) + 0(0) = 0$$
$$z_5 = 0(0) + 0(0) + 0(1) = 0$$

Because the objective function coefficient of x_1 is $c_1 = 50$, the value of $c_1 - z_1$ is $50 - 0 = 50$. Then the net result of bringing one unit of x_1 into the current basis will be an increase in profit of $50. Hence, in the net evaluation row corresponding to x_1, we enter 50. In the same manner, we can calculate the $c_j - z_j$ values for the remaining variables. The result is the following initial simplex tableau:

The simplex tableau is nothing more than a table that helps keep track of the simplex method calculations. Reconstructing the original problem can be accomplished from the initial simplex tableau.

		x_1	x_2	s_1	s_2	s_3	
Basis	c_B	50	40	0	0	0	
s_1	0	3	5	1	0	0	150
s_2	0	0	1	0	1	0	20
s_3	0	8	5	0	0	1	300
z_j		0	0	0	0	0	**0**
$c_j - z_j$		50	40	0	0	0	↑

Value of the
Objective Function

In this tableau we also see a boldfaced 0 in the z_j row in the last column. This zero is the value of the objective function associated with the current basic feasible solution. It was computed by multiplying the objective function coefficients in the c_B column by the corresponding values of the basic variables shown in the last column of the tableau—that is, $0(150) + 0(20) + 0(300) = 0$.

Try Problem 5(a) for practice in setting up the complete initial simplex tableau for a problem with less-than-or-equal-to constraints.

The initial simplex tableau is now complete. It shows that the initial basic feasible solution ($x_1 = 0, x_2 = 0, s_1 = 150, s_2 = 20$, and $s_3 = 300$) has an objective function value, or profit, of $0. In addition, the $c_j - z_j$ or net evaluation row has values that will guide us in improving the solution by moving to a better basic feasible solution.

17.4 IMPROVING THE SOLUTION

From the net evaluation row, we see that each unit of the Deskpro (x_1) increases the value of the objective function by 50 and each unit of the Portable (x_2) increases the value of the objective function by 40. Because x_1 causes the largest per-unit increase, we choose it as the variable to bring into the basis. We must next determine which of the current basic variables to make nonbasic.

In discussing how to compute the z_j values, we noted that each of the coefficients in the x_1 column indicates the amount of decrease in the corresponding basic variable that would result from increasing x_1 by one unit. Considering the first row, we see that every unit of the Deskpro produced will use 3 hours of assembly time, reducing s_1 by 3. In the current solution, $s_1 = 150$ and $x_1 = 0$. Thus—considering this row only—the maximum possible value of x_1 can be calculated by solving

$$3x_1 = 150$$

which provides

$$x_1 = 50$$

If x_1 is 50 (and x_2 remains a nonbasic variable with a value of 0), s_1 will have to be reduced to zero in order to satisfy the first constraint:

$$3x_1 + 5x_2 + 1s_1 = 150$$

Considering the second row, $0x_1 + 1x_2 + 1s_2 = 20$, we see that the coefficient of x_1 is 0. Thus, increasing x_1 will not have any effect on s_2; that is, increasing x_1 cannot drive the basic variable in the second row (s_2) to zero. Indeed, increases in x_1 will leave s_2 unchanged.

Finally, with 8 as the coefficient of x_1 in the third row, every unit that we increase x_1 will cause a decrease of eight units in s_3. Because the value of s_3 is currently 300, we can solve

$$8x_1 = 300$$

to find the maximum possible increase in x_1 before s_3 will become nonbasic at a value of zero; thus, we see that x_1 cannot be any larger than $^{300}/_8 = 37.5$.

Considering the three rows (constraints) simultaneously, we see that row 3 is the most restrictive. That is, producing 37.5 units of the Deskpro will force the corresponding slack variable to become nonbasic at a value of $s_3 = 0$.

In making the decision to produce as many Deskpro units as possible, we must change the set of variables in the basic feasible solution, which means obtaining a new basis. The simplex method moves from one basic feasible solution to another by selecting a nonbasic variable to replace one of the current basic variables. This process of moving from one basic feasible solution to another is called an **iteration.** We now summarize the rules for selecting a nonbasic variable to be made basic and for selecting a current basic variable to be made nonbasic.

Criterion for Entering a New Variable into the Basis

Look at the net evaluation row ($c_j - z_j$), and select the variable to enter the basis that will cause the largest per-unit improvement in the value of the objective function. In the case of a tie, follow the convention of selecting the variable to enter the basis that corresponds to the leftmost of the columns.

To determine which basic variable will become nonbasic, only the positive coefficients in the incoming column correspond to basic variables that will decrease in value when the new basic variable enters.

Criterion for Removing a Variable from the Current Basis (Minimum Ratio Test)

Suppose the incoming basic variable corresponds to column j in the A portion of the simplex tableau. For each row i, compute the ratio b_i/a_{ij} for each a_{ij} greater than zero. The basic variable that will be removed from the basis corresponds to the minimum of these ratios. In case of a tie, we follow the convention of selecting the variable that corresponds to the uppermost of the tied rows.

To illustrate the computations involved, we add an extra column to the right of the tableau showing the b_i/a_{ij} ratios.

Basis	c_B	x_1 50	x_2 40	s_1 0	s_2 0	s_3 0		$\dfrac{b_i}{a_{i1}}$
s_1	0	3	5	1	0	0	150	$\dfrac{150}{3} = 50$
s_2	0	0	1	0	1	0	20	—
s_3	0	⑧	5	0	0	1	300	$\dfrac{300}{8} = 37.5$
z_j		0	0	0	0	0	0	
$c_j - z_j$		50	40	0	0	0		

We see that $c_1 - z_1 = 50$ is the largest positive value in the $c_j - z_j$ row. Hence, x_1 is selected to become the new basic variable. Checking the ratios b_i/a_{i1} for values of a_{i1} greater than zero, we see that $b_3/a_{31} = 300/8 = 37.5$ is the minimum of these ratios. Thus, the current basic variable associated with row 3 (s_3) is the variable selected to leave the basis. In the tableau we have circled $a_{31} = 8$ to indicate that the variable corresponding to the first column is to enter the basis and that the basic variable corresponding to the third row is to leave the basis. Adopting the usual linear programming terminology, we refer to this circled element as the **pivot element.** The column and the row containing the pivot element are called the **pivot column** and the **pivot row,** respectively.

The circled value is the pivot element; the corresponding column and row are called the pivot

To improve the current solution of $x_1 = 0$, $x_2 = 0$, $s_1 = 150$, $s_2 = 20$, and $s_3 = 300$, we should increase x_1 to 37.5. The production of 37.5 units of the Deskpro results in a profit of $50(37.5) = 1875$. In producing 37.5 units of the Deskpro, s_3 will be reduced to zero. Hence, x_1 will become the new basic variable, replacing s_3 in the previous basis.

17.5   CALCULATING THE NEXT TABLEAU

We now want to update the simplex tableau in such a fashion that the column associated with the new basic variable is a unit column; in this way its value will be given by the right-hand-side value of the corresponding row. We would like the column in the new tableau corresponding to x_1 to look just like the column corresponding to s_3 in the original tableau, so our goal is to make the column in the A matrix corresponding to x_1 appear as

$$0$$
$$0$$
$$1$$

The way in which we transform the simplex tableau so that it still represents an equivalent system of constraint equations is to use the following **elementary row operations.**

Elementary Row Operations

1. Multiply any row (equation) by a nonzero number.
2. Replace any row (equation) by the result of adding or subtracting a multiple of another row (equation) to it.

The application of these elementary row operations to a system of simultaneous linear equations will not change the solution to the system of equations; however, the elementary row operations will change the coefficients of the variables and the values of the right-hand sides.

The objective in performing elementary row operations is to transform the system of constraint equations into a form that makes it easy to identify the new basic feasible solution. Consequently, we must perform the elementary row operations in such a manner that we transform the column for the variable entering the basis into a unit column. We emphasize that the feasible solutions to the original constraint equations are the same as the feasible solutions to the modified constraint equations obtained by performing elementary row operations. However, many of the numerical values in the simplex tableau will change as the result of performing these row operations. Thus, the present method of referring to elements in the simplex tableau may lead to confusion.

Until now we made no distinction between the A matrix and b column coefficients in the tableau form of the problem and the corresponding coefficients in the simplex tableau. Indeed, we showed that the initial simplex tableau is formed by properly placing the a_{ij}, c_j, and b_i elements as given in the tableau form of the problem into the simplex tableau. To avoid confusion in subsequent simplex tableaus, we will refer to the portion of the simplex tableau that initially contained the a_{ij} values with the symbol $\bar{A}$, and the portion of the tableau that initially contained the b_i values with the symbol $\bar{b}$. In terms of the simplex tableau, elements in $\bar{A}$ will be denoted by $\bar{a}_{ij}$, and elements in $\bar{b}$ will be denoted by $\bar{b}_i$. In subsequent simplex tableaus, elementary row operations will change the tableau elements. The overbar notation should avoid any confusion when we wish to distinguish between (1) the original constraint coefficient values a_{ij} and right-hand-side values b_i of the tableau form, and (2) the simplex tableau elements $\bar{a}_{ij}$ and $\bar{b}_i$.

Now let us see how elementary row operations are used to create the next simplex tableau for the HighTech problem. Recall that the goal is to transform the column in the $\bar{A}$ portion of the simplex tableau corresponding to x_1 to a unit column; that is,

$$\bar{a}_{11} = 0$$
$$\bar{a}_{21} = 0$$
$$\bar{a}_{31} = 1$$

To set $\bar{a}_{31} = 1$, we perform the first elementary row operation by multiplying the pivot row (row 3) by $\frac{1}{8}$ to obtain the equivalent equation

$$\tfrac{1}{8}(8x_1 + 5x_2 + 0s_1 + 0s_2 + 1s_3) = \tfrac{1}{8}(300)$$

or

$$1x_1 + \tfrac{5}{8}x_2 + 0s_1 + 0s_2 + \tfrac{1}{8}s_3 = \tfrac{75}{2} \qquad (17.9)$$

We refer to equation (17.9) in the updated simplex tableau as the *new pivot row.*

To set $\bar{a}_{11} = 0$, we perform the second elementary row operation by first multiplying the new pivot row by 3 to obtain the equivalent equation

$$3(1x_1 + \tfrac{5}{8}x_2 + 0s_1 + 0s_2 + \tfrac{1}{8}s_3) = 3(\tfrac{75}{2})$$

or

$$3x_1 + \tfrac{15}{8}x_2 + 0s_1 + 0s_2 + \tfrac{3}{8}s_3 = \tfrac{225}{2} \qquad (17.10)$$

Subtracting equation (17.10) from the equation represented by row 1 of the simplex tableau completes the application of the second elementary row operation; thus, after dropping the terms with zero coefficients, we obtain

$$(3x_1 + 5x_2 + 1s_1) - (3x_1 + \tfrac{15}{8}x_2 + \tfrac{3}{8}s_3) = 150 - \tfrac{225}{2}$$

or

$$0x_1 + \tfrac{25}{8}x_2 + 1s_1 - \tfrac{3}{8}s_3 = \tfrac{75}{2} \qquad (17.11)$$

Because $\bar{a}_{21} = 0$, no row operations need be performed on the second row of the simplex tableau. Replacing rows 1 and 3 with the coefficients in equations (17.11) and (17.9), respectively, we obtain the new simplex tableau

Basis	c_B	x_1 50	x_2 40	s_1 0	s_2 0	s_3 0	
s_1	0	0	$\tfrac{25}{8}$	1	0	$-\tfrac{3}{8}$	$\tfrac{75}{2}$
s_2	0	0	1	0	1	0	20
x_1	50	1	$\tfrac{5}{8}$	0	0	$\tfrac{1}{8}$	$\tfrac{75}{2}$
z_j							1875
$c_j - z_j$							

Assigning zero values to the nonbasic variables x_2 and s_3 permits us to identify the following new basic feasible solution:

$$s_1 = \tfrac{75}{2}$$
$$s_2 = 20$$
$$x_1 = \tfrac{75}{2}$$

This solution is also provided by the last column in the new simplex tableau. The profit associated with this solution is obtained by multiplying the solution values for the basic variables as given in the $\bar{b}$ column by their corresponding objective function coefficients as given in the c_B column; that is,

$$0(\tfrac{75}{2}) + 0(20) + 50(\tfrac{75}{2}) = 1875$$

Interpreting the Results of an Iteration

In our example, the initial basic feasible solution was

$$
\begin{aligned}
x_1 &= 0 \\
x_2 &= 0 \\
s_1 &= 150 \\
s_2 &= 20 \\
s_3 &= 300
\end{aligned}
$$

with a corresponding profit of $0. One iteration of the simplex method moved us to another basic feasible solution with an objective function value of $1875. This new basic feasible solution is

$$
\begin{aligned}
x_1 &= {}^{75}\!/_2 \\
x_2 &= 0 \\
s_1 &= {}^{75}\!/_2 \\
s_2 &= 20 \\
s_3 &= 0
\end{aligned}
$$

In Figure 17.2 we see that the initial basic feasible solution corresponds to extreme point ①. The first iteration moved us in the direction of the greatest increase per unit in profit—that is, along the x_1 axis. We moved away from extreme point ① in the x_1 direction until we could not move farther without violating one of the constraints. The tableau we obtained after one iteration provides the basic feasible solution corresponding to extreme point ②.

The first iteration moves us from the origin in Figure 17.2 to extreme point 2.

We note from Figure 17.2 that at extreme point ② the warehouse capacity constraint is binding with $s_3 = 0$ and that the other two constraints contain slack. From the simplex tableau, we see that the amount of slack for these two constraints is given by $s_1 = {}^{75}\!/_2$ and $s_2 = 20$.

Moving Toward a Better Solution

To see whether a better basic feasible solution can be found, we need to calculate the z_j and $c_j - z_j$ rows for the new simplex tableau. Recall that the elements in the z_j row are the sum of the products obtained by multiplying the elements in the c_B column of the simplex tableau by the corresponding elements in the columns of the $\bar{A}$ matrix. Thus, we obtain

$$
\begin{aligned}
z_1 &= 0(0) & + 0(0) + 50(1) &= 50 \\
z_2 &= 0(^{25}\!/_8) & + 0(1) + 50(^{5}\!/_8) &= {}^{250}\!/_8 \\
z_3 &= 0(1) & + 0(0) + 50(0) &= 0 \\
z_4 &= 0(0) & + 0(1) + 50(0) &= 0 \\
z_5 &= 0(-^{3}\!/_8) & + 0(0) + 50(^{1}\!/_8) &= {}^{50}\!/_8
\end{aligned}
$$

FIGURE 17.2   FEASIBLE REGION AND EXTREME POINTS FOR THE HIGHTECH INDUSTRIES PROBLEM

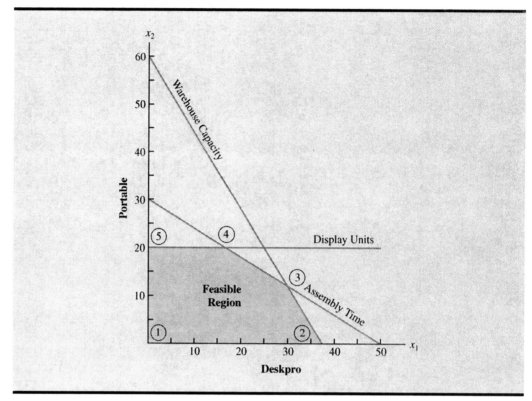

Subtracting z_j from c_j to compute the new net evaluation row, we obtain the following simplex tableau:

		x_1	x_2	s_1	s_2	s_3	
Basis	c_B	50	40	0	0	0	
s_1	0	0	$^{25}/_8$	1	0	$-^3/_8$	$^{75}/_2$
s_2	0	0	1	0	1	0	**20**
x_1	50	1	$^5/_8$	0	0	$^1/_8$	$^{75}/_2$
z_j		50	$^{250}/_8$	0	0	$^{50}/_8$	**1875**
$c_j - z_j$		0	$^{70}/_8$	0	0	$-^{50}/_8$	

Let us now analyze the $c_j - z_j$ row to see whether we can introduce a new variable into the basis and continue to improve the value of the objective function. Using the rule for determining which variable should enter the basis next, we select x_2 because it has the highest positive coefficient in the $c_j - z_j$ row.

To determine which variable will be removed from the basis when x_2 enters, we must compute for each row i the ratio $\bar{b}_i/\bar{a}_{i2}$ (remember, though, that we should compute this ratio only if $\bar{a}_{i2}$ is greater than zero); then we select the variable to leave the basis that corresponds to the minimum ratio. As before, we will show these ratios in an extra column of the simplex tableau:

Basis	c_B	x_1 50	x_2 40	s_1 0	s_2 0	s_3 0		$\dfrac{\bar{b}_i}{\bar{a}_{i2}}$
s_1	0	0	㉕⁄₈	1	0	$-\tfrac{3}{8}$	$\tfrac{75}{2}$	$\dfrac{75/2}{25/8} = 12$
s_2	0	0	1	0	1	0	20	$\dfrac{20}{1} = 20$
x_1	50	1	$\tfrac{5}{8}$	0	0	$\tfrac{1}{8}$	$\tfrac{75}{2}$	$\dfrac{75/2}{5/8} = 60$
z_j		50	$\tfrac{250}{8}$	0	0	$\tfrac{50}{8}$	1875	
$c_j - z_j$		0	$\tfrac{70}{8}$	0	0	$-\tfrac{50}{8}$		

With 12 as the minimum ratio, s_1 will leave the basis. The pivot element is $\bar{a}_{12} = \tfrac{25}{8}$, which is circled in the preceding tableau. The nonbasic variable x_2 must now be made a basic variable in row 1. This requirement means that we must perform the elementary row operations that will convert the x_2 column into a unit column with a 1 in row 1; that is, we will have to transform the second column in the tableau to the form

$$1$$
$$0$$
$$0$$

We can make this change by performing the following elementary row operations:

Step 1. Multiply every element in row 1 (the pivot row) by $\tfrac{8}{25}$ in order to make $\bar{a}_{12} = 1$.
Step 2. Subtract the new row 1 (the new pivot row) from row 2 to make $\bar{a}_{22} = 0$.
Step 3. Multiply the new pivot row by $\tfrac{5}{8}$, and subtract the result from row 3 to make $\bar{a}_{32} = 0$.

The new simplex tableau resulting from these row operations is as follows:

Basis	c_B	x_1 50	x_2 40	s_1 0	s_2 0	s_3 0	
x_2	40	0	1	$\tfrac{8}{25}$	0	$-\tfrac{3}{25}$	12
s_2	0	0	0	$-\tfrac{8}{25}$	1	$\tfrac{3}{25}$	8
x_1	50	1	0	$-\tfrac{5}{25}$	0	$\tfrac{5}{25}$	30
z_j		50	40	$\tfrac{14}{5}$	0	$\tfrac{26}{5}$	1980
$c_j - z_j$		0	0	$-\tfrac{14}{5}$	0	$-\tfrac{26}{5}$	

Note that the values of the basic variables are $x_2 = 12$, $s_2 = 8$, and $x_1 = 30$, and the corresponding profit is $40(12) + 0(8) + 50(30) = 1980$.

We must now determine whether to bring any other variable into the basis and thereby move to another basic feasible solution. Looking at the net evaluation row, we see that every element is zero or negative. Because $c_j - z_j$ is less than or equal to zero for both of the nonbasic variables s_1 and s_3, any attempt to bring a nonbasic variable into the basis at this point will result in a lowering of the current value of the objective function. Hence, this tableau represents the optimal solution. In general, the simplex method uses the following criterion to determine when the optimal solution has been obtained.

Optimality Criterion

The optimal solution to a linear programming problem has been reached when all of the entries in the net evaluation row $(c_j - z_j)$ are zero or negative. In such cases, the optimal solution is the current basic feasible solution.

Referring to Figure 17.2, we can see graphically the process that the simplex method used to determine an optimal solution. The initial basic feasible solution corresponds to the origin ($x_1 = 0$, $x_2 = 0$, $s_1 = 150$, $s_2 = 20$, $s_3 = 300$). The first iteration caused x_1 to enter the basis and s_3 to leave. The second basic feasible solution corresponds to extreme point ② ($x_1 = {}^{75}\!/_2$, $x_2 = 0$, $s_1 = {}^{75}\!/_2$, $s_2 = 20$, $s_3 = 0$). At the next iteration, x_2 entered the basis and s_1 left. This iteration brought us to extreme point ③ and the optimal solution ($x_1 = 30$, $x_2 = 12$, $s_1 = 0$, $s_2 = 8$, $s_3 = 0$).

For the HighTech problem with only two decision variables, we had a choice of using the graphical or simplex method. For problems with more than two variables, we shall always use the simplex method.

Interpreting the Optimal Solution

Using the final simplex tableau, we find the optimal solution to the HighTech problem consists of the basic variables x_1, x_2, and s_2 and nonbasic variables s_1 and s_3 with:

$$x_1 = 30$$
$$x_2 = 12$$
$$s_1 = 0$$
$$s_2 = 8$$
$$s_3 = 0$$

The value of the objective function is $1980. If management wants to maximize the total profit contribution, HighTech should produce 30 units of the Deskpro and 12 units of the Portable. When $s_2 = 8$, management should note that there will be eight unused Portable display units. Moreover, because $s_1 = 0$ and $s_3 = 0$, no slack is associated with the assembly time constraint and the warehouse capacity constraint; in other words, these constraints are both binding. Consequently, if it is possible to obtain additional assembly time and/or additional warehouse space, management should consider doing so.

Figure 17.3 shows the computer solution to the HighTech problem using The Management Scientist software package. The optimal solution with $x_1 = 30$ and $x_2 = 12$ is shown to have an objective function value of $1980. The values of the slack variables complete the optimal solution with $s_1 = 0$, $s_2 = 8$, and $s_3 = 0$. The values in the Reduced Costs column are from the net evaluation row of the final simplex tableau. Note that the $c_j - z_j$ values in columns corresponding to x_1 and x_2 are both 0. The dual prices are the z_j values for the three slack variables in the final simplex tableau. Referring to the final tableau, we see that the dual price for constraint 1 is the z_j value corresponding to s_1 where ${}^{14}\!/_5 = 2.8$. Similarly, the dual price for constraint 2 is 0, and the dual price for constraint 3 is ${}^{26}\!/_5 = 5.2$. The use of the simplex method to compute dual prices will be discussed further when we cover sensitivity analysis in Chapter 18.

FIGURE 17.3   THE MANAGEMENT SCIENTIST SOLUTION FOR THE HIGHTECH INDUSTRIES PROBLEM

```
OPTIMAL SOLUTION

Objective Function Value =            1980.000

        Variable              Value           Reduced Costs
    -------------        ---------------      ----------------
          X1                 30.000                0.000
          X2                 12.000                0.000

      Constraint         Slack/Surplus          Dual Prices
    -------------        ---------------      ----------------
          1                  0.000                 2.800
          2                  8.000                 0.000
          3                  0.000                 5.200
```

Summary of the Simplex Method

Let us now summarize the steps followed to solve a linear program using the simplex method. We assume that the problem has all less-than-or-equal-to constraints and involves maximization.

Step 1. Formulate a linear programming model of the problem.

Step 2. Add slack variables to each constraint to obtain standard form. This also provides the tableau form necessary to identify an initial basic feasible solution for problems involving all less-than-or-equal-to constraints with nonnegative right-hand-side values.

Step 3. Set up the initial simplex tableau.

Step 4. Choose the nonbasic variable with the largest entry in the net evaluation row to bring into the basis. This variable identifies the pivot column: the column associated with the incoming variable.

Step 5. Choose as the pivot row that row with the smallest ratio of $\bar{b}_i/\bar{a}_{ij}$ for $\bar{a}_{ij} > 0$ where j is the pivot column. This pivot row is the row of the variable leaving the basis when variable j enters.

Step 6. Perform the necessary elementary row operations to convert the column for the incoming variable to a unit column with a 1 in the pivot row.

   a. Divide each element of the pivot row by the pivot element (the element in the pivot row and pivot column).

   b. Obtain zeroes in all other positions of the pivot column by adding or subtracting an appropriate multiple of the new pivot row. Once the row operations have been completed, the value of the new basic feasible solution can be read from the $\bar{b}$ column of the tableau.

Step 7. Test for optimality. If $c_j - z_j \leq 0$ for all columns, the solution is optimal. If not, return to step 4.

To test your ability to solve a problem employing the simplex method, try Problem 6.

The steps are basically the same for problems with equality and greater-than-or-equal-to constraints except that setting up tableau form requires a little more work. We discuss what is involved in Section 17.6. The modification necessary for minimization problems is covered in Section 17.7.

NOTES AND COMMENTS

The entries in the net evaluation row provide the reduced costs that appear in the computer solution to a linear program. Recall that in Chapter 3 we defined the reduced cost as the amount by which an objective function coefficient would have to improve before it would be possible for the corresponding variable to assume a positive value in the optimal solution. In general, the reduced costs are the absolute values of the entries in the net evaluation row.

17.6   TABLEAU FORM: THE GENERAL CASE

This section explains how to get started with the simplex method for problems with greater-than-or-equal-to and equality constraints.

When a linear program contains all less-than-or-equal-to constraints with nonnegative right-hand-side values, it is easy to set up the tableau form; we simply add a slack variable to each constraint. However, obtaining tableau form is somewhat more complex if the linear program contains greater-than-or-equal-to constraints, equality constraints, and/or negative right-hand-side values. In this section we describe how to develop tableau form for each of these situations and also how to solve linear programs involving equality and greater-than-or-equal-to constraints using the simplex method.

Greater-Than-or-Equal-to Constraints

Suppose that in the HighTech Industries problem, management wanted to ensure that the combined total production for both models would be at least 25 units. This requirement means that the following constraint must be added to the current linear program:

$$1x_1 + 1x_2 \geq 25$$

Adding this constraint results in the following modified problem:

$$\text{Max} \quad 50x_1 + 40x_2$$

s.t.

$$
\begin{aligned}
3x_1 + 5x_2 &\leq 150 \quad \text{Assembly time} \\
1x_2 &\leq 20 \quad \text{Portable display} \\
8x_1 + 5x_2 &\leq 300 \quad \text{Warehouse space} \\
1x_1 + 1x_2 &\leq 25 \quad \text{Minimum total production} \\
x_1, x_2 &\geq 0
\end{aligned}
$$

First, we use three slack variables and one surplus variable to write the problem in standard form. This provides the following:

$$\text{Max} \quad 50x_1 + 40x_2 + 0s_1 + 0s_2 + 0s_3 + 0s_4$$

s.t.

$$
\begin{aligned}
3x_1 + 5x_2 + 1s_1 &= 150 \quad (17.12)\\
1x_2 + 1s_2 &= 20 \quad (17.13)\\
8x_1 + 5x_2 + 1s_3 &= 300 \quad (17.14)\\
1x_1 + 1x_2 - 1s_4 &= 25 \quad (17.15)\\
x_1, x_2, s_1, s_2, s_3, s_4 &\geq 0
\end{aligned}
$$

Now let us consider how we obtain an initial basic feasible solution to start the simplex method. Previously, we set $x_1 = 0$ and $x_2 = 0$ and selected the slack variables as the initial basic variables. The extension of this notion to the modified HighTech problem would suggest setting $x_1 = 0$ and $x_2 = 0$ and selecting the slack and surplus variables as the initial basic variables. Doing so results in the basic solution

$$
\begin{aligned}
x_1 &= 0 \\
x_2 &= 0 \\
s_1 &= 150 \\
s_2 &= 20 \\
s_3 &= 300 \\
s_4 &= -25
\end{aligned}
$$

Clearly this solution is not a basic feasible solution because $s_4 = -25$ violates the nonnegativity requirement. The difficulty is that the standard form and the tableau form are not equivalent when the problem contains greater-than-or-equal-to constraints.

To set up the tableau form, we shall resort to a mathematical "trick" that will enable us to find an initial basic feasible solution in terms of the slack variables s_1, s_2, and s_3 and a new variable we shall denote a_4. The new variable constitutes the mathematical trick. Variable a_4 really has nothing to do with the HighTech problem; it merely enables us to set up the tableau form and thus obtain an initial basic feasible solution. This new variable, which has been artificially created to start the simplex method, is referred to as an **artificial variable.**

Artificial variables are appropriately named; they have no physical meaning in the real problem.

The notation for artificial variables is similar to the notation used to refer to the elements of the A matrix. To avoid any confusion between the two, recall that the elements of the A matrix (constraint coefficients) always have two subscripts, whereas artificial variables have only one subscript.

With the addition of an artificial variable, we can convert the standard form of the problem into tableau form. We add artificial variable a_4 to constraint equation (17.15) to obtain the following representation of the system of equations in tableau form:

$$
\begin{aligned}
3x_1 + 5x_2 + 1s_1 &&&&&= 150 \\
1x_2 &&+ 1s_2 &&&= 20 \\
8x_1 + 5x_2 &&&+ 1s_3 &&= 300 \\
1x_1 + 1x_2 &&&&- 1s_4 + 1a_4 &= 25
\end{aligned}
$$

Note that the subscript on the artificial variable identifies the constraint with which it is associated. Thus, a_4 is the artificial variable associated with the fourth constraint.

Because the variables s_1, s_2, s_3, and a_4 each appear in a different constraint with a coefficient of 1, and the right-hand-side values are nonnegative, both requirements of the tableau form have been satisfied. We can now obtain an initial basic feasible solution by setting $x_1 = x_2 = s_4 = 0$. The complete solution is

$$
\begin{aligned}
x_1 &= 0 \\
x_2 &= 0 \\
s_1 &= 150 \\
s_2 &= 20 \\
s_3 &= 300 \\
s_4 &= 0 \\
a_4 &= 25
\end{aligned}
$$

Is this solution feasible in terms of the real HighTech problem? No, it is not. It does not satisfy the constraint 4 combined total production requirement of 25 units. We must make an important distinction between a basic feasible solution for the tableau form and a feasible solution for the real problem. A basic feasible solution for the tableau form of a linear programming problem is not always a feasible solution for the real problem.

A basic feasible solution containing one or more artificial variables at positive values is not feasible for the real problem.

The reason for creating the tableau form is to obtain the initial basic feasible solution that is required to start the simplex method. Thus, we see that whenever it is necessary to introduce artificial variables, the initial simplex solution will not in general be feasible for the real problem. This situation is not as difficult as it might seem, however, because the only time we must have a feasible solution for the real problem is at the last iteration of the simplex method. Thus, devising a way to guarantee that any artificial variable would be eliminated from the basic feasible solution before the optimal solution is reached would eliminate the difficulty.

The way in which we guarantee that artificial variables will be eliminated before the optimal solution is reached is to assign each artificial variable a very large cost in the objective function. For example, in the modified HighTech problem, we could assign a very large negative number as the profit coefficient for artificial variable a_4. Hence, if this variable is in the basis, it will substantially reduce profits. As a result, this variable will be eliminated from the basis as soon as possible, which is precisely what we want to happen.

As an alternative to picking a large negative number such as $-100,000$ for the profit coefficient, we will denote the profit coefficient of each artificial variable by $-M$. Here it is assumed that M represents a very large number—in other words, a number of large magnitude and hence, the letter M. This notation will make it easier to keep track of the elements of the simplex tableau that depend on the profit coefficients of the artificial variables. Using $-M$ as the profit coefficient for artificial variable a_4 in the modified HighTech problem, we can write the objective function for the tableau form of the problem as follows:

$$\text{Max}\quad 50x_1 + 40x_2 + 0s_1 + 0s_2 + 0s_3 + 0s_4 - Ma_4$$

The initial simplex tableau for the problem is shown here.

Basis	c_B	x_1 50	x_2 40	s_1 0	s_2 0	s_3 0	s_4 0	a_4 $-M$	
s_1	0	3	5	1	0	0	0	0	150
s_2	0	0	1	0	1	0	0	0	20
s_3	0	8	5	0	0	1	0	0	300
a_4	$-M$	①	1	0	0	0	-1	1	25
z_j		$-M$	$-M$	0	0	0	M	$-M$	$-25M$
$c_j - z_j$		$50 + M$	$40 + M$	0	0	0	$-M$	0	

This tableau corresponds to the solution $s_1 = 150$, $s_2 = 20$, $s_3 = 300$, $a_4 = 25$, and $x_1 = x_2 = s_4 = 0$. In terms of the simplex tableau, this solution is a basic feasible solution because all the variables are greater than or equal to zero, and $n - m = 7 - 4 = 3$ of the variables are equal to zero.

Because $c_1 - z_1 = 50 + M$ is the largest value in the net evaluation row, we see that x_1 will become a basic variable during the first iteration of the simplex method. Further calculations with the simplex method show that x_1 will replace a_4 in the basic solution. The following simplex tableau is the result of the first iteration.

Result of Iteration 1

Basis	c_B	x_1 50	x_2 40	s_1 0	s_2 0	s_3 0	s_4 0	a_4 $-M$	
s_1	0	0	2	1	0	0	3	-3	75
s_2	0	0	1	0	1	0	0	0	20
s_3	0	0	-3	0	0	1	8	-8	100
x_1	50	1	1	0	0	0	-1	1	25
z_j		50	50	0	0	0	-50	50	1250
$c_j - z_j$		0	-10	0	0	0	50	$-M - 50$	

When the artificial variable $a_4 = 0$, we have a situation in which the basic feasible solution contained in the simplex tableau is also a feasible solution to the real HighTech problem. In addition, because a_4 is an artificial variable that was added simply to obtain an initial basic feasible solution, we can now drop its associated column from the simplex tableau. Indeed, whenever artificial variables are used, they can be dropped from the simplex tableau as soon as they have been eliminated from the basic feasible solution.

When artificial variables are required to obtain an initial basic feasible solution, the iterations required to eliminate the artificial variables are referred to as **phase I** of the simplex method. When all the artificial variables have been eliminated from the basis, phase I is complete, and a basic feasible solution to the real problem has been obtained. Thus, by dropping the column associated with a_4 from the current tableau, we obtain the following simplex tableau at the end of phase I.

Basis	c_B	x_1 50	x_2 40	s_1 0	s_2 0	s_3 0	s_4 0	
s_1	0	0	2	1	0	0	3	75
s_2	0	0	1	0	1	0	0	20
s_3	0	0	-3	0	0	1	⑧	100
x_1	50	1	1	0	0	0	-1	25
z_j		50	50	0	0	0	-50	1250
$c_j - z_j$		0	-10	0	0	0	50	

We are now ready to begin phase II of the simplex method. This phase simply continues the simplex method computations after all artificial variables have been removed. At the next iteration, variable s_4 with $c_j - z_j = 50$ is entered into the solution and variable s_3 is eliminated. The simplex tableau after this iteration is:

Basis	c_B	x_1 50	x_2 40	s_1 0	s_2 0	s_3 0	s_4 0	
s_1	0	0	$\boxed{25/8}$	1	0	$-3/8$	0	$75/2$
s_2	0	0	1	0	1	0	0	20
s_4	0	0	$-3/8$	0	0	$1/8$	1	$25/2$
x_1	50	1	$5/8$	0	0	$1/8$	0	$75/2$
z_j		50	$250/8$	0	0	$50/8$	0	1875
$c_j - z_j$		0	$70/8$	0	0	$-50/8$	0	

One more iteration is required. This time x_2 comes into the solution, and s_1 is eliminated. After performing this iteration, the following simplex tableau shows that the optimal solution has been reached.

Basis	c_B	x_1 50	x_2 40	s_1 0	s_2 0	s_3 0	s_4 0	
x_2	40	0	1	$8/25$	0	$-3/25$	0	12
s_2	0	0	0	$-8/25$	1	$3/25$	0	8
s_4	0	0	0	$3/25$	0	$2/25$	1	17
x_1	50	1	0	$-5/25$	0	$5/25$	0	30
z_j		50	40	$14/5$	0	$26/5$	0	1980
$c_j - z_j$		0	0	$-14/5$	0	$-26/5$	0	

It turns out that the optimal solution to the modified HighTech problem is the same as the solution for the original problem. However, the simplex method required more iterations to reach this extreme point, because an extra iteration was needed to eliminate the artificial variable (a_4) in phase I.

Fortunately, once we obtain an initial simplex tableau using artificial variables, we need not concern ourselves with whether the basic solution at a particular iteration is feasible for the real problem. We need only follow the rules for the simplex method. If we reach the optimality criterion (all $c_j - z_j \leq 0$) and all the artificial variables have been eliminated from the solution, then we have found the optimal solution. On the other hand, if we reach the optimality criterion and one or more of the artificial variables remain in solution at a positive value, then there is no feasible solution to the problem. This special case will be discussed further in Section 17.8.

Equality Constraints

When an equality constraint occurs in a linear programming problem, we need to add an artificial variable to obtain tableau form and an initial basic feasible solution. For example, if constraint 1 is

$$6x_1 + 4x_2 - 5x_3 = 30$$

we would simply add an artificial variable a_1 to create a basic feasible solution in the initial simplex tableau. With the artificial variable, the constraint equation becomes

$$6x_1 + 4x_2 - 5x_3 + 1a_1 = 30$$

Now a_1 can be selected as the basic variable for this row, and its value is given by the right-hand side. Once we have created tableau form by adding an artificial variable to each equality constraint, the simplex method proceeds exactly as before.

Eliminating Negative Right-Hand-Side Values

One of the properties of the tableau form of a linear program is that the values on the right-hand sides of the constraints have to be nonnegative. In formulating a linear programming problem, we may find one or more of the constraints have negative right-hand-side values. To see how this situation might happen, suppose that the management of HighTech has specified that the number of units of the Portable model, x_2, has to be less than or equal to the number of units of the Deskpro model, x_1, after setting aside five units of the Deskpro for internal company use. We could formulate this constraint as

$$x_2 \, x_1 - 5 \tag{17.16}$$

Subtracting x_1 from both sides of the inequality places both variables on the left-hand side of the inequality. Thus,

$$-x_1 + x_2 \leq -5 \tag{17.17}$$

Because this constraint has a negative right-hand-side value, we can develop an equivalent constraint with a nonnegative right-hand-side value by multiplying both sides of the constraint by -1. In doing so, we recognize that multiplying an inequality constraint by -1 changes the direction of the inequality.

Thus, to convert inequality (17.17) to an equivalent constraint with a nonnegative right-hand-side value, we multiply by -1 to obtain

$$-x_1 + x_2 \geq -5 \tag{17.18}$$

We now have an acceptable nonnegative right-hand-side value. Tableau form for this constraint can now be obtained by subtracting a surplus variable and adding an artificial variable.

For a greater-than-or-equal-to constraint, multiplying by -1 creates an equivalent less-than-or-equal-to constraint. For example, suppose we had the following greater-than-or-equal-to constraint:

$$6x_1 + 3x_2 - 4x_3 \geq -20$$

Multiplying by -1 to obtain an equivalent constraint with a nonnegative right-hand-side value leads to the following less-than-or-equal-to constraint

$$-6x_1 - 3x_2 + 4x_3 \leq 20$$

Tableau form can be created for this constraint by adding a slack variable.

For an equality constraint with a negative right-hand-side value, we simply multiply by -1 to obtain an equivalent constraint with a nonnegative right-hand-side value. An artificial variable can then be added to create the tableau form.

Summary of the Steps to Create Tableau Form

Step 1. If the original formulation of the linear programming problem contains one or more constraints with negative right-hand-side values, multiply each of these constraints by -1. Multiplying by -1 will change the direction of the inequalities. This step will provide an equivalent linear program with nonnegative right-hand-side values.

Step 2. For $\leq$ constraints, add a slack variable to obtain an equality constraint. The coefficient of the slack variable in the objective function is assigned a value of zero. It provides the tableau form for the constraint, and the slack variable becomes one of the basic variables in the initial basic feasible solution.

Step 3. For $\geq$ constraints, subtract a surplus variable to obtain an equality constraint, and then add an artificial variable to obtain the tableau form. The coefficient of the surplus variable in the objective function is assigned a value of zero. The coefficient of the artificial variable in the objective function is assigned a value of $-M$. The artificial variable becomes one of the basic variables in the initial basic feasible solution.

Step 4. For equality constraints, add an artificial variable to obtain the tableau form. The coefficient of the artificial variable in the objective function is assigned a value of $-M$. The artificial variable becomes one of the basic variables in the initial basic feasible solution.

To obtain some practice in applying these steps, convert the following example problem into tableau form, and then set up the initial simplex tableau:

$$\text{Max} \quad 6x_1 + 3x_2 + 4x_3 + 1x_4$$
$$\text{s.t.}$$
$$-2x_1 - \tfrac{1}{2}x_2 + 1x_3 - 6x_4 = -60$$
$$1x_1 \qquad\quad + 1x_3 + \tfrac{2}{3}x_4 \leq 20$$
$$-1x_2 - 5x_3 \qquad\qquad \leq -50$$
$$x_1, x_2, x_3, x_4 \geq 0$$

To eliminate the negative right-hand-side values in constraints 1 and 3, we apply step 1. Multiplying both constraints by -1, we obtain the following equivalent linear program:

$$\text{Max} \quad 6x_1 + 3x_2 + 4x_3 + 1x_4$$
$$\text{s.t.}$$
$$2x_1 + \tfrac{1}{2}x_2 - 1x_3 + 6x_4 = 60$$
$$1x_1 \qquad\quad + 1x_3 + \tfrac{2}{3}x_4 \leq 20$$
$$1x_2 + 5x_3 \qquad\qquad \geq 50$$
$$x_1, x_2, x_3, x_4 \geq 0$$

Note that the direction of the $\leq$ inequality in constraint 3 has been reversed as a result of multiplying the constraint by -1. By applying step 4 for constraint 1, step 2 for constraint 2, and step 3 for constraint 3, we obtain the following tableau form:

$$\text{Max} \quad 6x_1 + 3x_2 + 4x_3 + 1x_4 + 0s_2 + 0s_3 - Ma_1 - Ma_3$$

s.t.

$$
\begin{aligned}
2x_1 + \tfrac{1}{2}x_2 - 1x_3 + 6x_4 && + 1a_1 && = 60 \\
1x_1 && + 1x_3 + \tfrac{2}{3}x_4 + 1s_2 && = 20 \\
1x_2 + 5x_3 && - 1s_3 && + 1a_3 = 50 \\
x_1, x_2, x_3, x_4, s_2, s_3, a_1, a_3 \geq 0
\end{aligned}
$$

The initial simplex tableau corresponding to this tableau form is

Basis	c_B	x_1	x_2	x_3	x_4	s_2	s_3	a_1	a_3	
		6	3	4	1	0	0	$-M$	$-M$	
a_1	$-M$	2	$\tfrac{1}{2}$	-1	⑥	0	0	1	0	60
s_2	0	1	0	1	$\tfrac{2}{3}$	1	0	0	0	20
a_3	$-M$	0	1	5	0	0	-1	0	1	50
z_j		$-2M$	$-\tfrac{3}{2}M$	$-4M$	$-6M$	0	M	$-M$	$-M$	$-110M$
$c_j - z_j$		$6 + 2M$	$3 + \tfrac{3}{2}M$	$4 + 4M$	$1 + 6M$	0	$-M$	0	0	

For practice setting up tableau form and developing the initial simplex tableau for problems with any constraint form, try Problem 15.

Note that we have circled the pivot element indicating that x_4 will enter and a_1 will leave the basis at the first iteration.

NOTES AND COMMENTS

We have shown how to convert constraints with negative right-hand sides to equivalent constraints with positive right-hand sides. Actually, nothing is wrong with formulating a linear program and including negative right-hand sides. But if you want to use the ordinary simplex method to solve the linear program, you must first alter the constraints to eliminate the negative right-hand sides.

17.7 SOLVING A MINIMIZATION PROBLEM

We can use the simplex method to solve a minimization problem in two ways. The first approach requires that we change the rule used to introduce a variable into the basis. Recall that in the maximization case, we select the variable with the largest positive $c_j - z_j$ as the variable to introduce next into the basis, because the value of $c_j - z_j$ tells us the amount the objective function will increase if one unit of the variable in column j is brought into solution. To solve the minimization problem, we simply reverse this rule. That is, we select the variable with the most negative $c_j - z_j$ as the one to introduce next. Of course, this approach means the stopping rule for the optimal solution will also have to be changed. Using this approach to solve a minimization problem, we would stop when every value in the net evaluation row is zero or positive.

The second approach to solving a minimization problem is the one we shall employ in this book. It is based on the fact that any minimization problem can be converted to an equivalent maximization problem by multiplying the objective function by -1. Solving the resulting maximization problem will provide the optimal solution to the minimization problem.

In keeping with the general notation of this chapter, we are using x_1 and x_2 to represent units of product A and product B.

Let us illustrate this second approach by using the simplex method to solve the M&D Chemicals problem introduced in Chapter 2. Recall that in this problem, management wanted to minimize the cost of producing two products subject to a demand constraint for product A, a minimum total production quantity requirement, and a constraint on available processing time. The mathematical statement of the M&D Chemicals problem is shown here.

$$\text{Min} \quad 2x_1 + 3x_2$$
$$\text{s.t.}$$

$$\begin{aligned}
1x_1 & & \geq 125 & \quad \text{Demand for product A} \\
1x_1 + 1x_2 & & \geq 350 & \quad \text{Total production} \\
2x_1 + 1x_2 & & \leq 600 & \quad \text{Processing time} \\
x_1, x_2 & \geq 0 &
\end{aligned}$$

We convert a minimization problem to a maximization problem by multiplying the objective function by −1.

To solve this problem using the simplex method, we first multiply the objective function by −1 to convert the minimization problem into the following equivalent maximization problem:

$$\text{Max} \quad -2x_1 - 3x_2$$
$$\text{s.t.}$$

$$\begin{aligned}
1x_1 & & \geq 125 & \quad \text{Demand for product A} \\
1x_1 + 1x_2 & & \geq 350 & \quad \text{Total production} \\
2x_1 + 1x_2 & & \leq 600 & \quad \text{Processing time} \\
x_1, x_2 & \geq 0 &
\end{aligned}$$

The tableau form for this problem is as follows:

$$\text{Max} \quad -2x_1 - 3x_2 + 0s_1 + 0s_2 + 0s_3 - Ma_1 - Ma_2$$
$$\text{s.t.}$$

$$\begin{aligned}
1x_1 & & - 1s_1 & & + 1a_1 & & = 125 \\
1x_1 + 1x_2 & & - 1s_2 & & & + 1a_2 & = 350 \\
2x_1 + 1x_2 & & & + 1s_3 & & & = 600 \\
x_1, x_2, s_1, s_2, s_3, a_1, a_2 & \geq 0
\end{aligned}$$

The initial simplex tableau is shown here:

		x_1	x_2	s_1	s_2	s_3	a_1	a_2	
Basis	c_B	-2	-3	0	0	0	$-M$	$-M$	
a_1	$-M$	①	0	-1	0	0	1	0	125
a_2	$-M$	1	1	0	-1	0	0	1	350
s_3	0	2	1	0	0	1	0	0	600
z_j		$-2M$	$-M$	M	M	0	$-M$	$-M$	$-475M$
$c_j - z_j$		$-2 + 2M$	$-3 + M$	$-M$	$-M$	0	0	0	

At the first iteration, x_1 is brought into the basis and a_1 is removed. After dropping the a_1 column from the tableau, the result of the first iteration is as follows:

Basis	c_B	x_1 -2	x_2 -3	s_1 0	s_2 0	s_3 0	a_2 $-M$	
x_1	-2	1	0	-1	0	0	0	125
a_2	$-M$	0	1	1	-1	0	1	225
s_3	0	0	1	②	0	1	0	350
z_j		-2	$-M$	$2-M$	M	0	$-M$	$-250-225M$
$c_j - z_j$		0	$-3+M$	$-2+M$	$-M$	0	0	

Continuing with two more iterations of the simplex method provides the following final simplex tableau:

Basis	c_B	x_1 -2	x_2 -3	s_1 0	s_2 0	s_3 0	
x_1	-2	1	0	0	1	1	250
x_2	-3	0	1	0	-2	-1	100
s_1	0	0	0	1	1	1	125
z_j		-2	-3	0	4	1	-800
$c_j - z_j$		0	0	0	-4	-1	

The value of the objective function -800 must be multiplied by -1 to obtain the value of the objective function for the original minimization problem. Thus, the minimum total cost of the optimal solution is $800.

Try Problem 17 for practice solving a minimization problem with the simplex method.

In the next section we discuss some important special cases that may occur when trying to solve any linear programming problem. We will only consider the case for maximization problems, recognizing that all minimization problems can be converted into an equivalent maximization problem by multiplying the objective function by -1.

17.8   SPECIAL CASES

In Chapter 2 we discussed how infeasibility, unboundedness, and alternative optimal solutions could occur when solving linear programming problems using the graphical solution procedure. These special cases can also arise when using the simplex method. In addition, a special case referred to as *degeneracy* can theoretically cause difficulties for the simplex method. In this section we show how these special cases can be recognized and handled when the simplex method is used.

Infeasibility

Infeasibility occurs whenever no solution to the linear program can be found that satisfies all the constraints, including the nonnegativity constraints. Let us now see how infeasibility is recognized when the simplex method is used.

In Section 17.6, when discussing artificial variables, we mentioned that infeasibility can be recognized when the optimality criterion indicates that an optimal solution has been obtained and one or more of the artificial variables remain in the solution at a positive value. As an illustration of this situation, let us consider another modification of the HighTech Industries problem. Suppose management imposed a minimum combined total production requirement of 50 units. The revised problem formulation is shown as follows.

$$\text{Max} \quad 50x_1 + 40x_2$$
$$\text{s.t.}$$

$$
\begin{array}{rcll}
3x_1 + 5x_2 & \leq & 150 & \text{Assembly time} \\
1x_2 & \leq & 20 & \text{Portable display} \\
8x_1 + 5x_2 & \leq & 300 & \text{Warehouse space} \\
1x_1 + 1x_2 & \geq & 50 & \text{Minimum total production} \\
x_1, x_2 & \geq & 0 &
\end{array}
$$

Two iterations of the simplex method will provide the following tableau:

		x_1	x_2	s_1	s_2	s_3	s_4	a_4	
Basis	c_B	50	40	0	0	0	0	$-M$	
x_2	40	0	1	$8/25$	0	$-3/25$	0	0	12
s_2	0	0	0	$-8/25$	1	$3/25$	0	0	8
x_1	50	1	0	$-5/25$	0	$5/25$	0	0	30
a_4	$-M$	0	0	$-3/25$	0	$-2/25$	-1	1	8
z_j		50	40	$\dfrac{70 + 3M}{25}$	0	$\dfrac{130 + 2M}{25}$	M	$-M$	$1980 - 8M$
$c_j - z_j$		0	0	$\dfrac{-70 - 3M}{25}$	0	$\dfrac{-130 - 2M}{25}$	$-M$	0	

If an artificial variable is positive, the solution is not feasible for the real problem.

Note that $c_j - z_j \leq 0$ for all the variables; therefore, according to the optimality criterion, it should be the optimal solution. But this solution is *not feasible* for the modified HighTech problem because the artificial variable $a_4 = 8$ appears in the solution. The solution $x_1 = 30$ and $x_2 = 12$ results in a combined total production of 42 units instead of the constraint 4 requirement of at least 50 units. The fact that the artificial variable is in solution at a value of $a_4 = 8$ tells us that the final solution violates the fourth constraint ($1x_1 + 1x_2 \geq 50$) by eight units.

If management is interested in knowing which of the first three constraints is preventing us from satisfying the total production requirement, a partial answer can be obtained from the final simplex tableau. Note that $s_2 = 8$, but that s_1 and s_3 are zero. This tells us that the assembly time and warehouse capacity constraints are binding. Because not enough assembly time and warehouse space are available, we cannot satisfy the minimum combined total production requirement.

The management implications here are that additional assembly time and/or warehouse space must be made available to satisfy the total production requirement. If more time and/or space cannot be made available, management will have to relax the total production requirement by at least eight units.

Try Problem 23 to practice recognizing when there is no feasible solution to a problem using the simplex method.

In summary, a linear program is infeasible if no solution satisfies all the constraints simultaneously. *We recognize infeasibility when one or more of the artificial variables remain in the final solution at a positive value.* In closing, we note that linear programming problems with all $\leq$ constraints and nonnegative right-hand sides will always have a feasible solution. Because it is not necessary to introduce artificial variables to set up the initial simplex tableau for these types of problems, the final solution cannot possibly contain an artificial variable.

Unboundedness

Usually a constraint has been overlooked if unboundedness occurs.

For maximization problems, we say that a linear program is unbounded if the value of the solution may be made infinitely large without violating any constraints. Thus, when unboundedness occurs, we can generally look for an error in the formulation of the problem.

The coefficients in the column of the $\bar{A}$ matrix associated with the incoming variable indicate how much each of the current basic variables will decrease if one unit of the incoming variable is brought into solution. Suppose then, that for a particular linear programming problem, we reach a point where the rule for determining which variable should enter the basis results in the decision to enter variable x_2. Assume that for this variable, $c_2 - z_2 = 5$, and that all $\bar{a}_{i2}$ in column 2 are ≤ 0. Thus, each unit of x_2 brought into solution increases the objective function by five units. Furthermore, because $\bar{a}_{i2} \leq 0$ for all i, none of the current basic variables will be driven to zero, no matter how many units of x_2 we introduce. Thus, we can introduce an infinite amount of x_2 into solution and still maintain feasibility. Because each unit of x_2 increases the objective function by 5, we will have an unbounded solution. Hence, *the way we recognize the unbounded situation is that all the $\bar{a}_{ij}$ are less than or equal to zero in the column associated with the incoming variable.*

To illustrate this concept, let us consider the following example of an unbounded problem.

$$\text{Max} \quad 20x_1 + 10x_2$$
$$\text{s.t.} \quad 1x_1 \quad\quad\quad \geq 2$$
$$1x_2 \leq 5$$
$$x_1, x_2 \geq 0$$

We subtract a surplus variable s_1 from the first constraint equation and add a slack variable s_2 to the second constraint equation to obtain the standard-form representation. We then add an artificial variable a_1 to the first constraint equation to obtain the tableau form. In the initial simplex tableau the basic variables are a_1 and s_2. After bringing in x_1 and removing a_1 at the first iteration, the simplex tableau is as follows:

		x_1	x_2	s_1	s_2	
Basis	c_B	20	10	0	0	
x_1	20	1	0	-1	0	**2**
s_2	0	0	1	0	1	**5**
z_j		20	0	-20	0	**40**
$c_j - z_j$		0	10	20	0	

Because s_1 has the largest positive $c_j - z_j$, we know we can increase the value of the objective function most rapidly by bringing s_1 into the basis. But $\bar{a}_{13} = -1$ and $\bar{a}_{23} = 0$; hence, we cannot form the ratio $\bar{b}_i / \bar{a}_{i3}$ for any $\bar{a}_{i3} > 0$ because no values of $\bar{a}_{i3}$ are greater than zero.

This result indicates that the solution to the linear program is unbounded because each unit of s_1 that is brought into solution provides one extra unit of x_1 (since $\bar{a}_{13} = -1$) and drives zero units of s_2 out of solution (since $\bar{a}_{23} = 0$). Because s_1 is a surplus variable and can be interpreted as the amount of x_1 over the minimum amount required, the simplex tableau indicates we can introduce as much of s_1 as we desire without violating any constraints; the interpretation is that we can make as much as we want above the minimum amount of x_1 required. Because the objective function coefficient associated with x_1 is positive, there will be no upper bound on the value of the objective function.

In summary, a maximization linear program is unbounded if it is possible to make the value of the optimal solution as large as desired without violating any of the constraints. When employing the simplex method, an unbounded linear program exists if *at some iteration, the simplex method tells us to introduce variable j into the solution and all the $\bar{a}_{ij}$ are less than or equal to zero in the jth column.*

Try Problem 25 for another example of an unbounded problem.

We emphasize that the case of an unbounded solution will never occur in real cost minimization or profit maximization problems because it is not possible to reduce costs to minus infinity or to increase profits to plus infinity. Thus, if we encounter an unbounded solution to a linear programming problem, we should carefully reexamine the formulation of the problem to determine whether a formulation error has occurred.

Alternative Optimal Solutions

A linear program with two or more optimal solutions is said to have alternative optimal solutions. When using the simplex method, we cannot recognize that a linear program has alternative optimal solutions until the final simplex tableau is reached. Then if the linear program has alternative optimal solutions, $c_j - z_j$ will equal zero for one or more nonbasic variables.

To illustrate the case of alternative optimal solutions when using the simplex method, consider changing the objective function for the HighTech problem from $50x_1 + 40x_2$ to $30x_1 + 50x_2$; in doing so, we obtain the revised linear program:

$$\text{Max} \quad 30x_1 + 50x_2$$
$$\text{s.t.}$$
$$3x_1 + 5x_2 \leq 150$$
$$1x_2 \leq 20$$
$$8x_1 + 5x_2 \leq 300$$
$$x_1, x_2 \geq 0$$

The final simplex tableau for this problem is shown here:

		x_1	x_2	s_1	s_2	s_3	
Basis	c_B	30	50	0	0	0	
x_2	50	0	1	0	1	0	20
s_3	0	0	0	$-\frac{8}{3}$	$\frac{25}{3}$	1	$\frac{200}{3}$
x_1	30	1	0	$\frac{1}{3}$	$-\frac{5}{3}$	0	$\frac{50}{3}$
z_j		30	50	10	0	0	1500
$c_j - z_j$		0	0	-10	0	0	

All values in the net evaluation row are less than or equal to zero, indicating that an optimal solution has been found. This solution is given by $x_1 = 50/3$, $x_2 = 20$, $s_1 = 0$, $s_2 = 0$, and $s_3 = 200/3$. The value of the objective function is 1500.

In looking at the net evaluation row in the optimal simplex tableau, we see that the $c_j - z_j$ value for nonbasic variable s_2 is equal to zero. It indicates that the linear program may have alternative optimal solutions. In other words, because the net evaluation row entry for s_2 is zero, we can introduce s_2 into the basis without changing the value of the solution. The tableau obtained after introducing s_2 follows:

		x_1	x_2	s_1	s_2	s_3	
Basis	c_B	30	50	0	0	0	
x_2	50	0	1	$8/25$	0	$-3/25$	12
s_2	0	0	0	$-8/25$	1	$3/25$	8
x_1	30	1	0	$-5/25$	0	$5/25$	30
z_j		30	50	10	0	0	1500
$c_j - z_j$		0	0	-10	0	0	

Try Problem 24 for another example of alternative optimal solutions.

As shown, we have a different basic feasible solution: $x_1 = 30$, $x_2 = 12$, $s_1 = 0$, $s_2 = 8$, and $s_3 = 0$. However, this new solution is also optimal because $c_j - z_j \leq 0$ for all j. Another way to confirm that this solution is still optimal is to note that the value of the solution has remained equal to 1500.

In summary, *when using the simplex method, we can recognize the possibility of alternative optimal solutions if $c_j - z_j$ equals zero for one or more of the nonbasic variables in the final simplex tableau.*

Degeneracy

A linear program is said to be degenerate if one or more of the basic variables have a value of zero. **Degeneracy** does not cause any particular difficulties for the graphical solution procedure; however, degeneracy can theoretically cause difficulties when the simplex method is used to solve a linear programming problem.

To see how a degenerate linear program could occur, consider a change in the right-hand-side value of the assembly time constraint for the HighTech problem. For example, what if the number of hours available had been 175 instead of 150? The modified linear program is shown here.

$$\text{Max} \quad 50x_1 + 40x_2$$

s.t.

$$3x_1 + 5x_2 \leq 175 \quad \text{Assembly time increased to 175 hours}$$
$$1x_2 \leq 20 \quad \text{Portable display}$$
$$8x_1 + 5x_2 \leq 300 \quad \text{Warehouse space}$$
$$x_1, x_2 \geq 0$$

The simplex tableau after one iteration is as follows:

Basis	c_B	x_1 50	x_2 40	s_1 0	s_2 0	s_3 0	
s_1	0	0	$25/8$	1	0	$-3/8$	$125/2$
s_2	0	0	1	0	1	0	20
x_1	50	1	$5/8$	0	0	$1/8$	$75/2$
z_j		50	$250/8$	0	0	$50/8$	1875
$c_j - z_j$		0	$70/8$	0	0	$-50/8$	

The entries in the net evaluation row indicate that x_2 should enter the basis. By calculating the appropriate ratios to determine the pivot row, we obtain

$$\frac{\bar{b}_1}{\bar{a}_{12}} = \frac{125/2}{25/8} = 20$$

$$\frac{\bar{b}_2}{\bar{a}_{22}} = \frac{20}{1} = 20$$

$$\frac{\bar{b}_3}{\bar{a}_{32}} = \frac{75/2}{5/8} = 60$$

We see that the first and second rows tie, which indicates that we will have a degenerate basic feasible solution at the next iteration. Recall that in the case of a tie, we follow the convention of selecting the uppermost row as the pivot row. Here, it means that s_1 will leave the basis. But from the tie for the minimum ratio we see that the basic variable in row 2, s_2, will also be driven to zero. Because it does not leave the basis, we will have a basic variable with a value of zero after performing this iteration. The simplex tableau after this iteration is as follows:

Basis	c_B	x_1 50	x_2 40	s_1 0	s_2 0	s_3 0	
x_2	40	0	1	$8/25$	0	$-3/25$	20
s_2	0	0	0	$-8/25$	1	$3/25$	0
x_1	50	1	0	$-5/25$	0	$5/25$	25
z_j		50	40	$70/25$	0	$130/25$	2050
$c_j - z_j$		0	0	$-70/25$	0	$-130/25$	

As expected, we have a basic feasible solution with one of the basic variables, s_2, equal to zero. Whenever we have a tie in the minimum $\bar{b}_i/\bar{a}_{ij}$ ratio, the next tableau will always have a basic variable equal to zero. Because we are at the optimal solution in the preceding case, we do not care that s_2 is in solution at a zero value. However, if degeneracy occurs at some iteration prior to reaching the optimal solution, it is theoretically possible for the simplex method to cycle; that is, the procedure could possibly alternate between the same set of nonoptimal basic feasible solutions and never reach the optimal solution. Cycling has not proven to be a significant difficulty in practice. Therefore, we do not recommend introducing any special steps into the simplex method to eliminate the possibility that degeneracy will occur. If while performing the iterations of the simplex algorithm a tie occurs for the minimum $\bar{b}_i/\bar{a}_{ij}$ ratio, then we recommend simply selecting the upper row as the pivot row.

NOTES AND COMMENTS

1. We stated that infeasibility is recognized when the stopping rule is encountered but one or more artificial variables are in solution at a positive value. This requirement does not necessarily mean that all artificial variables must be nonbasic to have a feasible solution. An artificial variable could be in solution at a zero value.

2. An unbounded feasible region must exist for a problem to be unbounded, but it does not guarantee that a problem will be unbounded. A minimization problem may be bounded, whereas a maximization problem with the same feasible region is unbounded.

SUMMARY

In this chapter the simplex method was introduced as an algebraic procedure for solving linear programming problems. Although the simplex method can be used to solve small linear programs by hand calculations, it becomes too cumbersome as problems get larger. As a result, a computer software package must be used to solve large linear programs in any reasonable length of time. The computational procedures of most computer software packages are based on the simplex method.

We described how developing the tableau form of a linear program is a necessary step in preparing a linear programming problem for solution using the simplex method, including how to convert greater-than-or-equal-to constraints, equality constraints, and constraints with negative right-hand-side values into tableau form.

For linear programs with greater-than-or-equal-to constraints and/or equality constraints, artificial variables are used to obtain tableau form. An objective function coefficient of $-M$, where M is a very large number, is assigned to each artificial variable. If there is a feasible solution to the real problem, all artificial variables will be driven out of solution (or to zero) before the simplex method reaches its optimality criterion. The iterations required to remove the artificial variables from solution constitute what is called phase I of the simplex method.

Two techniques were mentioned for solving minimization problems. The first approach involved changing the rule for introducing a variable into solution and changing the optimality criterion. The second approach involved multiplying the objective function by -1 to obtain an equivalent maximization problem. With this change, any minimization problem can be solved using the steps required for a maximization problem, but the value of the optimal solution must be multiplied by -1 to obtain the optimal value of the original minimization problem.

As a review of the material in this chapter we now present a detailed step-by-step procedure for solving linear programs using the simplex method.

Step 1. Formulate a linear programming model of the problem.
Step 2. Define an equivalent linear program by performing the following operations:
   a. Multiply each constraint with a negative right-hand-side value by -1, and change the direction of the constraint inequality.
   b. For a minimization problem, convert the problem to an equivalent maximization problem by multiplying the objective function by -1.

Step 3. Set up the standard form of the linear program by adding appropriate slack and surplus variables.

Step 4. Set up the tableau form of the linear program to obtain an initial basic feasible solution. All linear programs must be set up this way before the initial simplex tableau can be obtained.

Step 5. Set up the initial simplex tableau to keep track of the calculations required by the simplex method.

Step 6. Choose the nonbasic variable with the largest $c_j - z_j$ to bring into the basis. The column associated with that variable is the pivot column.

Step 7. Choose as the pivot row that row with the smallest ratio of $\bar{b}_i/\bar{a}_{ij}$ for $\bar{a}_{ij} > 0$. This ratio is used to determine which variable will leave the basis when variable j enters the basis. This ratio also indicates how many units of variable j can be introduced into solution before the basic variable in the ith row equals zero.

Step 8. Perform the necessary elementary row operations to convert the pivot column to a unit column.

a. Divide each element in the pivot row by the pivot element. The result is a new pivot row containing a 1 in the pivot column.

b. Obtain zeroes in all other positions of the pivot column by adding or subtracting an appropriate multiple of the new pivot row.

Step 9. Test for optimality. If $c_j - z_j \leq 0$ for all columns, we have the optimal solution. If not, return to step 6.

In Section 17.8 we discussed how the special cases of infeasibility, unboundedness, alternative optimal solutions, and degeneracy can occur when solving linear programming problems with the simplex method.

GLOSSARY

Simplex method   An algebraic procedure for solving linear programming problems. The simplex method uses elementary row operations to iterate from one basic feasible solution (extreme point) to another until the optimal solution is reached.

Basic solution   Given a linear program in standard form, with n variables and m constraints, a basic solution is obtained by setting $n - m$ of the variables equal to zero and solving the constraint equations for the values of the other m variables. If a unique solution exists, it is a basic solution.

Nonbasic variable   One of $n - m$ variables set equal to zero in a basic solution.

Basic variable   One of the m variables not required to equal zero in a basic solution.

Basic feasible solution   A basic solution that is also feasible; that is, it satisfies the nonnegativity constraints. A basic feasible solution corresponds to an extreme point.

Tableau form   The form in which a linear program must be written before setting up the initial simplex tableau. When a linear program is written in tableau form, its A matrix contains m unit columns corresponding to the basic variables, and the values of these basic variables are given by the values in the b column. A further requirement is that the entries in the b column be greater than or equal to zero.

Simplex tableau   A table used to keep track of the calculations required by the simplex method.

Unit column or unit vector   A vector or column of a matrix that has a zero in every position except one. In the nonzero position there is a 1. There is a unit column in the simplex tableau for each basic variable.

Basis   The set of variables that are not restricted to equal zero in the current basic solution. The variables that make up the basis are termed basic variables, and the remaining variables are called nonbasic variables.

Net evaluation row   The row in the simplex tableau that contains the value of $c_j - z_j$ for every variable (column).

Iteration   The process of moving from one basic feasible solution to another.

Pivot element   The element of the simplex tableau that is in both the pivot row and the pivot column.

Pivot column   The column in the simplex tableau corresponding to the nonbasic variable that is about to be introduced into solution.

Pivot row   The row in the simplex tableau corresponding to the basic variable that will leave the solution.

Elementary row operations   Operations that may be performed on a system of simultaneous equations without changing the solution to the system of equations.

Artificial variable   A variable that has no physical meaning in terms of the original linear programming problem, but serves merely to enable a basic feasible solution to be created for starting the simplex method. Artificial variables are assigned an objective function coefficient of $-M$, where M is a very large number.

Phase I   When artificial variables are present in the initial simplex tableau, phase I refers to the iterations of the simplex method that are required to eliminate the artificial variables. At the end of phase I, the basic feasible solution in the simplex tableau is also feasible for the real problem.

Degeneracy   When one or more of the basic variables has a value of zero.

PROBLEMS

1. Consider the following system of linear equations:

$$3x_1 + x_2 \quad\quad = 6$$
$$2x_1 + 4x_2 + x_3 = 12$$

    a.   Find the basic solution with $x_1 = 0$.
    b.   Find the basic solution with $x_2 = 0$.
    c.   Find the basic solution with $x_3 = 0$.
    d.   Which of the preceding solutions would be basic feasible solutions for a linear program?

2. Consider the following linear program:

$$\text{Max} \quad x_1 + 2x_2$$
$$\text{s.t.}$$
$$x_1 + 5x_2 \le 10$$
$$2x_1 + 6x_2 \le 16$$
$$x_1, x_2 \ge 0$$

a. Write the problem in standard form.
b. How many variables will be set equal to zero in a basic solution for this problem?
c. Find all the basic solutions, and indicate which are also feasible.
d. Find the optimal solution by computing the value of each basic feasible solution.

3. Consider the following linear program:

$$\text{Max} \quad 5x_1 + 9x_2$$
$$\text{s.t.}$$
$$\tfrac{1}{2}x_1 + 1x_2 \leq 8$$
$$1x_1 + 1x_2 \geq 10$$
$$\tfrac{1}{4}x_1 + \tfrac{3}{2}x_2 \geq 6$$
$$x_1, x_2 \geq 0$$

a. Write the problem in standard form.
b. How many variables will be set equal to zero in a basic solution for this problem? Explain.
c. Find the basic solution that corresponds to s_1 and s_2 equal to zero.
d. Find the basic solution that corresponds to x_1 and s_3 equal to zero.
e. Are your solutions for parts (c) and (d) basic feasible solutions? Extreme-point solutions? Explain.
f. Use the graphical approach to identify the solutions found in parts (c) and (d). Do the graphical results agree with your answer to part (e)? Explain.

4. Consider the following linear programming problem:

$$\text{Max} \quad 60x_1 + 90x_2$$
$$\text{s.t.}$$
$$15x_1 + 45x_2 \leq 90$$
$$5x_1 + 5x_2 \leq 20$$
$$x_1, x_2 \geq 0$$

a. Write the problem in standard form.
b. Develop the portion of the simplex tableau involving the objective function coefficients, the coefficients of the variables in the constraints, and the constants for the right-hand sides.

5. A partially completed initial simplex tableau is given:

Basis	c_B	x_1 5	x_2 9	s_1 0	s_2 0	
s_1	0	10	9	1	0	90
s_2	0	−5	3	0	1	15
z_j						
$c_j - z_j$						

a. Complete the initial tableau.
b. Which variable would be brought into solution at the first iteration?
c. Write the original linear program.

6. The following partial initial simplex tableau is given:

		x_1	x_2	x_3	s_1	s_2	s_3	
Basis	c_B	5	20	25	0	0	0	
		2	1	0	1	0	0	40
		0	2	1	0	1	0	30
		3	0	$-\frac{1}{2}$	0	0	1	15
z_j								
$c_j - z_j$								

a. Complete the initial tableau.
b. Write the problem in tableau form.
c. What is the initial basis? Does this basis correspond to the origin? Explain.
d. What is the value of the objective function at this initial solution?
e. For the next iteration, which variable should enter the basis, and which variable should leave the basis?
f. How many units of the entering variable will be in the next solution? Before making this first iteration, what do you think will be the value of the objective function after the first iteration?
g. Find the optimal solution using the simplex method.

7. Solve the following linear program using the graphical approach:

$$\text{Max} \quad 4x_1 + 5x_2$$
$$\text{s.t.}$$
$$2x_1 + 2x_2 \leq 20$$
$$3x_1 + 7x_2 \leq 42$$
$$x_1, x_2 \geq 0$$

Put the linear program in tableau form, and solve using the simplex method. Show the sequence of extreme points generated by the simplex method on your graph.

8. Recall the problem for Par, Inc., introduced in Section 2.1. The mathematical model for this problem is restated as follows:

$$\text{Max} \quad 10x_1 + 9x_2$$
$$\text{s.t.}$$
$$\frac{7}{10}x_1 + 1x_2 \leq 630 \quad \text{Cutting and dyeing}$$
$$\frac{1}{2}x_1 + \frac{5}{6}x_2 \leq 600 \quad \text{Sewing}$$
$$1x_1 + \frac{2}{3}x_2 \leq 708 \quad \text{Finishing}$$
$$\frac{1}{10}x_1 + \frac{1}{4}x_2 \leq 135 \quad \text{Inspection and packaging}$$
$$x_1, x_2 \geq 0$$

where

$$x_1 = \text{number of standard bags produced}$$
$$x_2 = \text{number of deluxe bags produced}$$

a. Use the simplex method to determine how many bags of each model Par should manufacture.
b. What is the profit Par can earn with these production quantities?

c.   How many hours of production time will be scheduled for each operation?

d.   What is the slack time in each operation?

9. RMC, Inc., is a small firm that produces a variety of chemical products. In a particular production process, three raw materials are blended (mixed together) to produce two products: a fuel additive and a solvent base. Each ton of fuel additive is a mixture of $\frac{2}{5}$ ton of material 1 and $\frac{3}{5}$ ton of material 3. A ton of solvent base is a mixture of $\frac{1}{2}$ ton of material 1, $\frac{1}{5}$ ton of material 2, and $\frac{3}{10}$ ton of material 3. After deducting relevant costs, the profit contribution is $40 for every ton of fuel additive produced and $30 for every ton of solvent base produced.

RMC's production is constrained by a limited availability of the three raw materials. For the current production period, RMC has available the following quantities of each raw material:

Raw Material	Amount Available for Production
Material 1	20 tons
Material 2	5 tons
Material 3	21 tons

Assuming that RMC is interested in maximizing the total profit contribution, the problem formulation is shown here:

$$\text{Max} \quad 40x_1 + 30x_2$$
$$\text{s.t.}$$
$$
\begin{aligned}
\tfrac{2}{5}x_1 + \tfrac{1}{2}x_2 &\le 20 \quad \text{Material 1} \\
\tfrac{1}{5}x_2 &\le 5 \quad \text{Material 2} \\
\tfrac{3}{5}x_1 + \tfrac{3}{10}x_2 &\le 21 \quad \text{Material 3} \\
x_1, x_2 &\ge 0
\end{aligned}
$$

where

$$x_1 = \text{tons of fuel additive produced}$$
$$x_2 = \text{tons of solvent base produced}$$

Solve the RMC problem using the simplex method. At each iteration, locate the basic feasible solution found by the simplex method on the graph of the feasible region.

10. Solve the following linear program:

$$\text{Max} \quad 5x_1 + 5x_2 + 24x_3$$
$$\text{s.t.}$$
$$
\begin{aligned}
15x_1 + 4x_2 + 12x_3 &\le 2800 \\
15x_1 + 8x_2 \quad &\le 6000 \\
x_1 \quad + 8x_3 &\le 1200 \\
x_1, x_2, x_3 &\ge 0
\end{aligned}
$$

11. Solve the following linear program using both the graphical and the simplex methods:

$$\text{Max} \quad 2x_1 + 8x_2$$

s.t.

$$3x_1 + 9x_2 \leq 45$$
$$2x_1 + 1x_2 \geq 12$$
$$x_1, x_2 \geq 0$$

Show graphically how the simplex method moves from one basic feasible solution to another. Find the coordinates of all extreme points of the feasible region.

12. Suppose a company manufactures three products from two raw materials. The amount of raw material in each unit of each product is given.

Raw Material	Product A	Product B	Product C
I	7 lb	6 lb	3 lb
II	5 lb	4 lb	2 lb

If the company has available 100 pounds of material I and 200 pounds of material II, and if the profits for the three products are $20, $20, and $15, respectively, how much of each product should be produced to maximize profits?

13. Liva's Lumber, Inc., manufactures three types of plywood. The following table summarizes the production hours per unit in each of three production operations and other data for the problem.

Plywood	Operations (hours)			Profit/Unit
	I	II	III	
Grade A	2	2	4	$40
Grade B	5	5	2	$30
Grade X	10	3	2	$20
Maximum time available	900	400	600	

How many units of each grade of lumber should be produced?

14. Ye Olde Cording Winery in Peoria, Illinois, makes three kinds of authentic German wine: Heidelberg Sweet, Heidelberg Regular, and Deutschland Extra Dry. The raw materials, labor, and profit for a gallon of each of these wines are summarized here:

Wine	Grade A Grapes (bushels)	Grade B Grapes (bushels)	Sugar (pounds)	Labor (hours)	Profit/ Gallon
Heidelberg Sweet	1	1	2	2	$1.00
Heidelberg Regular	2	0	1	3	$1.20
Deutschland Extra Dry	0	2	0	1	$2.00

If the winery has 150 bushels of grade A grapes, 150 bushels of grade B grapes, 80 pounds of sugar, and 225 labor-hours available during the next week, what product mix of wines will maximize the company's profit?

a. Solve using the simplex method.

b. Interpret all slack variables.

c. An increase in which resources could improve the company's profit?

15. Set up the tableau form for the following linear program (do not attempt to solve):

$$\text{Max} \quad 4x_1 + 2x_2 - 3x_3 + 5x_4$$

s.t.

$$2x_1 - 1x_2 + 1x_3 + 2x_4 \geq 50$$
$$3x_1 \qquad - 1x_3 + 2x_4 \leq 80$$
$$1x_1 + 1x_2 \qquad + 1x_4 = 60$$
$$x_1, x_2, x_3, x_4 \geq 0$$

16. Set up the tableau form for the following linear program (do not attempt to solve):

$$\text{Min} \quad 4x_1 + 5x_2 + 3x_3$$

s.t.

$$4x_1 \qquad + 2x_3 \geq 20$$
$$1x_2 - 1x_3 \leq -8$$
$$1x_1 - 2x_2 \qquad = -5$$
$$2x_1 + 1x_2 + 1x_3 \leq 12$$
$$x_1, x_2, x_3 \geq 0$$

17. Solve the following linear program:

$$\text{Min} \quad 3x_1 + 4x_2 + 8x_3$$

s.t.

$$4x_1 + 2x_2 \qquad \geq 12$$
$$4x_2 + 8x_3 \geq 16$$
$$x_1, x_2, x_3 \geq 0$$

18. Solve the following linear program:

$$\text{Min} \quad 84x_1 + 4x_2 + 30x_3$$

s.t.

$$8x_1 + 1x_2 + 3x_3 \leq 240$$
$$16x_1 + 1x_2 + 7x_3 \geq 480$$
$$8x_1 - 1x_2 + 4x_3 \geq 160$$
$$x_1, x_2, x_3 \geq 0$$

19. Captain John's Yachts, Inc., located in Fort Lauderdale, Florida, rents three types of ocean-going boats: sailboats, cabin cruisers, and Captain John's favorite, the luxury yachts. Captain John advertises his boats with his famous "you rent—we pilot" slogan, which means that the company supplies the captain and crew for each rented boat. Each rented boat has one captain, of course, but the crew sizes (deck hands, galley hands, etc.) differ. The crew requirements, in addition to a captain, are one for sailboats, two for cabin cruisers, and three for yachts. Ten employees are captains, and an additional 18 employees fill the various crew positions. Currently,

Captain John has rental requests for all of his boats: four sailboats, eight cabin cruisers, and three luxury yachts. If Captain John's daily profit contribution is $50 for sailboats, $70 for cruisers, and $100 for luxury yachts, how many boats of each type should he rent?

20. The Our-Bags-Don't-Break (OBDB) plastic bag company manufactures three plastic refuse bags for home use: a 20-gallon garbage bag, a 30-gallon garbage bag, and a 33-gallon leaf-and-grass bag. Using purchased plastic material, three operations are required to produce each end product: cutting, sealing, and packaging. The production time required to process each type of bag in every operation and the maximum production time available for each operation are shown (note that the production time figures in this table are per box of each type of bag).

Type of Bag	Production Time (seconds/box)		
	Cutting	Sealing	Packaging
20 gallons	2	2	3
30 gallons	3	2	4
33 gallons	3	3	5
Time available	2 hours	3 hours	4 hours

If OBDB's profit contribution is $0.10 for each box of 20-gallon bags produced, $0.15 for each box of 30-gallon bags, and $0.20 for each box of 33-gallon bags, what is the optimal product mix?

21. Kirkman Brothers ice cream parlors sell three different flavors of Dairy Sweet ice milk: chocolate, vanilla, and banana. Due to extremely hot weather and a high demand for its products, Kirkman has run short of its supply of ingredients: milk, sugar, and cream. Hence, Kirkman will not be able to fill all the orders received from its retail outlets, the ice cream parlors. Due to these circumstances, Kirkman decided to make the most profitable amounts of the three flavors, given the constraints on supply of the basic ingredients. The company will then ration the ice milk to the retail outlets.

Kirkman collected the following data on profitability of the various flavors, availability of supplies, and amounts required for each flavor.

Flavor	Profit/ Gallon	Usage/Gallon		
		Milk (gallons)	Sugar (pounds)	Cream (gallons)
Chocolate	$1.00	0.45	0.50	0.10
Vanilla	$0.90	0.50	0.40	0.15
Banana	$0.95	0.40	0.40	0.20
Maximum available		200	150	60

Determine the optimal product mix for Kirkman Brothers. What additional resources could be used profitably?

22. Uforia Corporation sells two brands of perfume: Incentive and Temptation No. 1. Uforia sells exclusively through department stores and employs a three-person sales staff to call on its customers. The amount of time necessary for each sales representative to sell one case of each product varies with experience and ability. Data on the average time for each of Uforia's three sales representatives is presented here.

	Average Sales Time per Case (minutes)	
Salesperson	Incentive	Temptation No. 1
John	10	15
Brenda	15	10
Red	12	6

Each sales representative spends approximately 80 hours per month in the actual selling of these two products. Cases of Incentive and Temptation No. 1 sell at profits of $30 and $25, respectively. How many cases of each perfume should each person sell during the next month to maximize the firm's profits? (*Hint:* Let x_1 = number of cases of Incentive sold by John, x_2 = number of cases of Temptation No. 1 sold by John, x_3 = number of cases of Incentive sold by Brenda, and so on.)

Note: In Problems 23–29, we provide examples of linear programs that result in one or more of the following situations:

* Optimal solution
* Infeasible solution
* Unbounded solution
* Alternative optimal solutions
* Degenerate solution

For each linear program, determine the solution situation that exists, and indicate how you identified each situation using the simplex method. For the problems with alternative optimal solutions, calculate at least two optimal solutions.

23.

$$\text{Max} \quad 4x_1 + 8x_2$$
s.t.
$$2x_1 + 2x_2 \leq 10$$
$$-1x_1 + 1x_2 \geq 8$$
$$x_1, x_2 \geq 0$$

24.

$$\text{Min} \quad 3x_1 + 3x_2$$
s.t.
$$2x_1 + 0.5x_2 \geq 10$$
$$2x_1 \qquad \geq 4$$
$$4x_1 + 4x_2 \geq 32$$
$$x_1, x_2 \geq 0$$

25.

$$\text{Min} \quad 1x_1 + 1x_2$$
s.t.
$$8x_1 + 6x_2 \geq 24$$
$$4x_1 + 6x_2 \geq -12$$
$$2x_2 \geq 4$$
$$x_1, x_2 \geq 0$$

26.

$$\text{Max} \quad 2x_1 + 1x_2 + 1x_3$$
s.t.
$$4x_1 + 2x_2 + 2x_3 \geq 4$$
$$2x_1 + 4x_2 \qquad \leq 20$$
$$4x_1 + 8x_2 + 2x_3 \leq 16$$
$$x_1, x_2, x_3 \geq 0$$

27.
$$\text{Max} \quad 2x_1 + 4x_2$$
s.t.
$$1x_1 + \tfrac{1}{2}x_2 \leq 10$$
$$1x_1 + 1x_2 = 12$$
$$1x_1 + \tfrac{3}{4}x_2 \leq 18$$
$$x_1, x_2 \geq 0$$

28.
$$\text{Min} \quad -4x_1 + 5x_2 + 5x_3$$
s.t.
$$1x_2 + 1x_3 \geq 2$$
$$-1x_1 + 1x_2 + 1x_3 \geq 1$$
$$-1x_3 \geq 1$$
$$x_1, x_2, x_3 \geq 0$$

29. Solve the following linear program and identify any alternative optimal solutions.

$$\text{Max} \quad 120x_1 + 80x_2 + 14x_3$$
s.t.
$$4x_1 + 8x_2 + x_3 \leq 200$$
$$2x_2 + 1x_3 \leq 300$$
$$32x_1 + 4x_2 + 2x_3 = 400$$
$$x_1, x_2, x_3 \geq 0$$

30. Supersport Footballs, Inc., manufactures three kinds of footballs: an All-Pro model, a College model, and a High School model. All three footballs require operations in the following departments: cutting and dyeing, sewing, and inspection and packaging. The production times and maximum production availabilities are shown here.

| | Production Time (minutes) | | |
Model	Cutting and Dyeing	Sewing	Inspection and Packaging
All-Pro	12	15	3
College	10	15	4
High School	8	12	2
Time available	300 hours	200 hours	100 hours

Current orders indicate that at least 1000 All-Pro footballs must be manufactured.
  a. If Supersport realizes a profit contribution of $3 for each All-Pro model, $5 for each College model, and $4 for each High School model, how many footballs of each type should be produced? What occurs in the solution of this problem? Why?
  b. If Supersport can increase sewing time to 300 hours and inspection and packaging time to 150 hours by using overtime, what is your recommendation?

Chapter 17

1. a. With $x_1 = 0$, we have

$$x_2 = 6 \quad (1)$$
$$4x_2 + x_3 = 12 \quad (2)$$

From (1), we have $x_2 = 6$; substituting for x_2 in (2) yields

$$4(6) + x_3 = 12$$
$$x_3 = 12 - 24 = -12$$

Basic solution: $x_1 = 0, x_2 = 6, x_3 = -12$

b. With $x_2 = 0$, we have

$$3x_1 = 6 \quad (3)$$
$$2x_1 + x_3 = 12 \quad (4)$$

From (3), we find $x_1 = 2$; substituting for x_1 in (4) yields

$$2(2) + x_3 = 12$$
$$x_3 = 12 - 4 = 8$$

Basic solution: $x_1 = 2, x_2 = 0, x_3 = 8$

c. With $x_3 = 0$, we have

$$3x_1 + x_2 = 6 \quad (5)$$
$$2x_1 + 4x_2 = 12 \quad (6)$$

Multiplying (6) by $\frac{3}{2}$ and subtracting from (5) yields

$$3x_1 + x_2 = 6$$
$$-(3x_1 + 6x_2) = -18$$
$$\overline{\hspace{1.5cm}-5x_2 = -12}$$
$$x_2 = \tfrac{12}{5}$$

Substituting $x_2 = \tfrac{12}{5}$ into (5) yields

$$3x_1 + \tfrac{12}{5} = 6$$
$$3x_1 = \tfrac{18}{5}$$
$$x_1 = \tfrac{6}{5}$$

Basic solution: $x_1 = \tfrac{6}{5}, x_2 = \tfrac{12}{5}, x_3 = 0$

d. The basic solutions found in parts (b) and (c) are basic feasible solutions. The one in part (a) is not because $x_3 = -12$.

2. a. Max $x_1 + 2x_2$
   s.t.

$$x_1 + 5x_2 + s_1 = 10$$
$$2x_1 + 6x_2 + s_2 = 16$$
$$x_1, x_2, s_1, s_2 \geq 0$$

b. 2

c. $x_1 = 0, x_2 = 0, s_1 = 10, s_2 = 16$; feasible
$x_1 = 0, x_2 = 2, s_1 = 0, s_2 = 4$; feasible
$x_1 = 0, x_2 = \tfrac{8}{3}, s_1 = -\tfrac{10}{3}, s_2 = 0$; not feasible
$x_1 = 10, x_2 = 0, s_1 = 0, s_2 = -4$; not feasible
$x_1 = 8, x_2 = 0, s_1 = 2, s_2 = 0$; feasible
$x_1 = 5, x_2 = 1, s_1 = 0, s_2 = 0$; feasible

d. $x_1 = 8, x_2 = 0$; Value $= 8$

4. a. Standard form:

Max $60x_1 + 90x_2$
s.t.

$$15x_1 + 45x_2 + s_1 = 90$$
$$5x_1 + 5x_2 + s_2 = 20$$
$$x_1, x_2, s_1, s_2 \geq 0$$

b. Partial initial simple tableau:

x_1	x_2	s_1	s_2	
60	90	0	0	
15	45	1	0	90
5	5	0	1	20

5. a. Initial tableau:

		x_1	x_2	s_1	s_2	
Basis	c_B	5	9	0	0	
s_1	0	10	9	1	0	90
s_2	0	-5	3	0	1	15
z_j		0	0	0	0	0
$c_j - z_j$		5	9	0	0	

b. Introduce x_2 at the first iteration

c. Max $5x_1 + 9x_2$
   s.t.

$$10x_1 + 9x_2 \leq 90$$
$$-5x_1 + 3x_2 \leq 15$$
$$x_1, x_2 \geq 0$$

6. a.

	z_j	0	0	0	0	0	0	0
	$c_j - z_j$	5	20	25	0	0	0	

b. Max $5x_1 + 20x_2 + 25x_3 + 0s_1 + 0s_2 + 0s_3$
   s.t.

$$2x_1 + 1x_2 + 1s_1 = 40$$
$$2x_2 + 1x_3 + 1s_2 = 30$$
$$3x_1 - \tfrac{1}{2}x_3 + 1s_3 = 15$$
$$x_1, x_2, x_3, s_1, s_2, s_3 \geq 0$$

c. s_1, s_2, s_3; it is the origin

d. 0
e. x_3 enters, s_2 leaves
f. 30, 750
g. $x_1 = 10, s_1 = 20$
$x_2 = 0, s_2 = 0$, Value = 800
$x_3 = 30, s_3 = 0$

8. a. $x_1 = 540, x_2 = 252$
b. $7668
c. 630, 480, 708, 117
d. 0, 120, 0, 18

10. $x_2 = 250, x_3 = 150, s_2 = 4000$
Value = 4850

12. A = 0, B = 0, C = 33⅓; Profit = 500

14. a. $x_1 = 0, x_2 = 50, x_3 = 75$; Profit = $210
c. Grade B grapes and labor

15. Max $4x_1 + 2x_2 - 3x_3 + 5x_4 + 0s_1 - Ma_1 + 0s_2 - Ma_3$
s.t.

$$2x_1 - 1x_2 + 1x_3 + 2x_4 - 1s_1 + 1a_1 = 50$$
$$3x_1 - 1x_3 + 2x_4 + 1s_2 = 80$$
$$1x_1 + 1x_2 + 1x_4 + 1a_3 = 60$$
$$x_1, x_2, x_3, x_4, s_1, s_2, a_1, a_3 \geq 0$$

16.
Max $-4x_1 - 5x_2 - 3x_3 + 0s_1 + 0s_2 + 0s_4 - Ma_1 - Ma_2 - Ma_3$
s.t.

$$4x_1 + 2x_3 - 1s_1 + 1a_1 = 20$$
$$-1x_2 + 1x_3 - 1s_2 + 1a_2 = 8$$
$$-1x_1 + 2x_2 + 1a_3 = 5$$
$$2x_1 + 1x_2 + 1x_3 + 1s_4 = 12$$
$$x_1, x_2, x_3, s_1, s_2, s_4, a_1, a_2, a_3 \geq 0$$

17. Converting to a max problem and solving using the simplex method, the final simplex tableau is

Basis	c_B	x_1	x_2	x_3	s_1	s_2	
		−3	−4	−8	0	0	
x_1	−3	1	0	−1	−¼	⅛	**1**
x_2	−4	0	1	2	0	−¼	**4**
z_j		−3	−4	−5	¾	⅝	**−19**
$c_j - z_j$		0	0	−3	−¾	−⅝	

18. $x_2 = 60, x_3 = 60, s_3 = 20$; Value = 2040

20. 2400 boxes of 33 gallon bags
Profit = $480

22. $x_1 = 480, x_4 = 480, x_6 = 800$; Value = 46,400

23. Final simplex tableau:

Basis	c_B	x_1	x_2	s_1	s_2	a_2	
		4	8	0	0	$-M$	
x_2	8	1	1	½	0	0	**5**
a_2	$-M$	−2	0	−½	−1	1	**3**
z_j		$8 + 2M$	8	$4 + M/2$	$+M$	$-M$	**$40 - 3M$**
$c_j - z_j$		$-4 - 2M$	0	$-4 - M/2$	$-M$	0	

Infeasible; optimal solution condition is reached with the artificial variable a_2 still in the solution

24. Alternative optimal solutions:

Basis	c_B	x_1	x_2	s_1	s_2	s_3	
		−3	−3	0	0	0	
s_2	0	0	0	−⅓	1	⅙	**4**
x_1	−3	1	0	−⅔	0	1/12	**4**
x_2	−3	0	1	⅔	0	−⅓	**4**
z_j		−3	−3	0	0	¾	**−24**
$c_j - z_j$		0	0	0	0	−¾	

↑ Indicates alternative optimal solutions exist:
$x_1 = 4, x_2 = 4, z = 24$
$x_1 = 8, x_2 = 0, z = 24$

25. Unbounded solution:

Basis	c_B	x_1	x_2	s_1	s_2	s_3	
		1	1	0	0	0	
s_3	0	⅛	0	−⅓	0	1	**4**
s_2	0	4	0	−1	1	0	**36**
x_2	1	⅓	1	−⅙	0	0	**4**
z_j		⅓	1	−⅙	0	0	**4**
$c_j - z_j$		−⅓	0	⅙	0	0	

↑ Incoming column

26. Alternative optimal solution: $x_1 = 4, x_2 = 0, x_3 = 0$
$x_1 = 0, x_2 = 0, x_3 = 8$

28. Infeasible

30. a. Infeasible solution; not enough sewing time
b. Alternative optimal solutions: $x_1 = 1000, x_2 = 0, x_3 = 250$ or $x_1 = 1000, x_2 = 200, x_3 = 0$
Profit = $4000

Simplex-Based Sensitivity Analysis and Duality

CONTENTS

In Chapter 3 we defined sensitivity analysis as the study of how the changes in the coefficients of a linear program affect the optimal solution. In this chapter we discuss how sensitivity analysis information such as the ranges for the objective function coefficients, dual prices, and the ranges for the right-hand-side values can be obtained from the final simplex tableau. The topic of duality is also introduced. We will see that associated with every linear programming problem is a dual problem that has an interesting economic interpretation.

18.1   SENSITIVITY ANALYSIS WITH THE SIMPLEX TABLEAU

The usual sensitivity analysis for linear programs involves computing ranges for the objective function coefficients and the right-hand-side values, as well as the dual prices.

Objective Function Coefficients

Sensitivity analysis for an objective function coefficient involves placing a range on the coefficient's value. We call this range the **range of optimality.** As long as the actual value of the objective function coefficient is within the range of optimality, *the current basic feasible solution will remain optimal.* The range of optimality for a basic variable defines the objective function coefficient values for which that variable will remain part of the current optimal basic feasible solution. The range of optimality for a nonbasic variable defines the objective function coefficient values for which that variable will remain nonbasic.

In computing the range of optimality for an objective function coefficient, all other coefficients in the problem are assumed to remain at their original values; in other words, *only one coefficient is allowed to change at a time.* To illustrate the process of computing ranges for objective function coefficients, recall the HighTech Industries problem introduced in Chapter 17. The linear program for this problem is restated as follows:

$$\text{Max} \quad 50x_1 + 40x_2$$

s.t.

$$
\begin{aligned}
3x_1 + 5x_2 &\leq 150 \quad \text{Assembly time} \\
1x_2 &\leq 20 \quad \text{Portable display} \\
8x_1 + 5x_2 &\leq 300 \quad \text{Warehouse capacity} \\
x_1, x_2 &\geq 0
\end{aligned}
$$

where

$$
\begin{aligned}
x_1 &= \text{number of units of the Deskpro} \\
x_2 &= \text{number of units of the Portable}
\end{aligned}
$$

The final simplex tableau for the HighTech problem is as follows.

Basis	c_B	x_1 50	x_2 40	s_1 0	s_2 0	s_3 0	
x_2	40	0	1	$8/25$	0	$-3/25$	12
s_2	0	0	0	$-8/25$	1	$3/25$	8
x_1	50	1	0	$-5/25$	0	$5/25$	30
z_j		50	40	$14/5$	0	$26/5$	1980
$c_j - z_j$		0	0	$-14/5$	0	$-26/5$	

Recall that when the simplex method is used to solve a linear program, an optimal solution is recognized when all entries in the net evaluation row $(c_j - z_j)$ are ≤ 0. Because the preceding simplex tableau satisfies this criterion, the solution shown is optimal. However, if a change in one of the objective function coefficients were to cause one or more of the $c_j - z_j$ values to become positive, then the current solution would no longer be optimal; in such a case, one or more additional simplex iterations would be necessary to find the new optimal solution. *The range of optimality for an objective function coefficient is determined by those coefficient values that maintain*

$$c_j - z_j \leq 0 \tag{18.1}$$

for all values of j.

Let us illustrate this approach by computing the range of optimality for c_1, the profit contribution per unit of the Deskpro. Using c_1 (instead of 50) as the objective function coefficient of x_1, the final simplex tableau is as follows:

		x_1	x_2	s_1	s_2	s_3	
Basis	c_B	c_1	40	0	0	0	
x_2	40	0	1	$8/25$	0	$-3/25$	12
s_2	0	0	0	$-8/25$	1	$3/25$	8
x_1	c_1	1	0	$-5/25$	0	$5/25$	30
z_j		c_1	40	$\dfrac{64 - c_1}{5}$	0	$\dfrac{c_1 - 24}{5}$	$480 + 30c_1$
$c_j - z_j$		0	0	$\dfrac{c_1 - 64}{5}$	0	$\dfrac{24 - c_1}{5}$	

Changing an objective function coefficient will result in changes in the z_j and $c_j - z_j$ rows, but not in the variable values.

Note that this tableau is the same as the previous optimal tableau except that c_1 replaces 50. Thus, we have a c_1 in the objective function coefficient row and the c_B column, and the z_j and $c_j - z_j$ rows have been recomputed using c_1 instead of 50. The current solution will remain optimal as long as the value of c_1 results in all $c_j - z_j \leq 0$. Hence, from the column for s_1 we must have

$$\frac{c_1 - 64}{5} \leq 0$$

and from the column for s_3, we must have

$$\frac{24 - c_1}{5} \leq 0$$

Using the first inequality, we obtain

$$c_1 - 64 \leq 0$$

or

$$c_1 \leq 64 \qquad (18.2)$$

Similarly, from the second inequality, we obtain

$$24 - c_1 \leq 0$$

or

$$24 \leq c_1 \qquad (18.3)$$

Because c_1 must satisfy both inequalities (18.2) and (18.3), the range of optimality for c_1 is given by

$$24 \leq c_1 \leq 64 \qquad (18.4)$$

To see how management of HighTech can make use of this sensitivity analysis information, suppose an increase in material costs reduces the profit contribution per unit for the Deskpro to $30. The range of optimality indicates that the current solution ($x_1 = 30$, $x_2 = 12$, $s_1 = 0$, $s_2 = 8$, $s_3 = 0$) is still optimal. To verify this solution, let us recompute the final simplex tableau after reducing the value of c_1 to 30.

We have simply set $c_1 = 30$ everywhere it appears in the previous tableau.

Basis	c_B	x_1 30	x_2 40	s_1 0	s_2 0	s_3 0	
x_2	40	0	1	$8/25$	0	$-3/25$	12
s_2	0	0	0	$-8/25$	1	$3/25$	8
x_1	30	1	0	$-5/25$	0	$5/25$	30
z_j		30	40	$34/5$	0	$6/5$	1380
$c_j - z_j$		0	0	$-34/5$	0	$-6/5$	

Because $c_j - z_j \leq 0$ for all variables, the solution with $x_1 = 30$, $x_2 = 12$, $s_1 = 0$, $s_2 = 8$, and $s_3 = 0$ is still optimal. That is, the optimal solution with $c_1 = 30$ is the same as the optimal solution with $c_1 = 50$. Note, however, that the decrease in profit contribution per unit of the Deskpro has caused a reduction in total profit from $1980 to $1380.

What if the profit contribution per unit were reduced even further—say, to $20? Referring to the range of optimality for c_1 given by expression (18.4), we see that $c_1 = 20$ is outside the range; thus, we know that a change this large will cause a new basis to be optimal. To verify this new basis, we have modified the final simplex tableau by replacing c_1 by 20.

Basis	c_B	x_1 20	x_2 40	s_1 0	s_2 0	s_3 0	
x_2	40	0	1	$\frac{8}{25}$	0	$-\frac{3}{25}$	12
s_2	0	0	0	$-\frac{8}{25}$	1	$\frac{3}{25}$	8
x_1	20	1	0	$-\frac{5}{25}$	0	$\frac{5}{25}$	30
z_j		20	40	$\frac{44}{5}$	0	$-\frac{4}{5}$	1080
$c_j - z_j$		0	0	$-\frac{44}{5}$	0	$\frac{4}{5}$	

As expected, the current solution ($x_1 = 30$, $x_2 = 12$, $s_1 = 0$, $s_2 = 8$, and $s_3 = 0$) is no longer optimal because the entry in the s_3 column of the net evaluation row is greater than zero. This result implies that at least one more simplex iteration must be performed to reach the optimal solution. Continue to perform the simplex iterations in the previous tableau to verify that the new optimal solution will require the production of $16\frac{2}{3}$ units of the Deskpro and 20 units of the Portable.

At the endpoints of the range, the corresponding variable is a candidate for entering the basis if it is currently out or for leaving the basis if it is currently in.

The procedure we used to compute the range of optimality for c_1 can be used for any basic variable. The procedure for computing the range of optimality for nonbasic variables is even easier because a change in the objective function coefficient for a nonbasic variable causes only the corresponding $c_j - z_j$ entry to change in the final simplex tableau. To illustrate the approach, we show the following final simplex tableau for the original HighTech problem after replacing 0, the objective function coefficient for s_1, with the coefficient c_{s_1}:

Basis	c_B	x_1 50	x_2 40	s_1 c_{s_1}	s_2 0	s_3 0	
x_2	40	0	1	$\frac{8}{25}$	0	$-\frac{3}{25}$	12
s_2	0	0	0	$-\frac{8}{25}$	1	$\frac{3}{25}$	8
x_1	50	1	0	$-\frac{5}{25}$	0	$\frac{5}{25}$	30
z_j		50	40	$\frac{14}{5}$	0	$\frac{26}{5}$	1980
$c_j - z_j$		0	0	$c_{s_1} - \frac{14}{5}$	0	$-\frac{26}{5}$	

Note that the only changes in the tableau are in the s_1 column. In applying inequality (18.1) to compute the range of optimality, we get

$$c_{s_1} - 14/5 \leq 0$$

and hence

$$c_{s_1} \leq 14/5$$

Therefore, as long as the objective function coefficient for s_1 is less than or equal to $\frac{14}{5}$, the current solution will be optimal. With no lower bound on how much the coefficient may be decreased, we write the range of optimality for c_{s_1} as

$$c_{s_1} \leq 14/5$$

The same approach works for all nonbasic variables. In a maximization problem, the range of optimality has no lower limit, and the upper limit is given by z_j. Thus, the range of optimality for the objective function coefficient of any nonbasic variable is given by

$$c_j \leq z_j \tag{18.5}$$

Let us summarize the steps necessary to compute the range of optimality for objective function coefficients. In stating the following steps, we assume that computing the range of optimality for c_k, the coefficient of x_k, in a maximization problem is the desired goal. Keep in mind that x_k in this context may refer to one of the original decision variables, a slack variable, or a surplus variable.

Steps to Compute the Range of Optimality

Step 1. Replace the numerical value of the objective function coefficient for x_k with c_k everywhere it appears in the final simplex tableau.

Step 2. Recompute $c_j - z_j$ for each nonbasic variable (if x_k is a nonbasic variable, it is only necessary to recompute $c_k - z_k$).

Step 3. Requiring that $c_j - z_j \leq 0$, solve each inequality for any upper or lower bounds on c_k. If two or more upper bounds are found for c_k, the smallest of these is the upper bound on the range of optimality. If two or more lower bounds are found, the largest of these is the lower bound on the range of optimality.

Step 4. If the original problem is a minimization problem that was converted to a maximization problem in order to apply the simplex method, multiply the inequalities obtained in step 3 by -1, and change the direction of the inequalities to obtain the ranges of optimality for the original minimization problem.

Can you compute the range of optimality for objective function coefficients by working with the final simplex tableau? Try Problem 1.

By using the range of optimality to determine whether a change in an objective function coefficient is large enough to cause a change in the optimal solution, we can often avoid the process of formulating and solving a modified linear programming problem.

Right-Hand-Side Values

In many linear programming problems, we can interpret the right-hand-side values (the b_i's) as the resources available. For instance, in the HighTech Industries problem, the right-hand side of constraint 1 represents the available assembly time, the right-hand side of constraint 2 represents the available Portable displays, and the right-hand side of constraint 3 represents the available warehouse space. Dual prices provide information on the value of additional resources in these cases; the ranges over which these dual prices are valid are given by the ranges for the right-hand-side values.

Dual Prices   In Chapter 3 we stated that the improvement in the value of the optimal solution per unit increase in a constraint's right-hand-side value is called a **dual price.**[1] When the simplex method is used to solve a linear programming problem, the values of the dual

---

[1]The closely related term *shadow price* is used by some authors. The shadow price is the same as the dual price for maximization problems; for minimization problems, the dual and shadow prices are equal in absolute value but have opposite signs. LINGO and The Management Scientist provide dual prices as part of the computer output. Some software packages, such as Premium Solver for Education, provide shadow prices.

prices are easy to obtain. They are found in the z_j row of the final simplex tableau. To illustrate this point, the final simplex tableau for the HighTech problem is again shown.

Basis	c_B	x_1 50	x_2 40	s_1 0	s_2 0	s_3 0	
x_2	40	0	1	$8/25$	0	$-3/25$	12
s_2	0	0	0	$-8/25$	1	$3/25$	8
x_1	50	1	0	$-5/25$	0	$5/25$	30
z_j		50	40	$14/5$	0	$26/5$	1980
$c_j - z_j$		0	0	$-14/5$	0	$-26/5$	

The z_j values for the three slack variables are $14/5$, 0, and $26/5$, respectively. Thus, the dual prices for the assembly time constraint, Portable display constraint, and warehouse capacity constraint are, respectively, $14/5 = \$2.80$, 0.00, and $26/5 = \$5.20$. The dual price of \$5.20 shows that more warehouse space will have the biggest positive impact on HighTech's profit.

To see why the z_j values for the slack variables in the final simplex tableau are the dual prices, let us first consider the case for slack variables that are part of the optimal basic feasible solution. Each of these slack variables will have a z_j value of zero, implying a dual price of zero for the corresponding constraint. For example, consider slack variable s_2, a basic variable in the HighTech problem. Because $s_2 = 8$ in the optimal solution, HighTech will have eight Portable display units unused. Consequently, how much would management of HighTech Industries be willing to pay to obtain additional Portable display units? Clearly the answer is nothing because at the optimal solution HighTech has an excess of this particular component. Additional amounts of this resource are of no value to the company, and, consequently, the dual price for this constraint is zero. In general, if a slack variable is a basic variable in the optimal solution, the value of z_j—and hence, the dual price of the corresponding resource—is zero.

Consider now the nonbasic slack variables—for example, s_1. In the previous subsection we determined that the current solution will remain optimal as long as the objective function coefficient for s_1 (denoted c_{s_1}) stays in the following range:

$$c_{s_1} \leq 14/5$$

It implies that the variable s_1 should not be increased from its current value of zero unless it is worth more than $14/5 = \$2.80$ to do so. We can conclude then that \$2.80 is the marginal value to HighTech of 1 hour of assembly time used in the production of Deskpro and Portable computers. Thus, if additional time can be obtained, HighTech should be willing to pay up to \$2.80 per hour for it. A similar interpretation can be given to the z_j value for each of the nonbasic slack variables.

With a greater-than-or-equal-to constraint, the value of the dual price will be less than or equal to zero because a one-unit increase in the value of the right-hand side cannot be helpful; a one-unit increase makes it more difficult to satisfy the constraint. For a maximization problem, then, the optimal value can be expected to decrease when the right-hand side of a greater-than-or-equal-to constraint is increased. The dual price gives the amount of the expected improvement—a negative number, because we expect a decrease. As a result, the dual price for a greater-than-or-equal-to constraint is given by the negative of the z_j entry for the corresponding surplus variable in the optimal simplex tableau.

TABLE 18.1   TABLEAU LOCATION OF DUAL PRICE BY CONSTRAINT TYPE

Constraint Type	Dual Price Given by
$\leq$	z_j value for the slack variable associated with the constraint
$\geq$	Negative of the z_j value for the surplus variable associated with the constraint
$=$	z_j value for the artificial variable associated with the constraint

Finally, it is possible to compute dual prices for equality constraints. They are given by the z_j values for the corresponding artificial variables. We will not develop this case in detail here because we have recommended dropping each artificial variable column from the simplex tableau as soon as the corresponding artificial variable leaves the basis.

To summarize, when the simplex method is used to solve a linear programming problem, the dual prices for the constraints are contained in the final simplex tableau. Table 18.1 summarizes the rules for determining the dual prices for the various constraint types in a maximization problem solved by the simplex method.

Try Problem 3, parts (a), (b), and (c), for practice in finding dual prices from the optimal simplex tableau.

Recall that we convert a minimization problem to a maximization problem by multiplying the objective function by -1 before using the simplex method. Nevertheless, the dual price is given by the same z_j values because improvement for a minimization problem is a decrease in the optimal value.

To illustrate the approach for computing dual prices for a minimization problem, recall the M&D Chemicals problem that we solved in Section 17.7 as an equivalent maximization problem by multiplying the objective function by -1. The linear programming model for this problem and the final simplex tableau are restated as follows, with x_1 and x_2 representing manufacturing quantities of products A and B, respectively.

$$\text{Min} \quad 2x_1 + 3x_2$$
$$\text{s.t.}$$
$$1x_1 \qquad \geq 125 \quad \text{Demand for product A}$$
$$1x_1 + 1x_2 \geq 350 \quad \text{Total production}$$
$$2x_1 + 1x_2 \leq 600 \quad \text{Processing time}$$
$$x_1, x_2 \geq 0$$

		x_1	x_2	s_1	s_2	s_3	
Basis	c_B	-2	-3	0	0	0	
x_1	-2	1	0	0	1	1	**250**
x_2	-3	0	1	0	-2	-1	**100**
s_1	0	0	0	1	1	1	**125**
z_j		-2	-3	0	4	1	**-800**
$c_j - z_j$		0	0	0	-4	-1	

Following the rules in Table 18.1 for identifying the dual price for each constraint type, the dual prices for the constraints in the M&D Chemicals problem are given in Table 18.2.

TABLE 18.2   DUAL PRICES FOR M&D CHEMICALS PROBLEM

Constraint	Constraint Type	Dual Price
Demand for product A	≥	0
Total production	≥	−4
Processing time	≤	1

Constraint 1 is not binding, and its dual price is zero. The dual price for constraint 2 shows that the marginal cost of increasing the total production requirement is $4 per unit. Finally, the dual price of one for the third constraint shows that the per-unit value of additional processing time is $1.

Range of Feasibility   As we have just seen, the z_j row in the final simplex tableau can be used to determine the dual price and, as a result, predict the change in the value of the objective function corresponding to a unit change in a b_i. This interpretation is only valid, however, as long as the change in b_i is not large enough to make the current basic solution infeasible. Thus, we will be interested in calculating a range of values over which a particular b_i can vary without any of the current basic variables becoming infeasible (i.e., less than zero). This range of values will be referred to as the **range of feasibility.**

A change in b_i does not affect optimality ($c_j − z_j$ is unchanged), but it does affect feasibility. One of the current basic variables may become negative.

To demonstrate the effect of changing a b_i, consider increasing the amount of assembly time available in the HighTech problem from 150 to 160 hours. Will the current basis still yield a feasible solution? If so, given the dual price of $2.80 for the assembly time constraint, we can expect an increase in the value of the solution of 10(2.80) = 28. The final simplex tableau corresponding to an increase in the assembly time of 10 hours is shown here.

		x_1	x_2	s_1	s_2	s_3	
Basis	c_B	50	40	0	0	0	
x_2	40	0	1	$8/25$	0	$-3/25$	15.2
s_2	0	0	0	$-8/25$	1	$3/25$	4.8
x_1	50	1	0	$-5/25$	0	$5/25$	28.0
z_j		50	40	$14/5$	0	$26/5$	2008
$c_j − z_j$		0	0	$-14/5$	0	$-26/5$	

The same basis, consisting of the basic variables x_2, s_2, and x_1, is feasible because all the basic variables are nonnegative. Note also that, just as we predicted using the dual price, the value of the optimal solution has increased by 10($2.80) = $28, from $1980 to $2008.

You may wonder whether we had to re-solve the problem completely to find this new solution. The answer is no! The only changes in the final simplex tableau (as compared with the final simplex tableau with $b_1 = 150$) are the differences in the values of the basic variables and the value of the objective function. That is, only the last column of the simplex tableau changed. The entries in this new last column of the simplex tableau were obtained by adding 10 times the first four entries in the s_1 column to the last column in the previous tableau:

	Old solution	Change in b_1	s_1 column	New solution

$$\text{New solution} = \begin{bmatrix} 12 \\ 8 \\ 30 \\ 1980 \end{bmatrix} + 10 \begin{bmatrix} \frac{8}{25} \\ -\frac{8}{25} \\ -\frac{5}{25} \\ \frac{14}{5} \end{bmatrix} = \begin{bmatrix} 15.2 \\ 4.8 \\ 28.0 \\ 2008 \end{bmatrix}$$

Let us now consider why this procedure can be used to find the new solution. First, recall that each of the coefficients in the s_1 column indicates the amount of decrease in a basic variable that would result from increasing s_1 by one unit. In other words, these coefficients tell us how many units of each of the current basic variables will be driven out of solution if one unit of variable s_1 is brought into solution. Bringing one unit of s_1 into solution, however, is the same as reducing the availability of assembly time (decreasing b_1) by one unit; increasing b_1, the available assembly time, by one unit has just the opposite effect. Therefore, the entries in the s_1 column can also be interpreted as the changes in the values of the current basic variables corresponding to a one-unit increase in b_1.

To practice finding the new solution after a change in a right-hand side without re-solving the problem when the same basis remains feasible, try Problem 3, parts (d) and (e).

The change in the value of the objective function corresponding to a one-unit increase in b_1 is given by the value of z_j in that column (the dual price). In the foregoing case, the availability of assembly time increased by 10 units; thus, we multiplied the first four entries in the s_1 column by 10 to obtain the change in the value of the basic variables and the optimal value.

How do we know when a change in b_1 is so large that the current basis will become infeasible? We shall first answer this question specifically for the HighTech Industries problem and then state the general procedure for less-than-or-equal-to constraints. The approach taken with greater-than-or-equal-to and equality constraints will then be discussed.

We begin by showing how to compute upper and lower bounds for the maximum amount that b_1 can be changed before the current optimal basis becomes infeasible. We have seen how to find the new basic feasible solution values given a 10-unit increase in b_1. In general, given a change in b_1 of Δb_1, the new values for the basic variables in the HighTech problem are given by

$$\begin{bmatrix} x_2 \\ s_2 \\ x_1 \end{bmatrix} = \begin{bmatrix} 12 \\ 8 \\ 30 \end{bmatrix} + \Delta b_1 \begin{bmatrix} \frac{8}{25} \\ -\frac{8}{25} \\ -\frac{5}{25} \end{bmatrix} = \begin{bmatrix} 12 + \frac{8}{25}\Delta b_1 \\ 8 - \frac{8}{25}\Delta b_1 \\ 30 - \frac{5}{25}\Delta b_1 \end{bmatrix} \tag{18.6}$$

As long as the new value of each basic variable remains nonnegative, the current basis will remain feasible and therefore optimal. We can keep the basic variables nonnegative by limiting the change in b_1 (i.e., Δb_1) so that we satisfy each of the following conditions:

$$12 + \frac{8}{25}\Delta b_1 \geq 0 \tag{18.7}$$

$$8 - \frac{8}{25}\Delta b_1 \geq 0 \tag{18.8}$$

$$30 - \frac{5}{25}\Delta b_1 \geq 0 \tag{18.9}$$

The left-hand sides of these inequalities represent the new values of the basic variables after b_1 has been changed by Δb_1.

Solving for Δb_1 in inequalities (18.7), (18.8), and (18.9), we obtain

$$\Delta b_1 \geq \; (^{25}\!/_8)(-12) = -37.5$$
$$\Delta b_1 \leq \; (-^{25}\!/_8)(-8) = 25$$
$$\Delta b_1 \leq (-^{25}\!/_5)(-30) = 150$$

Because all three inequalities must be satisfied, the most restrictive limits on b_1 must be satisfied for all the current basic variables to remain nonnegative. Therefore, Δb_1 must satisfy

$$-37.5 \leq \Delta b_1 \leq 25 \qquad\qquad (18.10)$$

The initial amount of assembly time available was 150 hours. Therefore, $b_1 = 150 + \Delta b_1$, where b_1 is the amount of assembly time available. We add 150 to each of the three terms in expression (18.10) to obtain

$$150 - 37.5 \leq 150 + \Delta b_1 \leq 150 + 25 \qquad\qquad (18.11)$$

Replacing $150 + \Delta b_1$ with b_1, we obtain the range of feasibility for b_1:

$$112.5 \leq b_1 \leq 175$$

This range of feasibility for b_1 indicates that as long as the available assembly time is between 112.5 and 175 hours, the current optimal basis will remain feasible, which is why we call this range the range of feasibility.

Because the dual price for b_1 (assembly time) is $^{14}\!/_5$, we know profit can be increased by \$2.80 by obtaining an additional hour of assembly time. Suppose then that we increase b_1 by 25; that is, we increase b_1 to the upper limit of its range of feasibility, 175. The profit will increase to $\$1980 + (\$2.80)25 = \$2050$, and the values of the optimal basic variables become

$$x_2 = 12 + 25(^8\!/_{25}) \quad = 20$$
$$s_2 = \; 8 + 25(-^8\!/_{25}) = \; 0$$
$$x_1 = 30 + 25(-^5\!/_{25}) = 25$$

What happened to the solution? The increased assembly time caused a revision in the optimal production plan. HighTech should produce more of the Portable and less of the Deskpro. Overall, the profit will be increased by $(\$2.80)(25) = \$70$. Note that although the optimal solution changed, the basic variables that were optimal before are still optimal.

The procedure for determining the range of feasibility has been illustrated with the assembly time constraint. The procedure for calculating the range of feasibility for the right-hand side of any less-than-or-equal-to constraint is the same. The first step for a general constraint i is to calculate the range of values for b_i that satisfies the following inequalities.

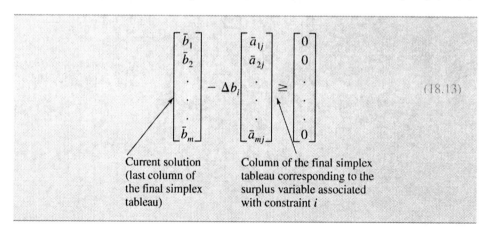

$$\begin{bmatrix} \bar{b}_1 \\ \bar{b}_2 \\ \cdot \\ \cdot \\ \cdot \\ \bar{b}_m \end{bmatrix} + \Delta b_i \begin{bmatrix} \bar{a}_{1j} \\ \bar{a}_{2j} \\ \cdot \\ \cdot \\ \cdot \\ \bar{a}_{mj} \end{bmatrix} \geq \begin{bmatrix} 0 \\ 0 \\ \cdot \\ \cdot \\ \cdot \\ 0 \end{bmatrix} \qquad (18.12)$$

Current solution (last column of the final simplex tableau)

Column of the final simplex tableau corresponding to the slack variable associated with constraint i

The inequalities are used to identify lower and upper limits on Δb_i. The range of feasibility can then be established by the maximum of the lower limits and the minimum of the upper limits.

Similar arguments can be used to develop a procedure for determining the range of feasibility for the right-hand-side value of a greater-than-or-equal-to constraint. Essentially the procedure is the same, with the column corresponding to the surplus variable associated with the constraint playing the central role. For a general greater-than-or-equal-to constraint i, we first calculate the range of values for Δb_i that satisfy the inequalities shown in inequality (18.13).

$$\begin{bmatrix} \bar{b}_1 \\ \bar{b}_2 \\ \cdot \\ \cdot \\ \cdot \\ \bar{b}_m \end{bmatrix} - \Delta b_i \begin{bmatrix} \bar{a}_{1j} \\ \bar{a}_{2j} \\ \cdot \\ \cdot \\ \cdot \\ \bar{a}_{mj} \end{bmatrix} \geq \begin{bmatrix} 0 \\ 0 \\ \cdot \\ \cdot \\ \cdot \\ 0 \end{bmatrix} \qquad (18.13)$$

Current solution (last column of the final simplex tableau)

Column of the final simplex tableau corresponding to the surplus variable associated with constraint i

Once again, these inequalities establish lower and upper limits on Δb_i. Given these limits, the range of feasibility is easily determined.

Try Problem 4 to make sure you can compute the range of feasibility by working with the final simplex tableau.

A range of feasibility for the right-hand side of an equality constraint can also be computed. To do so for equality constraint i, one could use the column of the final simplex tableau corresponding to the artificial variable associated with constraint i in equation (18.12). Because we have suggested dropping the artificial variable columns from the simplex tableau as soon as the artificial variable becomes nonbasic, these columns will not be available in the final tableau. Thus, more involved calculations are required to compute a range of feasibility for equality constraints. Details may be found in more advanced texts.

Changes that force b_i outside its range of feasibility are normally accompanied by changes in the dual prices.

As long as the change in a right-hand-side value is such that b_i stays within its range of feasibility, the same basis will remain feasible and optimal. Changes that force b_i outside its range of feasibility will force us to re-solve the problem to find the new optimal solution consisting of a different set of basic variables. (More advanced linear programming texts show how it can be done without completely re-solving the problem.) In any case, the calculation of the range of feasibility for each b_i is valuable management information and should be included as part of the management report on any linear programming project. The range of feasibility is typically made available as part of the computer solution to the problem.

Simultaneous Changes

In reviewing the procedures for developing the range of optimality and the range of feasibility, we note that only one coefficient at a time was permitted to vary. Our statements concerning changes within these ranges were made with the understanding that no other coefficients are permitted to change. However, sometimes we can make the same statements when either two or more objective function coefficients or two or more right-hand sides are varied simultaneously. When the simultaneous changes satisfy the 100 percent rule, the same statements are applicable. The 100 percent rule was explained in Chapter 3, but we will briefly review it here.

Let us define allowable increase as the amount a coefficient can be increased before reaching the upper limit of its range, and allowable decrease as the amount a coefficient can be decreased before reaching the lower limit of its range. Now suppose simultaneous changes are made in two or more objective function coefficients. For each coefficient changed, we compute the percentage of the allowable increase, or allowable decrease, represented by the change. If the sum of the percentages for all changes does not exceed 100 percent, we say that the 100 percent rule is satisfied and that the simultaneous changes will not cause a change in the optimal solution. However, just as with a single objective function coefficient change, the value of the solution will change because of the change in the coefficients.

Similarly, if two or more changes in constraint right-hand-side values are made, we again compute the percentage of allowable increase or allowable decrease represented by each change. If the sum of the percentages for all changes does not exceed 100 percent, we say that the 100 percent rule is satisfied. The dual prices are then valid for determining the change in value of the objective function associated with the right-hand-side changes.

NOTES AND COMMENTS

1. Sometimes, interpreting dual prices and choosing the appropriate sign can be confusing. It often helps to think of this process as follows. Relaxing a $\geq$ constraint means decreasing its right-hand side, and relaxing a $\leq$ constraint means increasing its right-hand side. Relaxing a constraint permits improvement in value; restricting a constraint (decreasing the right-hand side of a $\leq$ constraint or increasing the right-hand side of a $\geq$ constraint) has the opposite effect. In every case, the absolute value of the dual price gives the improvement in the optimal value associated with relaxing the constraint.

2. The Notes and Comments in Chapter 3 concerning sensitivity analysis are also applicable here. In particular, recall that the 100 percent rule cannot be applied to simultaneous changes in the objective function *and* the right-hand sides; it applies only to simultaneous changes in one or the other. Also note that this rule *does not* mean that simultaneous changes that do not satisfy the rule will necessarily cause a change in the solution. For instance, any proportional change in *all* the objective function coefficients will leave the optimal solution unchanged, and any proportional change in *all* the right-hand sides will leave the dual prices unchanged.

18.2   DUALITY

Every linear programming problem has an associated linear programming problem called the **dual problem.** Referring to the original formulation of the linear programming problem as the **primal problem,** we will see how the primal can be converted into its corresponding dual. Then we will solve the dual linear programming problem and interpret the results. A fundamental property of the primal-dual relationship is that the optimal solution to either the primal or the dual problem also provides the optimal solution to the other. In cases where the primal and the dual problems differ in terms of computational difficulty, we can choose the easier problem to solve.

Let us return to the HighTech Industries problem. The original formulation—the primal problem—is as follows:

$$\text{Max} \quad 50x_1 + 40x_2$$
$$\text{s.t.}$$
$$
\begin{array}{llll}
3x_1 + & 5x_2 \le 150 & \text{Assembly time} \\
        & 1x_2 \le \ \ 20 & \text{Portable display} \\
8x_1 + & 5x_2 \le 300 & \text{Warehouse space} \\
x_1, x_2 \ge 0
\end{array}
$$

A maximization problem with all less-than-or-equal-to constraints and nonnegativity requirements for the variables is said to be in **canonical form.** For a maximization problem in canonical form, such as the HighTech Industries problem, the conversion to the associated dual linear program is relatively easy. Let us state the dual of the HighTech problem and then identify the steps taken to make the primal-dual conversion. The HighTech dual problem is as follows:

$$\text{Min} \quad 150u_1 + 20u_2 + 300u_3$$
$$\text{s.t.}$$
$$
\begin{array}{lll}
3u_1 & + & 8u_3 \ge 50 \\
5u_1 + 1u_2 + & 5u_3 \ge 40 \\
u_1, u_2, u_3 \ge 0
\end{array}
$$

This **canonical form for a minimization problem** is a minimization problem with all greater-than-or-equal-to constraints and nonnegativity requirements for the variables. Thus, the dual of a maximization problem in canonical form is a minimization problem in canonical form. The variables u_1, u_2, and u_3 are referred to as **dual variables.**

With the preceding example in mind, we make the following general statements about the *dual of a maximization problem in canonical form.*

1. The dual is a minimization problem in canonical form.
2. When the primal has n decision variables ($n = 2$ in the HighTech problem), the dual will have n constraints. The first constraint of the dual is associated with variable x_1 in the primal, the second constraint in the dual is associated with variable x_2 in the primal, and so on.
3. When the primal has m constraints ($m = 3$ in the HighTech problem), the dual will have m decision variables. Dual variable u_1 is associated with the first primal constraint, dual variable u_2 is associated with the second primal constraint, and so on.

4. The right-hand sides of the primal constraints become the objectiv
   ficients in the dual.
5. The objective function coefficients of the primal become the right-han
   dual constraints.
6. The constraint coefficients of the ith primal variable become the coeffici
   ith constraint of the dual.

Try part (a) of Problem 17 for practice in finding the dual of a maximization problem in canonical form.

These six statements are the general requirements that must be satisfied when co
ing a maximization problem in canonical form to its associated dual: a minimization p
lem in canonical form. Even though these requirements may seem cumbersome at fir
practice with a few simple problems will show that the primal-dual conversion process i.
relatively easy to implement.

We have formulated the HighTech dual linear programming problem, so let us now proceed to solve it. With three variables in the dual, we will use the simplex method. After subtracting surplus variables s_1 and s_2 to obtain the standard form, adding artificial variables a_1
and a_2 to obtain the tableau form, and multiplying the objective function by -1 to convert
the dual problem to an equivalent maximization problem, we arrive at the following initial
simplex tableau.

Basis	c_B	u_1 -150	u_2 -20	u_3 -300	s_1 0	s_2 0	a_1 $-M$	a_2 $-M$	
a_1	$-M$	3	0	⑧	-1	0	1	0	50
a_2	$-M$	5	1	5	0	-1	0	1	40
z_j		$-8M$	$-M$	$-13M$	M	M	$-M$	$-M$	$-90M$
$c_j - z_j$		$-150 + 8M$	$-20 + M$	$-300 + 13M$	$-M$	$-M$	0	0	

At the first iteration, u_3 is brought into the basis, and a_1 is removed. At the second iteration, u_1 is brought into the basis, and a_2 is removed. At this point, the simplex tableau appears as follows.

Basis	c_B	u_1 -150	u_2 -20	u_3 -300	s_1 0	s_2 0	
u_3	-300	0	$-\frac{3}{25}$	1	$-\frac{5}{25}$	$\frac{3}{25}$	$\frac{26}{5}$
u_1	-150	1	$\frac{8}{25}$	0	$\frac{5}{25}$	$-\frac{8}{25}$	$\frac{14}{5}$
z_j		-150	-12	-300	30	12	-1980
$c_j - z_j$		0	-8	0	-30	-12	

Because all the entries in the net evaluation row are less than or equal to zero, the opti-
mal solution has been reached; it is $u_1 = \frac{14}{5}$, $u_2 = 0$, $u_3 = \frac{26}{5}$, $s_1 = 0$, and $s_2 = 0$. We have
been maximizing the negative of the dual objective function; therefore, the value of the ob-
jective function for the optimal dual solution must be $-(-1980) = 1980$.

The final simplex tableau for the original HighTech Industries problem is shown here.

Basis	c_B	x_1 50	x_2 40	s_1 0	s_2 0	s_3 0	
x_2	40	0	1	$8/25$	0	$-3/25$	12
s_2	0	0	0	$-8/25$	1	$3/25$	8
x_1	50	1	0	$-5/25$	0	$5/25$	30
z_j		50	40	$14/5$	0	$26/5$	1980
$c_j - z_j$		0	0	$-14/5$	0	$-26/5$	

The optimal solution to the primal problem is $x_1 = 30$, $x_2 = 12$, $s_1 = 0$, $s_2 = 8$, and $s_3 = 0$. The optimal value of the objective function is 1980.

What observation can we make about the relationship between the optimal value of the objective function in the primal and the optimal value in the dual for the HighTech problem? The optimal value of the objective function is the same (1980) for both. This relationship is true for all primal and dual linear programming problems and is stated as property 1.

Property 1

If the dual problem has an optimal solution, the primal problem has an optimal solution, and vice versa. Furthermore, the values of the optimal solutions to the dual and primal problems are equal.

This property tells us that if we solved only the dual problem, we would know that High-Tech could make a maximum of $1980.

Economic Interpretation of the Dual Variables

Before making further observations about the relationship between the primal and the dual solutions, let us consider the meaning or interpretation of the dual variables u_1, u_2, and u_3. Remember that in setting up the dual problem, each dual variable is associated with one of the constraints in the primal. Specifically, u_1 is associated with the assembly time constraint, u_2 with the Portable display constraint, and u_3 with the warehouse space constraint.

To understand and interpret these dual variables, let us return to property 1 of the primal-dual relationship, which stated that the objective function values for the primal and dual problems must be equal. At the optimal solution, the primal objective function results in

$$50x_1 + 40x_2 = 1980 \tag{18.14}$$

while the dual objective function is

$$150u_1 + 20u_2 + 300u_3 = 1980 \tag{18.15}$$

Using equation (18.14), let us restrict our interest to the interpretation of the primal objective function. With x_1 and x_2 as the number of units of the Deskpro and the Portable that are assembled respectively, we have

$$\begin{pmatrix}\text{Dollar value}\\\text{per unit of}\\\text{Deskpro}\end{pmatrix}\begin{pmatrix}\text{Number of}\\\text{units of}\\\text{Deskpro}\end{pmatrix} + \begin{pmatrix}\text{Dollar value}\\\text{per unit of}\\\text{Portable}\end{pmatrix}\begin{pmatrix}\text{Number of}\\\text{units of}\\\text{Portable}\end{pmatrix} = \begin{matrix}\text{Total dollar}\\\text{value of}\\\text{production}\end{matrix}$$

From equation (18.15), we see that the coefficients of the dual objective function (150, 20, and 300) can be interpreted as the number of units of resources available. Thus, because the primal and dual objective functions are equal at optimality, we have

$$\begin{pmatrix}\text{Units of}\\\text{resource}\\1\end{pmatrix}u_1 + \begin{pmatrix}\text{Units of}\\\text{resource}\\2\end{pmatrix}u_2 + \begin{pmatrix}\text{Units of}\\\text{resource}\\3\end{pmatrix}u_3 = \begin{matrix}\text{Total dollar value}\\\text{of production}\end{matrix}$$

Thus, we see that the dual variables must carry the interpretations of being the value per unit of resource. For the HighTech problem,

$$u_1 = \text{dollar value per hour of assembly time}$$
$$u_2 = \text{dollar value per unit of the Portable display}$$
$$u_3 = \text{dollar value per square foot of warehouse space}$$

Have we attempted to identify the value of these resources previously? Recall that in Section 18.1, when we considered sensitivity analysis of the right-hand sides, we identified the value of an additional unit of each resource. These values were called dual prices and are helpful to the decision maker in determining whether additional units of the resources should be made available.

The analysis in Section 18.1 led to the following dual prices for the resources in the HighTech problem.

Resource	Value per Additional Unit (dual price)
Assembly time	$2.80
Portable display	$0.00
Warehouse space	$5.20

The dual variables are the shadow prices, but in a maximization problem, they also equal the dual prices. For a minimization problem, the dual prices are the negative of the dual variables.

Let us now return to the optimal solution for the HighTech dual problem. The values of the dual variables at the optimal solution are $u_1 = \frac{14}{5} = 2.80$, $u_2 = 0$, and $u_3 = \frac{26}{5} = 5.20$. For this maximization problem, the values of the dual variables and the dual prices are the same. For a minimization problem, the dual prices and the dual variables are the same in absolute value but have opposite signs. Thus, the optimal values of the dual variables identify the dual prices of each additional resource or input unit at the optimal solution.

In light of the preceding discussion, the following interpretation of the primal and dual problems can be made when the primal is a product-mix problem.

Primal Problem Given a per-unit value of each product, determine how much of each should be produced to maximize the value of the total production. Constraints require the amount of each resource used to be less than or equal to the amount available.

Dual Problem   Given the availability of each resource, determine the per-unit value such that the total value of the resources used is minimized. Constraints require the resource value per unit be greater than or equal to the value of each unit of output.

Using the Dual to Identify the Primal Solution

At the beginning of this section, we mentioned that an important feature of the primal-dual relationship is that when an optimal solution is reached, the value of the optimal solution for the primal problem is the same as the value of the optimal solution for the dual problem; see property 1. However, the question remains: If we solve only the dual problem, can we identify the optimal values for the primal variables?

Recall that in Section 18.1 we showed that when a primal problem is solved by the simplex method, the optimal values of the primal variables appear in the right-most column of the final tableau, and the dual prices (values of the dual variables) are found in the z_j row. The final simplex tableau of the dual problem provides the optimal values of the dual variables, and therefore the values of the primal variables should be found in the z_j row of the optimal dual tableau. This result is, in fact, the case and is formally stated as property 2.

Property 2

Given the simplex tableau corresponding to the optimal dual solution, the optimal values of the primal decision variables are given by the z_j entries for the surplus variables; furthermore, the optimal values of the primal slack variables are given by the negative of the $c_j - z_j$ entries for the u_j variables.

To test your ability to find the primal solution from the optimal simplex tableau for the dual and interpret the dual variables, try parts (b) and (c) of Problem 17.

This property enables us to use the final simplex tableau for the dual of the HighTech problem to determine the optimal primal solution of $x_1 = 30$ units of the Deskpro and $x_2 = 12$ units of the Portable. These optimal values of x_1 and x_2, as well as the values for all primal slack variables, are given in the z_j and $c_j - z_j$ rows of the final simplex tableau of the dual problem, which is shown again here.

Basis	c_B	u_1 -150	u_2 -20	u_3 -300	s_1 0	s_2 0	
u_3	-300	0	$-3/25$	1	$-5/25$	$3/25$	$26/5$
u_1	-150	1	$8/25$	0	$5/25$	$-8/25$	$14/5$
z_j		-150	-12	-300	30	12	-1980
$c_j - z_j$		0	-8	0	-30	-12	

Finding the Dual of Any Primal Problem

The HighTech Industries primal problem provided a good introduction to the concept of duality because it was formulated as a maximization problem in canonical form. For this form of primal problem, we demonstrated that conversion to the dual problem is rather easy. If the primal problem is a minimization problem in canonical form, then the dual is a maximization problem in canonical form. Therefore, finding the dual of a minimization problem in canonical form is also easy. Consider the following linear program in canonical form for a minimization problem:

$$\text{Min} \quad 6x_1 + 2x_2$$
$$\text{s.t.}$$
$$5x_1 - 1x_2 \geq 13$$
$$3x_1 + 7x_2 \geq 9$$
$$x_1, x_2 \geq 0$$

The dual is the following maximization problem in canonical form:

$$\text{Max} \quad 13u_1 + 9u_2$$
$$\text{s.t.}$$
$$5u_1 + 3u_2 \leq 6$$
$$-1u_1 + 7u_2 \leq 2$$
$$u_1, u_2 \geq 0$$

Try Problem 18 for practice in finding the dual of a minimization problem in canonical form.

Although we could state a special set of rules for converting each type of primal problem into its associated dual, we believe it is easier to first convert any primal problem into an equivalent problem in canonical form. Then, we follow the procedures already established for finding the dual of a maximization or minimization problem in canonical form.

Let us illustrate the procedure for finding the dual of any linear programming problem by finding the dual of the following minimization problem:

$$\text{Min} \quad 2x_1 - 3x_2$$
$$\text{s.t.}$$
$$1x_1 + 2x_2 \leq 12$$
$$4x_1 - 2x_2 \geq 3$$
$$6x_1 - 1x_2 = 10$$
$$x_1, x_2 \geq 0$$

For this minimization problem, we obtain the canonical form by converting all constraints to greater-than-or-equal-to form. The necessary steps are as follows:

Step 1. Convert the first constraint to greater-than-or-equal-to form by multiplying both sides of the inequality by (-1). Doing so yields

$$-x_1 - 2x_2 \geq -12$$

Step 2. Constraint 3 is an equality constraint. For an equality constraint, we first create two inequalities: one with $\leq$ form, the other with $\geq$ form. Doing so yields

$$6x_1 - 1x_2 \geq 10$$
$$6x_1 - 1x_2 \leq 10$$

Then, we multiply the $\leq$ constraint by (-1) to get two $\geq$ constraints.

$$6x_1 - 1x_2 \geq 10$$
$$-6x_1 + 1x_2 \geq -10$$

Now the original primal problem has been restated in the following equivalent form:

$$\text{Min} \quad 2x_1 - 3x_2$$

s.t.

$$
\begin{aligned}
-1x_1 - 2x_2 &\geq -12 \\
4x_1 - 2x_2 &\geq 3 \\
6x_1 - 1x_2 &\geq 10 \\
-6x_1 + 1x_2 &\geq -10 \\
x_1, x_2 &\geq 0
\end{aligned}
$$

With the primal problem now in canonical form for a minimization problem, we can easily convert to the dual problem using the primal-dual procedure presented earlier in this section. The dual becomes[2]

$$\text{Max} \quad -12u_1 + 3u_2 + 10u_3' - 10u_3''$$

s.t.

$$
\begin{aligned}
-1u_1 + 4u_2 + 6u_3' - 6u_3'' &\leq 2 \\
-2u_1 - 2u_2 - 1u_3' + 1u_3'' &\leq -3 \\
u_1, u_2, u_3', u_3'' &\geq 0
\end{aligned}
$$

The equality constraint required two $\geq$ constraints, so we denoted the dual variables associated with these constraints as u_3' and u_3''. This notation reminds us that u_3' and u_3'' both refer to the third constraint in the initial primal problem. Because two dual variables are associated with an equality constraint, the interpretation of the dual variable must be modified slightly. The dual variable for the equality constraint $6x_1 - 1x_2 = 10$ is given by the value of $u_3' - u_3''$ in the optimal solution to the dual. Hence, the dual variable for an equality constraint can be negative.

Can you write the dual of any linear programming problem? Try Problem 19.

SUMMARY

In this chapter we showed how sensitivity analysis can be performed using the information in the final simplex tableau. This sensitivity analysis includes computing the range of optimality for objective function coefficients, dual prices, and the range of feasibility for the right-hand sides. Sensitivity information is routinely made available as part of the solution report provided by most linear programming computer packages.

We stress here that sensitivity analysis is based on the assumption that only one coefficient is allowed to change at a time; all other coefficients are assumed to remain at their original values. It is possible to do some limited sensitivity analysis on the effect of changing more than one coefficient at a time; the 100 percent rule was mentioned as being useful in this context.

In studying duality, we saw how the original linear programming problem, called the primal, can be converted into its associated dual linear programming problem. Solving either the primal or the dual provides the solution to the other. We learned that the value of the dual variable identifies the economic contribution or value of additional resources in the primal problem.

---

[2]Note that the right-hand side of the second constraint is negative. Thus, we must multiply both sides of the constraint by -1 to obtain a positive value for the right-hand side before attempting to solve the problem with the simplex method.

GLOSSARY

Range of optimality   The range of values over which an objective function coefficient may vary without causing any change in the optimal solution (i.e., the values of all the variables will remain the same, but the value of the objective function may change).

Dual price   The improvement in value of the optimal solution per unit increase in a constraint's right-hand-side value.

Range of feasibility   The range of values over which a b_i may vary without causing the current basic solution to become infeasible. The values of the variables in the solution will change, but the same variables will remain basic. The dual prices for constraints do not change within these ranges.

Dual problem   A linear programming problem related to the primal problem. Solution of the dual also provides the solution to the primal.

Primal problem   The original formulation of a linear programming problem.

Canonical form for a maximization problem   A maximization problem with all less-than-or-equal-to constraints and nonnegativity requirements for the decision variables.

Canonical form for a minimization problem   A minimization problem with all greater-than-or-equal-to constraints and nonnegativity requirements for the decision variables.

Dual variable   The variable in a dual linear programming problem. Its optimal value provides the dual price for the associated primal resource.

PROBLEMS

1. Consider the following linear programming problem.

$$\text{Max} \quad 5x_1 + 6x_2 + 4x_3$$
$$\text{s.t.}$$
$$3x_1 + 4x_2 + 2x_3 \leq 120$$
$$x_1 + 2x_2 + x_3 \leq 50$$
$$x_1 + 2x_2 + 3x_3 \geq 30$$
$$x_1, x_2, x_3 \geq 0$$

The optimal simplex tableau is

		x_1	x_2	x_3	s_1	s_2	s_3	
Basic	c_B	5	6	4	0	0	0	
s_3	0	0	4	0	−2	7	1	**80**
x_3	4	0	2	1	−1	3	0	**30**
x_1	5	1	0	0	1	−2	0	**20**
z_j		5	8	4	1	2	0	**220**
$c_j - z_j$		0	−2	0	−1	−2	0	

    a.   Compute the range of optimality for c_1.

    b.   Compute the range of optimality for c_2.

    c.   Compute the range of optimality for c_{s_1}.

2. For the HighTech problem, we found the range of optimality for c_1, the profit contribution per unit of the Deskpro. The final simplex tableau is given in Section 18.1. Find the following:

    a.   The range of optimality for c_2.

    b.   The range of optimality for c_{s_2}.

    c.   The range of optimality for c_{s_3}.

    d.   Suppose the per-unit profit contribution of the Portable (c_2) dropped to \$35. How would the optimal solution change? What is the new value for total profit?

3. Refer to the problem formulation and optimal simplex tableau given in Problem 1.

    a.   Find the dual price for the first constraint.

    b.   Find the dual price for the second constraint.

    c.   Find the dual price for the third constraint.

    d.   Suppose the right-hand side of the first constraint is increased from 120 to 125. Find the new optimal solution and its value.

    e.   Suppose the right-hand side of the first constraint is decreased from 120 to 110. Find the new optimal solution and its value.

4. Refer again to the problem formulation and optimal simplex tableau given in Problem 1.

    a.   Find the range of feasibility for b_1.

    b.   Find the range of feasibility for b_2.

    c.   Find the range of feasibility for b_3.

5. For the HighTech problem, we found the range of feasibility for b_1, the assembly time available (see Section 18.1).

    a.   Find the range of feasibility for b_2.

    b.   Find the range of feasibility for b_3.

    c.   How much will HighTech's profit increase if there is a 20-square-foot increase in the amount of warehouse space available (b_3)?

6. Recall the Par, Inc., problem introduced in Chapter 2. The linear program for this problem is

$$\text{Max} \quad 10x_1 + 9x_2$$

s.t.

$$
\begin{aligned}
\tfrac{7}{10}x_1 + 1x_2 &\le 630 \quad \text{Cutting and dyeing time} \\
\tfrac{1}{2}x_1 + \tfrac{5}{6}x_2 &\le 600 \quad \text{Sewing time} \\
1x_1 + \tfrac{2}{3}x_2 &\le 708 \quad \text{Finishing time} \\
\tfrac{1}{10}x_1 + \tfrac{1}{4}x_2 &\le 135 \quad \text{Inspection and packaging time} \\
x_1, x_2 &\ge 0
\end{aligned}
$$

where

$$x_1 = \text{number of standard bags produced}$$
$$x_2 = \text{number of deluxe bags produced}$$

The final simplex tableau is

Basis	c_B	x_1 10	x_2 9	s_1 0	s_2 0	s_3 0	s_4 0	
x_2	9	0	1	$^{30}/_{16}$	0	$-^{21}/_{16}$	0	252
s_2	0	0	0	$-^{15}/_{16}$	1	$^{5}/_{32}$	0	120
x_1	10	1	0	$-^{20}/_{16}$	0	$^{30}/_{16}$	0	540
s_4	0	0	0	$-^{11}/_{32}$	0	$^{9}/_{64}$	1	18
z_j		10	9	$^{70}/_{16}$	0	$^{111}/_{16}$	0	7668
$c_j - z_j$		0	0	$-^{70}/_{16}$	0	$-^{111}/_{16}$	0	

a. Calculate the range of optimality for the profit contribution of the standard bag.
b. Calculate the range of optimality for the profit contribution of the deluxe bag.
c. If the profit contribution per deluxe bag drops to $7 per unit, how will the optimal solution be affected?
d. What unit profit contribution would be necessary for the deluxe bag before Par, Inc., would consider changing its current production plan?
e. If the profit contribution of the deluxe bags can be increased to $15 per unit, what is the optimal production plan? State what you think will happen before you compute the new optimal solution.

7. For the Par, Inc., problem (Problem 6):
a. Calculate the range of feasibility for b_1 (cutting and dyeing capacity).
b. Calculate the range of feasibility for b_2 (sewing capacity).
c. Calculate the range of feasibility for b_3 (finishing capacity).
d. Calculate the range of feasibility for b_4 (inspection and packaging capacity).
e. Which of these four departments would you be interested in scheduling for overtime? Explain.

8. a. Calculate the final simplex tableau for the Par, Inc., problem (Problem 6) after increasing b_1 from 630 to $682^4/_{11}$.
b. Would the current basis be optimal if b_1 were increased further? If not, what would be the new optimal basis?

9. For the Par, Inc., problem (Problem 6):
a. How much would profit increase if an additional 30 hours became available in the cutting and dyeing department (i.e., if b_1 were increased from 630 to 660)?
b. How much would profit decrease if 40 hours were removed from the sewing department?
c. How much would profit decrease if, because of an employee accident, only 570 hours instead of 630 were available in the cutting and dyeing department?

10. The following are additional conditions encountered by Par, Inc. (Problem 6).
a. Suppose because of some new machinery Par, Inc., was able to make a small reduction in the amount of time it took to do the cutting and dyeing (constraint 1) for a standard bag. What effect would this reduction have on the objective function?
b. Management believes that by buying a new sewing machine, the sewing time for standard bags can be reduced from $\frac{1}{2}$ to $\frac{1}{3}$ hour. Do you think this machine would be a good investment? Why?

11. Recall the RMC problem (Chapter 17, Problem 9). The problem formulation is shown here:

$$\text{Max} \quad 40x_1 + 30x_2$$

s.t.

$$\begin{aligned} \tfrac{2}{5}x_1 + \tfrac{1}{2}x_2 &\le 20 \quad \text{Material 1}\\ \tfrac{1}{5}x_2 &\le 5 \quad \text{Material 2}\\ \tfrac{3}{5}x_1 + \tfrac{3}{10}x_2 &\le 21 \quad \text{Material 3}\\ x_1, x_2 &\ge 0 \end{aligned}$$

where

$$x_1 = \text{tons of fuel additive produced}$$
$$x_2 = \text{tons of solvent base produced}$$

The final simplex tableau is

		x_1	x_2	s_1	s_2	s_3	
Basis	c_B	40	30	0	0	0	
x_2	30	0	1	$\tfrac{10}{3}$	0	$-\tfrac{20}{9}$	**20**
s_2	0	0	0	$-\tfrac{2}{3}$	1	$\tfrac{4}{9}$	**1**
x_1	40	1	0	$-\tfrac{5}{3}$	0	$\tfrac{25}{9}$	**25**
z_j		40	30	$\tfrac{100}{3}$	0	$\tfrac{400}{9}$	**1600**
$c_j - z_j$		0	0	$-\tfrac{100}{3}$	0	$-\tfrac{400}{9}$	

a. Compute the ranges of optimality for c_1 and c_2.
b. Suppose that because of an increase in production costs, the profit per ton on the fuel additive is reduced to $30 per ton. What effect will this change have on the optimal solution?
c. What is the dual price for the material 1 constraint? What is the interpretation?
d. If RMC had an opportunity to purchase additional materials, which material would be the most valuable? How much should the company be willing to pay for this material?

12. Refer to Problem 11.
a. Compute the range of feasibility for b_1 (material 1 availability).
b. Compute the range of feasibility for b_2 (material 2 availability).
c. Compute the range of feasibility for b_3 (material 3 availability).
d. What is the dual price for material 3? Over what range of values for b_3 is this dual price valid?

13. Consider the following linear program:

$$\text{Max} \quad 3x_1 + 1x_2 + 5x_3 + 3x_4$$

s.t.

$$\begin{aligned} 3x_1 + 1x_2 + 2x_3 \qquad\quad &= 30\\ 2x_1 + 1x_2 + 3x_3 + 1x_4 &\ge 15\\ 2x_2 \qquad\quad + 3x_4 &\le 25\\ x_1, x_2, x_3, x_4 &\ge 0 \end{aligned}$$

a. Find the optimal solution.
b. Calculate the range of optimality for c_3.
c. What would be the effect of a four-unit decrease in c_3 (from 5 to 1) on the optimal solution and the value of that solution?
d. Calculate the range of optimality for c_2.
e. What would be the effect of a three-unit increase in c_2 (from 1 to 4) on the optimal solution and the value of that solution?

14. Consider the final simplex tableau shown here.

		x_1	x_2	x_3	x_4	s_1	s_2	s_3	
Basis	c_B	4	6	3	1	0	0	0	
x_3	3	$3/60$	0	1	$1/2$	$3/10$	0	$-6/30$	125
s_2	0	$195/60$	0	0	$-1/2$	$-5/10$	1	-1	425
x_2	6	$39/60$	1	0	$1/2$	$-1/10$	0	$12/30$	25
z_j		$81/20$	6	3	$9/2$	$3/10$	0	$54/30$	525
$c_j - z_j$		$-1/20$	0	0	$-7/2$	$-3/10$	0	$-54/30$	

The original right-hand-side values were $b_1 = 550$, $b_2 = 700$, and $b_3 = 200$.
a. Calculate the range of feasibility for b_1.
b. Calculate the range of feasibility for b_2.
c. Calculate the range of feasibility for b_3.

15. Consider the following linear program:

$$\text{Max} \quad 15x_1 + 30x_2 + 20x_3$$

s.t.

$$
\begin{aligned}
1x_1 \quad\quad\quad + \; 1x_3 &\le 4 \\
0.5x_1 + \; 2x_2 + \; 1x_3 &\le 3 \\
1x_1 + \; 1x_2 + \; 2x_3 &\le 6 \\
x_1, x_2, x_3 &\ge 0
\end{aligned}
$$

Solve using the simplex method, and answer the following questions:
a. What is the optimal solution?
b. What is the value of the objective function?
c. Which constraints are binding?
d. How much slack is available in the nonbinding constraints?
e. What are the dual prices associated with the three constraints? Which right-hand-side value would have the greatest effect on the value of the objective function if it could be changed?
f. Develop the appropriate ranges for the coefficients of the objective function. What is your interpretation of these ranges?
g. Develop and interpret the ranges of feasibility for the right-hand-side values.

16. Innis Investments manages funds for a number of companies and wealthy clients. The investment strategy is tailored to each client's needs. For a new client, Innis has been authorized to invest up to $1.2 million in two investment funds: a stock fund and a money

market fund. Each unit of the stock fund costs $50 and provides an annual rate of return of 10%; each unit of the money market fund costs $100 and provides an annual rate of return of 4%.

The client wants to minimize risk subject to the requirement that the annual income from the investment be at least $60,000. According to Innis's risk measurement system, each unit invested in the stock fund has a risk index of 8, and each unit invested in the money market fund has a risk index of 3; the higher risk index associated with the stock fund simply indicates that it is the riskier investment. Innis's client also specified that at least $300,000 be invested in the money market fund. Innis needs to determine how many units of each fund to purchase for the client to minimize the total risk index for the portfolio. Letting

$$x_1 = \text{units purchased in the stock fund}$$
$$x_2 = \text{units purchased in the money market fund}$$

leads to the following formulation:

$$
\begin{array}{lll}
\text{Min} & 8x_1 + \quad 3x_2 & \text{Total risk} \\
\text{s.t.} & & \\
& 50x_1 + 100x_2 \le 1{,}200{,}000 & \text{Funds available} \\
& 5x_1 + \quad 4x_2 \ge \quad 60{,}000 & \text{Annual income} \\
& \qquad\quad 1x_2 \ge \quad\; 3{,}000 & \text{Minimum units in money market} \\
& x_1, x_2 \ge 0 &
\end{array}
$$

a. Solve this problem using the simplex method.
b. The value of the optimal solution is a measure of the riskiness of the portfolio. What effect will increasing the annual income requirement have on the riskiness of the portfolio?
c. Find the range of feasibility for b_2.
d. How will the optimal solution and its value change if the annual income requirement is increased from $60,000 to $65,000?
e. How will the optimal solution and its value change if the risk measure for the stock fund is increased from 8 to 9?

 SELF test

17. Suppose that in a product-mix problem x_1, x_2, x_3, and x_4 indicate the units of products 1, 2, 3, and 4, respectively, and we have

$$
\begin{array}{ll}
\text{Max} & 4x_1 + 6x_2 + 3x_3 + 1x_4 \\
\text{s.t.} & \\
& 1.5x_1 + 2x_2 + 4x_3 + 3x_4 \le 550 \quad \text{Machine A hours} \\
& 4x_1 + 1x_2 + 2x_3 + 1x_4 \le 700 \quad \text{Machine B hours} \\
& 2x_1 + 3x_2 + 1x_3 + 2x_4 \le 200 \quad \text{Machine C hours} \\
& x_1, x_2, x_3, x_4 \ge 0
\end{array}
$$

a. Formulate the dual to this problem.
b. Solve the dual. Use the dual solution to show that the profit-maximizing product mix is $x_1 = 0$, $x_2 = 25$, $x_3 = 125$, and $x_4 = 0$.
c. Use the dual variables to identify the machine or machines that are producing at maximum capacity. If the manager can select one machine for additional production capacity, which machine should have priority? Why?

18. Find the dual for the following linear program:

$$\text{Min} \quad 2800x_1 + 6000x_2 + 1200x_3$$

s.t.

$$15x_1 + 15x_2 + 1x_3 \geq 5$$
$$4x_1 + 8x_2 \qquad \geq 5$$
$$12x_1 \qquad + 8x_3 \geq 24$$
$$x_1, x_2, x_3 \geq 0$$

19. Write the following primal problem in canonical form, and find its dual.

$$\text{Max} \quad 3x_1 + 1x_2 + 5x_3 + 3x_4$$

s.t.

$$3x_1 + 1x_2 + 2x_3 \qquad = 30$$
$$2x_1 + 1x_2 + 3x_3 + 1x_4 \geq 15$$
$$2x_2 \qquad + 3x_4 \leq 25$$
$$x_1, x_2, x_3, x_4 \geq 0$$

20. Photo Chemicals produces two types of photograph-developing fluids at a cost of $1.00 per gallon. Let

$$x_1 = \text{gallons of product 1}$$
$$x_2 = \text{gallons of product 2}$$

Photo Chemicals management requires that at least 30 gallons of product 1 and at least 20 gallons of product 2 be produced. They also require that at least 80 pounds of a perishable raw material be used in production. A linear programming formulation of the problem is as follows:

$$\text{Min} \quad 1x_1 + 1x_2$$

s.t.

$$1x_1 \qquad \geq 30 \quad \text{Minimum product 1}$$
$$1x_2 \geq 20 \quad \text{Minimum product 2}$$
$$1x_1 + 2x_2 \geq 80 \quad \text{Minimum raw material}$$
$$x_1, x_2 \geq 0$$

a. Write the dual problem.
b. Solve the dual problem. Use the dual solution to show that the optimal production plan is $x_1 = 30$ and $x_2 = 25$.
c. The third constraint involves a management request that the current 80 pounds of a perishable raw material be used. However, after learning that the optimal solution calls for an excess production of five units of product 2, management is reconsidering the raw material requirement. Specifically, you have been asked to identify the cost effect if this constraint is relaxed. Use the dual variable to indicate the change in the cost if only 79 pounds of raw material have to be used.

21. Consider the following linear programming problem:

$$\text{Min} \quad 4x_1 + 3x_2 + 6x_3$$

s.t.

$$1x_1 + 0.5x_2 + 1x_3 \geq 15$$
$$2x_2 + 1x_3 \geq 30$$
$$1x_1 + 1x_2 + 2x_3 \geq 20$$
$$x_1, x_2, x_3 \geq 0$$

a. Write the dual problem.

b. Solve the dual.

c. Use the dual solution to identify the optimal solution to the original primal problem.

d. Verify that the optimal values for the primal and dual problems are equal.

22. A sales representative who sells two products is trying to determine the number of sales calls that should be made during the next month to promote each product. Based on past experience, representatives earn an average $10 commission for every call on product 1 and a $5 commission for every call on product 2. The company requires at least 20 calls per month for each product and not more than 100 calls per month on any one product. In addition, the sales representative spends about 3 hours on each call for product 1 and 1 hour on each call for product 2. If 175 selling hours are available next month, how many calls should be made for each of the two products to maximize the commission?

a. Formulate a linear program for this problem.

b. Formulate and solve the dual problem.

c. Use the final simplex tableau for the dual problem to determine the optimal number of calls for the products. What is the maximum commission?

d. Interpret the values of the dual variables.

23. Consider the linear program

$$\text{Max} \quad 3x_1 + 2x_2$$
$$\text{s.t.}$$
$$1x_1 + 2x_2 \leq 8$$
$$2x_1 + 1x_2 \leq 10$$
$$x_1, x_2 \geq 0$$

a. Solve this problem using the simplex method. Keep a record of the value of the objective function at each extreme point.

b. Formulate and solve the dual of this problem using the graphical procedure.

c. Compute the value of the dual objective function for each extreme-point solution of the dual problem.

d. Compare the values of the objective function for each primal and dual extreme-point solution.

e. Can a dual feasible solution yield a value less than a primal feasible solution? Can you state a result concerning bounds on the value of the primal solution provided by any feasible solution to the dual problem?

24. Suppose the optimal solution to a three-variable linear programming problem has $x_1 = 10$, $x_2 = 30$, and $x_3 = 15$. It is later discovered that the following two constraints were inadvertently omitted when formulating the problem.

$$6x_1 + 4x_2 - 1x_3 \leq 170$$
$$\tfrac{1}{4}x_1 + 1x_2 \quad \geq 25$$

Find the new optimal solution if possible. If it is not possible, state why it is not possible.

Self-Test Solutions and Answers to Even-Numbered Problems

Chapter 18

1. a. Recomputing the $c_j - z_j$ values for the nonbasic variables with c_1 as the coefficient of x_1 leads to the following inequalities that must be satisfied:

   For x_2, we get no inequality because of the zero in the x_2 column for the row in which x_1 is a basic variable

   For s_1, we get

   $$0 + 4 - c_1 \leq 0$$
   $$c_1 \geq 4$$

   For s_2, we get

   $$0 - 12 + 2c_1 \leq 0$$
   $$2c_1 \leq 12$$
   $$c_1 \leq 6$$
   $$\text{Range: } 4 \leq c_1 \leq 6$$

   b. Because x_2 is nonbasic, we have

   $$c_2 \leq 8$$

   c. Because s_1 is nonbasic, we have

   $$c_{s_1} \leq 1$$

2. a. $31.25 \leq c_2 \leq 83.33$
   b. $-43.33 \leq c_{s_2} \leq 8.75$
   c. $c_{s_3} \leq {}^{26}\!/_5$
   d. Variables do not change; Value = $1920

3. a. It is the z_j value for s_1; dual price = 1
   b. It is the z_j value for s_2; dual price = 2
   c. It is the z_j value for s_3; dual price = 0
   d.
   $$s_3 = 80 + 5(-2) = 70$$
   $$x_3 = 30 + 5(-1) = 25$$
   $$x_1 = 20 + 5(1) = 25$$
   $$\text{Value} = 220 + 5(1) = 225$$
   e.
   $$s_3 = 80 - 10(-2) = 100$$
   $$x_3 = 30 - 10(-1) = 40$$
   $$x_1 = 20 - 10(1) = 10$$
   $$\text{Value} = 220 - 10(1) = 210$$

4. a. $80 + \Delta b_1(-2) \geq 0 \qquad \Delta b_1 \leq 40$
   $30 + \Delta b_1(-1) \geq 0 \qquad \Delta b_1 \leq 30$
   $20 + \Delta b_1(1) \geq 0 \qquad \Delta b_1 \geq -20$
   $\qquad\qquad -20 \leq \Delta b_1 \leq 30$
   $\qquad\qquad 100 \leq b_1 \leq 150$
   b. $80 + \Delta b_2(7) \geq 0 \qquad \Delta b_2 \geq -80/7$
   $30 + \Delta b_2(3) \geq 0 \qquad \Delta b_2 \geq -10$
   $20 + \Delta b_2(-2) \geq 0 \qquad \Delta b_2 \leq 10$
   $\qquad\qquad -10 \leq \Delta b_2 \leq 10$
   $\qquad\qquad 40 \leq b_2 \leq 60$
   c. $80 - \Delta b_3(1) \geq 0 \rightarrow \Delta b_3 \leq 80$
   $30 - \Delta b_3(0) \geq 0$

$$20 - \Delta b_3(0) \geq 0$$
$$\Delta b_3 \leq 80$$
$$b_3 \leq 110$$

6. a. $6.3 \leq c_1 \leq 13.5$
   b. $6^2\!/_3 \leq c_2 \leq 14^2\!/_7$
   c. Variables do not change; Value = $7164
   d. Below $6^2\!/_3$ or above $14^2\!/_7$
   e. $x_1 = 300$, $x_2 = 420$; Value = $9300

8. a. $x_1 = 5220/11$, $x_2 = 3852/11$; Value = 86,868/11
   b. No, s_1 would enter the basis

10. a. Increase in profit
    b. No

12. a. $14 \leq b_1 \leq 21\frac{1}{2}$
    b. $4 \leq b_2$
    c. $18^3\!/_4 \leq b_3 \leq 30$
    d. Dual price = 400/9; Range: $18^3\!/_4 \leq b_3 \leq 30$

14. a. $400/3 \leq b_1 \leq 800$
    b. $275 \leq b_2$
    c. $275/2 \leq b_3 \leq 625$

16. a. $x_1 = 4000$, $x_2 = 10,000$; Total risk = 62,000
    b. Increase it by 2.167 per unit
    c. $48,000 \leq b_2 \leq 102,000$
    d. $x_1 = 5667$, $x_2 = 9167$; Total risk = 72,833
    e. Variables do not change; Total risk = 66,000

17. a. The dual is given by:

    Min $550u_1 + 700u_2 + 200u_3$
    s.t.
    $$1.5u_1 + 4u_2 + 2u_3 \geq 4$$
    $$2u_1 + 1u_2 + 3u_3 \geq 6$$
    $$4u_1 + 2u_2 + 1u_3 \geq 3$$
    $$3u_1 + 1u_2 + 2u_3 \geq 1$$
    $$u_1, u_2, u_3 \geq 0$$

    b. Optimal solution: $u_1 = 3/10$; $u_2 = 0$, $u_3 = 54/30$
    The z_j values for the four surplus variables of the dual show $x_1 = 0$, $x_2 = 25$, $x_3 = 125$, and $x_4 = 0$
    c. Because $u_1 = 3/10$, $u_2 = 0$, and $u_3 = 54/30$, machines A and C ($u_j > 0$) are operating at capacity; machine C is the priority machine since each hour is worth 54/30

18. The dual is given by

    Max $5u_1 + 5u_2 + 24u_3$
    s.t.
    $$15u_1 + 4u_2 + 12u_3 \leq 2800$$
    $$15u_1 + 8u_2 \leq 6000$$
    $$u_1 + 8u_3 \leq 1200$$
    $$u_1, u_2, u_3 \geq 0$$

19. The canonical form is

Max $\quad 3x_1 + x_2 + 5x_3 + 3x_4$
s.t.

$$3x_1 + 1x_2 + 2x_3 \qquad \leq \quad 30$$
$$-3x_1 - 1x_2 - 2x_3 \qquad \leq -30$$
$$-2x_1 - 1x_2 - 3x_3 - x_4 \leq -15$$
$$2x_2 \qquad + 3x_4 \leq \quad 25$$
$$x_1, x_2, x_3, x_4 \geq 0$$

The dual is

Min $\quad 30u_1' - 30u_1'' - 15u_2 + 25u_3$
s.t.

$$3u_1' - 3u_1'' - 2u_2 \qquad\qquad \geq 3$$
$$u_1' - u_1'' - u_2 + 2u_3 \geq 1$$
$$2u_1' - 2u_1'' - 3u_2 \qquad\qquad \geq 5$$
$$- u_2 + 3u_3 \geq 3$$
$$u_1', u_1'', u_2, u_3 \geq 0$$

20. a. Max $\quad 30u_1 + 20u_2 + 80u_3$
   s.t.

$$u_1 \qquad + u_3 \leq 1$$
$$u_2 + 2u_3 \leq 1$$
$$u_1, u_2, u_3 \geq 0$$

b. $x_1 = 30, x_2 = 25$

c. Reduce cost by \$0.50

22. a. Max $\quad 10x_1 + 5x_2$
   s.t.

$$x_1 \qquad\qquad \geq 20$$
$$x_2 \geq 20$$
$$x_1 \qquad\qquad \leq 100$$
$$x_2 \leq 100$$
$$3x_1 + x_2 \leq 175$$
$$x_1, x_2 \geq 0$$

b. Min $\quad -20u_1 - 20u_2 + 100u_3 + 100u_4 + 175u_5$
   s.t.

$$-u_1 \qquad + u_3 \qquad + 3u_5 \geq 10$$
$$- u_2 \qquad + u_4 + u_5 \geq 5$$
$$u_1, u_2, u_3, u_4, u_5 \geq 0$$

Solution: $u_4 = \frac{5}{3}, u_5 = \frac{10}{3}$

c. $x_1 = 25, x_2 = 100$; commission = \$750

24. Check both constraints with $x_1 = 10, x_2 = 30, x_3 = 15$
   Both constraints are satisfied; solution remains optimal

CHAPTER 19

Solution Procedures for Transportation and Assignment Problems

CONTENTS

In Chapter 6, we introduced the **transportation** and **assignment problems** and showed how each could by solved using linear programming. In this chapter, we return to these two problems and describe special solution procedures that simplify the computations required to obtain an optimal solution.

19.1   TRANSPORTATION SIMPLEX METHOD: A SPECIAL-PURPOSE SOLUTION PROCEDURE

Solving transportation problems with a general-purpose linear programming code is fine for small to medium-sized problems. However, these problems often grow very large (a problem with 100 origins and 1000 destinations would have 100,000 variables), and more efficient solution procedures may be needed. The network structure of the transportation problem has enabled management scientists to develop special-purpose solution procedures that greatly simplify the computations.

In Section 6.1 we introduced the Foster Generators transportation problem and showed how to formulate and solve it as a linear program. The linear programming formulation involved 12 variables and 7 constraints. In this section we describe a special-purpose solution procedure, called the **transportation simplex method,** that takes advantage of the network structure of the transportation problem and makes possible the solution of large transportation problems efficiently on a computer and small transportation problems by hand.

The transportation simplex method, like the simplex method for linear programs, is a two-phase procedure; it involves first finding an initial feasible solution and then proceeding iteratively to make improvements in the solution until an optimal solution is reached. To summarize the data conveniently and to keep track of the calculations, we utilize a **transportation tableau.** The transportation tableau for the Foster Generators problem is presented in Table 19.1.

Note that the 12 *cells* in the tableau correspond to the 12 routes from one origin to one destination. Thus, each cell in the transportation tableau corresponds to a variable in the linear programming formulation. The entries in the right-hand margin of the tableau indicate the supply at each origin, and the entries in the bottom margin indicate the demand at each destination. Each row corresponds to a supply node, and each column corresponds to a demand node in the network model of the problem. The number of rows plus the number of columns equals the number of constraints in the linear programming formulation of the problem. The entries in the upper right-hand corner of each cell show the transportation cost per unit shipped over the corresponding route. Note also that for the Foster Generators problem total supply equals total demand. The transportation simplex method can be applied only to a balanced problem (total supply = total demand); if a problem is not balanced, a dummy origin or dummy destination must be added. The use of dummy origins and destinations will be discussed later in this section.

Phase I: Finding an Initial Feasible Solution

The first phase of the transportation simplex method involves finding an initial feasible solution. Such a solution provides arc flows that satisfy each demand constraint without shipping more from any origin node than the supply available. The procedures most often used to find an initial feasible solution to a transportation problem are called heuristics. A **heuristic** is a commonsense procedure for quickly finding a solution to a problem.

Several heuristics have been developed to find an initial feasible solution to a transportation problem. Although some heuristics can find an initial feasible solution quickly, often the solution they find is not especially good in terms of minimizing total cost. Other

TABLE 19.1   TRANSPORTATION TABLEAU FOR THE FOSTER GENERATORS
TRANSPORTATION PROBLEM

Origin	Destination				Origin Supply
	Boston	Chicago	St. Louis	Lexington	
Cleveland	3	2	7	6	5000
Bedford	7	5	2	3	6000
York	2	5	4	5	2500
Destination Demand	6000	4000	2000	1500	13,500

Cell corresponding
to shipments from
Bedford to Boston

Total supply
and total demand

heuristics may not find an initial feasible solution as quickly, but the solution they find is often good in terms of minimizing total cost. The heuristic we describe for finding an initial feasible solution to a transportation problem is called the **minimum cost method.** This heuristic strikes a compromise between finding a feasible solution quickly and finding a feasible solution that is close to the optimal solution.

We begin by allocating as much flow as possible to the minimum cost arc. In Table 19.1 we see that the Cleveland–Chicago, Bedford–St. Louis, and York–Boston routes each qualifies as the minimum cost arc because they each have a transportation cost of $2 per unit. When ties between arcs occur, we follow the convention of selecting the arc to which the most flow can be allocated. In this case it corresponds to shipping 4000 units from Cleveland to Chicago, so we write 4000 in the Cleveland–Chicago cell of the transportation tableau. This selection reduces the supply at Cleveland from 5000 to 1000; hence, we cross out the 5000-unit supply value and replace it with the reduced value of 1000. In addition, allocating 4000 units to this arc satisfies the demand at Chicago, so we reduce the Chicago demand to zero and eliminate the corresponding column from further consideration by drawing a line through it. The transportation tableau now appears as shown in Table 19.2.

Now we look at the reduced tableau consisting of all unlined cells to identify the next minimum cost arc. The Bedford–St. Louis and York–Boston routes tie with transportation cost of $2 per unit. More units of flow can be allocated to the York–Boston route, so we choose it for the next allocation. This step results in an allocation of 2500 units over the York–Boston route. To update the tableau, we reduce the Boston demand by 2500 units to

TABLE 19.2   TRANSPORTATION TABLEAU AFTER ONE ITERATION OF THE MINIMUM COST METHOD

	Boston	Chicago	St. Louis	Lexington	Supply
Cleveland	3	2 4000	7	6	1000 ~~5000~~
Bedford	7	5	2	3	6000
York	2	5	4	5	2500
Demand	6000	~~4000~~ 0	2000	1500	

3500, reduce the York supply to zero, and eliminate this row from further consideration by lining through it. Continuing the process results in an allocation of 2000 units over the Bedford–St. Louis route and the elimination of the St. Louis column because its demand goes to zero. The transportation tableau obtained after carrying out the second and third iterations is shown in Table 19.3.

TABLE 19.3   TRANSPORTATION TABLEAU AFTER THREE ITERATIONS OF THE MINIMUM COST METHOD

	Boston	Chicago	St. Louis	Lexington	Supply
Cleveland	3	2 4000	7	6	1000 ~~5000~~
Bedford	7	5	2 2000	3	4000 ~~6000~~
York	2 ~~2500~~	5	4	5	0 ~~2500~~
Demand	~~6000~~ 3500	~~4000~~ 0	~~2000~~ 0	1500	

TABLE 19.4   TRANSPORTATION TABLEAU AFTER FIVE ITERATIONS
OF THE MINIMUM COST METHOD

	Boston	Chicago	St. Louis	Lexington	Supply
Cleveland	3 ~~1000~~	2 ~~4000~~	7	6	0 ~~1000~~ ~~5000~~
Bedford	7	5	2 2000	3 1500	2500 ~~4000~~ ~~6000~~
York	2 ~~2500~~	5	4	5	0 ~~2500~~
Demand	~~6000~~ ~~3500~~ 2500	~~4000~~ 0	~~2000~~ 0	~~1500~~ 0	

We now have two arcs that qualify for the minimum cost arc with a value of 3:
Cleveland–Boston and Bedford–Lexington. We can allocate a flow of 1000 units to the
Cleveland–Boston route and a flow of 1500 to the Bedford–Lexington route, so we allocate
1500 units to the Bedford–Lexington route. Doing so results in a demand of zero at
Lexington and eliminates this column. The next minimum cost allocation is 1000 over the
Cleveland–Boston route. After we make these two allocations, the transportation tableau
appears as shown in Table 19.4.

The only remaining unlined cell is Bedford–Boston. Allocating 2500 units to the corresponding arc uses up the remaining supply at Bedford and satisfies all the demand at
Boston. The resulting tableau is shown in Table 19.5.

This solution is feasible because all the demand is satisfied and all the supply is
used. The total transportation cost resulting from this initial feasible solution is calculated
in Table 19.6. Phase I of the transportation simplex method is now complete; we have
an initial feasible solution. The total transportation cost associated with this solution is
$42,000.

Summary of the Minimum Cost Method   Before applying phase II of the transportation
simplex method, let us summarize the steps for obtaining an initial feasible solution using
the minimum cost method.

Step 1. Identify the cell in the transportation tableau with the lowest cost, and allocate
as much flow as possible to this cell. In case of a tie, choose the cell corresponding to the arc over which the most units can be shipped. If ties still exist,
choose any of the tied cells.

Step 2. Reduce the row supply and the column demand by the amount of flow allocated
to the cell identified in step 1.

TABLE 19.5   FINAL TABLEAU SHOWING THE INITIAL FEASIBLE SOLUTION OBTAINED USING THE MINIMUM COST METHOD

	Boston	Chicago	St. Louis	Lexington	Supply
Cleveland	3 1000	2 4000	7	6	0 ~~1000~~ ~~5000~~
Bedford	7 2500	5	2 2000	3 1500	0 ~~2500~~ ~~4000~~ ~~6000~~
York	2 2500	5	4	5	0 ~~2500~~
Demand	~~6000~~ ~~3500~~ ~~2500~~ 0	~~4000~~ 0	~~2000~~ 0	~~1500~~ 0	

To test your ability to use the minimum cost method to find an initial feasible solution, try part (a) of Problem 2.

Step 3. If *all* row supplies and column demands have been exhausted, then stop; the allocations made will provide an initial feasible solution. Otherwise, continue with step 4.

Step 4. If the row supply is now zero, eliminate the row from further consideration by drawing a line through it. If the column demand is now zero, eliminate the column by drawing a line through it.

Step 5. Continue with step 1 for all unlined rows and columns.

TABLE 19.6   TOTAL COST OF THE INITIAL FEASIBLE SOLUTION OBTAINED USING THE MINIMUM COST METHOD

| Route | | Units | Cost | |
From	To	Shipped	per Unit	Total Cost
Cleveland	Boston	1000	$3	$ 3,000
Cleveland	Chicago	4000	$2	8,000
Bedford	Boston	2500	$7	17,500
Bedford	St. Louis	2000	$2	4,000
Bedford	Lexington	1500	$3	4,500
York	Boston	2500	$2	5,000
				$42,000

Phase II: Iterating to the Optimal Solution

Phase II of the transportation simplex method is a procedure for iterating from the initial feasible solution identified in phase I to the optimal solution. Recall that each cell in the transportation tableau corresponds to an arc (route) in the network model of the transportation problem. The first step at each iteration of phase II is to identify an incoming arc. The **incoming arc** is the currently unused route (unoccupied cell) where making a flow allocation will cause the largest per-unit reduction in total cost. Flow is then assigned to the incoming arc, and the amounts being shipped over all other arcs to which flow had previously been assigned (occupied cells) are adjusted as necessary to maintain a feasible solution. In the process of adjusting the flow assigned to the occupied cells, we identify and drop an **outgoing arc** from the solution. Thus, at each iteration in phase II, we bring a currently unused arc (unoccupied cell) into the solution, and remove an arc to which flow had previously been assigned (occupied cell) from the solution.

To show how phase II of the transportation simplex method works, we must explain how to identify the incoming arc (cell), how to make the adjustments to the other occupied cells when flow is allocated to the incoming arc, and how to identify the outgoing arc (cell). We first consider identifying the incoming arc.

As mentioned, the incoming arc is the one that will cause the largest reduction per unit in the total cost of the current solution. To identify this arc, we must compute for each unused arc the amount by which total cost will be reduced by shipping one unit over that arc. The *mo*dified *di*stribution or **MODI method** is a way to make this computation.

The MODI method requires that we define an index u_i for each row of the tableau and an index v_j for each column of the tableau. Computing these row and column indexes requires that the cost coefficient for each occupied cell equal $u_i + v_j$. Thus, when c_{ij} is the cost per unit from origin i to destination j, then $u_i + v_j = c_{ij}$ for each occupied cell. Let us return to the initial feasible solution for the Foster Generators problem, which we found using the minimum cost method (see Table 19.7), and use the MODI method to identify the incoming arc.

TABLE 19.7   INITIAL FEASIBLE SOLUTION FOR THE FOSTER GENERATORS PROBLEM

	Boston	Chicago	St. Louis	Lexington	Supply
Cleveland	3 — 1000	2 — 4000	7	6	5000
Bedford	7 — 2500	5	2 — 2000	3 — 1500	6000
York	2 — 2500	5	4	5	2500
Demand	6000	4000	2000	1500	

Requiring that $u_i + v_j = c_{ij}$ for all the occupied cells in the initial feasible solution leads to a system of six equations and seven indexes, or variables:

Occupied Cell	$u_i + v_j = c_{ij}$
Cleveland–Boston	$u_1 + v_1 = 3$
Cleveland–Chicago	$u_1 + v_2 = 2$
Bedford–Boston	$u_2 + v_1 = 7$
Bedford–St. Louis	$u_2 + v_3 = 2$
Bedford–Lexington	$u_2 + v_4 = 3$
York–Boston	$u_3 + v_1 = 2$

With one more index (variable) than equation in this system, we can freely pick a value for one of the indexes and then solve for the others. We will always choose $u_1 = 0$ and then solve for the values of the other indexes. Setting $u_1 = 0$, we obtain

$$0 + v_1 = 3$$
$$0 + v_2 = 2$$
$$u_2 + v_1 = 7$$
$$u_2 + v_3 = 2$$
$$u_2 + v_4 = 3$$
$$u_3 + v_1 = 2$$

Solving these equations leads to the following values for $u_1, u_2, u_3, v_1, v_2, v_3,$ and v_4:

$$
\begin{array}{ll}
u_1 = 0 & v_1 = 3 \\
u_2 = 4 & v_2 = 2 \\
u_3 = -1 & v_3 = -2 \\
& v_4 = -1
\end{array}
$$

Management scientists have shown that for each *unoccupied* cell, $e_{ij} = c_{ij} - u_i - v_j$ provides the change in total cost per unit that will be obtained by allocating one unit of flow to the corresponding arc. Thus, we will call e_{ij} the **net evaluation index.** Because of the way u_i and v_j are computed, the net evaluation index for each occupied cell equals zero.

Rewriting the tableau containing the initial feasible solution for the Foster Generators problem and replacing the previous marginal information with the values of u_i and v_j, we obtain Table 19.8. We computed the net evaluation index (e_{ij}) for each unoccupied cell, which is the circled number in the cell. Thus, shipping one unit over the route from origin 1 to destination 3 (Cleveland–St. Louis) will increase total cost by $9; shipping one unit from origin 1 to destination 4 (Cleveland–Lexington) will increase total cost by $7; shipping one unit from origin 2 to destination 2 (Bedford–Chicago) will decrease total cost by $1; and so on.

On the basis of the net evaluation indexes, the best arc in terms of cost reduction (a net evaluation index of -1) is associated with the Bedford–Chicago route (origin 2–destination 2); thus, the cell in row 2 and column 2 is chosen as the incoming cell. Total cost decreases by $1 for every unit of flow assigned to this arc. The question now is: How much flow should we assign to this arc? Because the total cost decreases by $1 per unit assigned, we want to allocate the maximum possible flow. To find that maximum, we must recognize that, to maintain feasibility, each unit of flow assigned to this arc will require adjustments in the flow over the other currently used arcs. The **stepping-stone method** can be used to determine the adjustments necessary and to identify an outgoing arc.

TABLE 19.8 NET EVALUATION INDEXES FOR THE INITIAL FEASIBLE SOLUTION TO THE FOSTER GENERATORS PROBLEM COMPUTED USING THE MODI METHOD

u_i	v_j			
	3	2	−2	−1
0	3 1000	2 4000	7 ⑨	6 ⑦
4	7 2500	5 (−1)	2 2000	3 1500
−1	2 2500	5 ④	4 ⑦	5 ⑦

The Stepping-Stone Method Suppose that we allocate one unit of flow to the incoming arc (the Bedford–Chicago route). To maintain feasibility—that is, not exceed the number of units to be shipped to Chicago—we would have to reduce the flow assigned to the Cleveland–Chicago arc to 3999. But then we would have to increase the flow on the Cleveland–Boston arc to 1001 so that the total Cleveland supply of 5000 units could be shipped. Finally, we would have to reduce the flow on the Bedford–Boston arc by 1 to satisfy the Boston demand exactly. Table 19.9 summarizes this cycle of adjustments.

The cycle of adjustments needed in making an allocation to the Bedford–Chicago cell required changes in four cells: the incoming cell (Bedford–Chicago) and three currently occupied cells. We can view these four cells as forming a stepping-stone path in the tableau, where the corners of the path are currently occupied cells. The idea behind the stepping-stone name is to view the tableau as a pond with the occupied cells as stones sticking up in it. To identify the stepping-stone path for an incoming cell, we start at the incoming cell and move horizontally and vertically using occupied cells as the stones at the corners of the path; the objective is to step from stone to stone and return to the incoming cell where we started. To focus attention on which occupied cells are part of the stepping-stone path, we draw each occupied cell in the stepping-stone path as a cylinder, which should reinforce the image of these cells as stones sticking up in the pond. Table 19.10 depicts the stepping-stone path associated with the incoming arc of the Bedford–Chicago route.

In Table 19.10 we placed a plus sign (+) or a minus sign (−) in each occupied cell on the stepping-stone path. A plus sign indicates that the allocation to that cell will increase by the same amount we allocate to the incoming cell. A minus sign indicates that the allocation to that cell will decrease by the amount allocated to the incoming cell. Thus, to determine the maximum amount that may be allocated to the incoming cell, we simply look to the cells on the stepping-stone path identified with a minus sign. Because no arc can have a negative flow, the minus-sign cell with the *smallest amount* allocated to it will determine the maximum amount that can be allocated to the incoming cell. After allocating this

TABLE 19.9   CYCLE OF ADJUSTMENTS IN OCCUPIED CELLS NECESSARY TO MAINTAIN FEASIBILITY WHEN SHIPPING ONE UNIT FROM BEDFORD TO CHICAGO

	Boston	Chicago	St. Louis	Lexington	Supply
Cleveland	3 1001 ~~1000~~	2 3999 ~~4000~~	7	6	5000
Bedford	7 2499 ~~2500~~	5 1	2 2000	3 1500	6000
York	2 2500	5	4	5	2500
Demand	6000	4000	2000	1500	

TABLE 19.10   STEPPING-STONE PATH WITH BEDFORD–CHICAGO AS THE INCOMING ROUTE

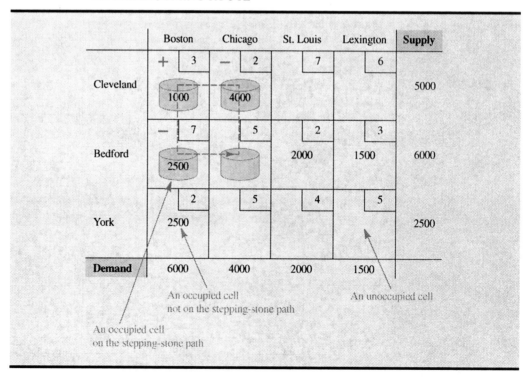

	Boston	Chicago	St. Louis	Lexington	Supply
Cleveland	+ 3 1000	− 2 4000	7	6	5000
Bedford	− 7 2500	5	2 2000	3 1500	6000
York	2 2500	5	4	5	2500
Demand	6000	4000	2000	1500	

An occupied cell
not on the stepping-stone path

An unoccupied cell

An occupied cell
on the stepping-stone path

TABLE 19.11   NEW SOLUTION AFTER ONE ITERATION IN PHASE II OF THE TRANSPORTATION SIMPLEX METHOD

	Boston	Chicago	St. Louis	Lexington	Supply
Cleveland	3 / 3500	2 / 1500	7	6	5000
Bedford	7	5 / 2500	2 / 2000	3 / 1500	6000
York	2 / 2500	5	4	5	2500
Demand	6000	4000	2000	1500	

maximum amount to the incoming cell, we then make all the adjustments necessary on the stepping-stone path to maintain feasibility. The incoming cell becomes an occupied cell, and the outgoing cell is dropped from the current solution.

In the Foster Generators problem, the Bedford–Boston and Cleveland–Chicago cells are the ones where the allocation will decrease (the ones with a minus sign) as flow is allocated to the incoming arc (Bedford–Chicago). The 2500 units currently assigned to Bedford–Boston is less than the 4000 units assigned to Cleveland–Chicago, so we identify Bedford–Boston as the outgoing arc. We then obtain the new solution by allocating 2500 units to the Bedford–Chicago arc, making the appropriate adjustments on the stepping-stone path and dropping Bedford–Boston from the solution (its allocation has been driven to zero). Table 19.11 shows the tableau associated with the new solution. Note that the only changes from the previous tableau are located on the stepping-stone path originating in the Bedford–Chicago cell.

We now try to improve on the current solution. Again, the first step is to apply the MODI method to find the best incoming arc, so we recompute the row and column indexes by requiring that $u_i + v_j = c_{ij}$ for all occupied cells. The values of u_i and v_j can easily be computed directly on the tableau. Recall that we begin the MODI method by setting $u_1 = 0$. Thus, for the two occupied cells in row 1 of the table, $v_j = c_{1j}$; as a result, $v_1 = 3$ and $v_2 = 2$. Moving down the column associated with each newly computed column index, we compute the row index associated with each occupied cell in that column by subtracting v_j from c_{ij}. Doing so for the newly found column indexes, v_1 and v_2, we find that $u_3 = 2 - 3 = -1$ and that $u_2 = 5 - 2 = 3$. Next, we use these row indexes to compute the column indexes for occupied cells in the associated rows, obtaining $v_3 = 2 - 3 = -1$ and $v_4 = 3 - 3 = 0$. Table 19.12 shows these new row and column indexes.

Also shown in Table 19.12 are the net changes (the circled numbers) in the value of the solution that will result from allocating one unit to each unoccupied cell. Recall that these are the net evaluation indexes given by $e_{ij} = c_{ij} - u_i - v_j$. Note that the net evaluation index

TABLE 19.12   MODI EVALUATION OF EACH CELL IN SOLUTION

u_i	v_j = 3	2	−1	0
0	3 3500	2 1500	7 (8)	6 (6)
3	7 (1)	5 2500	2 2000	3 1500
−1	2 2500	5 (4)	4 (6)	5 (6)

for every unoccupied cell is now greater than or equal to zero. This condition shows that if current unoccupied cells are used, the cost will actually increase. Without an arc to which flow can be assigned to decrease the total cost, we have reached the optimal solution. Table 19.13 summarizes the optimal solution and shows its total cost.

Maintaining $m + n − 1$ Occupied Cells   Recall that m represents the number of origins and n represents the number of destinations. A solution to a transportation problem that has less than $m + n − 1$ cells with positive allocations is said to be **degenerate.** The solution to the Foster Generators problem is not degenerate; six cells are occupied and $m + n − 1 = 3 + 4 − 1 = 6$. The problem with degeneracy is that $m + n − 1$ occupied cells are required by the MODI method to compute all the row and column indexes. When degeneracy occurs, we must artificially create an occupied cell in order to compute the row and column indexes. Let us illustrate how degeneracy could occur and how to deal with it.

TABLE 19.13   OPTIMAL SOLUTION TO THE FOSTER GENERATORS TRANSPORTATION PROBLEM

| Route | | Units | Cost | |
From	To	Shipped	per Unit	Total Cost
Cleveland	Boston	3500	$3	$10,500
Cleveland	Chicago	1500	$2	3,000
Bedford	Chicago	2500	$5	12,500
Bedford	St. Louis	2000	$2	4,000
Bedford	Lexington	1500	$3	4,500
York	Boston	2500	$2	5,000
				$39,500

TABLE 19.14   TRANSPORTATION TABLEAU WITH A DEGENERATE INITIAL FEASIBLE SOLUTION

u_i	v_j 3	6		Supply
0	3 35	6 25	7	60
−1	8	5 30	7	30
	4	9	11 30	30
Demand	35	55	30	

Table 19.14 shows the initial feasible solution obtained using the minimum cost method for a transportation problem involving $m = 3$ origins and $n = 3$ destinations. To use the MODI method for this problem, we must have $m + n - 1 = 3 + 3 - 1 = 5$ occupied cells. Since the initial feasible solution has only four occupied cells, the solution is degenerate.

Suppose that we try to use the MODI method to compute row and column indexes to begin phase II for this problem. Setting $u_1 = 0$ and computing the column indexes for each occupied cell in row 1, we obtain $v_1 = 3$ and $v_2 = 6$ (see Table 19.14). Continuing, we then compute the row indexes for all occupied cells in columns 1 and 2. Doing so yields $u_2 = 5 - 6 = -1$. At this point, we cannot compute any more row and column indexes because no cells in columns 1 and 2 of row 3 and no cells in rows 1 or 2 of column 3 are occupied.

To compute all the row and column indexes when fewer than $m + n - 1$ cells are occupied, we must create one or more "artificially" occupied cells with a flow of zero. In Table 19.14 we must create one artificially occupied cell to have five occupied cells. Any currently unoccupied cell can be made an artificially occupied cell if doing so makes it possible to compute the remaining row and column indexes. For instance, treating the cell in row 2 and column 3 of Table 19.14 as an artificially occupied cell will enable us to compute v_3 and u_3, but placing it in row 2 and column 1 will not.

As we previously stated, whenever an artificially occupied cell is created, we assign a flow of zero to the corresponding arc. Table 19.15 shows the results of creating an artificially occupied cell in row 2 and column 3 of Table 19.14. Creation of the artificially occupied cell results in five occupied cells, so we can now compute the remaining row and column indexes. Using the row 2 index ($u_2 = -1$) and the artificially occupied cell in row 2, we compute the column index for column 3; thus, $v_3 = c_{23} - u_2 = 7 - (-1) = 8$. Then, using the column 3 index ($v_3 = 8$) and the occupied cell in row 3 and column 3 of the tableau, we compute the row 3 index: $u_3 = c_{33} - v_3 = 11 - 8 = 3$. Table 19.15 shows the complete set of row and column indexes and the net evaluation index for each unoccupied cell.

TABLE 19.15   TRANSPORTATION TABLEAU WITH AN ARTIFICIAL CELL IN ROW 2 AND COLUMN 3

u_i	v_j 3	6	8	Supply
0	3 35	6 25	7 (−1)	60
−1	8 (6)	5 30	7 0	30
3	4 (−2)	9 (0)	11 30	30
Demand	35	55	30	

Artificially occupied cell

Reviewing the net evaluation indexes in Table 19.15, we identify the cell in row 3 and column 1 (net evaluation index = −2) as the incoming cell. The stepping-stone path and the adjustments necessary to maintain feasibility are shown in Table 19.16. Note that the stepping-stone path can be more complex than the simple one obtained for the incoming cell in the Foster Generators problem. The path in Table 19.16 requires adjustments in all

TABLE 19.16   STEPPING-STONE PATH FOR THE INCOMING CELL IN ROW 3 AND COLUMN 1

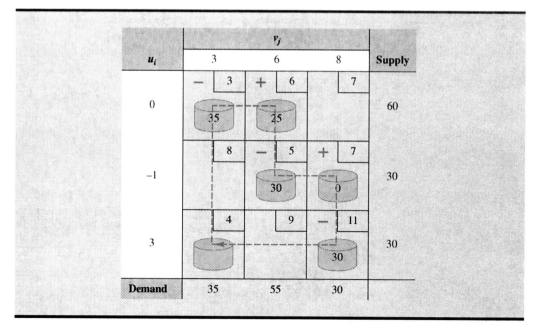

five occupied cells to maintain feasibility. Again, the plus- and minus-sign labels simply show where increases and decreases in the allocation will occur as units of flow are added to the incoming cell. The smallest flow in a decreasing cell is a tie between the cell in row 2 and column 2 and the cell in row 3 and column 3.

Because the smallest amount in a decreasing cell is 30, the allocation we make to the incoming cell is 30 units. However, when 30 units are allocated to the incoming cell and the appropriate adjustments are made to the occupied cells on the stepping-stone path, the allocation to two cells goes to zero (row 2, column 2 and row 3, column 3). We may choose either one as the outgoing cell, but not both. One will be treated as unoccupied; the other will become an artificially occupied cell with a flow of zero allocated to it. The reason we cannot let both become unoccupied cells is that doing so would lead to a degenerate solution, and as before, we could not use the MODI method to compute the row and column indexes for the next iteration. When ties occur in choosing the outgoing cell, we can choose any one of the tied cells as the artificially occupied cell and then use the MODI method to recompute the row and column indexes. As long as no more than one cell is dropped at each iteration, the MODI method will work.

The solution obtained after allocating 30 units to the incoming cell in row 3 and column 1 and making the appropriate adjustments on the stepping-stone path leads to the tableau shown in Table 19.17. Note that we treated the cell in row 2 and column 2 as the artificially occupied cell. After computing the new row and column indexes, we see that the cell in row 1 and column 3 will be the next incoming cell. Each unit allocated to this cell will further decrease the value of the solution by 1. The stepping-stone path associated with this incoming cell is shown in Table 19.18. The cell in row 2 and column 3 is the outgoing cell; the tableau after this iteration is shown in Table 19.19. Note that we have found the optimal solution and that, even though several earlier iterations were degenerate, the final solution is not degenerate.

TABLE 19.17   NEW ROW AND COLUMN INDEXES OBTAINED AFTER ALLOCATING
30 UNITS TO THE INCOMING CELL

u_i	v_j			Supply
	3	6	8	
0	3	6	7	60
	5	55	(−1)	
−1	8	5	7	30
	(6)	0	30	
1	4	9	11	30
	30	(2)	(2)	
Demand	35	55	30	

TABLE 19.18   STEPPING-STONE PATH ASSOCIATED WITH THE INCOMING CELL IN ROW 1 AND COLUMN 3

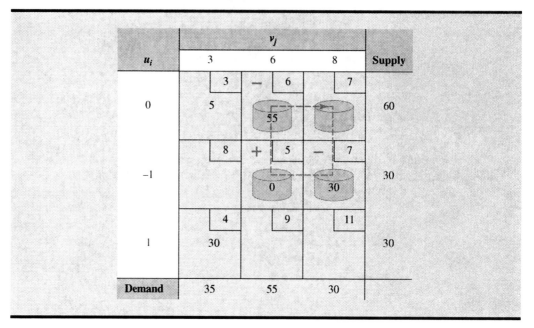

	v_j			
u_i	3	6	8	**Supply**
0	3 5	— 6 55	7	60
–1	8	+ 5 0	— 7 30	30
1	4 30	9	11	30
Demand	35	55	30	

TABLE 19.19   OPTIMAL SOLUTION TO A PROBLEM WITH A DEGENERATE INITIAL FEASIBLE SOLUTION

	v_j			
u_i	3	6	7	**Supply**
0	3 5	6 25	7 30	60
–1	8 ⑥	5 30	7 ①	30
1	4 30	9 ②	11 ③	30
Demand	35	55	30	

Summary of the Transportation Simplex Method

The transportation simplex method is a special-purpose solution procedure applicable to any network model having the special structure of the transportation problem. It is actually a clever implementation of the general simplex method for linear programming that takes advantage of the special mathematical structure of the transportation problem; but because of the special structure, the transportation simplex method is hundreds of times faster than the general simplex method.

Try part (b) of Problem 2 for practice using the transportation simplex method.

To apply the transportation simplex method, you must have a transportation problem with total supply equal to total demand; thus, for some problems you may need to add a dummy origin or dummy destination to put the problem in this form. The transportation simplex method takes the problem in this form and applies a two-phase solution procedure. In phase I, apply the minimum cost method to find an initial feasible solution. In phase II, begin with the initial feasible solution and iterate until you reach an optimal solution. The steps of the transportation simplex method for a minimization problem are summarized as follows.

Phase I

Find an initial feasible solution using the minimum cost method.

Phase II

Step 1. If the initial feasible solution is degenerate with less than $m + n - 1$ occupied cells, add an artificially occupied cell or cells so that $m + n - 1$ occupied cells exist in locations that enable use of the MODI method.

Step 2. Use the MODI method to compute row indexes, u_i, and column indexes, v_j.

Step 3. Compute the net evaluation index $e_{ij} = c_{ij} - u_i - v_j$ for each unoccupied cell.

Step 4. If $e_{ij} \geq 0$ for all unoccupied cells, stop; you have reached the minimum cost solution. Otherwise, proceed to step 5.

Step 5. Identify the unoccupied cell with the smallest (most negative) net evaluation index and select it as the incoming cell.

Step 6. Find the stepping-stone path associated with the incoming cell. Label each cell on the stepping-stone path whose flow will increase with a plus sign and each cell whose flow will decrease with a minus sign.

Step 7. Choose as the outgoing cell the minus-sign cell on the stepping-stone path with the smallest flow. If there is a tie, choose any one of the tied cells. The tied cells that are not chosen will be artificially occupied with a flow of zero at the next iteration.

Step 8. Allocate to the incoming cell the amount of flow currently given to the outgoing cell; make the appropriate adjustments to all cells on the stepping-stone path, and continue with step 2.

Problem Variations

The following problem variations can be handled, with slight adaptations, by the transportation simplex method:

1. Total supply not equal to total demand
2. Maximization objective function
3. Unacceptable routes

The case where the total supply is not equal to the total demand can be handled easily by the transportation simplex method if we first introduce a dummy origin or a dummy destination. If total supply is greater than total demand, we introduce a **dummy destination** with demand equal to the excess of supply over demand. Similarly, if total demand is greater than total supply, we introduce a **dummy origin** with supply equal to the excess of demand over supply. In either case, the use of a dummy destination or a dummy origin will equalize total supply and total demand so that we can use the transportation simplex method. When a dummy destination or origin is present, we assign cost coefficients of zero to every arc into a dummy destination and to every arc out of a dummy origin. The reason is that no shipments will actually be made from a dummy origin or to a dummy destination when the solution is implemented and thus a zero cost per unit is appropriate.

The transportation simplex method also can be used to solve maximization problems. The only modification necessary involves the selection of an incoming cell. Instead of picking the cell with the smallest or most negative e_{ij} value, we pick that cell for which e_{ij} is largest. That is, we pick the cell that will cause the largest increase per unit in the objective function. If $e_{ij} \leq 0$ for all unoccupied cells, we stop; the maximization solution has been reached.

To handle unacceptable routes in a minimization problem, infeasible arcs must carry an extremely high cost, denoted M, to keep them out of the solution. Thus, if we have a route (arc) from an origin to a destination that for some reason cannot be used, we simply assign this arc a cost per unit of M, and it will not enter the solution. Unacceptable arcs would be assigned a profit per unit of $-M$ in a maximization problem.

NOTES AND COMMENTS

1. Research devoted to developing efficient special-purpose solution procedures for network problems has shown that the transportation simplex method is one of the best. It is used in the transportation and assignment modules of The Management Scientist software package. A simple extension of this method also can be used to solve transshipment problems.

2. As we previously noted, each cell in the transportation tableau corresponds to an arc (route) in the network model of the problem and a variable in the linear programming formulation. Phase II of the transportation simplex method is thus the same as phase II of the simplex method

for linear programming. At each iteration, one variable is brought into solution and another variable is dropped from solution. The reason the method works so much better for transportation problems is that the special mathematical structure of the constraint equations means that only addition and subtraction operations are necessary. We can implement the entire procedure in a transportation tableau that has one row for each origin and one column for each destination. A simplex tableau for such a problem would require a row for each origin, a row for each destination, and a column for each arc; thus, the simplex tableau would be much larger.

19.2 ASSIGNMENT PROBLEM: A SPECIAL-PURPOSE SOLUTION PROCEDURE

As mentioned previously, the assignment problem is a special case of the transportation problem. Thus, the transportation simplex method can be used to solve the assignment problem. However, the assignment problem has an even more special structure: All supplies and demands equal 1. Because of this additional special structure, special-purpose solution procedures have been specifically designed to solve the assignment problem; one such procedure is called the **Hungarian method.** In this section we will show how the Hungarian method can be used to solve the Fowle Marketing Research problem.

TABLE 19.20   ESTIMATED PROJECT COMPLETION TIMES (DAYS) FOR THE FOWLE
ASSIGNMENT PROBLEM

		Client	
Project Leader	1	2	3
Terry	10	15	9
Carle	9	18	5
McClymonds	6	14	3

Recall that the Fowle problem (see Section 6.2) involved assigning project leaders to clients; three project leaders were available and three research projects were to be completed for three clients. Fowle's assignment alternatives and estimated project completion times in days are restated in Table 19.20.

The Hungarian method involves what is called *matrix reduction*. Subtracting and adding appropriate values in the matrix yields an optimal solution to the assignment problem. Three major steps are associated with the procedure. Step 1 involves row and column reduction.

Step 1.   Reduce the initial matrix by subtracting the smallest element in each row from every element in that row. Then, using the row-reduced matrix, subtract the smallest element in each column from every element in that column.

Thus, we first reduce the matrix in Table 19.20 by subtracting the minimum value in each row from each element in the row. With the minimum values of 9 for row 1, 5 for row 2, and 3 for row 3, the row-reduced matrix becomes

	1	2	3
Terry	1	6	0
Carle	4	13	0
McClymonds	3	11	0

The assignment problem represented by this reduced matrix is equivalent to the original assignment problem in the sense that the same solution will be optimal. To understand why, first note that the row 1 minimum element, 9, has been subtracted from every element in the first row. Terry must still be assigned to one of the clients, so the only change is that in this revised problem the time for any assignment will be 9 days less. Similarly, Carle and McClymonds are shown with completion times requiring 5 and 3 fewer days, respectively.

Continuing with step 1 in the matrix reduction process, we now subtract the minimum element in each column of the row-reduced matrix from every element in the column. This operation also leads to an equivalent assignment problem; that is, the same solution will still be optimal, but the times required to complete each project are reduced. With the minimum values of 1 for column 1, 6 for column 2, and 0 for column 3, the reduced matrix becomes

	1	2	3
Terry	0	0	0
Carle	3	7	0
McClymonds	2	5	0

The goal of the Hungarian method is to continue reducing the matrix until the value of one of the solutions is zero—that is, until an assignment of project leaders to clients can be made that, in terms of the reduced matrix, requires a total time expenditure of zero days. Then, as long as there are no negative elements in the matrix, the zero-valued solution will be optimal. The way in which we perform this further reduction and recognize when we have reached an optimal solution is described in the following two steps.

Step 2. Find the minimum number of straight lines that must be drawn through the rows and the columns of the current matrix so that all the zeros in the matrix will be covered. If the minimum number of straight lines is the same as the number of rows (or equivalently, columns), an optimal assignment with a value of zero can be made. If the minimum number of lines is less than the number of rows, go to step 3.

Applying step 2, we see that the minimum number of lines required to cover all the zeros is 2. Thus, we must continue to step 3.

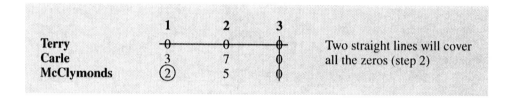

Step 3. Subtract the value of the smallest unlined element from every unlined element, and add this same value to every element at the intersection of two lines. All other elements remain unchanged. Return to step 2, and continue until the minimum number of lines necessary to cover all the zeros in the matrix is equal to the number of rows.

The minimum unlined element is 2. In the preceding matrix we circled this element. Subtracting 2 from all unlined elements and adding 2 to the intersection element for Terry and client 3 produces the new matrix:

	1	2	3
Terry	0	0	2
Carle	1	5	0
McClymonds	0	3	0

Returning to step 2, we find that the minimum number of straight lines required to cover all the zeros in the current matrix is 3. The following matrix illustrates the step 2 calculations.

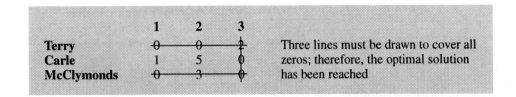

	1	2	3
Terry	0	0	2
Carle	1	5	0
McClymonds	0	3	0

Three lines must be drawn to cover all zeros; therefore, the optimal solution has been reached

According to step 2, then, it must be possible to find an assignment with a value of zero. To do so we first locate any row or column that contains only one zero. If all have more than one zero, we choose the row or column with the fewest zeros. We draw a square around a zero in the chosen row or column, indicating an assignment, and eliminate that row and column from further consideration. Row 2 has only one zero in the Fowle problem, so we assign Carle to client 3 and eliminate row 2 and column 3 from further consideration. McClymonds must then be assigned to client 1 (the only remaining zero in row 3) and, finally, Terry to client 2. The solution to the Fowle problem, in terms of the reduced matrix, requires a time expenditure of zero days, as follows:

	1	2	3
Terry	0	[0]	2
Carle	1	5	[0]
McClymonds	[0]	3	0

We obtain the value of the optimal assignment by referring to the original assignment problem and summing the solution times associated with the optimal assignment—in this case, 15 for Terry to client 2, 5 for Carle to client 3, and 6 for McClymonds to client 1. Thus, we obtain the solution time of $15 + 5 + 6 = 26$ days.

Finding the Minimum Number of Lines

Sometimes it is not obvious how the lines should be drawn through rows and columns of the matrix in order to cover all the zeros with the smallest number of lines. In these cases, the following heuristic works well. Choose any row or column with a single zero. If it is a row, draw a line through the column the zero is in; if it is a column, draw a line through the row the zero is in. Continue in this fashion until you cover all the zeros.

Can you solve an assignment problem using the Hungarian method? Try Problem 6.

If you make the mistake of drawing too many lines to cover the zeros in the reduced matrix and thus conclude incorrectly that you have reached an optimal solution, you will be unable to identify a zero-value assignment. Thus, if you think you have reached the optimal solution, but cannot find a set of zero-value assignments, go back to the preceding step and check to see whether you can cover all the zeros with fewer lines.

Problem Variations

We now discuss how to handle the following problem variations with the Hungarian method:

1. Number of agents not equal to number of tasks
2. Maximization objective function
3. Unacceptable assignments

TABLE 19.21   ESTIMATED PROJECT COMPLETION TIME (DAYS) FOR THE FOWLE
ASSIGNMENT PROBLEM WITH FOUR PROJECT LEADERS

	Client		
Project Leader	1	2	3
Terry	10	15	9
Carle	9	18	5
McClymonds	6	14	3
Higley	8	16	6

Number of Agents Not Equal to Number of Tasks   The Hungarian method requires that
the number of rows (agents) equal the number of columns (tasks). Suppose that in the Fowle
problem four project leaders (agents) had been available for assignment to the three new
clients (tasks). Fowle still faces the same basic problem, namely, which project leaders
should be assigned to which clients to minimize the total days required. Table 19.21 shows
the project completion time estimates with a fourth project leader.

We know how to apply the Hungarian method when the number of rows and the number of columns are equal. We can apply the same procedure if we can add a new client. If
we do not have another client, we simply add a *dummy column*, or a dummy client. This
dummy client is nonexistent, so the project leader assigned to the dummy client in the optimal assignment solution, in effect, will be the unassigned project leader.

What project completion time estimates should we show in this new dummy column?
The dummy client assignment will not actually take place, which means that a zero project
completion time for all project leaders seems logical. Table 19.22 shows the Fowle assignment problem with a dummy client, labeled D. Problem 8 at the end of the chapter asks you
to use the Hungarian method to determine the optimal solution to this problem.

Note that if we had considered the case of four new clients and only three project leaders, we would have had to add a *dummy row* (dummy project leader) in order to apply the
Hungarian method. The client receiving the dummy leader would not actually be assigned
a project leader immediately and would have to wait until one becomes available. To obtain
a problem form compatible with the solution algorithm, adding several dummy rows or
dummy columns, but never both, may be necessary.

Maximization Objective   To illustrate how maximization assignment problems can be
handled, let us consider the problem facing management of Salisbury Discounts, Inc.

TABLE 19.22   ESTIMATED PROJECT COMPLETION TIME (DAYS) FOR THE FOWLE
ASSIGNMENT PROBLEM WITH A DUMMY CLIENT

	Client				Dummy client
Project Leader	1	2	3	D
Terry	10	15	9	0
Carle	9	18	5	0
McClymonds	6	14	3	0
Higley	8	16	6	0

TABLE 19.23   ESTIMATED ANNUAL PROFIT ($1000s) FOR EACH DEPARTMENT-LOCATION COMBINATION

	Location			
Department	1	2	3	4
Shoe	10	6	12	8
Toy	15	18	5	11
Auto parts	17	10	13	16
Housewares	14	12	13	10
Video	14	16	6	12

Suppose that Salisbury Discounts has just leased a new store and is attempting to determine where various departments should be located within the store. The store manager has four locations that have not yet been assigned a department and is considering five departments that might occupy the four locations. The departments under consideration are shoes, toys, auto parts, housewares, and videos. After a careful study of the layout of the remainder of the store, the store manager has made estimates of the expected annual profit for each department in each location. These estimates are presented in Table 19.23.

This assignment problem requires a maximization objective. However, the problem also involves more rows than columns. Thus, we must first add a dummy column, corresponding to a dummy or fictitious location, in order to apply the Hungarian method. After adding a dummy column, we obtain the 5 × 5 Salisbury Discounts, Inc., assignment problem shown in Table 19.24.

We can obtain an equivalent minimization assignment problem by converting all the elements in the matrix to **opportunity losses.** We do so by subtracting every element in each column from the largest element in the column. Finding the assignment that minimizes opportunity loss leads to the same solution that maximizes the value of the assignment in the original problem. Thus, any maximization assignment problem can be converted to a minimization problem by converting the assignment matrix to one in which the elements represent opportunity losses. Hence, we begin the solution to this maximization assignment problem by developing an assignment matrix in which each element represents the opportunity loss for not making the "best" assignment. Table 19.25 presents the opportunity losses.

The opportunity loss from putting the shoe department in location 1 is $7000. That is, if we put the shoe department, instead of the best department (auto parts), in that location, we forgo the opportunity to make an additional $7000 in profit. The opportunity loss

TABLE 19.24   ESTIMATED ANNUAL PROFIT ($1000s) FOR EACH DEPARTMENT-LOCATION COMBINATION, INCLUDING A DUMMY LOCATION

	Location					Dummy location
Department	1	2	3	4	5	
Shoe	10	6	12	8	0	
Toy	15	18	5	11	0	
Auto parts	17	10	13	16	0	
Housewares	14	12	13	10	0	
Video	14	16	6	12	0	

TABLE 19.25   OPPORTUNITY LOSS ($1000s) FOR EACH DEPARTMENT-LOCATION COMBINATION

Department	Location 1	2	3	4	5 (Dummy location)
Shoe	7	12	1	8	0
Toy	2	0	8	5	0
Auto parts	0	8	0	0	0
Housewares	3	6	0	6	0
Video	3	2	7	4	0

associated with putting the toy department in location 2 is zero because it yields the highest profit in that location. What about the opportunity losses associated with the dummy column? The assignment of a department to this dummy location means that the department will not be assigned a store location in the optimal solution. All departments earn the same amount from this dummy location, zero, making the opportunity loss for each department zero.

Try Problem 9 for practice in using the Hungarian method for a maximization problem.

Using steps 1, 2, and 3 of the Hungarian method on Table 19.25 will minimize opportunity loss and determine the maximum profit assignment.

Unacceptable Assignments   As an illustration of how we can handle unacceptable assignments, suppose that in the Salisbury Discounts, Inc., assignment problem the store manager believed that the toy department should not be considered for location 2 and that the auto parts department should not be considered for location 4. Essentially the store manager is saying that, based on other considerations, such as size of the area, adjacent departments, and so on, these two assignments are unacceptable alternatives.

Using the same approach for the assignment problem as we did for the transportation problem, we define a value of M for unacceptable minimization assignments and a value of $-M$ for unacceptable maximization assignments, where M is an arbitrarily large value. In fact, we assume M to be so large that M plus or minus any value is still extremely large. Thus, an M-valued cell in an assignment matrix retains its M value throughout the matrix reduction calculations. An M-valued cell can never be zero, so it can never be an assignment in the final solution.

Problem 10 at the end of this chapter asks you to solve this assignment problem.

The Salisbury Discounts, Inc., assignment problem with the two unacceptable assignments is shown in Table 19.26. When this assignment matrix is converted to an opportunity loss matrix, the $-M$ profit value will be changed to M.

TABLE 19.26   ESTIMATED PROFIT FOR THE SALISBURY DEPARTMENT-LOCATION COMBINATIONS

Department	Location 1	2	3	4	5
Shoe	10	6	12	8	0
Toy	15	$-M$	5	11	0
Auto parts	17	10	13	$-M$	0
Housewares	14	12	13	10	0
Video	14	16	6	12	0

GLOSSARY

Transportation problem   A network flow problem that often involves minimizing the cost of shipping goods from a set of origins to a set of destinations; it can be formulated and solved as a linear program by including a variable for each arc and a constraint for each node.

Assignment problem   A network flow problem that often involves the assignment of agents to tasks; it can be formulated as a linear program and is a special case of the transportation problem.

Transportation simplex method   A special-purpose solution procedure for the transportation problem.

Transportation tableau   A table representing a transportation problem in which each cell corresponds to a variable, or arc.

Heuristic   A commonsense procedure for quickly finding a solution to a problem. Heuristics are used to find initial feasible solutions for the transportation simplex method and in other applications.

Minimum cost method   A heuristic used to find an initial feasible solution to a transportation problem; it is easy to use and usually provides a good (but not optimal) solution.

Incoming arc   The unused arc (represented by an unoccupied cell in the transportation tableau) to which flow is assigned during an iteration of the transportation simplex method.

Outgoing arc   The arc corresponding to an occupied cell that is dropped from solution during an iteration of the transportation simplex method.

MODI method   A procedure in which a modified distribution method determines the incoming arc in the transportation simplex method.

Net evaluation index   The per-unit change in the objective function associated with assigning flow to an unused arc in the transportation simplex method.

Stepping-stone method   Using a sequence or path of occupied cells to identify flow adjustments necessary when flow is assigned to an unused arc in the transportation simplex method. This identifies the outgoing arc.

Degenerate solution   A solution to a transportation problem in which fewer than $m + n - 1$ arcs (cells) have positive flow; m is the number of origins and n is the number of destinations.

Dummy destination   A destination added to a transportation problem to make the total supply equal to the total demand. The demand assigned to the dummy destination is the difference between the total supply and the total demand.

Dummy origin   An origin added to a transportation problem in order to make the total supply equal to the total demand. The supply assigned to the dummy origin is the difference between the total demand and the total supply.

Hungarian method   A special-purpose solution procedure for solving an assignment problem.

Opportunity loss   For each cell in an assignment matrix, the difference between the largest value in the column and the value in the cell. The entries in the cells of an assignment matrix must be converted to opportunity losses to solve maximization problems using the Hungarian method.

PROBLEMS

1. Consider the following transportation tableau with four origins and four destinations.

Origin	Destination				Supply
	D_1	D_2	D_3	D_4	
O_1	5 / 25	7	10 / 50	5	75
O_2	6	5	8 / 100	2 / 75	175
O_3	6 / 100	6	12	7	100
O_4	8	5 / 100	14	4 / 50	150
Demand	125	100	150	125	

a. Use the MODI method to determine whether this solution provides the minimum transportation cost. If it is not the minimum cost solution, find that solution. If it is the minimum cost solution, what is the total transportation cost?

b. Does an alternative optimal solution exit? Explain. If so, find the alternative optimal solution. What is the total transportation cost associated with this solution?

2. Consider the following minimum cost transportation problem.

Origin	Destination			Supply
	Los Angeles	San Francisco	San Diego	
San Jose	4	10	6	100
Las Vegas	8	16	6	300
Tucson	14	18	10	300
Demand	200	300	200	700

      a. Use the minimum cost method to find an initial feasible solution.

      b. Use the transportation simplex method to find an optimal solution.

      c. How would the optimal solution change if you must ship 100 units on the Tucson–San Diego route?

      d. Because of road construction, the Las Vegas–San Diego route is now unacceptable. Re-solve the initial problem.

3. Consider the following network representation of a transportation problem. The supplies, demands, and transportation costs per unit are shown on the network.

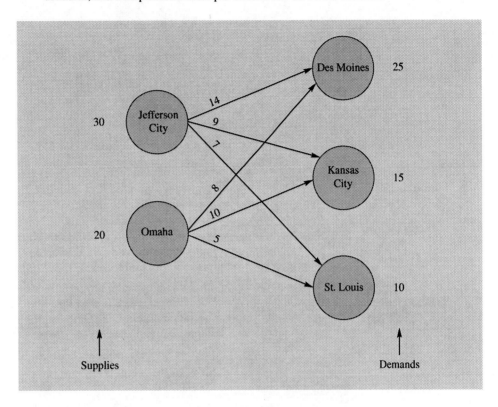

      a. Set up the transportation tableau for the problem.

      b. Use the minimum cost method to find an initial feasible solution.

4. A product is produced at three plants and shipped to three warehouses. The transportation costs per unit are shown in the following table.

Plant	Warehouse			Plant Capacity
	W_1	W_2	W_3	
P_1	20	16	24	300
P_2	10	10	8	500
P_3	12	18	10	100
Warehouse demand	200	400	300	

Use the transportation simplex method to find an optimal solution.

5. Consider the following minimum cost transportation problem.

Origin	Destination			Supply
	D_1	D_2	D_3	
O_1	6	8	8	250
O_2	18	12	14	150
O_3	8	12	10	100
Demand	150	200	150	

a. Use the minimum cost method to find an initial feasible solution.
b. Use the transportation simplex method to find an optimal solution.
c. Using your solution to part (b), identify an alternative optimal solution.

SELF test

6. Scott and Associates, Inc., is an accounting firm that has three new clients. Project leaders will be assigned to the three clients. Based on the different backgrounds and experiences of the leaders, the various leader-client assignments differ in terms of projected completion times. The possible assignments and the estimated completion times in days are

Project Leader	Client		
	1	2	3
Jackson	10	16	32
Ellis	14	22	40
Smith	22	24	34

Use the Hungarian method to obtain the optimal solution.

7. CarpetPlus sells and installs floor covering for commercial buildings. Brad Sweeney, a CarpetPlus account executive, was just awarded the contract for five jobs. Brad must now assign a CarpetPlus installation crew to each of the five jobs. Because the commission Brad will earn depends on the profit CarpetPlus makes, Brad would like to determine an assignment that will minimize total installation costs. Currently, five installation crews are available for assignment. Each crew is identified by a color code, which aids in tracking of job progress on a large white board. The following table shows the costs (in hundreds of dollars) for each crew to complete each of the five jobs.

Crew	Job 1	2	3	4	5
Red	30	44	38	47	31
White	25	32	45	44	25
Blue	23	40	37	39	29
Green	26	38	37	45	28
Brown	26	34	44	43	28

Use the Hungarian method to obtain the optimal solution.

8. Fowle Marketing Research has four project leaders available for assignment to three clients. Find the assignment of project leaders to clients that will minimize the total time to complete all projects. The estimated project completion times in days are as follows:

Project Leader	Client 1	2	3
Terry	10	15	9
Carle	9	18	5
McClymonds	6	14	3
Higley	8	16	6

Use the Hungarian method to obtain the optimal solution.

9. Use the Hungarian method to solve the Salisbury Discount, Inc., problem using the profit data in Table 19.23.

10. Use the Hungarian method to solve the Salisbury Discount, Inc., problem using the profit data in Table 19.26.

Chapter 19

2. a. An initial solution is

	Los Angeles	San Francisco	San Diego
San Jose	4 100	10	6
Las Vegas	8 100	16	6 200
Tucson	14	18 300	10

Total cost = $7800

b. Note that the initial solution is degenerate because only 4 cells are occupied; a zero is assigned to the cell in row 3 and column 1 so that the row and column indexes can be computed

u_i	v_j 4	8	2
0	4 100	10 ②	6 ④
4	8 100	16 ④	6 200
10	14 0	18 300	10 (−2)

Cell in row 3 and column 3 is identified as an incoming cell; however, 0 units can be added to this cell. Initial solution remains optimal

c.

San Jose–San Francisco:	100
Las Vegas–Los Angeles:	200
Las Vegas–San Diego:	100
Tucson–San Francisco:	200
Tucson–San Diego	100
Total Cost = $7800	

Note that this total cost is the same as for part (a); thus, we have alternative optimal solutions

d. The final transportation tableau is shown; the total transportation cost is $8000, an increase of $200 over the solution to part (a)

u_i	v_j 2	10	2	
0	4 ②	10 100	6 ④	100
6	8 200	16 100	M $(M-8)$	300
8	14 ④	18 100	10 200	300
	200	300	200	700

4. b. $x_{12} = 300$, $x_{21} = 100$, $x_{22} = 100$, $x_{23} = 300$, $x_{31} = 100$
    Cost = 10,400

6. Subtract 10 from row 1, 14 from row 2, and 22 from row 3 to obtain:

	1	2	3
Jackson	0	6	22
Ellis	0	8	26
Smith	0	2	12

Subtract 0 from column 1, 2 from column 2, and 12 from column 3 to obtain:

	1	2	3
Jackson	0	④	10
Ellis	0	6	14
Smith	0	0	0

Two lines cover the zeros; the minimum unlined element is 4; step 3 yields:

	1	2	3
Jackson	0	[0]	6
Ellis	[0]	2	10
Smith	0	0	[0]

Optimal solution: Jackson–2
                  Ellis–1
                  Smith–3
Time requirement is 64 days

8. Terry 2; Carle 3; MacClymonds 1; Higley unassigned
   Time = 26 days

9. We start with the opportunity loss matrix:

	1	2	3	4	D*
Shoe	4	11	0	5	[0]
Toy	0	[0]	8	3	1
Auto	0	10	2	[0]	3
Houseware	1	6	[0]	4	1
Video	[0]	1	6	1	0

*D = Dummy

	Optimal Solution	Profit
Toy	2	18
Auto	4	16
Housewares	3	13
Video	1	14
	Total	61

10. Toy: 2; Auto: 4; Housewares: 3; Video: 1

7	12	1	8	0		5	12	①	6	0
②	0	8	5	0		0	0	8	3	0
0	8	0	0	0	→	0	10	2	0	2
3	6	0	6	0		1	6	0	4	0
3	2	7	4	0		1	2	7	2	0

APPENDIXES

The purpose of this appendix is twofold. First, we provide an overview of Excel and discuss the basic operations needed to work with Excel workbooks and worksheets. Second, we provide an introduction to building mathematical models using Excel, including a discussion of how to find and use particular Excel functions, how to design and build good spreadsheet models, and how to ensure that these models are free of errors.

OVERVIEW OF MICROSOFT EXCEL

When using Excel for modeling, the data and the model are displayed in workbooks, each of which contains a series of worksheets. Figure A.1 shows the layout of a blank workbook created each time Excel is opened. The workbook is named Book1 and consists of three worksheets named Sheet1, Sheet2, and Sheet3. Excel highlights the worksheet currently displayed (Sheet1) by setting the name on the worksheet tab in bold. To select a different worksheet, simply click on the corresponding tab. Note that cell A1 is initially selected.

A workbook is a file containing one or more worksheets.

The wide bar located across the top of the workbook is referred to as the Ribbon. Tabs, located at the top of the Ribbon, provide quick access to groups of related commands. There are eight tabs: Home, Insert, Page Layout, Formulas, Data, Review, View, and Add-Ins. Each tab contains several groups of related commands. Note that the Home tab is selected when Excel is opened. Four of the seven groups are displayed in Figure A.2. Under the Home tab there are seven groups of related commands: Clipboard, Font, Alignment, Number, Styles, Cells, and Editing. Commands are arranged within each group. For example, to change selected text to boldface, click the Home tab and click the Bold button in the Font group.

Figure A.3 illustrates the location of the File tab, the Quick Access Toolbar, and the Formula Bar. When you click the File tab, Excel provides a list of workbook options such as opening, saving, and printing (worksheets). The Quick Access Toolbar allows you to quickly access these workbook options. For instance, the Quick Access Toolbar shown in Figure A.3 includes a Save button 🔲 that can be used to save files without having to first click the File tab. To add or remove features on the Quick Access Toolbar click the Customize Quick Access Toolbar button ⏷ on the Quick Access Toolbar.

The Formula Bar contains a Name box, the Insert Function button *fx*, and a Formula box. In Figure A.3, "A1" appears in the Name box because cell A1 is selected. You can select any other cell in the worksheet by using the mouse to move the cursor to another cell and clicking or by typing the new cell location in the name box and pressing the enter key. The Formula box is used to display the formula in the currently selected cell. For instance, if you had entered $=A1+A2$ into cell A3, whenever you select cell A3, the formula $=A1+A2$ will be shown in the Formula box. This feature makes it very easy to see and edit a formula in a particular cell. The Insert Function button allows you to quickly access all of the functions available in Excel. Later, we show how to find and use a particular function.

FIGURE A.1   BLANK WORKBOOK CREATED WHEN EXCEL IS STARTED

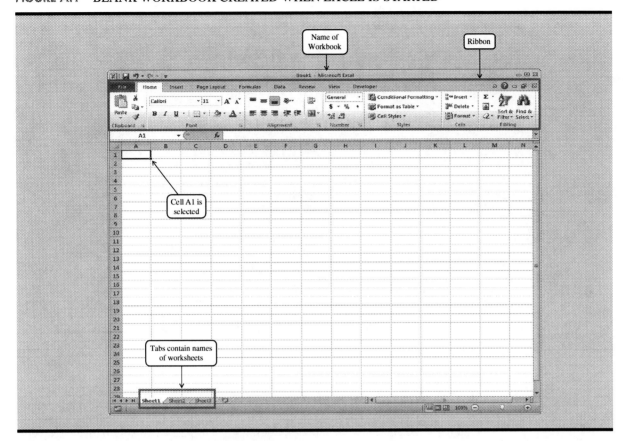

FIGURE A.2   PORTION OF THE HOME TAB

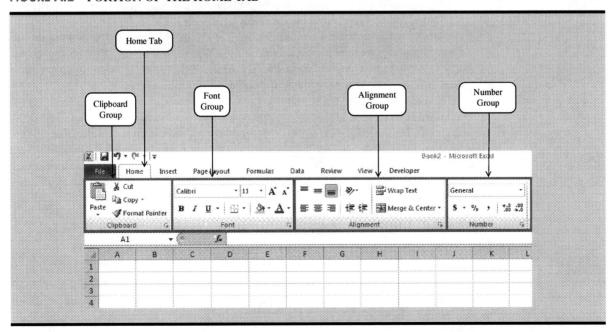

FIGURE A.3   EXCEL FILE TAB, QUICK ACCESS TOOLBAR, AND
              FORMULA BAR

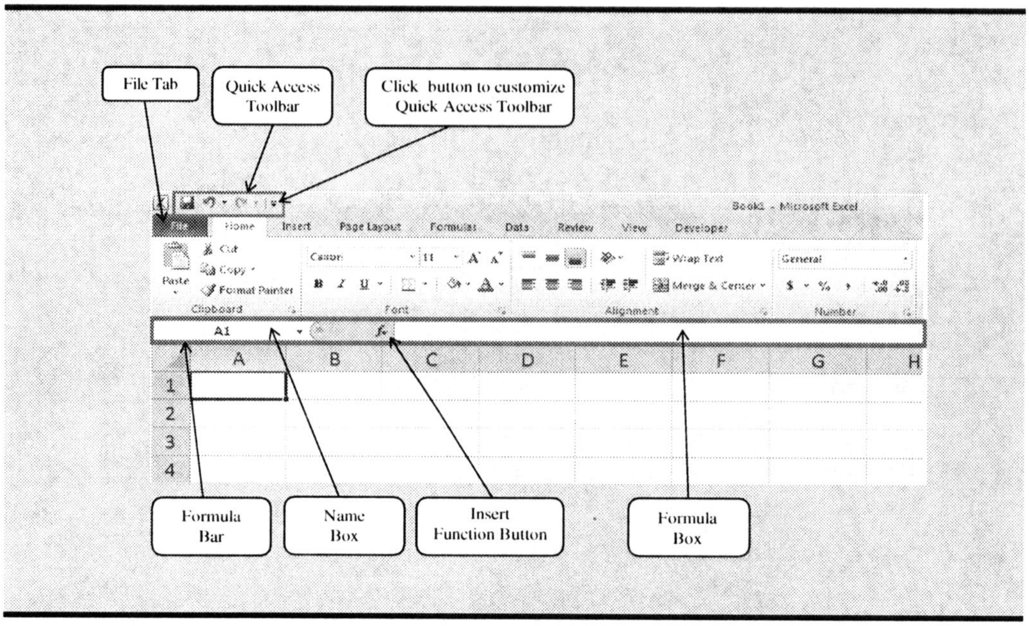

BASIC WORKBOOK OPERATIONS

Figure A.4 illustrates the worksheet options that can be performed after right clicking on a worksheet tab. For instance, to change the name of the current worksheet from "Sheet1" to "NowlinModel," right click the worksheet tab named "Sheet1" and select the Rename option. The current worksheet name (Sheet1) will be highlighted. Then, simply type the new name (NowlinModel) and press the Enter key to rename the worksheet.

Suppose that you wanted to create a copy of "Sheet 1." After right clicking the tab named "Sheet1," select the Move or Copy option. When the Move or Copy dialog box appears, select Create a Copy and click OK. The name of the copied worksheet will appear as "Sheet1 (2)." You can then rename it, if desired.

To add a worksheet to the workbook, right click any worksheet tab and select the Insert option; when the Insert dialog box appears, select Worksheet and click OK. An additional blank worksheet titled "Sheet 4" will appear in the workbook. You can also insert a new worksheet by clicking the Insert Worksheet tab button 🔲 that appears to the right of the last worksheet tab displayed. Worksheets can be deleted by right clicking the worksheet tab and choosing Delete. After clicking Delete, a window will appear warning you that any data appearing in the worksheet will be lost. Click Delete to confirm that you do want to delete the worksheet. Worksheets can also be moved to other workbooks or a different position in the current workbook by using the Move or Copy option.

Creating, Saving, and Opening Files

As an illustration of manually entering, saving, and opening a file, we will use the Nowlin Plastics production example from Chapter 1. The objective is to compute the breakeven

**FIGURE A.4   WORKSHEET OPTIONS OBTAINED AFTER RIGHT CLICKING ON A
WORKSHEET TAB**

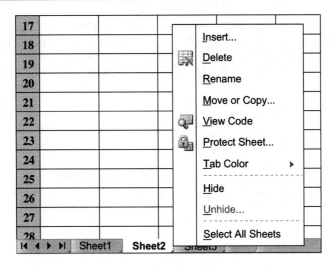

point for a product that has a fixed cost of $3000, a variable cost per unit of $2, and a selling price per unit of $5. We begin by creating a worksheet containing the problem data.

If you have just opened Excel, a blank workbook containing three worksheets will be displayed. The Nowlin data can now be entered manually by simply typing the fixed cost of $3000, the variable cost of $2, and the selling price of $5 into one of the worksheets. If Excel is currently running and no blank workbook is displayed, you can create a new blank workbook using the following steps:

Step 1. Click the **File** tab
Step 2. Click **New** in the list of options
Step 3. When the New Workbook dialog box appears:
   Double click **Blank Workbook**

A new workbook containing three worksheets labeled Sheet1, Sheet2, and Sheet3 will appear.

We will place the data for the Nowlin example in the top portion of Sheet1 of the new workbook. First, we enter the label "Nowlin Plastics" into cell A1. To identify each of the three data values we enter the label "Fixed Cost" into cell A3, the label "Variable Cost Per Unit" into cell A5, and the label "Selling Price Per Unit" into cell A7. Next, we enter the actual cost and price data into the corresponding cells in column B: the value of $3000 in cell B3; the value of $2 in cell B5; and the value of $5 into cell B7. Finally, we will change the name of the worksheet from "Sheet1" to "NowlinModel" using the procedure described previously. Figure A.5 shows a portion of the worksheet we have just developed.

Before we begin the development of the model portion of the worksheet, we recommend that you first save the current file; this will prevent you from having to reenter the data in case something happens that causes Excel to close. To save the workbook using the filename "Nowlin," we perform the following steps:

Step 1. Click the **File** tab
Step 2. Click **Save** in the list of options
Step 3. When the **Save As** dialog box appears:
    Select the location where you want to save the file
    Type the file name "Nowlin" in the **File name** box
    Click **Save**

Excel's Save command is designed to save the file as an Excel workbook. As you work with and build models in Excel, you should follow the practice of periodically saving the file so you will not lose any work. Simply follow the procedure described above, using the Save command.

Keyboard shortcut: To save the file, press CTRL S.

Sometimes you may want to create a copy of an existing file. For instance, suppose you change one or more of the data values and would like to save the modified file using the filename "NowlinMod." The following steps show how to save the modified workbook using filename "NowlinMod."

Step 1. Click the **File** tab
Step 2. Position the mouse pointer over **Save As**
Step 3. Click **Excel Workbook** from the list of options
Step 4. When the **Save As** dialog box appears:
    In the **Save in** box select the location where you want to save the file
    Type the filename "NowlinMod" in the **File name** box
    Click **Save**

FIGURE A.5   NOWLIN PLASTICS DATA

	A	B
1	**Nowlin Plastics**	
2		
3	**Fixed Cost**	$3,000
4		
5	**Variable Cost Per Unit**	$2
6		
7	**Selling Price Per Unit**	$5
8		
9		
10		
11		
12		
13		
14		
15		
16		
17		
18		

Once the NowlinMod workbook has been saved, you can continue to work with the file to perform whatever type of analysis is appropriate. When you are finished working with the file, simply click the close window button ▨ located at the top right-hand corner of the Ribbon.

You can easily access a saved file at another point in time. For example, the following steps show how to open the previously saved Nowlin workbook.

Step 1. Click the **File** tab
Step 2. Click **Open** in the list of options
Step 3. When the **Open** dialog box appears:
Select the location where you previously saved the file
Type the filename "Nowlin" in the **File name** box
Click **Open**

The procedures we showed for saving or opening a workbook begin by clicking on the File tab to access the Save and Open commands. Once you have used Excel for a while, you will probably find it more convenient to add these commands to the Quick Access Toolbar.

CELLS, REFERENCES, AND FORMULAS IN EXCEL

Assume that the Nowlin workbook is open again and that we would like to develop a model that can be used to compute the profit or loss associated with a given production volume. We will use the bottom portion of the worksheet shown in Figure A.5 to develop the model. The model will contain formulas that *refer to the location of the data cells* in the upper section of the worksheet. By putting the location of the data cells in the formula, we will build a model that can be easily updated with new data. This will be discussed in more detail later in this appendix in the section Principles for Building Good Spreadsheet Models.

We enter the label "Models" into cell A10 to provide a visual reminder that the bottom portion of this worksheet will contain the model. Next, we enter the labels "Production Volume" into cell A12, "Total Cost" into cell A14, "Total Revenue" into cell A16, and "Total Profit (Loss)" into cell A18. Cell B12 is used to contain a value for the production volume. We will now enter formulas into cells B14, B16, and B18 that use the production volume in cell B12 to compute the values for total cost, total revenue, and total profit or loss.

Total cost is the sum of the fixed cost (cell B3) and the total variable cost. The total variable cost is the product of the variable cost per unit (cell B5) and production volume (cell B12). Thus, the formula for total variable cost is B5*B12 and to compute the value of total cost, we enter the formula =B3+B5*B12 into cell B14. Next, total revenue is the product of the selling price per unit (cell B7) and the number of units produced (cell B12), which we enter in cell B16 as the formula =B7*B12. Finally, the total profit or loss is the difference between the total revenue (cell B16) and the total cost (cell B14). Thus, in cell B18 we enter the formula =B16-B14. Figure A.6 shows a portion of the formula worksheet just described.

We can now compute the total profit or loss for a particular production volume by entering a value for the production volume into cell B12. Figure A.7 shows the results after entering a value of 800 into cell B12. We see that a production volume of 800 units results in a total cost of $4600, a total revenue of $4000, and a loss of $600.

FIGURE A.6   NOWLIN PLASTICS DATA AND MODEL

	A	B
1	**Nowlin Plastics**	
2		
3	**Fixed Cost**	3000
4		
5	**Variable Cost Per Unit**	2
6		
7	**Selling Price Per Unit**	5
8		
9		
10	**Models**	
11		
12	**Production Volume**	
13		
14	**Total Cost**	=B3+B5*B12
15		
16	**Total Revenue**	=B7*B12
17		
18	**Total Profit (Loss)**	=B16-B14

FIGURE A.7   NOWLIN PLASTICS RESULTS

	A	B
1	**Nowlin Plastics**	
2		
3	**Fixed Cost**	$3,000
4		
5	**Variable Cost Per Unit**	$2
6		
7	**Selling Price Per Unit**	$5
8		
9		
10	**Models**	
11		
12	**Production Volume**	800
13		
14	**Total Cost**	$4,600
15		
16	**Total Revenue**	$4,000
17		
18	**Total Profit (Loss)**	−$600

USING EXCEL FUNCTIONS

Excel provides a wealth of built-in formulas or functions for developing mathematical models. If we know which function is needed and how to use it, we can simply enter the function into the appropriate worksheet cell. However, if we are not sure which functions are available to accomplish a task or are not sure how to use a particular function, Excel can provide assistance.

Finding the Right Excel Function

To identify the functions available in Excel, click the Formulas tab on the Ribbon and then click the Insert Function button in the Function Library group. Alternatively, click the Insert Function button f_x on the formula bar. Either approach provides the Insert Function dialog box shown in Figure A.8.

The Search for a function box at the top of the Insert Function dialog box enables us to type a brief description for what we want to do. After doing so and clicking Go, Excel will search for and display, in the Select a function box, the functions that may accomplish our task. In many situations, however, we may want to browse through an entire category of functions to see what is available. For this task, the Or select a category box is helpful.

It contains a dropdown list of several categories of functions provided by Excel. Figure A.8 shows that we selected the Math & Trig category. As a result, Excel's Math &

FIGURE A.8   INSERT FUNCTION DIALOG BOX

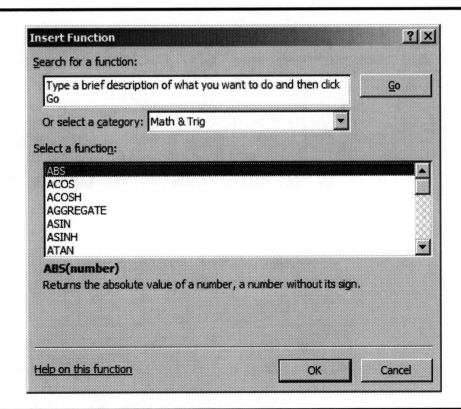

Trig functions appear in alphabetical order in the Select a function box. We see the ABS function listed first, followed by the ACOS function, and so on.

Colon Notation

Although many functions, such as the ABS function, have a single argument, some Excel functions depend on arrays. Colon notation provides an efficient way to convey arrays and matrices of cells to functions. The colon notation may be described as follows: B3:B5 means cell B1 "through" cell B5, namely the array of values stored in the locations (B1,B2,B3,B4,B5). Consider for example the following function =SUM(B1:B5). The sum function adds up the elements contained in the function's argument. Hence, =SUM(B1:B5) evaluates the following formula:

$$=B1+B2+B3+B4+B5$$

Inserting a Function into a Worksheet Cell

Through the use of an example, we will now show how to use the Insert Function and Function Arguments dialog boxes to select a function, develop its arguments, and insert

FIGURE A.9   DESCRIPTION OF THE SUMPRODUCT FUNCTION IN THE INSERT FUNCTION DIALOG BOX

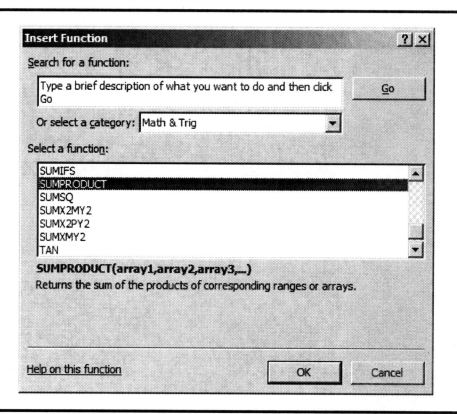

the function into a worksheet cell. We also illustrate the use of a very useful function, the SUMPRODUCT function, and how to use colon notation in the argument of a function.

The SUMPRODUCT function, as shown in Figure A.9, is used in many of the Solver examples in the textbook. Note that SUMPRODUCT is now highlighted, and that immediately below the Select a function box we see SUMPRODUCT(array1,array2,array3, . . .), which indicates that the SUMPRODUCT function contains the array arguments array1, array2, array3, ... In addition, we see that the description of the SUMPRODUCT function is "Returns the sum of the products of corresponding ranges or arrays." For example, the function =SUMPRODUCT(A1:A3, B1:B3) evaluates the formula A1*B1 + A2*B2 + A3*B3. As shown in the following example, this function can be very useful in calculations of cost, profit, and other such functions involving multiple arrays of numbers.

Figure A.10 displays an Excel worksheet for the Foster Generators Problem that appears in Chapter 6. This problem involves the transportation of a product from three plants (Cleveland, Bedford, and York) to four distribution centers (Boston, Chicago, St. Louis, and Lexington). The costs for each unit shipped from each plant to each distribution center are shown in cells B5:E7, and the values in cells B17:E19 are the number of units shipped from each plant to each distribution center. Cell B13 will contain the total transportation cost corresponding to the transportation cost values in cells B5:E7 and the values of the number of units shipped in cells B17:E19.

The following steps show how to use the SUMPRODUCT function to compute the total transportation cost for Foster Generators.

FIGURE A.10   EXCEL WORKSHEET USED TO CALCULATE TOTAL SHIPPING COSTS FOR THE FOSTER GENERATORS TRANSPORTATION PROBLEM

Foster Generators

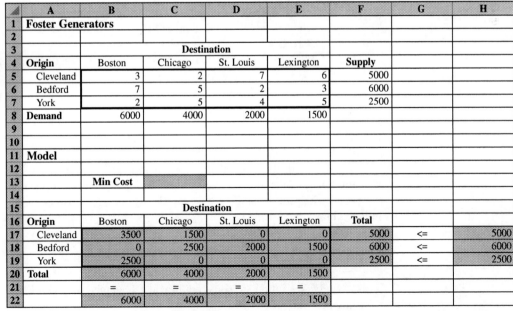

	A	B	C	D	E	F	G	H
1	**Foster Generators**							
2								
3			**Destination**					
4	**Origin**	Boston	Chicago	St. Louis	Lexington	**Supply**		
5	Cleveland	3	2	7	6	5000		
6	Bedford	7	5	2	3	6000		
7	York	2	5	4	5	2500		
8	**Demand**	6000	4000	2000	1500			
9								
10								
11	**Model**							
12								
13		**Min Cost**						
14								
15			**Destination**					
16	**Origin**	Boston	Chicago	St. Louis	Lexington	**Total**		
17	Cleveland	3500	1500	0	0	5000	<=	5000
18	Bedford	0	2500	2000	1500	6000	<=	6000
19	York	2500	0	0	0	2500	<=	2500
20	**Total**	6000	4000	2000	1500			
21		=	=	=	=			
22		6000	4000	2000	1500			

FIGURE A.11   COMPLETED FUNCTION ARGUMENTS DIALOG BOX FOR THE
SUMPRODUCT FUNCTION

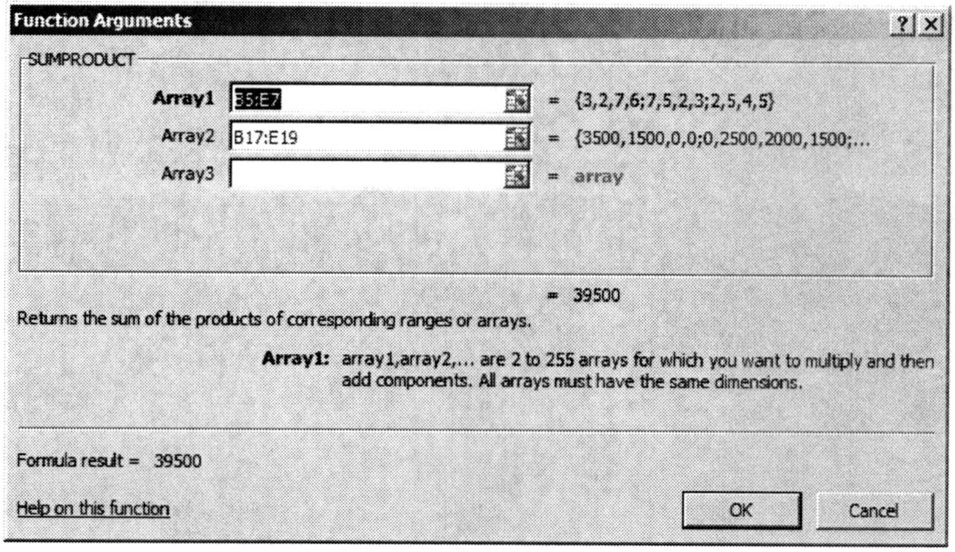

Step 1. Select **cell C13**
Step 2. Click f_x on the formula bar
Step 3. When the **Insert Function** dialog box appears:
Select **Math & Trig** in the **Or select a category** box
Select **SUMPRODUCT** in the **Select a function** box (as shown in Figure A.9)
Click **OK**
Step 4. When the **Function Arguments** box appears (see Figure A.11):
Enter B5:E7 in the **Array1** box
Enter B17:E19 in the **Array2** box
Click **OK**

The worksheet then appears as shown in Figure A.12. The value of the total transportation cost in cell C13 is 39500, or $39,500.

We illustrated the use of Excel's capability to provide assistance in using the SUMPRODUCT function. The procedure is similar for all Excel functions. This capability is especially helpful if you do not know which function to use or forget the proper name and/or syntax for a function.

ADDITIONAL EXCEL FUNCTIONS FOR MODELING

In this section we introduce some additional Excel functions that have proven useful in modeling decision problems.

FIGURE A.12   EXCEL WORKSHEET SHOWING THE USE OF EXCEL'S SUMPRODUCT FUNCTION TO CALCULATE TOTAL SHIPPING COSTS

	A	B	C	D	E	F	G	H
1	**Foster Generators**							
2								
3				**Destination**				
4	**Origin**	Boston	Chicago	St. Louis	Lexington	**Supply**		
5	Cleveland	3	2	7	6	5000		
6	Bedford	7	5	2	3	6000		
7	York	2	5	4	5	2500		
8	**Demand**	6000	4000	2000	1500			
9								
10								
11	**Model**							
12								
13		**Min Cost**	39500					
14								
15				**Destination**				
16	**Origin**	Boston	Chicago	St. Louis	Lexington	**Total**		
17	Cleveland	3500	1500	0	0	5000	<=	5000
18	Bedford	0	2500	2000	1500	6000	<=	6000
19	York	2500	0	0	0	2500	<=	2500
20	**Total**	6000	4000	2000	1500			
21		=	=	=	=			
22		6000	4000	2000	1500			

IF and COUNTIF Functions

Let us consider the case of Gambrell Manufacturing. Gambrell Manufacturing produces car stereos. Stereos are composed of a variety of components that the company must carry in inventory to keep production running smoothly. However, because inventory can be a costly investment, Gambrell generally likes to keep the amount of inventory of the components it uses in manufacturing to a minimum. To help monitor and control its inventory of components, Gambrell uses an inventory policy known as an "order up to" policy. This type of inventory policy and others are discussed in detail in Chapter 14.

The "order up to policy" is as follows. Whenever the inventory on hand drops below a certain level, enough units are ordered to return the inventory to that predetermined level. If the current number of units in inventory, denoted by H, drops below M units, we order enough to get the inventory level back up to M units. M is called the Order Up to Point. Stated mathematically, if Q is the amount we order, then

$$Q = M - H$$

An inventory model for Gambrell Manufacturing appears in Figure A.13. In this worksheet, labeled "OrderQuantity" in the upper half of the worksheet, the component ID number, inventory on hand (H), order up to point (M), and cost per unit are given for each of four components. Also given in this sheet is the fixed cost per order. The fixed cost is interpreted as follows: Each time a component is ordered, it costs Gambrell $120 to process the order. The fixed cost of $120 is incurred regardless of how many units are ordered.

FIGURE A.13   THE GAMBRELL MANUFACTURING COMPONENT ORDERING MODEL

	A	B	C	D	E	F
4	Component ID	570	578	741	755	
5	Inventory On-Hand	5	30	70	17	
6	Up to Order Point	100	55	70	45	
7	Cost per unit	$4.50	$12.50	$3.26	$4.15	
8						
9	Fixed Cost per Order	$120				
10						
11	**Model**					
12						
13	Component ID	570	578	741	755	
14	Order Quantity	95	25	0	28	
15	Cost of Goods	$384.75	$312.50	$0.00	$116.20	
16						
17	Total Number of Orders	3				
18						
19	Total Fixed costs	$360.00				
20	Total Cost of Goods	$813.45				
21	Total Cost	$1,173.45				
22						

WEB file

Gambrell

The model portion of the worksheet calculates the order quantity for each component. For example, for component 570, $M = 100$ and $H = 5$, so $Q = M - H = 100 - 5 = 95$. For component 741, $M = 70$ and $H = 70$ and no units are ordered because the on-hand inventory of 70 units is equal to the order point of 70. The calculations are similar for the other two components.

Depending on the number of units ordered, Gambrell receives a discount on the cost per unit. If 50 or more units are ordered, there is a quantity discount of 10% on every unit purchased. For example, for component 741, the cost per unit is $4.50 and 95 units are ordered. Because 95 exceeds the 50-unit requirement, there is a 10% discount and the cost per unit is reduced to $4.50 - 0.1(\$4.50) = \$4.50 - \$0.45 = \$4.05$. Not including the fixed cost, the cost of goods purchased is then $4.05(95) = \$384.75$.

The Excel functions used to perform these calculations are shown in Figure A.14. The IF function is used to calculate the purchase cost of goods for each component in row 15. The general form of the IF function is

$$=IF(\text{condition, result if condition is true, result if condition is false})$$

For example, in cell B15 we have =IF(B14>=50,0.9*B7,B7)*B14. This statement says if the order quantity (cell B14) is greater than or equal to 50, then the cost per unit is 0.9*B7 (there is a 10% discount); otherwise, there is no discount and the cost per unit is the amount given in cell B7. The purchase cost of goods for the other components are computed in a like manner.

The total cost in cell B21 is the sum of the purchase cost of goods ordered in row 15 and the fixed ordering costs. Because we place three orders (one each for components 570, 578, and 755), the fixed cost of the orders is 3*120 = $360.

FIGURE A.14   FORMULAS AND FUNCTIONS FOR GAMBRELL MANUFACTURING

	A	B	C	D	E
1					
2	**Gambrell Manufacturing**				
3					
4	Component ID	570	578	741	755
5	Inventory On-Hand	5	30	70	17
6	Up to Order Point	100	55	70	45
7	Cost per unit	4.5	12.5	3.26	4.15
8					
9	Fixed Cost per Order	120			
10					
11	**Model**				
12					
13	Component ID	=B4	=C4	=D4	=E4
14	Order Quantity	=B6-B5	=C6-C5	=D6-D5	=E6-E5
15	Cost of Goods	=IF(B14>=50,0.9*B7,B7)*B14	=IF(C14>=50, 0.9*C7,C7)*C14	=IF(D14>=50, 0.9*D7,D7)*D14	=IF(E14>=50, 0.9*E7,E7)*E14
16					
17	Total Number of Orders	=COUNTIF(B14:E14,">0")			
18					
19	Total Fixed Costs	=B17*B9			
20	Total Cost of Goods	=SUM(B15:E15)			
21	Total Cost	=SUM(B19:B20)			
22					

The COUNTIF function in cell B17 is used to count how many times we order. In particular, it counts the number of components having a positive order quantity. The general form of the COUNTIF function is

$$=COUNTIF(range, condition)$$

The *range* is the range to search for the *condition*. The condition is the test to be counted when satisfied. *Note that quotes are required for the condition with the COUNTIF function.* In the Gambrell model in Figure A.14, cell B17 counts the number of cells that are greater than zero in the range of cells B14:E14. In the model, because only cells B14, C14, and E14 are greater than zero, the COUNTIF function in cell B17 returns 3.

As we have seen, IF and COUNTIF are powerful functions that allow us to make calculations based on a condition holding (or not). There are other such conditional functions available in Excel. In the problems at the end of this appendix, we ask you to investigate one such function, the SUMIF function. Another conditional function that is extremely useful in modeling is the VLOOKUP function. We discuss the VLOOKUP function with an example in the next section.

VLOOKUP Function

Next, consider the workbook named *OM455* shown in Figure A.15. The worksheet named Grades is shown. This worksheet calculates the course grades for the course OM 455. There are 11 students in the course. Each student has a midterm exam score and a final exam score, and these are averaged in column D to get the course average. The scale given in the upper portion of the worksheet is used to determine the course grade for each student.

FIGURE A.15   OM455 GRADE SPREADSHEET

WEB file

OM455

	A	B	C	D	E	F
1	OM455					
2	Section 001					
3	Course Grading Scale Based on Course Average:					
4		Lower	Upper	Course		
5		Limit	Limit	Grade		
6		0	59	F		
7		60	69	D		
8		70	79	C		
9		80	89	B		
10		90	100	A		
11						
12		Midterm	Final	Course	Course	
13	Lastname	Score	Score	Average	Grade	
14	Benson	70	56	63.0	D	
15	Chin	95	91	93.0	A	
16	Choi	82	80	81.0	B	
17	Cruz	45	78	61.5	D	
18	Doe	68	45	56.5	F	
19	Honda	91	98	94.5	A	
20	Hume	87	74	80.5	B	
21	Jones	60	80	70.0	C	
22	Miranda	80	93	86.5	B	
23	Murigami	97	98	97.5	A	
24	Ruebush	90	91	90.5	A	
25						

Consider, for example, the performance of student Choi in row 16. This student earned an 82 on the midterm, an 80 on the final, and a course average of 81. From the grading scale, this equates to a course grade of B.

The course average is simply the average of the midterm and final scores, but how do we get Excel to look in the grading scale table and automatically assign the correct course letter grade to each student? The VLOOKUP function allows us to do just that. The formulas and functions used in *OM455* are shown in Figure A.16.

The VLOOKUP function allows the user to pull a subset of data from a larger table of data based on some criterion. The general form of the VLOOKUP function is

$$=VLOOKUP(arg1,arg2,arg3,arg4)$$

where arg1 is the value to search for in the first column of the table, arg2 is the table location, arg3 is the column location in the table to be returned, and arg4 is TRUE if looking for the first partial match of arg1 and FALSE for looking for an exact match of arg1. We will explain the difference between a partial and exact match in a moment. VLOOKUP assumes that the first column of the table is sorted in ascending order.

The VLOOKUP function for student Choi in cell E16 is as follows:

$$=VLOOKUP(D16,B6:D10,3,TRUE)$$

This function uses the course average from cell D16 and searches the first column of the table defined by B6:D10. In the first column of the table (column B), Excel searches from the top until it finds a number strictly greater than the value of D16 (81). It then backs up one row (to row 9). That is, it finds the last value in the first column less than or equal to 81.

FIGURE A.16   THE FORMULAS AND FUNCTIONS USED IN OM 455

	A	B	C	D	E
1	**OM 455**				
2	**Section 001**				
3	**Course Grading Scale Based on Course Average:**				
4		**Lower**	**Upper**	**Course**	
5		**Limit**	**Limit**	**Grade**	
6		0	59	F	
7		60	69	D	
8		70	79	C	
9		80	89	B	
10		90	100	A	
11					
12		Midterm	Final	Course	Course
13	Lastname	Score	Score	Average	Grade
14	Benson	70	56	=AVERAGE(B14:C14)	=VLOOKUP(D14,B6:D10,3,TRUE)
15	Chin	95	91	=AVERAGE(B15:C15)	=VLOOKUP(D15,B6:D10,3,TRUE)
16	Choi	82	80	=AVERAGE(B16:C16)	=VLOOKUP(D16,B6:D10,3,TRUE)
17	Cruz	45	78	=AVERAGE(B17:C17)	=VLOOKUP(D17,B6:D10,3,TRUE)
18	Doe	68	45	=AVERAGE(B18:C18)	=VLOOKUP(D18,B6:D10,3,TRUE)
19	Honda	91	98	=AVERAGE(B19:C19)	=VLOOKUP(D19,B6:D10,3,TRUE)
20	Hume	87	74	=AVERAGE(B20:C20)	=VLOOKUP(D20,B6:D10,3,TRUE)
21	Jones	60	80	=AVERAGE(B21:C21)	=VLOOKUP(D21,B6:D10,3,TRUE)
22	Miranda	80	93	=AVERAGE(B22:C22)	=VLOOKUP(D22,B6:D10,3,TRUE)
23	Murigami	97	98	=AVERAGE(B23:C23)	=VLOOKUP(D23,B6:D10,3,TRUE)
24	Ruebush	90	91	=AVERAGE(B24:C24)	=VLOOKUP(D24,B6:D10,3,TRUE)
25					

Because there is a 3 in the third argument of the VLOOKUP function, it takes the element in row 9 in the third column of the table, which is the letter "B." In summary, the VLOOKUP takes the first argument and searches the first column of the table for the last row that is less than or equal to the first argument. It then selects from that row the element in the column number of the third argument.

Note: If the last element of the VLOOKUP function is "False," the only change is that Excel searches for an exact match of the first argument in the first column of the data. VLOOKUP is very useful when you seek subsets of a table based on a condition.

PRINCIPLES FOR BUILDING GOOD SPREADSHEET MODELS

We have covered some of the fundamentals of building spreadsheet models. There are some generally accepted guiding principles for how to build a spreadsheet so that it is more easily used by others and so that the risk of error is mitigated. In this section we discuss some of those principles.

Separate the Data from the Model

One of the first principles of good modeling is to separate the data from the model. This enables the user to update the model parameters without fear of mistakenly typing over a formula or function. For this reason, it is good practice to have a data section at the top of the spreadsheet. A separate model section should contain all calculations and in general should not be updated by a user. For a what-if model or an optimization model, there might also be a separate section for decision cells (values that are not data or calculations, but are the outputs we seek from the model).

The Nowlin model in Figure A.6 is a good example. The data section is in the upper part of the spreadsheet followed by the model section that contains the calculations. The Gambrell model in Figure A.13 does not totally employ the principle of data/model separation. A better model would have the 50-unit hurdle and the 90% cost (10% discount) as data in the upper section. Then the formulas in row 15 would simply refer to the cells in the upper section. This would allow the user to easily change the discount, for example, without having to change all four formulas in row 15.

Document the Model

A good spreadsheet model is well documented. Clear labels and proper formatting and alignment make the spreadsheet easier to navigate and understand. For example, if the values in a worksheet are cost, currency formatting should be used. No cells should be unlabeled. A new user should be able to easily understand the model and its calculations. Figure A.17 shows a better-documented version of the Foster Generators model previously discussed (Figure A.10). The tables are more explicitly labeled, and shading focuses the user on the objective and the decision cells (amount to ship). The per-unit shipping cost data and total (Min) cost have been properly formatted as currency.

FIGURE A.17   A BETTER-DOCUMENTED FOSTER GENERATORS MODEL

Foster Rev

	A	B	C	D	E	F	G	H
1	**Foster Generators**							
2								
3	Origin to Destination—Cost per unit to ship							
4				**Destination**				
5	Origin	Boston	Chicago	St. Louis	Lexington	**Units Available**		
6	Cleveland	$3.00	$2.00	$7.00	$6.00	5000		
7	Bedford	$7.00	$5.00	$2.00	$3.00	6000		
8	York	$2.00	$5.00	$4.00	$5.00	2500		
9	**Units Demanded**	6000	4000	2000	1500			
10								
11								
12	**Model**							
13								
14		**Min Cost**	$39,500.00					
15								
16	Origin to Destination—Units Shipped							
17				**Destination**				
18	Origin	Boston	Chicago	St. Louis	Lexington	**Units Shipped**		
19	Cleveland	3500	1500	0	0	5000	<=	5000
20	Bedford	0	2500	2000	1500	6000	<=	6000
21	York	2500	0	0	0	2500	<=	2500
22	**Units Received**	6000	4000	2000	1500			
23		=	=	=	=			
24		6000	4000	2000	1500			

Use Simple Formulas and Cell Names

Clear formulas can eliminate unnecessary calculations, reduce errors, and make it easier to maintain your spreadsheet. Long and complex calculations should be divided into several cells. This makes the formula easier to understand and easier to edit. Avoid using numbers in a formula. Instead, put the number in a cell in the data section of your worksheet and refer to the cell location of the data in the formula. Building the formula in this manner avoids having to edit the formula for a simple data change.

Using cell names can make a formula much easier to understand. To assign a name to a cell, use the following steps:

Step 1. Select the cell or range of cells you would like to name
Step 2. Select the **Formulas** tab from the Ribbon
Step 3. Choose **Define Name** from the Define Names section
Step 4. The **New Name** dialog box will appear, as shown in Figure A.18
Enter the name you would like to use in the top portion of the dialog box and Click **OK**

Following this procedure and naming all cells in the *Nowlin Plastics* spreadsheet model leads to the model shown in Figure A.19. Compare this to Figure A.6 to easily understand the formulas in the model.

A name is also easily applied to range as follows. First, highlight the range of interest. Then click on the Name Box in the Formula Bar (refer back to Figure A.3) and type in the desired range name.

Use of Relative and Absolute Cell References

There are a number of ways to copy a formula from one cell to another in an Excel worksheet. One way to copy the a formula from one cell to another is presented here:

Step 1. Select the cell you would like to copy
Step 2. Right click on the mouse
Step 3. Click **Copy**
Step 4. Select the cell where you would like to put the copy
Step 5. Right click on the mouse
Step 6. Click **Paste**

When copying in Excel, one can use a relative or an absolute address. When copied, a relative address adjusts with the move of the copy, whereas an absolute address stays in its original form. Relative addresses are of the form C7. Absolute addresses have $ in front of the column and row, for example, $C$7. How you use relative and absolute addresses can have an impact on the amount of effort it takes to build a model and the opportunity for error in constructing the model.

Let us reconsider the OM455 grading spreadsheet previously discussed in this appendix and shown in Figure A.16. Recall that we used the VLOOKUP function to retrieve the appropriate letter grade for each student. The following formula is in cell E14:

$$=VLOOKUP(D14,B6:D10,3,TRUE)$$

FIGURE A.18   THE DEFINE NAME DIALOG BOX

Nowlin Plastics

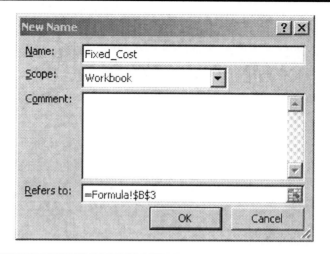

FIGURE A.19   THE NOWLIN PLASTIC MODEL FORMULAS WITH NAMED CELLS

	A	B
1	**Nowlin Plastics**	
2		
3	**Fixed Cost**	3000
4		
5	**Variable Cost Per Unit**	2
6		
7	**Selling Price Per Unit**	5
8		
9		
10	**Models**	
11		
12	**Production Volume**	800
13		
14	**Total Cost**	=Fixed_Cost+Variable_Cost*Production_Volume
15		
16	**Total Revenue**	=Selling_Price*Production_Volume
17		
18	**Total Profit (Loss)**	=Total_Revenue-Total_Cost

Note that this formula contains only relative addresses. If we copy this to cell E15, we get the following result:

$$=VLOOKUP(D15,B7:D11,3,TRUE)$$

Although the first argument has correctly changed to D15 (we want to calculate the letter grade for the student in row 15), the table in the function has also shifted to B7:D11. What we desired was for this table location to remain the same. A better approach would have been to use the following formula in cell E14:

$$=\text{VLOOKUP}(D14,\$B\$6:\$D\$10,3,\text{TRUE})$$

Copying this formula to cell E15 results in the following formula:

$$=\text{VLOOKUP}(D15,\$B\$6:\$D\$10,3,\text{TRUE})$$

This correctly changes the first argument to D15 and keeps the data table intact. Using absolute referencing is extremely useful if you have a function that has a reference that should not change when applied to another cell and you are copying the formula to other locations. In the case of the OM455 workbook, instead of typing the VLOOKUP for each student, we can use absolute referencing on the table and then copy from row 14 to rows 15 through 24.

In this section we have discussed guidelines for good spreadsheet model building. In the next section we discuss EXCEL tools available for checking and debugging spreadsheet models.

AUDITING EXCEL MODELS

EXCEL contains a variety of tools to assist you in the development and debugging of spreadsheet models. These tools are found in the Formula Auditing group of the Formulas Tab as shown in Figure A.20. Let us review each of the tools available in this group.

Trace Precedents and Dependents

The Trace Precedents button **Trace Precedents** creates arrows pointing to the selected cell from cells that are part of the formula in that cell. The Trace Dependents button **Trace Dependents**, on the other hand, shows arrows pointing from the selected cell, to cells that depend on the selected cell. Both of the tools are excellent for quickly ascertaining how parts of a model are linked.

An example of Trace Precedents is shown in Figure A.21. Here we have opened the *Foster Rev* worksheet, selected cell C14, and clicked the Trace Precedents button in the Formula Auditing Group. Recall that the cost in cell C14 is calculated as the SUMPRODUCT of the per-unit shipping cost and units shipped. In Figure A.21, to show this relationship, arrows are drawn to these respective areas of the spreadsheet to cell C14. These arrows may be removed by clicking on the Remove Arrows button in the Auditing Tools Group.

FIGURE A.20   THE FORMULA AUDITING GROUP OF THE FORMULAS TAB

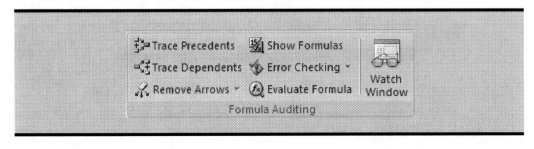

FIGURE A.21   TRACE PRECEDENTS FOR CELL C14 (COST) IN THE FOSTER
GENERATORS REV MODEL

	C14	▼	●	f_x	=SUMPRODUCT(B6:E8,B19:E21)			
	A	B	C	D	E	F	G	H
1	Foster Generators							
2								
3	Origin to Destination—Cost per unit to ship							
4				Destination				
5	Origin	Boston	Chicago	St. Louis	Lexington	Units Available		
6	Cleveland	$3.00	$2.00	$7.00	$6.00	5000		
7	Bedford	$7.00	$5.00	$2.00	$3.00	6000		
8	York	$2.00	$5.00	$4.00	$5.00	2500		
9	Units Demanded	6000	4000	2000	1500			
10								
11								
12	Model							
13								
14		Min Cost	$39,500.00					
15								
16	Origin to Destination—Units Shipped							
17				Destination				
18	Origin	Boston	Chicago	St. Louis	Lexington	Units Shipped		
19	Cleveland	3500	1500	0	0	5000	<=	5000
20	Bedford	0	2500	2000	1500	6000	<=	6000
21	York	2500	0	0	0	2500	<=	2500
22	Units Received	6000	4000	2000	1500			
23		=	=	=	=			
24		6000	4000	2000	1500			

WEB file

Foster Rev

An example of Trace Dependents is shown in Figure A.22. We have selected cell E20, the units shipped from Bedford to Lexington, and clicked on the Trace Dependents button in the Formula Auditing Group. As shown in Figure A.22, units shipped from Bedford to Lexington impacts the cost function in cell C14, the total units shipped from Bedford given in cell F20, and the total units shipped to Lexington in cell E22. These arrows may be removed by clicking on the Remove Arrows button in the Auditing Tools Group.

Trace Precedents and Trace Dependents can highlight errors in copying and formula construction by showing that incorrect sections of the worksheet are referenced.

Show Formulas

The Show Formulas button, 🔣 Show Formulas , does exactly that. To see the formulas in a worksheet, simply click on any cell in the worksheet and then click on Show Formulas. You will see the formulas that exist in that worksheet. To go back to hiding the formulas, click again on the Show Formulas button. Figure A.6 gives an example of the show formulas view. This allows you to inspect each formula in detail in its cell location.

Evaluate Formulas

The Evaluate Formula button, ⓐ Evaluate Formula , allows you to investigate the calculations of particular cell in great detail. To invoke this tool, we simply select a cell containing

FIGURE A.22   TRACE DEPENDENTS FOR CELL C14 (COST) IN THE FOSTER GENERATORS REV MODEL

	E20	▼	●	fx	1500			
	A	B	C	D	E	F	G	H
12	Model							
13								
14		Min Cost	$39,500.00					
15								
16	Origin to Destination—Units Shipped							
17				Destination				
18	Origin	Boston	Chicago	St. Louis	Lexington	Units Shipped		
19	Cleveland	3500	1500	0	0	5000	<=	5000
20	Bedford	0	2500	2000	1500	6000	<=	6000
21	York	2500	0	0	0	2500	<=	2500
22	Units Received	6000	4000	2000	1500			
23		=	=	=	=			
24		6000	4000	2000	1500			

a formula and click on the Evaluate Formula button in the Formula Auditing Group. As an example, we select cell B15 of the Gambrell Manufacturing model (see Figures A.13 and A.14). Recall we are calculating cost of goods based upon whether or not there is a quantity discount. Clicking on the Evaluate button allows you to evaluate this formula explicitly. The Evaluate Formula dialog box appears in Figure A.23. Figure A.24 shows the result of one click of the Evaluate button. The B14 has changed to its value of 95. Further clicks would evaluate in order, from left to right, the remaining components of the formula. We ask the reader to further explore this tool in an exercise at the end of this appendix.

The Evaluate Formula tool provides an excellent means of identifying the exact location of an error in a formula.

FIGURE A.23   THE EVALUATE FORMULA DIALOG BOX

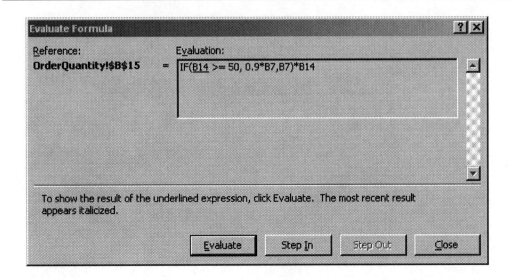

FIGURE A.24   THE EVALUATE FORMULA AFTER ONE CLICK OF THE
EVALUATE BUTTON

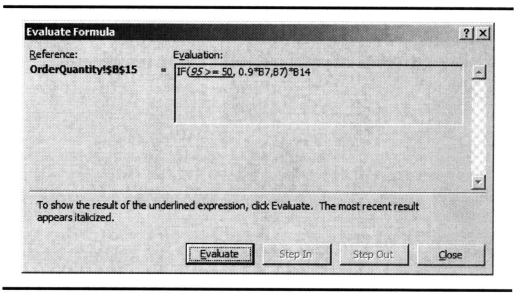

Error Checking

The Error Checking Button, 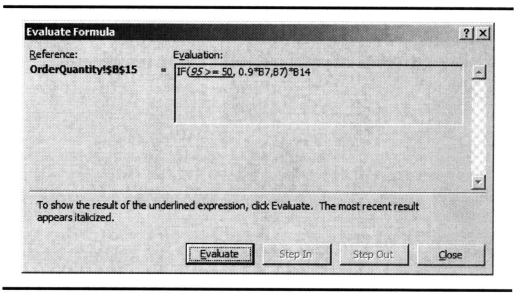 Error Checking ▾ , provides an automatic means of checking
for mathematical errors within formulas of a worksheet. Clicking on the Error Checking
button causes Excel to check every formula in the sheet for calculation errors. If an error is
found, the Error Checking dialog box appears. An example for a hypothetical division by
zero error is shown in Figure A.25. From this box, the formula can be edited or the calculation steps can be observed (as in the previous section on Evaluate Formulas).

FIGURE A.25   THE ERROR CHECKING DIALOG BOX FOR A DIVISION
BY ZERO ERROR

FIGURE A.26   THE WATCH WINDOW FOR THE GAMBRELL MANUFACTURING
MODEL

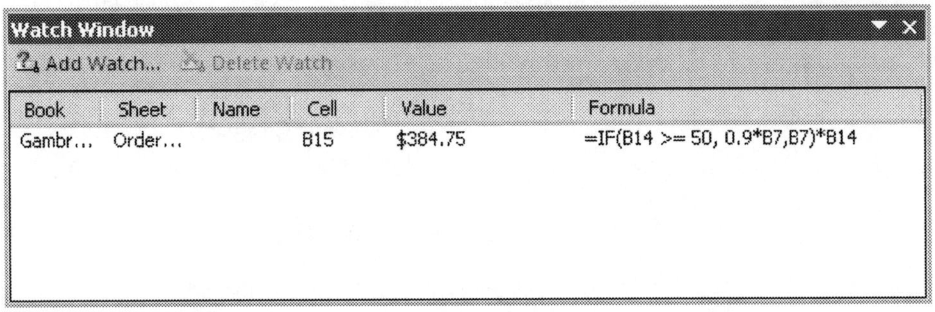

Watch Window					▾ ✕
🔍 Add Watch... ☷ Delete Watch					
Book	Sheet	Name	Cell	Value	Formula
Gambr...	Order...		B15	$384.75	=IF(B14 >= 50, 0.9*B7,B7)*B14

Watch Window

The Watch Window, located in the Formula Auditing Group, allows the user to observe the values of cells included in the Watch Window box list. This is useful for large models when not all the model is observable on the screen or when multiple worksheets are used. The user can monitor how the listed cells change with a change in the model without searching through the worksheet or changing from one worksheet to another.

A Watch Window for the Gambrell Manufacturing model is shown in Figure A.26. The following steps were used from the OrderQuantity worksheet to add cell B15 of the OrderQuantity worksheet to the watch list:

Step 1. Select the **Formulas** tab
Step 2. Select **Watch Window** from the Formula Auditing Group
  The Watch Window will appear
Step 3. Select **Add Watch**
Step 4. Click on the cell you would like to add to the watch list (in this case B15)

As shown in Figure A.26, the list gives the workbook name, worksheet name, cell name (if used), cell location, cell value, and cell formula. To delete a cell from the watch list, select the entry from the list and then click on the Delete Watch button in the upper part of the Watch Window.

The Watch Window, as shown in Figure A.26, allows us to monitor the value of B15 as we make changes elsewhere in the worksheet. Furthermore, if we had other worksheets in this workbook, we could monitor changes to B15 of the OrderQuantity worksheet even from these other worksheets. The Watch Window is observable regardless of where we are in any worksheet of a workbook.

SUMMARY

In this appendix we have discussed how to build effective spreadsheet models using Excel. We provided an overview on workbooks and worksheets and details on useful Excel functions. We also discussed a set of principles for good modeling and tools for auditing spreadsheet models.

PROBLEMS

Nowlin Plastics

1. Open the file *Nowlin Plastics*. Recall that we have modeled total profit for the product CD-50 in this spreadsheet. Suppose we have a second product called a CD-100, with the following characteristics:

$$\text{Fixed Cost} = \$2500$$
$$\text{Variable Cost per Unit} = \$1.67$$
$$\text{Selling Price per Unit} = \$4.40$$

Extend the model so that the profit is calculated for each product and then totaled to give an overall profit generated for the two products. Use a CD-100 production volume of 1200. Save this file as *Nowlin Plastics2*. *Hint:* Place the data for CD-100 in column C and copy the formulas in rows 14, 16, and 18 to column C.

2. Assume that in an empty Excel worksheet in cell A1 you enter the formula =B1*$F$3. You now copy this formula into cell E6. What is the modified formula that appears in E6?

Foster Rev

3. Open the file *Foster Rev*. Select cells B6:E8 and name these cells Shipping_Cost. Select cells B19:E21 and name these cells Units_Shipped. Use these names in the SUMPRODUCT function in cell C14 to compute cost and verify that you obtain the same cost ($39,500).

4. Open the file *Nowlin Plastics*. Recall that we have modeled total profit for the product CD-50 in this spreadsheet. Modify the spreadsheet to take into account production capacity and forecasted demand. If forecasted demand is less than or equal to capacity, Nowlin will produce only the forecasted demand; otherwise, they will produce the full capacity. For this example, use forecasted demand of 1200 and capacity of 1500. *Hint:* Enter demand and capacity into the data section of the model. Then use an IF statement to calculate production volume.

Cox Electric

5. Cox Electric makes electronic components and has estimated the following for a new design of one of its products:

$$\text{Fixed Cost} = \$10,000$$
$$\text{Revenue per unit} = \$0.65$$
$$\text{Material cost per unit} = \$0.15$$
$$\text{Labor cost per unit} = \$0.10$$

These data are given in the spreadsheet *Cox Electric*. Also in the spreadsheet in row 14 is a profit model that gives the profit (or loss) for a specified volume (cell C14).

   a. Use the Show Formula button in the Formula Auditing Group of the Formulas tab to see the formulas and cell references used in row 14.

   b. Use the Trace Precedents tool to see how the formulas are dependent on the elements of the data section.

   c. Use trial and error, by trying various values of volume in cell C14, to arrive at a breakeven volume.

6. Return to the Cox Electric spreadsheet. Build a table of profits based on different volume levels by doing the following: In cell C15, enter a volume of 20,000. Look at each formula in row 14 and decide which references should be absolute or relative for purposes of copying the formulas to row 15. Make the necessary changes to row 14 (change any references that should be absolute by putting in $). Copy cells D14:I14 to row 15. Continue this with new rows until a positive profit is found. Save your file as *Cox_Breakeven*.

OM455

7. Open the workbook *OM455*. Save the file under a new name, *OM455COUNTIF*. Suppose we wish to automatically count the number of each letter grade.
    a. Begin by putting the letters A, B, C, D, and F in cells C29:C33. Use the COUNTIF function in cells D29:D33 to count the number of each letter grade. *Hint:* Create the necessary COUNTIF function in cell D29. Use absolute referencing on the range ($E14:$E$24) and then copy the function to cells D30:D33 to count the number of each of the other letter grades.
    b. We are considering a different grading scale as follows:

Lower	Upper	Grade
0	69	F
70	76	D
77	84	C
85	92	B
93	100	A

For the current list of students, use the COUNTIF function to determine the number of A, B, C, D, and F letter grades earned under this new system.

OM455

8. Open the workbook *OM455*. Save the file under a new name, *OM4555Revised*. Suppose we wish to use a more refined grading system, as shown below:

Lower	Upper	Grade
0	59	F
60	69	D
70	72	C−
73	76	C−
77	79	C+
80	82	B−
83	86	B
87	89	B+
90	92	A−
93	100	A

Update the file to use this more refined grading system. How many of each letter grade are awarded under the new system? *Hint:* Build a new grading table and use VLOOKUP and an absolute reference to the table. Then use COUNTIF to count the number of each letter grade.

Newton_data

9. Newton Manufacturing produces scientific calculators. The models are N350, N450, and the N900. Newton has planned its distribution of these products around eight customer zones: Brazil, China, France, Malaysia, U.S. Northeast, U.S. Southeast, U.S. Midwest, and U.S. West. Data for the current quarter (volume to be shipped in thousands of units) for each product and each customer zone are given in the file *Newton_data*.

Newton would like to know the total number of units going to each customer zone and also the total units of each product shipped. There are several ways to get this information from the data set. One way is to use the SUMIF function.

The SUMIF function extends the SUM function by allowing the user to add the values of cells meeting a logical condition. This general form of the function is

$$=\text{SUMIF}(\textit{test range, condition, range to be summed})$$

The *test range* is an area to search to test the *condition,* and the *range to be summed* is the position of the data to be summed. So, for example, using the *Newton_data* file, we would use the following function to get the total units sent to Malaysia:

$$=SUMIF(A3:A26,A3,C3:C26)$$

Here, A3 is Malaysia, A3:A26 is the range of customer zones, and C3:C26 are the volumes for each product for these customer zones. The SUMIF looks for matches of Malaysia in column A and, if a match is found, adds the volume to the total. Use the SUMIF function to get each total volume by zone and each total volume by product.

Williamson

10. Consider the transportation model given in the Excel file *Williamson.* It is a model that is very similar to the Foster Generators model. Williamson produces a single product and has plants in Atlanta, Lexington, Chicago, and Salt Lake City and warehouses in Portland, St. Paul, Las Vegas, Tuscon, and Cleveland. Each plant has a capacity and each warehouse has a demand. Williamson would like to find a low-cost shipping plan. Mr. Williamson has reviewed the results and notices right away that the total cost is way out of line. Use the Formula Auditing Tools under the Formulas tab in Excel to find any errors in this model. Correct the errors. *Hint:* There are two errors in this model. Be sure to check every formula.

Appendix B   Areas for the Standard Normal Distribution

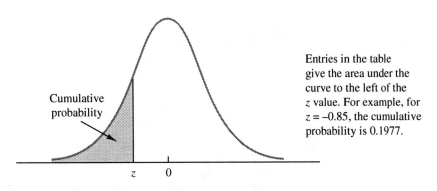

Cumulative probability

Entries in the table give the area under the curve to the left of the *z* value. For example, for *z* = –0.85, the cumulative probability is 0.1977.

z	0.00	0.01	0.02	0.03	0.04	0.05	0.06	0.07	0.08	0.09
−3.0	0.0013	0.0013	0.0013	0.0012	0.0012	0.0011	0.0011	0.0011	0.0010	0.0010
−2.9	0.0019	0.0018	0.0018	0.0017	0.0016	0.0016	0.0015	0.0015	0.0014	0.0014
−2.8	0.0026	0.0025	0.0024	0.0023	0.0023	0.0022	0.0021	0.0021	0.0020	0.0019
−2.7	0.0035	0.0034	0.0033	0.0032	0.0031	0.0030	0.0029	0.0028	0.0027	0.0026
−2.6	0.0047	0.0045	0.0044	0.0043	0.0041	0.0040	0.0039	0.0038	0.0037	0.0036
−2.5	0.0062	0.0060	0.0059	0.0057	0.0055	0.0054	0.0052	0.0051	0.0049	0.0048
−2.4	0.0082	0.0080	0.0078	0.0075	0.0073	0.0071	0.0069	0.0068	0.0066	0.0064
−2.3	0.0107	0.0104	0.0102	0.0099	0.0096	0.0094	0.0091	0.0089	0.0087	0.0084
−2.2	0.0139	0.0136	0.0132	0.0129	0.0125	0.0122	0.0119	0.0116	0.0113	0.0110
−2.1	0.0179	0.0174	0.0170	0.0166	0.0162	0.0158	0.0154	0.0150	0.0146	0.0143
−2.0	0.0228	0.0222	0.0217	0.0212	0.0207	0.0202	0.0197	0.0192	0.0188	0.0183
−1.9	0.0287	0.0281	0.0274	0.0268	0.0262	0.0256	0.0250	0.0244	0.0239	0.0233
−1.8	0.0359	0.0351	0.0344	0.0336	0.0329	0.0322	0.0314	0.0307	0.0301	0.0294
−1.7	0.0446	0.0436	0.0427	0.0418	0.0409	0.0401	0.0392	0.0384	0.0375	0.0367
−1.6	0.0548	0.0537	0.0526	0.0516	0.0505	0.0495	0.0485	0.0475	0.0465	0.0455
−1.5	0.0668	0.0655	0.0643	0.0630	0.0618	0.0606	0.0594	0.0582	0.0571	0.0559
−1.4	0.0808	0.0793	0.0778	0.0764	0.0749	0.0735	0.0721	0.0708	0.0694	0.0681
−1.3	0.0968	0.0951	0.0934	0.0918	0.0901	0.0885	0.0869	0.0853	0.0838	0.0823
−1.2	0.1151	0.1131	0.1112	0.1093	0.1075	0.1056	0.1038	0.1020	0.1003	0.0985
−1.1	0.1357	0.1335	0.1314	0.1292	0.1271	0.1251	0.1230	0.1210	0.1190	0.1170
−1.0	0.1587	0.1562	0.1539	0.1515	0.1492	0.1469	0.1446	0.1423	0.1401	0.1379
−0.9	0.1841	0.1814	0.1788	0.1762	0.1736	0.1711	0.1685	0.1660	0.1635	0.1611
−0.8	0.2119	0.2090	0.2061	0.2033	0.2005	0.1977	0.1949	0.1922	0.1894	0.1867
−0.7	0.2420	0.2389	0.2358	0.2327	0.2296	0.2266	0.2236	0.2206	0.2177	0.2148
−0.6	0.2743	0.2709	0.2676	0.2643	0.2611	0.2578	0.2546	0.2514	0.2483	0.2451
−0.5	0.3085	0.3050	0.3015	0.2981	0.2946	0.2912	0.2877	0.2843	0.2810	0.2776
−0.4	0.3446	0.3409	0.3372	0.3336	0.3300	0.3264	0.3228	0.3192	0.3156	0.3121
−0.3	0.3821	0.3783	0.3745	0.3707	0.3669	0.3632	0.3594	0.3557	0.3520	0.3483
−0.2	0.4207	0.4168	0.4129	0.4090	0.4052	0.4013	0.3974	0.3936	0.3897	0.3859
−0.1	0.4602	0.4562	0.4522	0.4483	0.4443	0.4404	0.4364	0.4325	0.4286	0.4247
−0.0	0.5000	0.4960	0.4920	0.4880	0.4840	0.4801	0.4761	0.4721	0.4681	0.4641

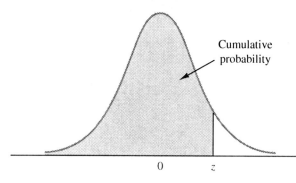

Cumulative probability

Entries in the table give the area under the curve to the left of the z value. For example, for $z = 1.25$, the cumulative probability is 0.8944.

z	0.00	0.01	0.02	0.03	0.04	0.05	0.06	0.07	0.08	0.09
0.0	0.5000	0.5040	0.5080	0.5120	0.5160	0.5199	0.5239	0.5279	0.5319	0.5359
0.1	0.5398	0.5438	0.5478	0.5517	0.5557	0.5596	0.5636	0.5675	0.5714	0.5753
0.2	0.5793	0.5832	0.5871	0.5910	0.5948	0.5987	0.6026	0.6064	0.6103	0.6141
0.3	0.6179	0.6217	0.6255	0.6293	0.6331	0.6368	0.6406	0.6443	0.6480	0.6517
0.4	0.6554	0.6591	0.6628	0.6664	0.6700	0.6736	0.6772	0.6808	0.6844	0.6879
0.5	0.6915	0.6950	0.6985	0.7019	0.7054	0.7088	0.7123	0.7157	0.7190	0.7224
0.6	0.7257	0.7291	0.7324	0.7357	0.7389	0.7422	0.7454	0.7486	0.7517	0.7549
0.7	0.7580	0.7611	0.7642	0.7673	0.7704	0.7734	0.7764	0.7794	0.7823	0.7852
0.8	0.7881	0.7910	0.7939	0.7967	0.7995	0.8023	0.8051	0.8078	0.8106	0.8133
0.9	0.8159	0.8186	0.8212	0.8238	0.8264	0.8289	0.8315	0.8340	0.8365	0.8389
1.0	0.8413	0.8438	0.8461	0.8485	0.8508	0.8531	0.8554	0.8577	0.8599	0.8621
1.1	0.8643	0.8665	0.8686	0.8708	0.8729	0.8749	0.8770	0.8790	0.8810	0.8830
1.2	0.8849	0.8869	0.8888	0.8907	0.8925	0.8944	0.8962	0.8980	0.8997	0.9015
1.3	0.9032	0.9049	0.9066	0.9082	0.9099	0.9115	0.9131	0.9147	0.9162	0.9177
1.4	0.9192	0.9207	0.9222	0.9236	0.9251	0.9265	0.9279	0.9292	0.9306	0.9319
1.5	0.9332	0.9345	0.9357	0.9370	0.9382	0.9394	0.9406	0.9418	0.9429	0.9441
1.6	0.9452	0.9463	0.9474	0.9484	0.9495	0.9505	0.9515	0.9525	0.9535	0.9545
1.7	0.9554	0.9564	0.9573	0.9582	0.9591	0.9599	0.9608	0.9616	0.9625	0.9633
1.8	0.9641	0.9649	0.9656	0.9664	0.9671	0.9678	0.9686	0.9693	0.9699	0.9706
1.9	0.9713	0.9719	0.9726	0.9732	0.9738	0.9744	0.9750	0.9756	0.9761	0.9767
2.0	0.9772	0.9778	0.9783	0.9788	0.9793	0.9798	0.9803	0.9808	0.9812	0.9817
2.1	0.9821	0.9826	0.9830	0.9834	0.9838	0.9842	0.9846	0.9850	0.9854	0.9857
2.2	0.9861	0.9864	0.9868	0.9871	0.9875	0.9878	0.9881	0.9884	0.9887	0.9890
2.3	0.9893	0.9896	0.9898	0.9901	0.9904	0.9906	0.9909	0.9911	0.9913	0.9913
2.4	0.9916	0.9920	0.9922	0.9925	0.9927	0.9929	0.9931	0.9932	0.9934	0.9936
2.5	0.9938	0.9940	0.9941	0.9943	0.9945	0.9946	0.9948	0.9949	0.9951	0.9952
2.6	0.9953	0.9955	0.9956	0.9957	0.9959	0.9960	0.9961	0.9962	0.9963	0.9964
2.7	0.9965	0.9966	0.9967	0.9968	0.9969	0.9970	0.9971	0.9972	0.9973	0.9974
2.8	0.9974	0.9975	0.9976	0.9977	0.9977	0.9978	0.9979	0.9979	0.9980	0.9981
2.9	0.9981	0.9982	0.9982	0.9983	0.9984	0.9984	0.9985	0.9985	0.9986	0.9986
3.0	0.9987	0.9987	0.9987	0.9988	0.9988	0.9989	0.9989	0.9989	0.9990	0.9990

Appendix C　Values of $e^{-\lambda}$

λ	$e^{-\lambda}$	λ	$e^{-\lambda}$	λ	$e^{-\lambda}$
0.05	0.9512	2.05	0.1287	4.05	0.0174
0.10	0.9048	2.10	0.1225	4.10	0.0166
0.15	0.8607	2.15	0.1165	4.15	0.0158
0.20	0.8187	2.20	0.1108	4.20	0.0150
0.25	0.7788	2.25	0.1054	4.25	0.0143
0.30	0.7408	2.30	0.1003	4.30	0.0136
0.35	0.7047	2.35	0.0954	4.35	0.0129
0.40	0.6703	2.40	0.0907	4.40	0.0123
0.45	0.6376	2.45	0.0863	4.45	0.0117
0.50	0.6065	2.50	0.0821	4.50	0.0111
0.55	0.5769	2.55	0.0781	4.55	0.0106
0.60	0.5488	2.60	0.0743	4.60	0.0101
0.65	0.5220	2.65	0.0707	4.65	0.0096
0.70	0.4966	2.70	0.0672	4.70	0.0091
0.75	0.4724	2.75	0.0639	4.75	0.0087
0.80	0.4493	2.80	0.0608	4.80	0.0082
0.85	0.4274	2.85	0.0578	4.85	0.0078
0.90	0.4066	2.90	0.0550	4.90	0.0074
0.95	0.3867	2.95	0.0523	4.95	0.0071
1.00	0.3679	3.00	0.0498	5.00	0.0067
1.05	0.3499	3.05	0.0474	5.05	0.0064
1.10	0.3329	3.10	0.0450	5.10	0.0061
1.15	0.3166	3.15	0.0429	5.15	0.0058
1.20	0.3012	3.20	0.0408	5.20	0.0055
1.25	0.2865	3.25	0.0388	5.25	0.0052
1.30	0.2725	3.30	0.0369	5.30	0.0050
1.35	0.2592	3.35	0.0351	5.35	0.0047
1.40	0.2466	3.40	0.0334	5.40	0.0045
1.45	0.2346	3.45	0.0317	5.45	0.0043
1.50	0.2231	3.50	0.0302	5.50	0.0041
1.55	0.2122	3.55	0.0287	5.55	0.0039
1.60	0.2019	3.60	0.0273	5.60	0.0037
1.65	0.1920	3.65	0.0260	5.65	0.0035
1.70	0.1827	3.70	0.0247	5.70	0.0033
1.75	0.1738	3.75	0.0235	5.75	0.0032
1.80	0.1653	3.80	0.0224	5.80	0.0030
1.85	0.1572	3.85	0.0213	5.85	0.0029
1.90	0.1496	3.90	0.0202	5.90	0.0027
1.95	0.1423	3.95	0.0193	5.95	0.0026
2.00	0.1353	4.00	0.0183	6.00	0.0025
				7.00	0.0009
				8.00	0.000335
				9.00	0.000123
				10.00	0.000045

Appendix D   References and Bibliography

Chapter 1   Introduction

Churchman, C. W., R. L. Ackoff, and E. L. Arnoff. *Introduction to Operations Research.* Wiley, 1957.

Horner, Peter. "The Sabre Story," *OR/MS Today* (June 2000).

Leon, Linda, Z. Przasnyski, and K. C. Seal. "Spreadsheets and OR/MS Models: An End-User Perspective," *Interfaces* (March/April 1996).

Powell, S. G. "Innovative Approaches to Management Science," *OR/MS Today* (October 1996).

Savage, S. "Weighing the Pros and Cons of Decision Technology and Spreadsheets," *OR/MS Today* (February 1997).

Winston, W. L. "The Teachers' Forum: Management Science with Spreadsheets for MBAs at Indiana University," *Interfaces* (March/April 1996).

Chapters 2 to 7   Linear, Distribution, Network, and Integer Programming

Ahuja, R. K., T. L. Magnanti, and J. B. Orlin. *Network Flows, Theory, Algorithms, and Applications.* Prentice Hall, 1993.

Bazarra, M. S., J. J. Jarvis, and H. D. Sherali. *Linear Programming and Network Flows,* 2d ed. Wiley, 1990.

Carino, H. F., and C. H. Le Noir, Jr. "Optimizing Wood Procurement in Cabinet Manufacturing," *Interfaces* (March/April 1988): 10–19.

Dantzig, G. B. *Linear Programming and Extensions.* Princeton University Press, 1963.

Davis, Morton D. *Game Theory: A Nontechnical Introduction.* Dover, 1997.

Evans, J. R., and E. Minieka. *Optimization Algorithms for Networks and Graphs,* 2d ed. Marcel Dekker, 1992.

Ford, L. R., and D. R. Fulkerson. *Flows and Networks.* Princeton University Press, 1962.

Geoffrion, A., and G. Graves. "Better Distribution Planning with Computer Models," *Harvard Business Review* (July/August 1976).

Greenberg, H. J. "How to Analyze the Results of Linear Programs—Part 1: Preliminaries," *Interfaces* 23, no. 4 (July/August 1993): 56–67.

Greenberg, H. J. "How to Analyze the Results of Linear Programs—Part 2: Price Interpretation," *Interfaces* 23, no. 5 (September/October 1993): 97–114.

Greenberg, H. J. "How to Analyze the Results of Linear Programs—Part 3: Infeasibility Diagnosis," *Interfaces* 23, no. 6 (November/December 1993): 120–139.

Lillien, G., and A. Rangaswamy. *Marketing Engineering: Computer-Assisted Marketing Analysis and Planning.* Addison-Wesley, 1998.

Martin, R. K. *Large Scale Linear and Integer Optimization: A Unified Approach.* Kluwer Academic Publishers, 1999.

McMillian, John. *Games, Strategies, and Managers.* Oxford University Press, 1992.

Myerson, Roger B. *Game Theory: Analysis of Conflict.* Harvard University Press, 1997.

Nemhauser, G. L., and L. A. Wolsey. *Integer and Combinatorial Optimization.* Wiley, 1999.

Osborne, Martin J. *An Introduction to Game Theory.* Oxford University Press, 2004.

Schrage, Linus. *Optimization Modeling with LINDO,* 4th ed. LINDO Systems Inc., 2000.

Sherman, H. D. "Hospital Efficiency Measurement and Evaluation," *Medical Care* 22, no. 10 (October 1984): 922–938.

Winston, W. L., and S. C. Albright. *Practical Management Science,* 2d ed. Duxbury Press, 2001.

Chapter 8   Nonlinear Optimization Models

Bazarra, M. S., H. D. Sherali, and C. M. Shetty. *Nonlinear Programming Theory and Applications.* Wiley, 1993.

Benninga, Simon. *Financial Modeling.* MIT Press, 2000.

Luenberger, D. *Linear and Nonlinear Programming,* 2d ed. Addison-Wesley, 1984.

Rardin, R. L. *Optimization in Operations Research.* Prentice Hall, 1998.

Chapter 9   Project Scheduling: PERT/CPM

Moder, J. J., C. R. Phillips, and E. W. Davis. *Project Management with CPM, PERT and Precedence Diagramming,* 3d ed. Blitz, 1995.

Wasil, E. A., and A. A. Assad. "Project Management on the PC: Software, Applications, and Trends," *Interfaces* 18, no. 2 (March/April 1988): 75–84.

Wiest, J., and F. Levy. *Management Guide to PERT-CPM,* 2d ed. Prentice Hall, 1977.

Chapter 10   Inventory Models

Fogarty, D. W., J. H. Blackstone, and T. R. Hoffman. *Production and Inventory Management,* 2d ed. South-Western, 1990.

Hillier, F., and G. J. Lieberman. *Introduction to Operations Research,* 7th ed. McGraw-Hill, 2000.

Narasimhan, S. L., D. W. McLeavey, and P. B. Lington. *Production Planning and Inventory Control,* 2d ed. Prentice Hall, 1995.

Orlicky, J., and G. W. Plossi. *Orlicky's Material Requirements Planning.* McGraw-Hill, 1994.

Vollmann, T. E., W. L. Berry, and D. C. Whybark. *Manufacturing Planning and Control Systems,* 4th ed. McGraw-Hill, 1997.

Zipkin, P. H. *Foundations of Inventory Management.* McGraw-Hill/Irwin, 2000.

Chapter 11   Waiting Line Models

Bunday, B. D. *An Introduction to Queueing Theory.* Wiley, 1996.

Gross, D., and C. M. Harris. *Fundamentals of Queueing Theory,* 3d ed. Wiley, 1997.

Hall, R. W. *Queueing Methods: For Services and Manufacturing.* Prentice Hall, 1997.

Hillier, F., and G. J. Lieberman. *Introduction to Operations Research,* 7th ed. McGraw-Hill, 2000.

Kao, E. P. C. *An Introduction to Stochastic Processes.* Duxbury, 1996.

Chapter 12   Simulation

Banks, J., J. S. Carson, and B. L. Nelson. *Discrete-Event System Simulation,* 2d ed. Prentice Hall, 1995.

Fishwick, P. A. *Simulation Model Design and Execution: Building Digital Worlds.* Prentice Hall, 1995.

Harrell, C. R., and K. Tumau. *Simulation Made Easy: A Manager's Guide.* Institute of Industrial Engineers, 1996.

Kelton, W. D., R. P. Sadowski, and D. A. Sadowski. *Simulation with Arena,* 4th ed. McGraw-Hill, 2007.

Law, A. M., and W. D. Kelton. *Simulation Modeling and Analysis,* 3d ed. McGraw-Hill, 1999.

Pidd, M. *Computer Simulation in Management Science,* 4th ed. Wiley, 1998.

Thesen, A., and L. E. Travis. *Simulation for Decision Making.* Wadsworth, 1992.

Chapter 13   Decision Analysis

Berger, J. O. *Statistical Decision Theory and Bayesian Analysis,* 2d ed. Springer-Verlag, 1985.

Chernoff, H., and L. E. Moses. *Elementary Decision Theory.* Dover, 1987.

Clemen, R. T., and T. Reilly. *Making Hard Decisions with Decision Tools.* Duxbury, 2001.

Goodwin, P., and G. Wright. *Decision Analysis for Management Judgment,* 2d ed. Wiley, 1999.

Gregory, G. *Decision Analysis.* Plenum, 1988.

Pratt, J. W., H. Raiffa, and R. Schlaifer. *Introduction to Statistical Decision Theory.* MIT Press, 1995.

Raiffa, H. *Decision Analysis.* McGraw-Hill, 1997.

Schlaifer, R. *Analysis of Decisions Under Uncertainty.* Krieger, 1978.

Chapter 14   Multicriteria Decisions

Dyer, J. S. "A Clarification of Remarks on the Analytic Hierarchy Process," *Management Science* 36, no. 3 (March 1990): 274–275.

Dyer, J. S. "Remarks on the Analytic Hierarchy Process," *Management Science* 36, no. 3 (March 1990): 249–258.

Harker, P. T., and L. G. Vargas. "Reply to Remarks on the Analytic Hierarchy Process by J. S. Dyer," *Management Science* 36, no. 3 (March 1990): 269–273.

Harker, P. T., and L. G. Vargas. "The Theory of Ratio Scale Estimation: Saaty's Analytic Hierarchy Process," *Management Science* 33, no. 11 (November 1987): 1383–1403.

Ignizio, J. *Introduction to Linear Goal Programming.* Sage, 1986.

Keeney, R. L., and H. Raiffa. *Decisions with Multiple Objectives: Preferences and Value Tradeoffs.* Cambridge, 1993.

Saaty, T. *Decision Making for Leaders: The Analytic Hierarchy Process for Decisions in a Complex World,* 3d ed. RWS, 1999.

Saaty, T. *Multicriteria Decision Making,* 2d ed. RWS, 1996.

Saaty, T. L. "An Exposition of the AHP in Reply to the Paper Remarks on the Analytic Hierarchy Process," *Management Science* 36, no. 3 (March 1990): 259–268.

Saaty, T. L. "Rank Generation, Preservation, and Reversal in the Analytic Hierarchy Decision Process," *Decision Sciences* 18 (1987): 157–177.

Winkler, R. L. "Decision Modeling and Rational Choice: AHP and Utility Theory," *Management Science* 36, no. 3 (March 1990): 247–248.

Chapter 15   Forecasting

Bowerman, B. L., and R. T. O'Connell. *Forecasting and Time Series: An Applied Approach,* 3d ed. Duxbury, 2000.

Box, G. E. P., G. M. Jenkins, and G. C. Reinsel. *Time Series Analysis: Forecasting and Control,* 3d ed. Prentice Hall, 1994.

Hanke, J. E., and A. G. Reitsch. *Business Forecasting,* 6th ed. Prentice Hall, 1998.

Makridakis, S. G., S. C. Wheelwright, and R. J. Hyndman. *Forecasting: Methods and Applications,* 3d ed. Wiley, 1997.

Wilson, J. H., and B. Keating. *Business Forecasting,* 3d ed. Irwin, 1998.

Chapter 16   Markov Processes

Bharucha-Reid, A. T. *Elements of the Theory of Markov Processes and Their Applications.* Dover, 1997.

Bhat, U. N. *Elements of Applied Stochastic Processes,* 2d ed. Wiley, 1984.

Filar, J. A., and K. Vrieze. *Competitive Markov Decision Processes.* Springer-Verlag, 1996.

Norris, J. *Markov Chains.* Cambridge, 1997.

Chapter 1

2. Define the problem; identify the alternatives; determine the criteria; evaluate the alternatives; choose an alternative.

4. A quantitative approach should be considered because the problem is large, complex, important, new, and repetitive.

6. Quicker to formulate, easier to solve, and/or more easily understood.

8. a. Max $10x + 5y$
   s.t.
   $$5x + 2y \leq 40$$
   $$x \geq 0, y \geq 0$$
   b. Controllable inputs: x and y
   Uncontrollable inputs: profit $(10, 5)$, labor-hours $(5, 2)$, and labor-hour availability (40)
   c. See Figure 1.8c.
   d. $x = 0, y = 20$; Profit $= \$100$ (solution by trial and error)
   e. Deterministic

10. a. Total units received $= x + y$
    b. Total cost $= 0.20x + 0.25y$
    c. $x + y = 5000$
    d. $x \leq 4000$ Kansas City
       $y \leq 3000$ Minneapolis
    e. Min $0.20x + 0.25y$
       s.t.
       $$x + \quad y = 5000$$
       $$x \quad\quad \leq 4000$$
       $$y \leq 3000$$
       $$x, y \geq 0$$

FIGURE 1.8c SOLUTION

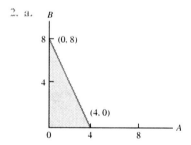

12. a. $TC = 1000 + 30x$
    b. $P = 40x - (1000 + 30x) = 10x - 1000$
    c. Break even when $P = 0$
       Thus, $10x - 1000 = 0$
       $$10x = 1000$$
       $$x = 100$$

14. a. 4706
    b. Loss of $12,000
    c. $23
    d. $11,800 profit

16. a. Max $6x + 4y$
    b. $50x + 30y \leq 80,000$
       $50x \quad\quad \leq 50,000$
       $$30y \leq 45,000$$

Chapter 2

1. Parts (a), (b), and (e) are acceptable linear programming relationships.
   Part (c) is not acceptable because of $-2x_2^2$.
   Part (d) is not acceptable because of $3\sqrt{x_1}$.
   Part (f) is not acceptable because of $1x_1x_2$.
   Parts (c), (d), and (f) could not be found in a linear programming model because they contain nonlinear terms.

2. a.

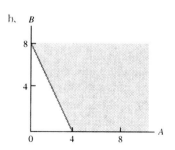

b.

c.

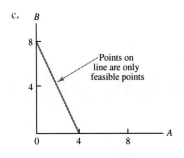

6. $7A + 10B = 420$
$6A + 4B = 420$
$-4A + 7B = 420$

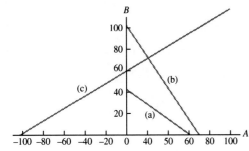

7.

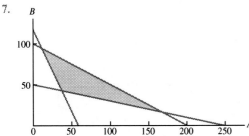

10.

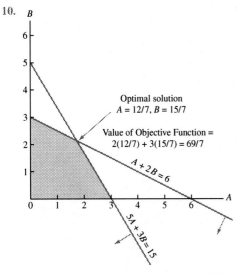

$$A + 2B = 6 \quad (1)$$
$$5A + 3B = 15 \quad (2)$$

Equation (1) times 5: $5A + 10B = 30 \quad (3)$
Equation (2) minus equation (3): $-7B = -15$
$B = 15/7$
From equation (1): $A = 6 - 2(15/7)$
$= 6 - 30/7 = 12/7$

12. a. $A = 3, B = 1.5$; value of optimal solution $= 13.5$
b. $A = 0, B = 3$; value of optimal solution $= 18$
c. Four: (0, 0), (4, 0), (3, 1.5), and (0.3)

13. a.

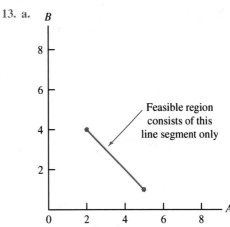

b. The extreme points are (5, 1) and (2, 4).
c.

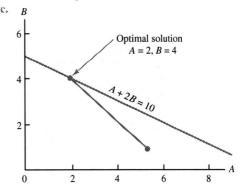

14. a. Let $F =$ number of tons of fuel additive
$S =$ number of tons of solvent base
Max $40F + 30S$
s.t.
$\frac{2}{5}F + \frac{1}{2}S \le 20$ Material 1
$\frac{1}{5}S \le 5$ Material 2
$\frac{3}{5}F + \frac{3}{10}S \le 21$ Material 3
$F, S \ge 0$
b. $F = 25, S = 20$
c. Material 2: 4 tons are used; 1 ton is unused.
d. No redundant constraints

16. a. $3S + 9D$
b. (0, 540)
c. 90, 150, 348, 0

17. Max $5A + 2B + 0s_1 + 0s_2 + 0s_3$
    s.t.
    $$1A - 2B + 1s_1 \qquad\qquad = 420$$
    $$2A + 3B - \qquad + 1s_2 \qquad = 610$$
    $$6A - 1B + \qquad\qquad + 1s_3 = 125$$
    $$A, B, s_1, s_2, s_3 \geq 0$$

18. b. $A = 18/7, B = 15/7$
    c. 0, 0, 4/7

20. b. $A = 3.43, B = 3.43$
    c. 2.86, 0, 1.43, 0

22. b.

Extreme Point	Coordinates	Profit ($)
1	(0, 0)	0
2	(1700, 0)	8500
3	(1400, 600)	9400
4	(800, 1200)	8800
5	(0, 1680)	6720

Extreme point 3 generates the highest profit.
c. $A = 1400, C = 600$
d. Cutting and dyeing constraint and the packaging constraint
e. $A = 800, C = 1200$; profit = $9200

24. a. Let R = number of units of regular model
    C = number of units of catcher's model

    Max $5R + 8C$
    $$1R + \tfrac{3}{2}C \leq 900 \quad \text{Cutting and sewing}$$
    $$\tfrac{1}{2}R + \tfrac{1}{3}C \leq 300 \quad \text{Finishing}$$
    $$\tfrac{1}{8}R + \tfrac{1}{4}C \leq 100 \quad \text{Packaging and shipping}$$
    $$R, C \geq 0$$

b.

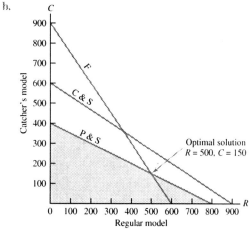

c. $5(500) + 8(150) = \$3700$
d. C & S $1(500) + \tfrac{3}{2}(150) = 725$
    F $\tfrac{1}{2}(500) + \tfrac{1}{3}(150) = 300$
    P & S $\tfrac{1}{8}(500) + \tfrac{1}{4}(150) = 100$

e.

Department	Capacity	Usage	Slack
Cutting and sewing	900	725	175 hours
Finishing	300	300	0 hours
Packaging and shipping	100	100	0 hours

26. a. Max $50N + 80R$
    s.t.
    $$N + \quad R = 1000$$
    $$N \qquad\quad \geq 250$$
    $$\qquad R \geq 250$$
    $$N - 2R \geq \quad 0$$
    $$N, R \geq 0$$
    b. $N = 666.67, R = 333.33$; Audience exposure = 60,000

28. a. Max $1W + 1.25M$
    s.t.
    $$5W + \quad 7M \leq 4480$$
    $$3W + \quad 1M \leq 2080$$
    $$2W + \quad 2M \leq 1600$$
    $$W, M \geq 0$$
    b. $W = 560, M = 240$; Profit = 860

30. a. Max $15E + 18C$
    s.t.
    $$40E + 25C \leq 50,000$$
    $$40E \qquad\quad \geq 15,000$$
    $$\qquad 25C \geq 10,000$$
    $$\qquad 25C \leq 25,000$$
    $$E, C \geq 0$$
    c. (375, 400); (1000, 400); (625, 1000); (375, 1000)
    d. $E = 625, C = 1000$
       Total return = $27,375

31.

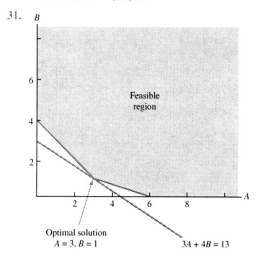

Objective function value = 13

32.

Extreme Points	Objective Function Value	Surplus Demand	Surplus Total Production	Slack Processing Time
(250, 100)	800	125	—	—
(125, 225)	925	—	—	125
(125, 350)	1300	—	125	—

34. a.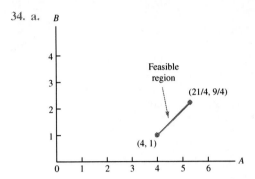

b. The two extreme points are
   $(A = 4, B = 1)$ and $(A = 21/4, B = 9/4)$

c. The optimal solution (see part (a)) is $A = 4, B = 1$.

35. a. Min $6A + 4B + 0s_1 + 0s_2 + 0s_3$
   s.t.

   $$2A + 1B - s_1 \qquad\qquad = 12$$
   $$1A + 1B \qquad - s_2 \qquad = 10$$
   $$1B \qquad\qquad + s_3 = 4$$
   $$A, B, s_1, s_2, s_3 \geq 0$$

b. The optimal solution is $A = 6, B = 4$.

c. $s_1 = 4, s_2 = 0, s_3 = 0$

36. a. Min $10{,}000T + 8{,}000P$
   s.t.

   $$T \qquad\qquad \geq 8$$
   $$P \geq 10$$
   $$T + \quad P \geq 25$$
   $$3T + \quad 2P \leq 84$$

c. (15, 10); (21.33, 10); (8, 30); (8, 17)

d. $T = 8, P = 17$
   Total cost = \$216,000

38. a. Min $7.50S + 9.00P$
   s.t.

   $$0.10S + 0.30P \geq 6$$
   $$0.06S + 0.12P \leq 3$$
   $$S + \quad P = 30$$
   $$S, P \geq 0$$

c. Optional solution is $S = 15, P = 15$.

d. No

e. Yes

40. $P_1 = 30, P_2 = 25$; Cost = \$55

42.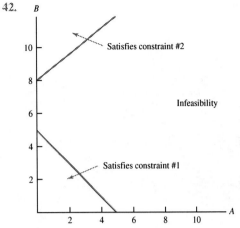

43.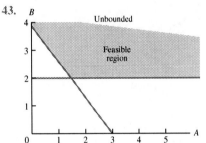

44. a. $A = {}^{30}/_{16}, B = {}^{30}/_{16}$; Value of optimal solution = ${}^{60}/_{16}$

b. $A = 0, B = 3$; Value of optimal solution = 6

46. a. 180, 20

b. Alternative optimal solutions

c. 120, 80

48. No feasible solution

50. $M = 65.45, R = 261.82$; Profit = \$45,818

52. $S = 384, O = 80$

54. a. Max $160M_1 + 345M_2$
   s.t.

   $$M_1 \qquad\qquad \leq 15$$
   $$M_2 \leq 10$$
   $$M_1 \qquad\qquad \geq 5$$
   $$M_2 \geq 5$$
   $$40M_1 + 50M_2 \leq 1000$$
   $$M_1, M_2 \geq 0$$

b. $M_1 = 12.5, M_2 = 10$

56. No, this could not make the problem infeasible. Changing an equality constraint to an inequality constraint can only make the feasible region larger, not smaller. No solutions have been eliminated and anything that was feasible before is still feasible.

58. The statement by the boss shows a fundamental misunderstanding of optimization models. If there were an optimal solution with 15 or less products, the model would find it,

because it is trying to minimize. If there is no solution with 15 or less, adding this constraint will make the model infeasible.

Chapter 3

1. a.

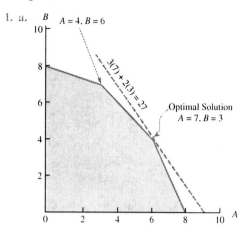

b. The same extreme point, $A = 7$ and $B = 3$, remains optimal; value of the objective function becomes $5(7) + 2(3) = 41$.

c. A new extreme point, $A = 4$ and $B = 6$, becomes optimal; value of the objective function becomes $3(4) + 4(6) = 36$.

d. The objective coefficient range for variable A is 2 to 6; the optimal solution, $A = 7$ and $B = 3$, does not change. The objective coefficient range for variable B is 1 to 3; re-solve the problem to find the new optimal solution.

2. a. The feasible region becomes larger with the new optimal solution of $A = 6.5$ and $B = 4.5$.

b. Value of the optimal solution to the revised problem is $3(6.5) + 2(4.5) = 28.5$; the one-unit increase in the right-hand side of constraint 1 improves the value of the optimal solution by $28.5 - 27 = 1.5$; therefore, the dual value for constraint 1 is 1.5.

c. The right-hand-side range for constraint 1 is 8 to 11.2; as long as the right-hand side stays within this range, the dual value of 1.5 is applicable.

d. The improvement in the value of the optimal solution will be 0.5 for every unit increase in the right-hand side of constraint 2 as long as the right-hand side is between 18 and 30.

4. a. $X = 2.5, Y = 2.5$
   b. -2
   c. 5 to 11
   d. -3 between 9 and 18

5. a. Regular glove = 500; Catcher's mitt = 150; Value = 3700

   b. The finishing, packaging, and shipping constraints are binding; there is no slack.

c. Cutting and sewing = 0
   Finishing = 3
   Packaging and shipping = 28
   Additional finishing time is worth $3 per unit, and additional packaging and shipping time is worth $28 per unit.

d. In the packaging and shipping department, each additional hour is worth $28.

6. a. 4 to 12
   3.33 to 10

   b. As long as the profit contribution for the regular glove is between $4.00 and $12.00, the current solution is optimal; as long as the profit contribution for the catcher's mitt stays between $3.33 and $10.00, the current solution is optimal; the optimal solution is not sensitive to small changes in the profit contributions for the gloves.

   c. The dual values for the resources are applicable over the following ranges:

Constraint	Right-Hand-Side Range
Cutting and sewing	725 to No upper limit
Finishing	133.33 to 400
Packaging and shipping	75 to 135

   d. Amount of increase = $(28)(20) = \$560$

8. a. More than $7.00
   b. More than $3.50
   c. None

10. a. $S = 4000, M = 10,000$; Total risk $= 62,000$
    b.

Variable	Objective Coefficient Range
S	3.75 to No upper limit
M	No lower limit to 6.4

    c. $5(4000) + 4(10,000) = \$60,000$
    d. $60,000/1,200,000 = 0.05$ or 5%
    e. 0.057 risk units
    f. $0.057(100) = 5.7\%$

12. a. $E = 80, S = 120, D = 0$
    Profit $= \$16,440$
    b. Fan motors and cooling coils
    c. Labor hours; 320 hours available
    d. Objective function coefficient range of optimality
       No lower limit to 159
    Because $150 is in this range, the optimal solution would not change.

13. a. Range of optimality
    E 47.5 to 75
    S 87 to 126
    D No lower limit to 159

b.

Model	Profit	Change	Allowable Increase/Decrease	%
E	$ 63	Increase $6(100)	$75 − $63 = $12	$\frac{6}{12}(100) = 50$
S	$ 95	Decrease $2	$95 − $87 = $8	$\frac{2}{8}(100) = 25$
D	$135	Increase $4	$159 − $135 = $24	$\frac{4}{24}(100) = \underline{17}$
				92

Because changes are 92% of allowable changes, the optimal solution of $E = 80$, $S = 120$, $D = 0$ will not change.
The change in total profit will be

$$
\begin{array}{lll}
E & 80 \text{ units @ } +\$6 = & \$480 \\
S & 120 \text{ units @ } -\$2 = & \underline{-240} \\
& & \$240
\end{array}
$$

∴ Profit $= \$16,440 + \$240 = \$16,680$

c. Range of feasibility
   Constraint 1   160 to 280
   Constraint 2   200 to 400
   Constraint 3   2080 to No upper limit

d. Yes, Fan motors $= 200 + 100 = 300$ is outside the range of feasibility; the dual value will change.

14. a. Manufacture 100 cases of A and 60 cases of B, and purchase 90 cases of B; Total cost $= \$2170$

b. Demand for A, demand for B, assembly time

c. $-12.25, -9.0, 0, 0.375$

d. Assembly time constraint

16. a. 100 suits, 150 sport coats
   Profit $= \$40,900$
   40 hours of cutting overtime

b. Optimal solution will not change.

c. Consider ordering additional material $34.50 is the maximum price.

d. Profit will improve by $875.

18. a. The linear programming model is as follows:
   Min $30AN + 50AO + 25BN + 40BO$
   s.t.

$$
\begin{array}{lrrr}
AN + & AO & & \geq 50,000 \\
& & BN + & BO \geq 70,000 \\
AN & + & BN & \leq 80,000 \\
& AO & + & BO \leq 60,000 \\
\end{array}
$$
$$AN, AO, BN, BO \geq 0$$

b. Optimal solution

	New Line	Old Line
Model A	50,000	0
Model B	30,000	40,000
Total cost: $3,850,000		

c. The first three constraints are binding.

d. Because the dual value is negative, increasing the right-hand side of constraint 3 will *decrease (improve)* the solution; thus, an increase in capacity for the new production line is desirable.

e. Because constraint 4 is not a binding constraint, any increase in the production line capacity of the old production line will have no effect on the optimal solution; thus, increasing the capacity of the old production line results in no benefit.

f. The reduced cost for model A made on the old production line is 5; thus, the cost would have to decrease by at least $5 before any units of model A would be produced on the old production line.

g. The right-hand-side range for constraint 2 shows a lower limit of 30,000; thus, if the minimum production requirement is reduced 10,000 units to 60,000, the dual value of 40 is applicable; thus, total cost would decrease by $10,000(40) = \$400,000$.

20. a. Max $0.07H + 0.12P + 0.09A$
   s.t.

$$
\begin{array}{rrrl}
H + & P + & A & = 1,000,000 \\
0.6H - & 0.4P - & 0.4A & \geq 0 \\
& P - & 0.6A & \leq 0 \\
\end{array}
$$
$$H, P, A \geq 0$$

b. $H = \$400,000$, $P = \$225,000$, $A = \$375,000$
   Total annual return $= \$88,750$
   Annual percentage return $= 8.875\%$

c. No change

d. Increase of $890

e. Increase of $312.50, or 0.031%

22. a. Min $30L + 25D + 18S$
   s.t.

$$
\begin{array}{rrrl}
L + & D + & S & = 100 \\
0.6L - & 0.4D & & \geq 0 \\
-0.15L - & 0.15D + & 0.85S & \geq 0 \\
-0.25L - & 0.25D + & S & \leq 0 \\
L & & & \leq 50 \\
\end{array}
$$
$$L, D, S \geq 0$$

b. $L = 48$, $D = 72$, $S = 30$
   Total cost $= \$3780$

c. No change

d. No change

24. a. 333.3, 0, 833.3; Risk $= 14,666.7$; Return $= 18,000$ or 9%

b. 1000, 0, 0, 2500; Risk $= 18,000$; Return $= 22,000$ or 11%

c. $4000

26. a. Let M_1 = units of component 1 manufactured
   M_2 = units of component 2 manufactured
   M_3 = units of component 3 manufactured
   P_1 = units of component 1 purchased
   P_2 = units of component 2 purchased
   P_3 = units of component 3 purchased

Min $4.50M_1 + 5.00M_2 + 2.75M_3 + 6.50P_1 + 8.80P_2 + 7.00P_3$
s.t.

$2M_1 + 3M_2 + 4M_3$	$\leq 21,600$	Production
$1M_1 + 1.5M_2 + 3M_3$	$\leq 15,000$	Assembly
$1.5M_1 + 2M_2 + 5M_3$	$\leq 18,000$	Testing & Packaging
$1M_1 + 1P_1$	$= 6,000$	Component 1
$1M_2 + 1P_2$	$= 4,000$	Component 2
$1M_3 + 1P_3$	$= 3,500$	Component 3

$M_1, M_2, M_3, P_1, P_2, P_3 \geq 0$

b.

Source	Component 1	Component 2	Component 3
Manufacture	2000	4000	1400
Purchase	4000		2100

Total cost = $73,550

c. Production: $54.36 per hour
   Testing & Packaging: $7.50 per hour
d. Dual values = $7.969; so it will cost Benson $7.969 to add a unit of component 2.

28. b. $G = 120,000$; $S = 30,000$; $M = 150,000$
    c. 0.15 to 0.60; No lower limit to 0.122; 0.02 to 0.20
    d. 4668
    e. $G = 48,000$; $S = 192,000$; $M = 60,000$
    f. The client's risk index and the amount of funds available

30. a. $L = 3, N = 7, W = 5, S = 5$
    b. Each additional minute of broadcast time increases cost by $100.
    c. If local coverage is increased by 1 minute, total cost will increase by $100.
    d. If the time devoted to local and national news is increased by 1 minute, total cost will increase by $100.
    e. Increasing the sports by 1 minute will have no effect because the dual value is 0.

32. a. Let P_1 = number of PT-100 battery packs produced at the Philippines plant
    P_2 = number of PT-200 battery packs produced at the Philippines plant
    P_3 = number of PT-300 battery packs produced at the Philippines plant
    M_1 = number of PT-100 battery packs produced at the Mexico plant
    M_2 = number of PT-200 battery packs produced at the Mexico plant
    M_3 = number of PT-300 battery packs produced at the Mexico plant

Min $1.13P_1 + 1.16P_2 + 1.52P_3 + 1.08M_1 + 1.16M_2 + 1.25M_3$
s.t.

$P_1 + M_1$			$= 200,000$
$P_2 + M_2$			$= 100,000$
$P_3 +$			$M_3 = 150,000$
$P_1 + P_2$			$\leq 175,000$
$M_1 + M_2$			$\leq 160,000$
P_3			$\leq 75,000$
			$M_3 \leq 100,000$

$P_1, P_2, P_3, M_1, M_2, M_3 \geq 0$

b. The optimal solution is as follows:

	Philippines	Mexico
PT-100	40,000	160,000
PT-200	100,000	0
PT-300	50,000	100,000

Total production and transportation cost is $535,000.
c. The range of optimality for the objective function coefficient for P_1 shows a lower limit of $1.08; thus, the production and/or shipping cost would have to decrease by at least 5 cents per unit.
d. The range of optimality for the objective function coefficient for M_1 shows a lower limit of $1.11; thus, the production and/or shipping cost would have to decrease by at least 5 cents per unit.

Chapter 4

1. a. Let T = number of television advertisements
   R = number of radio advertisements
   N = number of newspaper advertisements

Max $100,000T + 18,000R + 40,000N$
s.t.

$2000T +$	$300R +$	$600N \leq 18,200$	Budget
T		≤ 10	Max TV
	R	≤ 20	Max radio
		$N \leq 10$	Max news
$-0.5T +$	$0.5R -$	$0.5N \leq 0$	Max 50% radio
$0.9T -$	$0.1R -$	$0.1N \geq 0$	Min 10% TV

$T, R, N \geq 0$

		Budget $
Solution:	$T = 4$	$ 8000
	$R = 14$	4200
	$N = 10$	6000
		$18,200

Audience = 1,052,000

b. The dual value for the budget constraint is 51.30, meaning a $100 increase in the budget should provide an increase in audience coverage of approximately 5130; the right-hand-side range for the budget constraint will show that this interpretation is correct.

2. a. $x_1 = 77.89$, $x_2 = 63.16$, $3284.21
   b. Department A $15.79; Department B $47.37
   c. $x_1 = 87.21$, $x_2 = 65.12$, $3341.34
      Department A 10 hours; Department B 3.2 hours

4. a. $x_1 = 500$, $x_2 = 300$, $x_3 = 200$, $550
   b. $0.55
   c. Aroma, 75; Taste 84.4
   d. $-$0.60

6. 50 units of product 1; 0 units of product 2; 300 hours department A; 600 hours department B

8. Schedule 19 officers as follows:
3 begin at 8:00 A.M.; 3 begin at noon; 7 begin at 4:00 P.M.;
4 begin at midnight, 2 begin at 4:00 A.M.

9. a. Decision variables A, P, M, H, and G represent the fraction or proportion of the total investment in each alternative.

Max $0.073A + 0.103P + 0.064M + 0.075H + 0.045G$
s.t.

$$
\begin{array}{rrrrrl}
A + & P + & M + & H + & G & = 1 \\
0.5A + & 0.5P - & 0.5M - & 0.5H & & \leq 0 \\
-0.5A - & 0.5P + & 0.5M + & 0.5H & & \leq 0 \\
 & & -0.25M - & 0.25H + & G & \geq 0 \\
-0.6A + & 0.4P & & & & \leq 0 \\
\end{array}
$$
$A, P, M, H, G \geq 0$

Objective function = 0.079; $A = 0.178$; $P = 0.267$;
$M = 0.000$; $H = 0.444$; $G = 0.111$

b. Multiplying A, P, M, H, and G by the $100,000 invested provides the following:

Atlantic Oil	$ 17,800
Pacific Oil	26,700
Huber Steel	44,400
Government bonds	11,100
	$100,000

c. 0.079($100,000) = $7900
d. The marginal rate of return is 0.079.

10. a. 40.9%, 14.5%, 14.5%, 30.0%
Annual return = 5.4%
b. 0.0%, 36.0%, 36.0%, 28.0%
Annual return = 2.52%
c. 75.0%, 0.0%, 15.0%, 10.0%
Annual return = 8.2%
d. Yes

12.

Week	Buy	Sell	Store
1	80,000	0	100,000
2	0	0	100,000
3	0	100,000	0
4	25,000	0	25,000

14. b.

Quarter	Production	Ending Inventory
1	4000	2100
2	3000	1100
3	2000	100
4	1900	500

15. Let x_{11} = gallons of crude 1 used to produce regular
x_{12} = gallons of crude 1 used to produce high octane
x_{21} = gallons of crude 2 used to produce regular
x_{22} = gallons of crude 2 used to produce high octane

Min $0.10x_{11} + 0.10x_{12} + 0.15x_{21} + 0.15x_{22}$
s.t.

Each gallon of regular must have at least 40% A.

$x_{11} + x_{21}$ = amount of regular produced
$0.4(x_{11} + x_{21})$ = amount of A required for regular
$0.2x_{11} + 0.50x_{21}$ = amount of A in $(x_{11} + x_{21})$ gallons of regular gas
$\therefore 0.2x_{11} + 0.50x_{21} \geq 0.4x_{11} + 0.40x_{21}$
$\therefore -0.2x_{11} + 0.10x_{21} \geq 0$

Each gallon of high octane can have at most 50% B.

$x_{12} + x_{22}$ = amount high octane
$0.5(x_{12} + x_{22})$ = amount of B required for high octane
$0.60x_{12} + 0.30x_{22}$ = amount of B in $(x_{12} + x_{22})$ gallons of high octane
$\therefore 0.60x_{12} + 0.30x_{22} \leq 0.5x_{12} + 0.5x_{22}$
$\therefore 0.1x_{12} - 0.2x_{22} \leq 0$

$$x_{11} + x_{21} \geq 800,000$$
$$x_{12} + x_{22} \geq 500,000$$
$$x_{11}, x_{12}, x_{21}, x_{22} \geq 0$$

Optimal solution: $x_{11} = 266,667, x_{12} = 333,333, x_{21} = 533,333,$
$x_{22} = 166,667$
Cost = $165,000

16. x_i = number of 10-inch rolls processed by cutting alternative i
a. $x_1 = 0, x_2 = 125, x_3 = 500, x_4 = 1500, x_5 = 0, x_6 = 0,$
$x_7 = 0$; 2125 rolls with waste of 750 inches
b. 2500 rolls with no waste; however, $1\frac{1}{2}$-inch size is overproduced by 3000 units

18. a. 5 Super, 2 Regular, and 3 Econo-Tankers
Total cost $583,000; monthly operating cost $4650

19. a. Let x_{11} = amount of men's model in month 1
x_{21} = amount of women's model in month 1
x_{12} = amount of men's model in month 2
x_{22} = amount of women's model in month 2
s_{11} = inventory of men's model at end of month 1
s_{21} = inventory of women's model at end of month 1
s_{12} = inventory of men's model at end of month 2
s_{22} = inventory of women's model at end of month 2

Min $120x_{11} + 90x_{21} + 120x_{12} + 90x_{22} + 2.4s_{11} + 1.8s_{21} + 2.4s_{12} + 1.8s_{22}$
s.t.

$$
\left.
\begin{array}{rrrl}
x_{11} - & s_{11} & & = 130 \\
x_{21} - & s_{21} & & = 95 \\
s_{11} + & x_{12} - & s_{12} & = 200 \\
s_{21} + & x_{22} - & s_{22} & = 150 \\
\end{array}
\right\} \text{Satisfy demand}
$$

$$
\left.
\begin{array}{l}
s_{12} \geq 25 \\
s_{22} \geq 25 \\
\end{array}
\right\} \text{Ending inventory requirement}
$$

Labor-hours: Men's 2.0 + 1.5 = 3.5
Women's 1.6 + 1.0 = 2.6

$$
\left.
\begin{array}{rrl}
3.5x_{11} + 2.6x_{21} & & \geq 900 \\
3.5x_{11} + 2.6x_{21} & & \leq 1100 \\
3.5x_{11} + 2.6x_{21} - 3.5x_{12} - 2.6x_{22} \leq & 100 \\
-3.5x_{11} - 2.6x_{21} + 3.5x_{12} + 2.6x_{22} \leq & 100 \\
\end{array}
\right\} \text{Labor smoothing}
$$

$x_{11}, x_{12}, x_{21}, x_{22}, s_{11}, s_{12}, s_{21}, s_{22} \geq 0$

Solution: $x_{11} = 193$; $x_{21} = 95$; $x_{12} = 162$; $x_{22} = 175$
Total cost = $67,156
Inventory levels: $s_{11} = 63$; $s_{12} = 25$; $s_{21} = 0$; $s_{22} = 25$
Labor levels: Previous   1000 hours
           Month 1   922.25 hours
           Month 2   1022.25 hours

b. To accommodate the new policy, the right-hand sides of the four labor-smoothing constraints must be changed to 950, 1050, 50, and 50, respectively; the new total cost is $67,175.

20. Produce 10,250 units in March, 10,250 units in April, and 12,000 units in May.

22. b. 5, 515, 887 sq. in. of waste
Machine 3: 492 minutes

24. Investment strategy: 45.8% of A and 100% of B
Objective function = $4340.40
Savings/Loan schedule

	Period			
	1	**2**	**3**	**4**
Savings	242.11	—	—	341.04
Funds from loan	—	200.00	127.58	—

Chapter 5

2. b. $E = 0.924$
$wa = 0.074$
$wc = 0.436$
$we = 0.489$
c. D is relatively inefficient.
Composite requires 92.4 of D's resources.
d. 34.37 patient days (65 or older)
41.99 patient days (under 65)
e. Hospitals A, C, and E

4. b. $E = 0.960$
$wb = 0.074$
$wc = 0.000$
$wj = 0.436$
$wn = 0.489$
$ws = 0.000$
c. Yes; $E = 0.960$
d. More: $220 profit per week
Less: Hours of Operation 4.4 hours
       FTE Staff 2.6
       Supply Expense $185.61
d. Bardstown, Jeffersonville, and New Albany

6. a. 19, 18, 12, 18

b. PCQ = 8   PMQ = 0   POQ = 27
PCY = 4   PMY = 1   POY = 2
NCQ = 6   NMQ = 23   NOQ = 2
NCY = 4   NMY = 2   NOY = 1
CMQ = 37   CMY = 2
COQ = 11   COY = 3
c. PCQ = 8   PMQ = 1   POQ = 3
PCY = 4   PMY = 1   POY = 2
NCQ = 6   NMQ = 3   NOQ = 2
NCY = 4   NMY = 2   NOY = 1
CMQ = 3   CMY = 2
COQ = 7   COY = 3

8. b. 65.7% small-cap growth fund
34.3% of the portfolio in a small-cap value
Expected return = 18.5%
c. 10% foreign stock
50.8% small-cap growth fund
39.2% of the portfolio in a small-cap value
Expected return = 17.178%

10.

		Player B			
		b_1	b_2	b_3	Minimum
Player A	a_1	8	5	7	(5)
	a_2	2	4	10	4
	Maximum	8	(5)	7	Maximum

Minimum

The game has a pure strategy: Player A strategy a_1; Player B strategy b_2; and value of game = 5.

12. 2.5, 2.5, 1.5
Strategy a_1 or a_2
Expected payoff = 2.5

14. Pure strategies a_4 and b_3
Value = 10

16. a. The maximum of the row minimums is not equal to the minimum of the column maximums, so a mixed strategy exists.
Linear program for Player A:
Max   GAINA
s.t.   Player B strategy
      $5PA2 + 2PA3 - GAINA \geq 0$ (red chip)
   $-PA1 + 4PA2 + 3PA3 - GAINA \geq 0$ (white chip)
     $2PA1 - 3PA2 - 4PA3 - GAINA \geq 0$ (blue chip)
     $PA1 + PA2 + PA3 = 1$
     $PA1, PA2, PA3 \geq 0$
Player A: $P(\text{red}) = 0.7$, $P(\text{white}) = 0.3$, $P(\text{blue}) = 0.0$
From dual values:
Player B: $P(\text{red}) = 0.0$, $P(\text{white}) = 0.5$, $P(\text{blue}) = 0.5$
b. The value of the game is a 50-cent expected gain for Player A.
c. Player A

16. Company A: 0.0, 0.0, 0.8, 0.2
    Company B: 0.4, 0.6, 0.0, 0.0
    Expected gain for A = 2.8

Chapter 6

1.

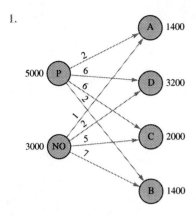

2. a. Let x_{11} = amount shipped from Jefferson City to Des Moines

   x_{12} = amount shipped from Jefferson City to Kansas City

   .
   .
   .

   x_{23} = amount shipped from Omaha to St. Louis

   Min $14x_{11} + 9x_{12} + 7x_{13} + 8x_{21} + 10x_{22} + 5x_{23}$
   s.t.

   $$
   \begin{aligned}
   x_{11} + x_{12} + x_{13} &\le 30 \\
   x_{21} + x_{22} + x_{23} &\le 20 \\
   x_{11} \quad\quad + x_{21} &= 25 \\
   x_{12} \quad\quad + x_{22} &= 15 \\
   x_{13} \quad\quad + x_{23} &= 10 \\
   \end{aligned}
   $$

   $x_{11}, x_{12}, x_{13}, x_{21}, x_{22}, x_{23} \ge 0$

b.

Optimal Solution	Amount	Cost
Jefferson City–Des Moines	5	70
Jefferson City–Kansas City	15	135
Jefferson City–St. Louis	10	70
Omaha–Des Moines	20	160
	Total	435

4. b.

Seattle–Denver	4000	Seattle–Los Angeles	5000
Columbus–Mobile	4000	New York–Pittsburgh	3000
New York–Mobile	1000	New York–Los Angeles	1000
New York–Washington	3000		

Cost = $150,000

c.

Seattle–Denver	4000	Seattle–Los Angeles	5000
Columbus–Mobile	5000	New York–Pittsburgh	4000
New York–Los Angeles	1000	New York–Washington	3000

Cost actually decreases by $9000

6. The network model, the linear programming formulation, and the optimal solution are shown. Note that the third constraint corresponds to the dummy origin; the variables x_{31}, x_{32}, x_{33}, and x_{34} are the amounts shipped out of the dummy origin and do not appear in the objective function because they are given a coefficient of zero.

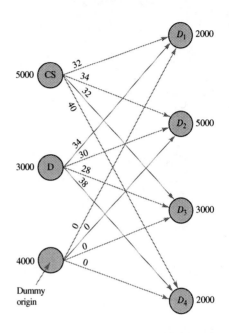

Max $32x_{11} + 34x_{12} + 32x_{13} + 40x_{14} + 34x_{21} + 30x_{22} + 28x_{23} + 38x_{24}$
s.t.

$$
\begin{aligned}
x_{11} + x_{12} + x_{13} + x_{14} &\le 5000 \\
x_{21} + x_{22} + x_{23} + x_{24} &\le 3000 \\
x_{31} + x_{32} + x_{33} + x_{34} &\le 4000 \\
x_{11} \quad + x_{21} \quad\quad + x_{31} &= 2000 \\
x_{12} \quad + x_{22} \quad\quad + x_{32} &= 5000 \\
x_{13} \quad + x_{23} \quad\quad + x_{33} &= 3000 \\
x_{14} \quad + x_{24} \quad\quad + x_{34} &= 2000 \\
\end{aligned}
$$

$x_{ij} \ge 0$ for all i, j

Optimal Solution	Units	Cost
Clifton Springs-D_2	4,000	$136,000
Clifton Springs-D_4	1,000	40,000
Danville-D_1	2,000	68,000
Danville-D_4	1,000	38,000
	Total	$282,000

Customer 2 demand has a shortfall of 1000; customer 3 demand of 3000 is not satisfied.

8. 1–A 300; 1–C 1200; 2–A 1200; 3–A 500; 3–B 500

9. a.

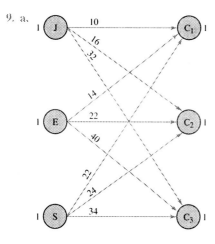

b.

Min $10x_{12} + 16x_{12} + 32x_{13} + 14x_{21} + 22x_{22} + 40x_{23} + 22x_{31} + 24x_{32} + 34x_{33}$

s.t.

$$x_{11} + x_{12} + x_{13} \leq 1$$
$$x_{21} + x_{22} + x_{23} \leq 1$$
$$x_{31} + x_{32} + x_{33} \leq 1$$
$$x_{11} + x_{21} + x_{31} = 1$$
$$x_{12} + x_{22} + x_{32} = 1$$
$$x_{13} + x_{23} + x_{33} = 1$$
$$x_{ij} \geq 0 \quad \text{for all } i, j$$

Solution $x_{12} = 1$, $x_{21} = 1$, $x_{33} = 1$; total completion time = 64

10. b.

Green:	Job 1	$ 26
Brown:	Job 2	34
Red:	Job 3	38
Blue:	Job 4	39
White:	Job 5	25
	Total Cost	$162

12. a. Plano: Kansas City and Dallas
   Flagstaff: Los Angeles
   Springfield: Chicago, Columbus, and Atlanta
   Boulder: Newark and Denver
   Cost = $216,000
   b. Nashville
   c. Columbus is switched from Springfield to Nashville.
   Cost = $227,000

14. A to MS, B to Ph.D., C to MBA, D to undergrad
   Maximum total rating = 13.3

16. a.

	Supplier					
Division	1	2	3	4	5	6
1	614	660	534	680	590	630
2	603	639	702	693	693	630
3	865	830	775	850	900	930
4	532	553	511	581	595	553
5	720	648	684	693	657	747

b. Optimal solution:

Supplier 1–Division 2	$ 603
Supplier 2–Division 5	648
Supplier 3–Division 3	775
Supplier 5–Division 1	590
Supplier 6–Division 4	553
Total	$3169

17. a.

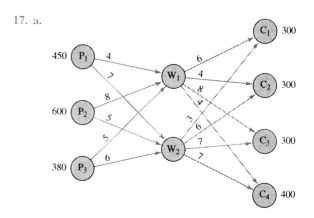

b.

Min $4x_{14} + 7x_{15} + 8x_{24} + 5x_{25} + 5x_{34} + 6x_{35} + 6x_{46} + 4x_{47} + 8x_{48} + 4x_{49} + 3x_{56} + 6x_{57} + 7x_{58} + 7x_{59}$

s.t.

$$x_{14} + x_{15} \leq 450$$
$$x_{24} + x_{25} \leq 600$$
$$x_{34} + x_{35} \leq 380$$
$$-x_{14} - x_{24} - x_{34} + x_{46} + x_{47} + x_{48} + x_{49} = 0$$
$$-x_{15} - x_{25} - x_{35} + x_{56} + x_{57} + x_{58} + x_{59} = 0$$
$$x_{46} + x_{56} = 300$$
$$x_{47} + x_{57} = 300$$
$$x_{48} + x_{58} = 300$$
$$x_{49} + x_{59} = 400$$

c.

	Warehouse	
Plant	1	2
1	450	—
2	—	600
3	250	—

Total cost = $11,850

	Customer			
Warehouse	1	2	3	4
1	—	300	—	400
2	300	—	300	—

18. c. $x_{14} = 320$, $x_{25} = 600$, $x_{47} = 300$, $x_{49} = 20$, $x_{56} = 300$, $x_{58} = 300$, $x_{39} = 380$
   Cost = $11,220

20.

Optimal Solution	Units Shipped	Cost
Muncie–Cincinnati	1	6
Cincinnati–Concord	3	84
Brazil–Louisville	6	18
Louisville–Macon	2	88
Louisville–Greenwood	4	136
Xenia–Cincinnati	5	15
Cincinnati–Chatham	3	72
	Total	419

Two rail cars must be held at Muncie until a buyer is found.

22. b. $x_{25} = 8$, $x_{31} = 8$, $x_{42} = 3$, $x_{53} = 5$, $x_{56} = 5$, $x_{74} = 6$, $x_{56} = 5$
Total cost = \$917

23. Min $7x_{12} + 9x_{13} + 18x_{14} + 3x_{23} + 5x_{25} + 3x_{32} + 4x_{35}$
$+ 3x_{46} + 5x_{52} + 4x_{53} + 2x_{56} + 6x_{57} + 2x_{65} + 3x_{67}$
s.t.

	Flow Out	Flow In		
Node 1	$x_{12} + x_{13} + x_{14}$		=	1
Node 2	$x_{23} + x_{25}$	$-x_{12} - x_{32} - x_{52}$	=	0
Node 3	$x_{32} + x_{35}$	$-x_{13} - x_{23} - x_{53}$	=	0
Node 4	x_{46}	$-x_{14}$	=	0
Node 5	$x_{52} + x_{53} + x_{56} + x_{57}$	$-x_{25} - x_{35} - x_{65}$	=	0
Node 6	$x_{65} + x_{67}$	$-x_{46} - x_{56}$	=	0
Node 7		$+x_{57} + x_{67}$	=	1

$x_{ij} \geq 0$ for all i and j
Optimal solution: $x_{12} = 1$, $x_{25} = 1$, $x_{56} = 1$, and $x_{67} = 1$
Shortest route 1–2–5–6–7
Length = 17

24. Route: 1–2–4–6
Travel time = 63 minutes

26. Route: 1–4–7–6
Distance = 40 miles

28. Replace years 2, 3, and 4
Total cost = \$2500

29. The capacitated transshipment problem to solve is given:

Max x_{61}
s.t.

$x_{12} + x_{13} + x_{14} - x_{61} = 0$
$x_{24} + x_{25} - x_{12} - x_{42} = 0$
$x_{34} + x_{36} - x_{13} - x_{43} = 0$
$x_{42} + x_{43} + x_{45} + x_{46} - x_{14} - x_{24} - x_{34} - x_{54} = 0$
$x_{54} + x_{56} - x_{25} - x_{45} = 0$
$x_{61} - x_{36} + x_{46} - x_{56} = 0$
$x_{12} \leq 2 \quad x_{13} \leq 6 \quad x_{14} \leq 3$
$x_{24} \leq 1 \quad x_{25} \leq 4$
$x_{34} \leq 3 \quad x_{36} \leq 2$
$x_{42} \leq 1 \quad x_{43} \leq 3 \quad x_{45} \leq 1 \quad x_{46} \leq 3$
$x_{54} \leq 1 \quad x_{56} \leq 6$
$x_{ij} \geq 0$ for all i, j

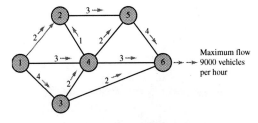

Maximum flow
9000 vehicles
per hour

30. Maximal flow = 11,000 vehicles per hour

32. a. 10 hours; 10,000 gallons per hour
b. 11.1 hours; flow reduced to 9000 gallons per hour

34. Maximal flow = 23 gallons/minute
The total flow from 3 to 5 must be 5 gallons/minute.

36. c. Regular month 1: 275; overtime month 1: 25; inventory
at end of month 1: 150
Regular month 2: 200; overtime month 2: 50; inventory
at end of month 2: 150
Regular month 3: 100; overtime month 3: 50; inventory
at end of month 3: 0

Chapter 7

2. a.

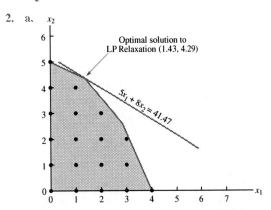

b. The optimal solution to the LP Relaxation is given by
$x_1 = 1.43$, $x_2 = 4.29$, with an objective function value
of 41.47. Rounding down gives the feasible integer
solution $x_1 = 1$, $x_2 = 4$; its value is 37.

c.

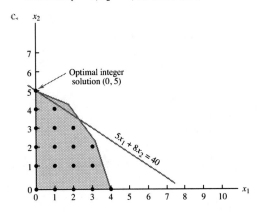

The optimal solution is given by $x_1 = 0$, $x_2 = 5$; its value is 40. It is not the same solution as found by rounding down; it provides a 3-unit increase in the value of the objective function.

4. a. $x_1 = 3.67$, $x_2 = 0$; Value = 36.7
       Rounded: $x_1 = 3$, $x_2 = 0$; Value = 30
       Lower bound = 30; Upper bound = 36.7
    b. $x_1 = 3$, $x_2 = 2$; Value = 36
    c. Alternative optimal solutions: $x_1 = 0$, $x_2 = 5$
       $x_1 = 2$, $x_2 = 4$

5. a. The feasible mixed-integer solutions are indicated by the boldface vertical lines in the graph.

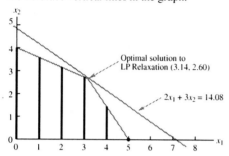

Optimal solution to
LP Relaxation (3.14, 2.60)

$2x_1 + 3x_2 = 14.08$

b. The optimal solution to the LP Relaxation is given by $x_1 = 3.14$, $x_2 = 2.60$; its value is 14.08.
    Rounding down the value of x_1 to find a feasible mixed-integer solution yields $x_1 = 3$, $x_2 = 2.60$ with a value of 13.8; this solution is clearly not optimal; with $x_1 = 3$, x_2 can be made larger without violating the constraints.
c. The optimal solution to the MILP is given by $x_1 = 3$, $x_2 = 2.67$; its value is 14, as shown in the following figure:

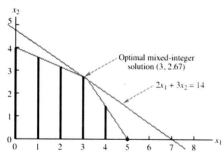

Optimal mixed-integer
solution (3, 2.67)

$2x_1 + 3x_2 = 14$

6. b. $x_1 = 1.96$, $x_2 = 5.48$; Value = 7.44
       Rounded: $x_1 = 1.96$, $x_2 = 5$; Value = 6.96
       Lower bound = 6.96; Upper bound = 7.44
    c. $x_1 = 1.29$, $x_2 = 6$; Value = 7.29

7. a. $x_1 + x_3 + x_5 + x_6 = 2$
    b. $x_3 - x_5 = 0$
    c. $x_1 + x_4 = 1$
    d. $x_4 \leq x_1$
       $x_4 \leq x_3$
    e. $x_4 \leq x_1$
       $x_4 \leq x_3$
       $x_4 \geq x_1 + x_3 - 1$

8. a. $x_3 = 1$, $x_4 = 1$, $x_6 = 1$; Value = 17,500
    b. Add $x_1 + x_2 \leq 1$
    c. Add $x_3 - x_4 = 0$

10. b. Choose locations B and E.

12. a. $P \leq 15 + 15Y_P$
        $D \leq 15 + 15Y_D$
        $J \leq 15 + 15Y_J$
        $Y_P + Y_D + Y_J \leq 1$
    b. $P = 15$, $D = 15$, $J = 30$
        $Y_P = 0$, $Y_D = 0$, $Y_J = 1$; Value = 50

13. a. Add the following multiple-choice constraint to the problem:
        $y_1 + y_2 = 1$
        New optimal solution: $y_1 = 1$, $y_3 = 1$, $x_{12} = 10$, $x_{31} = 30$, $x_{52} = 10$, $x_{53} = 20$
        Value = 940
    b. Because one plant is already located in St. Louis, it is only necessary to add the following constraint to the model:
        $y_3 = y_4 \leq 1$
        New optimal solution: $y_4 = 1$, $x_{42} = 20$, $x_{43} = 20$, $x_{51} = 30$
        Value = 860

14. b. Modernize plants 1 and 3 or plants 4 and 5.
    d. Modernize plants 1 and 3.

16. b. Use all part-time employees.
        Bring on as follows: 9:00 A.M.–6, 11:00 A.M.–2, 12:00 noon–6, 1:00 P.M.–1, 3:00 P.M.–6
        Cost = \$672
    c. Same as in part (b)
    d. New solution is to bring on 1 full-time employee at 9:00 A.M., 4 more at 11:00 A.M., and part-time employees as follows:
        9:00 A.M.–5, 12:00 noon–5, and 3:00 P.M.–2

18. a. 52, 49, 36, 83, 39, 70, 79, 59
    b. Thick crust, cheese blend, chunky sauce, medium sausage: Six of eight consumers will prefer this pizza (75%).

20. a. New objective function: Min $25x_1 + 40x_2 + 40x_3 + 40x_4 + 25x_5$
    b. $x_4 = x_5 = 1$; modernize the Ohio and California plants.
    c. Add the constraint $x_2 + x_3 = 1$.
    d. $x_1 = x_3 = 1$

22. $x_1 + x_2 + x_3 = 3y_1 + 5y_2 + 7y_3$
    $y_1 + y_2 + y_3 = 1$

24. a. $x_{111}, x_{112}, x_{121}$
    b. $x_{111} + x_{112} + x_{121} \leq 1$
    c. $x_{531} + x_{532} + x_{533} + x_{541} + x_{542} + x_{543} + x_{551} + x_{552} + x_{561} \leq 1$
    d. Only two screens are available.
    e. $x_{222} + x_{231} + x_{422} + x_{431} + x_{531} + x_{531} + x_{532} + x_{533} + x_{631} + x_{632} + x_{633} \leq 2$

Chapter 8

2. a. $X = 4.32$ and $Y = 0.92$, for an optimal solution value of 4.84.

    b. The dual value on the constraint $X + 4Y \leq 8$ is 0.88, which is the decrease in the optimal objective function value if we increase the right-hand-side from 8 to 9.

    c. The new optimal objective function value is 4.0, so the actual decrease is only 0.84 rather than 0.88.

4. a. $q_1 = 2150$
    $q_2 = 100$
    Gross profit = \$1,235,000

    b. $G = -1.5p_1^2 - 0.5p_2^2 + p_1p_2 + 2000p_1 + 3450p_2 - 11,465,000$

    c. $p_1 = \$2725$ and $p_2 = \$6175$; $q_1 = 1185$ and $q_2 = 230$; $G = \$1,911,875$

    d. Max $p_1q_1 + p_2q_2 - c_1 - c_2$
    s.t.
    $c_1 = 10000 + 1500q_1$
    $c_2 = 30000 + 4000q_2$
    $q_1 = 950 - 1.5p_1 + 0.7p_2$
    $q_2 = 2500 + 0.3p_1 - 0.5p_2$

5. a. If \$1000 is spent on radio and \$1000 is spent on direct mail, simply substitute those values into the sales function:
    $$S = -2R^2 - 10M^2 - 8RM + 18R + 34M$$
    $$= -2(2^2) - 10(1^2) - 8(2)(1) + 18(2) + 34(1)$$
    $$= 18$$
    Sales = \$18,000

    b. Max $-2R^2 - 10M^2 - 8RM + 18R + 34M$
    s.t.
    $$R + M \leq 3$$

    c. The optimal solution is Radio = \$2500 and Direct mail = \$500
    Total sales = \$37,000

6. a. Without the global solver option turned on, LINGO returns $X = 4.978$ and $Y = 1.402$ for a value of 0.3088137E-08, which is a local minimum.

    b. With the global solver option turned on, the optimal solution (which is a global minimum) is $X = 0.228$ and $Y = -1.626$ for an objective function value of -6.551.

8. b. $L = 2244.281$ and $C = 2618.328$; Optimal solution = \$374,046.9 (If Excel Solver is used for this problem, we recommend starting with an initial solution that has $L > 0$ and $C > 0$.)

10. a. Min $X^2 - X^2 + 5 + Y^2 + 2Y + 3$
    s.t.
    $$X + Y = 8$$
    $$X, Y \geq 0$$

    b. $X = 4.75$ and $Y = 3.25$; Optimal objective value = 42.875

11. The LINGO formulation:
    Min = (1/5)*((R1 − RBAR)^2 + (R2 − RBAR)^2 + (R3 − RBAR)^2 + (R4 − RBAR)^2 + (R5 − RBAR)^2;

.1006*FS + .1764*IB + .3241*LG + .3236*LV + .3344*SG + .2456*SV = R1;
.1312*FS + .0325*IB + .1871*LG + .2061*LV + .1940*SG + .2532*SV = R2;
.1347*FS + .0751*IB + .3328*LG + .1293*LV + .0385*SG + .0670*SV = R3;
.4542*FS + .0133*IB + .4146*LG + .0706*LV + .5868*SG + .0543*SV = R4;
−.2193*FS + .0736*IB + .2326*LG + .0537*LV + .0902*SG + .1731*SV = R5;
    FS +   IB +   LG +   LV +   SG +   SV = 50000;

(1/5)*(R1 + R2 + R3 + R4 + R5) = RBAR;

RBAR > RMIN;
RMIN = 5000;
@FREE(R1);
@FREE(R2);
@FREE(R3);
@FREE(R4);
@FREE(R5);

Optimal solution:

```
Local optimal solution found.
  Objective value:          6784038
  Total solver iterations:     19

Model Title: MARKOWITZ
   Variable        Value      Reduced Cost
       R1        9478.492       0.000000
     RBAR        5000.000       0.000000
       R2        5756.023       0.000000
       R3        2821.951       0.000000
       R4        4864.037       0.000000
       R5        2079.496       0.000000
       FS        7920.372       0.000000
       IB        26273.98       0.000000
       LG        2103.251       0.000000
       LV        0.000000       208.2068
       SG        0.000000       78.04764
       SV        13702.40       0.000000
     RMIN        5000.000       0.000000
```

(Excel Solver will produce the same optimal solution.)

12. Optimal value of $\alpha = 0.1743882$
    Sum of squared errors = 98.56

14. Optimal solution:

```
Local optimal solution found.
  Objective value:         0.1990478
  Total solver iterations:     12
  Model Title: MARKOWITZ

   Variable        Value      Reduced Cost
       R1      -0.1457056       0.000000
     RBAR       0.1518649       0.000000
       R2       0.7316081       0.000000
       R3       0.8905417       0.000000
       R4      -0.6823468E-02   0.000000
       R5      -0.3873745       0.000000
       R6      -0.5221017       0.000000
       R7       0.3499810       0.000000
       R8       0.2290317       0.000000
       R9       0.2276271       0.000000
     AAPL       0.1817734       0.000000
      AMD       0.1687534       0.000000
     ORCL       0.6494732       0.000000
```

15.

MODEL TITLE: MARKOWITZ:
! MINIMIZE VARIANCE OF THE PORTFOLIO:
MIN = (1/9) * ((R1 − RBAR)^2 + (R2 − RBAR)^2 + (R3 − RBAR)^2 +
(R4 − RBAR)^2 + (R5 − RBAR)^2 + (R6 − RBAR)^2 + (R7 − RBAR)^2 +
(R8 − RBAR)^2 + (R9 − RBAR)^2):
! SCENARIO 1 RETURN:
0.0962*AAPL − 0.5537*AMD − 0.1074*ORCL = R1:
! SCENARIO 2 RETURN:
0.8104*AAPL + 0.1272*AMD + 0.8666*ORCL = R2:
! SCENARIO 3 RETURN:
0.9236*AAPL + 0.4506*AMD + 0.9956*ORCL = R3:
! SCENARIO 4 RETURN:
−0.8753*AAPL + 0.3124*AMD + 0.1533*ORCL = R4:
! SCENARIO 5 RETURN:
0.1340*AAPL − 0.4270*AMD − 0.5230*ORCL = R5:
! SCENARIO 6 RETURN:
−0.5432*AAPL − 1.1194*AMD − 0.3610*ORCL = R6:
! SCENARIO 7 RETURN:
0.4517*AAPL + 1.0424*AMD + 0.1416*ORCL = R7:
! SCENARIO 8 RETURN:
1.2263*AAPL + 0.0613*AMD − 0.0065*ORCL = R8:
! SCENARIO 9 RETURN:
0.6749*AAPL + 0.9729*AMD − 0.0912*ORCL = R9:
! MUST BE FULLY INVESTED IN THE MUTUAL FUNDS:
AAPL + AMD + ORCL = 1:
! DEFINE THE MEAN RETURN:
(1/9) * (R1 + R2 + R3 + R4 + R5 + R6 + R7 + R8 + R9) = RBAR:
! THE MEAN RETURN MUST BE AT LEAST 10 PERCENT:
RBAR > 0.12:
! SCENARIO RETURNS MAY BE NEGATIVE:
@FREE(R1):
@FREE(R2):
@FREE(R3):
@FREE(R4):
@FREE(R5):
@FREE(R6):
@FREE(R7):
@FREE(R8):
@FREE(R9):
END

Optimal solution:

```
Local optimal solution found.
   Objective value:      0.4120213
   Total solver iterations:      8

   Model Title: MATCHING S&P INFO TECH
   RETURNS

       Variable      Value       Reduced Cost
          R1      −0.5266475E−01    0.000000
          R2       0.8458175        0.000000
          R3       0.9716207        0.000000
          R4      −0.1370104        0.000000
          R5      −0.3362695        0.000000
          R6      −0.4175977        0.000000
          R7       0.2353628        0.000000
          R8       0.3431437        0.000000
          R9       0.1328016        0.000000
        AAPL       0.2832558        0.000000
         AMD       0.6577707E−02    0.000000
        ORCL       0.7101665        0.000000
```

(Excel Solver produces the same return.)

16. Optimal solution:

```
Local optimal solution found.
   Objective value:        7.503540
   Total solver iterations:     18

Model Title: MARKOWITZ WITH SEMIVARIANCE

     Variable        Value       Reduced Cost
        D1N        0.000000        0.000000
        D2N        0.8595142       0.000000
        D3N        3.412762        0.000000
        D4N        2.343876        0.000000
        D5N        4.431505        0.000000
        FS         0.000000        6.491646
        IB         0.6908001       0.000000
        LG         0.6408726E−01   0.000000
        LV         0.000000       14.14185
        SG         0.8613837E−01   0.000000
        SV         0.1589743       0.000000
        R1        21.04766         0.000000
        R2         9.140486        0.000000
        R3         6.587238        0.000000
        R4         7.656124        0.000000
        R5         5.568495        0.000000
        RBAR      10.00000         0.000000
        RMIN      10.00000         0.000000
        D1P       11.04766         0.000000
        D2P        0.000000        0.3438057
        D3P        0.000000        1.365105
        D4P        0.000000        0.9375505
        D5P        0.000000        1.772602
```

The solution calls for investing 69.1% of the portfolio in the intermediate-term bond fund, 6.4% in the large-cap growth fund, 8.6% in the small-cap growth fund, and 15.9% in the small-cap value fund.

(Excel Solver may have trouble with this problem, depending upon the starting solution that is used; a starting solution of each fund at 0.167 will produce the optimal value.)

18. Call option price for Friday, August 25, 2006, is approximately $C = \$1.524709$.

20. Optimal solution: Produce 10 chairs at Aynor, cost = $1350; 30 chairs at Spartanburg, cost = $3150; Total cost = $4500

Chapter 9

2.

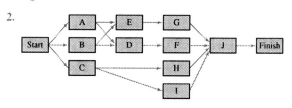

3.

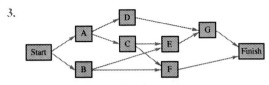

4. a. A–D–G
   b. No; Time = 15 months

6. a. Critical path: A–D–F–H
   b. 22 weeks
   c. No, it is a critical activity.
   d. Yes, 2 weeks
   e. Schedule for activity E:

Earliest start	3
Latest start	4
Earliest finish	10
Latest finish	11

8. b. B–C–E–F–H
   d. Yes, time = 49 weeks

10. a.

Activity	Optimistic	Most Probable	Pessimistic	Expected Times	Variance
A	4	5.0	6	5.00	0.11
B	8	9.0	10	9.00	0.11
C	7	7.5	11	8.00	0.44
D	7	9.0	10	8.83	0.25
E	6	7.0	9	7.17	0.25
F	5	6.0	7	6.00	0.11

   b. Critical activities: B–D–F
   Expected project completion time: $9.00 + 8.83 + 6.00 = 23.83$
   Variance of projection completion time: $0.11 + 0.25 + 0.11 = 0.47$

12. a. A–D–H–I
    b. 25.66 days
    c. 0.2578

13.

Activity	Expected Time	Variance
A	5	0.11
B	3	0.03
C	7	0.11
D	6	0.44
E	7	0.44
F	3	0.11
G	10	0.44
H	8	1.78

From Problem 6, A–D–F–H is the critical path, so
$E(T) = 5 + 6 + 3 + 8 = 22$.
$\sigma^2 = 0.11 + 0.44 + 0.11 + 1.78 = 2.44$
$$z = \frac{\text{Time} - E(T)}{\sigma} = \frac{\text{Time} - 22}{\sqrt{2.44}}$$

a. Time = 21: $z = -0.64$
   Cumulative Probability = 0.2611
   $P(21 \text{ weeks}) = 0.2611$
b. Time = 22: $z = 0$
   Cumulative Probability = 0.5000
   $P(22 \text{ weeks}) = 0.5000$
c. Time = 25: $z = +1.92$
   Cumulative Probability = 0.9726
   $P(25 \text{ weeks}) = 0.9726$

14. a. A–C–E–G–H
    b. 52 weeks (1 year)
    c. 0.0174
    d. 0.0934
    e. 10 month doubtful
       13 month very likely
       Estimate 12 months (1 year)

16. a.

E(T)	Variance
16	3.92
13	2.03
10	1.27

   b. 0.9783, approximately 1.00, approximately 1.00

18. c. A–B–D–G–H–I, 14.17 weeks
    d. 0.0951, yes

20. b. Crash B(1 week), D(2 weeks), E(1 week), F(1 week),
       G(1 week)
       Total cost = $2427
    c. All activities are critical.

21. a.

Activity	Earliest Start	Latest Start	Earliest Finish	Latest Finish	Slack	Critical Activity
A	0	0	3	3	0	Yes
B	0	1	2	3	1	
C	3	3	8	8	0	Yes
D	2	3	7	8	1	
E	8	8	14	14	0	Yes
F	8	10	10	12	2	
G	10	12	12	14	2	

   Critical path: A–C–E
   Project completion time $= t_A + t_C + t_E = 3 + 5 + 6 = 14$ days
   b. Total cost = $8400

22. a.

Activity	Max Crash Days	Crash Cost/Day
A	1	600
B	1	700
C	2	400
D	2	400
E	2	500
F	1	400
G	1	500

$\text{Min } 600Y_A + 700Y_B + 400Y_C + 400Y_D + 500Y_E + 400Y_F + 400Y_G$

s.t.

$$X_A + Y_A \geq 3$$
$$X_B + Y_B \geq 2$$
$$-X_A + X_C + Y_C \geq 5$$
$$-X_B + X_D + Y_D \geq 5$$
$$-X_C + X_E + Y_E \geq 6$$
$$-X_D + X_E + Y_E \geq 6$$
$$-X_C + X_F + Y_F \geq 2$$
$$-X_D + X_F + Y_F \geq 2$$
$$-X_F + X_G + Y_G \geq 2$$
$$-X_E + X_{FIN} \geq 0$$
$$-X_G + X_{FIN} \geq 0$$
$$X_{FIN} \leq 12$$
$$Y_A \leq 1$$
$$Y_B \leq 1$$
$$Y_C \leq 2$$
$$Y_D \leq 2$$
$$Y_E \leq 2$$
$$Y_F \leq 1$$
$$Y_G \leq 1$$

All $X, Y \geq 0$

b. Solution of the linear programming model in part (a) shows

Activity	Crash	Crashing Cost
C	1 day	$400
E	1 day	500
	Total	$900

c. Total cost = Normal cost + Crashing cost
= $8400 + $900 = $9300

24. c. A–B–C–F, 31 weeks
d. Crash A(2 weeks), B(2 weeks), C(1 week), D(1 week), E(1 week)
e. All activities are critical.
f. $112,500

Chapter 10

1. a. $Q^* = \sqrt{\dfrac{2DC_o}{C_h}} = \sqrt{\dfrac{2(3600)(20)}{0.25(3)}} = 438.18$

b. $r = dm = \dfrac{3600}{250}(5) = 72$

c. $T = \dfrac{250Q^*}{D} = \dfrac{250(438.18)}{3600} = 30.43$ days

d. $TC = \dfrac{1}{2}QC_h + \dfrac{D}{Q}C_o$

$= \dfrac{1}{2}(438.18)(0.25)(3) + \dfrac{3600}{438.18}(20) = \$328.63$

2. $164.32 for each; Total cost = $328.64

4. a. 1095.45
b. 240
c. 22.82 days
d. $273.86 for each; Total cost = $547.72

6. a. 15.95
b. $2106
c. 15.04
d. 16.62 days

8. $Q^* = 11.73$; use 12
5 classes per year
$225,200

10. $Q^* = 1414.21$
$T = 28.28$ days
Production runs of 7.07 days

12. $Q^* = 1000$; Total cost = $1200
Yes, the change saves $300 per year.

13. a. $Q^* = \sqrt{\dfrac{2DC_o}{(1 - D/P)C_h}}$

$= \sqrt{\dfrac{2(7200)(150)}{(1 - 7200/25,000)(0.18)(14.50)}} = 1078.12$

b. Number of production runs $= \dfrac{D}{Q^*} = \dfrac{7200}{1078.12} = 6.68$

c. $T = \dfrac{250Q}{D} = \dfrac{250(1078.12)}{7200} = 37.43$ days

d. Production run length $= \dfrac{Q}{P/250}$

$= \dfrac{1078.12}{25,000/250} = 10.78$ days

e. Maximum inventory $= \left(1 - \dfrac{D}{P}\right)Q$

$= \left(1 - \dfrac{7200}{25,000}\right)(1078.12)$

$= 767.62$

f. Holiday cost $= \dfrac{1}{2}\left(a - \dfrac{D}{P}\right)QC_h$

$= \dfrac{1}{2}\left(1 - \dfrac{7200}{25,000}\right)(1078.12)(0.18)(14.50)$

$= \$1001.74$

Ordering cost $= \dfrac{D}{Q}C_o = \dfrac{7200}{1078.12}(150) = \$1001.74$

Total cost $= \$2003.48$

g. $r = dm = \left(\dfrac{D}{250}\right)m = \dfrac{7200}{250}(15) = 432$

14. New $Q^* = 4509$

15. a. $Q^* = \sqrt{\dfrac{2DC_o}{C_h}\left(\dfrac{C_h + C_b}{C_b}\right)}$

$= \sqrt{\dfrac{2(12{,}000)(25)}{0.50}\left(\dfrac{0.50 + 5}{0.50}\right)} = 1148.91$

b. $S^* = Q^*\left(\dfrac{C_h}{C_h + C_b}\right) = 1148.91\left(\dfrac{0.50}{0.50 + 5}\right) = 104.45$

c. Max inventory $= Q^* - S^* = 1044.46$

d. $T = \dfrac{250Q^*}{D} = \dfrac{250(1148.91)}{12{,}000} = 23.94$ days

e. Holding $= \dfrac{(Q - S)^2}{2Q}C_h = \$237.38$

Ordering $= \dfrac{D}{Q}C_o = \$261.12$

Backorder $= \dfrac{S^2}{2Q}C_b = \$23.74$

Total cost $= \$522.24$

The total cost for the EOQ model in Problem 4 was $\$547.72$; allowing backorders reduces the total cost.

16. $135.55; r = dm - S;$ less than

18. $64, 24.44$

20. $Q^* = 100;$ Total cost $= \$3601.50$

21. $Q = \sqrt{\dfrac{2DC_o}{C_h}}$

$Q_1 = \sqrt{\dfrac{2(500)(40)}{0.20(10)}} = 141.42$

$Q_2 = \sqrt{\dfrac{2(500)(40)}{0.20(9.7)}} = 143.59$

Because Q_1 is over its limit of 99 units, Q_1 cannot be optimal (see Problem 23); use $Q_2 = 143.59$ as the optimal order quantity.

Total cost $= \dfrac{1}{2}QC_h + \dfrac{D}{Q}C_o + DC$

$= 139.28 + 139.28 + 4850.00 = \$5128.56$

22. $Q^* = 300;$ Savings $= \$480$

24. a. 500

b. 580.4

25. a. $c_o = 80 - 50 = 30$

$c_u = 125 - 80 = 45$

$P(D \le Q^*) = \dfrac{c_u}{c_u + c_o} = \dfrac{45}{45 + 30} = 0.60$

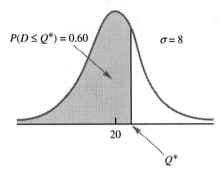

For the cumulative standard normal probability 0.60, $z = 0.25.$

$Q^* = 20 + 0.25(8) = 22$

b. $P(\text{Sell all}) = P(D \ge Q^*) = 1 - 0.60 = 0.40$

26. a. $\$150$

b. $\$240 - \$150 = \$90$

c. 47

d. 0.625

28. a. 440

b. 0.60

c. 710

d. $c_u = \$17$

29. a. $r = dm = (200/250)15 = 12$

b. $\dfrac{D}{Q} = \dfrac{200}{25} = 8$ orders/year

The limit of 1 stockout per year means that $P(\text{Stockout/cycle}) = 1/8 = 0.125.$

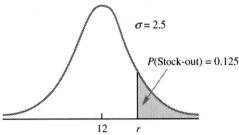

$P(\text{No Stockout/cycle}) = 1 - 0.125 = 0.875$

For cumulative probability 0.875, $z = 1.15$

Thus, $z = \dfrac{r - 12}{2.5} = 1.15$

$r = 12 + 1.15(2.5) = 14.875$ Use 15.

c. Safety stock $= 3$ units

Added cost $= 3(\$5) = \$15/$year

30. a. 13.68 (14)

b. 17.83 (18)

c. $2, \$10; 6, \$30$

32. a. 31.62
    b. 19.86 (20); 0.2108
    c. 5, $15

33. a. 1/52 = 0.0192
    b. P(No Stockout) = $1 - 0.0192 = 0.9808$
       For cumulative probability 0.9808, $z = 2.07$

       Thus, $z = \dfrac{M - 60}{12} = 2.07$

       $M = \mu + z\sigma = 60 + 2.07(12) = 85$
    c. $M = 35 + (0.9808)(85 - 35) = 84$

34. a. 243
    b. 93, $54.87
    c. 613
    d. 163, $96.17
    e. Yes, added cost would only be $41.30 per year.
    f. Yes, added cost would be $4130 per year.

36. a. 40
    b. 62.25; 7.9
    c. 54
    d. 36

Chapter 11

2. a. 0.4512
   b. 0.6988
   c. 0.3012

4. 0.3333, 0.2222, 0.1481, 0.0988; 0.1976

5. a. $P_0 = 1 - \dfrac{\lambda}{\mu} = 1 - \dfrac{10}{12} = 0.1667$

   b. $L_q = \dfrac{\lambda^2}{\mu(\mu - \lambda)} = \dfrac{10^2}{12(12 - 10)} = 4.1667$

   c. $W_q = \dfrac{L_q}{\lambda} = 0.4167$ hour (25 minutes)

   d. $W = W_q + \dfrac{1}{\lambda} = 0.5$ hour (30 minutes)

   e. $P_w = \dfrac{\lambda}{\mu} = \dfrac{10}{12} = 0.8333$

6. a. 0.3750
   b. 1.0417
   c. 0.8333 minutes (50 seconds)
   d. 0.6250
   e. Yes

8. 0.20, 3.2, 4, 3.2, 4, 0.80
   Slightly poorer service

10. a. New: 0.3333, 1.3333, 2, 0.6667, 1, 0.6667
       Experienced: 0.50, 0.50, 1, 0.25, 0.50, 0.50
    b. New $74; experienced $50; hire experienced

11. a. $\lambda = 2.5$; $\mu = \dfrac{60}{10} = 6$ customers per hour

$$L_q = \dfrac{\lambda^2}{\mu(\mu - \lambda)} = \dfrac{(2.5)^2}{6(6 - 2.5)} = 0.2976$$

$$L = L_q + \dfrac{\lambda}{\mu} = 0.7143$$

$$W_q = \dfrac{L_q}{\lambda} = 0.1190 \text{ hours (7.14 minutes)}$$

$$W = W_q + \dfrac{1}{\mu} = 0.2857 \text{ hours}$$

$$P_w = \dfrac{\lambda}{\mu} = \dfrac{2.5}{6} = 0.4167$$

b. No; $W_q = 7.14$ minutes; firm should increase the service rate (μ) for the consultant or hire a second consultant.

c. $\mu = \dfrac{60}{8} = 7.5$ customers per hour

$$L_q = \dfrac{\lambda^2}{\mu(\mu - \lambda)} = \dfrac{(2.5)^2}{7.5(7.5 - 2.5)} = 0.1667$$

$$W_q = \dfrac{L_q}{\lambda} = 0.0667 \text{ hours (4 minutes)}$$

The service goal is being met.

12. a. 0.25, 2.25, 3, 0.15 hours, 0.20 hours, 0.75
    b. The service needs improvement.

14. a. 8
    b. 0.3750
    c. 1.0417
    d. 12.5 minutes
    e. 0.6250
    f. Add a second consultant.

16. a. 0.50
    b. 0.50
    c. 0.10 hours (6 minutes)
    d. 0.20 hours (12 minutes)
    e. Yes, $W_q = 6$ minutes is most likely acceptable for a marina.

18. a. $k = 2$; $\lambda/\mu = 5.4/3 = 1.8$; $P_0 = 0.0526$

$$L_q = \dfrac{(\lambda/\mu)^2 \lambda\mu}{(k - 1)!(2\mu - \lambda)^2} P_0$$

$$= \dfrac{(1.8)^2(5.4)(3)}{(2 - 1)!(6 - 5.4)^2}(0.0526) = 7.67$$

$$L = L_q + \lambda/\mu = 7.67 + 1.8 = 9.47$$

$$W_q = \dfrac{L_q}{\lambda} = \dfrac{7.67}{5.4} = 1.42 \text{ minutes}$$

$$W = W_q + 1/\mu = 1.42 + 0.33 = 1.75 \text{ minutes}$$

$$P_w = \frac{1}{k!}\left(\frac{\lambda}{\mu}\right)^k \left(\frac{k\mu}{k\mu - \lambda}\right) P_0$$

$$= \frac{1}{2!}(1.8)^2\left(\frac{6}{6 - 5.4}\right)0.0526 = 0.8526$$

b. $L_q = 7.67$; Yes

c. $W = 1.75$ minutes

20. a. Use $k = 2$

   $W = 3.7037$ minutes

   $L = 4.4444$

   $P_w = 0.7111$

   b. For $k = 3$

   $W = 7.1778$ minutes

   $L = 15.0735$ customers

   $P_N = 0.8767$

   Expand post office.

21. From Problem 11, a service time of 8 minutes has $\mu = 60/8 = 7.5$.

$$L_q = \frac{\lambda^2}{\mu(\mu - \lambda)} = \frac{(2.5)^2}{7.5(7.5 - 2.5)} = 0.1667$$

$$L = L_q + \frac{\lambda}{\mu} = 0.50$$

Total cost = $\$25L + \$16$

   $= 25(0.50) + 16 = \$28.50$

Two channels: $\lambda = 2.5$; $\mu = 60/10 = 6$

With $P_0 = 0.6552$,

$$L_q = \frac{(\lambda/\mu)^2\lambda\mu}{1!(2\mu - \lambda)^2}P_0 = 0.0189$$

$$L = L_q + \frac{\lambda}{\mu} = 0.4356$$

Total cost $= 25(0.4356) + 2(16) = \$42.89$

Use one consultant with an 8-minute service time.

22.

Characteristic	A	B	C
a. P_0	0.2000	0.5000	0.4286
b. L_q	3.2000	0.5000	0.1524
c. L	4.0000	1.0000	0.9524
d. W_q	0.1333	0.0208	0.0063
e. W	0.1667	0.0417	0.0397
f. P_w	0.8000	0.5000	0.2286

The two-channel System C provides the best service.

24. a. 0.0466, 0.05

   b. 1.4

   c. 11:00 A.M.

25. $\lambda = 4$, $W = 10$ minutes

   a. $\mu = \frac{1}{2} = 0.5$

   b. $W_q = W - 1/\mu = 10 - 1/0.5 = 8$ minutes

   c. $L = \lambda W = 4(10) = 40$

26. a. 0.2668, 10 minutes, 0.6667

   b. 0.0667, 7 minutes, 0.4669

   c. $25.33; $33.34; one-channel

27. a. ⅔ hours = 0.25 per hour

   b. 1/3.2 hours = 0.3125 per hour

   c. $L_q = \dfrac{\lambda^2\sigma^2 + (\lambda/\mu)^2}{2(1 - \lambda/\mu)}$

   $= \dfrac{(0.25)^2(2)^2 + (2.5/0.3125)^2}{2(1 - 0.25/0.3125)} = 2.225$

   d. $W_q = \dfrac{L_q}{\lambda} = \dfrac{2.225}{0.25} = 8.9$ hours

   e. $W = W_q + \dfrac{1}{\mu} = 8.9 + \dfrac{1}{0.3125} = 12.1$ hours

   f. Same as $P_w = \dfrac{\lambda}{\mu} = \dfrac{0.25}{0.3125} = 0.80$

   The welder is busy 80% of the time.

28. a. 10, 9.6

   b. Design A with $\mu = 10$

   c. 0.05, 0.01

   d. A: 0.5, 0.3125, 0.8125, 0.0625, 0.1625, 0.5

   B: 0.4792, 0.2857, 0.8065, 0.0571, 0.1613, 0.5208

   e. Design B has slightly less waiting time.

30. a. $\lambda = 42$; $\mu = 20$

i	$(\lambda/\mu)^i/i!$
0	1.0000
1	2.1000
2	2.2050
3	1.5435
Total	6.8485

j	P_j	
0	1/6.8485	= 0.1460
1	2.1/6.8485	= 0.3066
2	2.2050/6.8485	= 0.3220
3	1.5435/6.8485	= 0.2254
		1.0000

b. 0.2254

c. $L = \lambda/\mu(1 - P_k) = 42/20(1 - 0.2254) = 1.6267$

d. Four lines will be necessary; the probability of denied access is 0.1499

32. a. 31.03%
    b. 27.59%
    c. 0.2759, 0.1092, 0.0351
    d. 3, 10.92%

34. $N = 5$; $\lambda = 0.025$; $\mu = 0.20$; $\lambda/\mu = 0.125$
    a.

n	$\dfrac{N!}{(N-n)!}\left(\dfrac{\lambda}{\mu}\right)^n$
0	1.0000
1	0.6250
2	0.3125
3	0.1172
4	0.0293
5	0.0037
Total	2.0877

$P_0 = 1/2.0877 = 0.4790$

b. $L_q = N - \left(\dfrac{\lambda + \mu}{\lambda}\right)(1 - P_0)$

$= 5 - \left(\dfrac{0.225}{0.025}\right)(1 - 0.4790) = 0.3110$

c. $L = L_q + (1 - P_0) = 0.3110 + (1 - 0.4790)$
$= 0.8321$

d. $W_q = \dfrac{L_q}{(N - L)\lambda} = \dfrac{0.3110}{(5 - 0.8321)(0.025)}$

$= 2.9854$ minutes

e. $W = W_q + \dfrac{1}{\mu} = 2.9854 + \dfrac{1}{0.20} = 7.9854$ minutes

f. Trips/day = (8 hours)(60 minutes/hour)(λ)
   $= (8)(60)(0.025) = 12$ trips
   Time at copier: $12 \times 7.9854 = 95.8$ minutes/day
   Wait time at copier: $12 \times 2.9854 = 35.8$ minutes/day

g. Yes, five assistants $\times$ 35.8 = 179 minutes (3 hours/day), so 3 hours per day are lost to waiting.
   (35.8/480)(100) = 7.5% of each assistant's day is spent waiting for the copier.

Chapter 12

2. a. c = variable cost per unit
      x = demand
      Profit = $(50 - c)x - 30,000$
   b. Base: Profit = $(50 - 20)1200 - 30,000 = 6,000$
      Worst: Profit = $(50 - 24)300 - 30,000 = -22,200$
      Best: Profit = $(50 - 16)2100 - 30,000 = 41,400$
   c. Simulation will be helpful in estimating the probability of a loss.

4. a.

Number of New Accounts	Interval
0	0.00 but less than 0.01
1	0.01 but less than 0.05
2	0.05 but less than 0.15
3	0.15 but less than 0.40
4	0.40 but less than 0.80
5	0.80 but less than 0.95
6	0.95 but less than 1.00

   b. 4, 3, 3, 5, 2, 6, 4, 4, 4, 2
      37 new accounts
   c. First-year commission = $185,000
      Cost of 10 seminars = $35,000
      Yes

5. a.

Stock Price Change	Interval
−2	0.00 but less than 0.05
−1	0.05 but less than 0.15
0	0.15 but less than 0.40
+1	0.40 but less than 0.60
+2	0.60 but less than 0.80
+3	0.80 but less than 0.90
+4	0.90 but less than 1.00

   b. Beginning price $39
      0.1091 indicates −1 change; $38
      0.9407 indicates +4 change; $42
      0.1941 indicates 0 change; $42
      0.8083 indicates +3 change; $45 (ending price)

6. a. 0.00–0.83, 0.83–0.89, 0.89–0.94, 0.94–0.96, 0.96–0.98, 0.98–0.99, 0.99–1.00
   b. 4 claims paid; Total = $22,000

8. a. Atlanta wins each game if random number is in interval 0.00–0.60, 0.00–0.55, 0.00–0.48, 0.00–0.45, 0.00–0.48, 0.00–0.55, 0.00–0.50.
   b. Atlanta wins games 1, 2, 4, and 6.
      Atlanta wins series 4 to 2.
   c. Repeat many times; record % of Atlanta wins.

9. a. Base-case based on most likely;
      Time = 6 + 5 + 14 + 8 = 33 weeks
      Worst: Time = 8 + 7 + 18 + 10 = 43 weeks
      Best: Time = 5 + 3 + 10 + 8 = 26 weeks
   b. 0.1778 for A: 5 weeks
      0.9617 for B: 7 weeks
      0.6849 for C: 14 weeks
      0.4503 for D: 8 weeks; Total = 34 weeks
   c. Simulation will provide an estimate of the probability of 35 weeks or less.

10. a.

Hand Value	Interval
17	0.0000 but less than 0.1654
18	0.1654 but less than 0.2717
19	0.2717 but less than 0.3780
20	0.3780 but less than 0.4797
21	0.4797 but less than 0.5769
Broke	0.5769 but less than 1.0000

   b, c, & d. Dealer wins 13 hands, Player wins 5, 2 pushes.
   e. Player wins 7, dealer wins 13.

FIGURE E12.14   WORKSHEET FOR THE MADEIRA MANUFACTURING SIMULATION

	A	B	C	D	E	F	G	H
1	Madeira Manufacturing Company							
2								
3	Selling Price per Unit		$50					
4	Fixed Cost		$30,000					
5								
6	Variable Cost (Uniform Distribution)				Demand (Normal Distribution)			
7	Smallest Value		$16		Mean		1200	
8	Largest Value		$24		Standard Deviation		300	
9								
10	Simulation trials							
11		Variable						
12	Trial	Cost per Unit	Demand	Profit				
13	1	$17.81	788	($4,681)				
14	2	$18.86	1078	$3,580				
15								

12. a. $7, $3, $12
   b. Purchase: 0.00–0.25, 0.25–0.70, 0.70–1.00
      Labor: 0.00–0.10, 0.10–0.35, 0.35–0.70, 0.70–1.00
      Transportation: 0.00–0.75, 0.75–1.00
   c. $5
   d. $7
   e. Provide probability profit less than $5/unit.

14. Selected cell formulas for the worksheet shown in
   Figure E12.14 are as follows:

Cell	Formula
B13	=$C$7+RAND()*($C$8−$C$7)
C13	=NORMINV(RAND(),$G$7,$G$8)
D13	=($C$3−B13)*C13−$C$4

   a. The mean profit should be approximately $6000; sim-
      ulation results will vary, with most simulations having
      a mean profit between $5500 and $6500.
   b. 120 to 150 of the 500 simulation trials should show a
      loss; thus, the probability of a loss should be between
      0.24 and 0.30.
   c. This project appears too risky.

16. a. About 36% of simulation runs will show $130,000 as
      the winning bid.
   b. $150,000; $10,000
   c. Recommended $140,000

18. Selected cell formulas for the worksheet shown in
   Figure E12.18 are as follows:

Cell	Formula
B11	=$C$4+RAND()*($C$5−$C$4)
C11	=NORMINV(RAND(),$H$4,$H$5)
D11	=MIN(B11:C11)
G11	=COUNTIF($D$11:$D$1010,">650")
H11	=G11/COUNT($D$11:$D$1010)

   a. $650,000 should win roughly 600 to 650 of the 1000
      times; the probability of winning the bid should be be-
      tween 0.60 and 0.65.
   b. The probability of $625,000 winning should be
      roughly 0.82, and the probability of $615,000 winning
      should be roughly 0.88; a contractor's bid of $625,000
      is recommended.

20. a. Results vary with each simulation run.
      Approximate results: 50,000 provided $230,000
                             60,000 provided $190,000
                             70,000 less than $100,000
   b. Recommend 50,000 units.
   c. Roughly 0.75

22. Very poor operation; some customers wait 30 minutes or
   more.

24. b. Waiting time is approximately 0.8 minutes.
   c. 30% to 35% of customers have to wait.

FIGURE E12.18   WORKSHEET FOR THE CONTRACTOR BIDDING SIMULATION

	A	B	C	D	E	F	G	H	I
1	**Contractor Bidding**								
2									
3	**Contractor A (Uniform Distribution)**					**Contractor B (Normal Distribution)**			
4	Smallest Value		$600			Mean		$700	
5	Largest Value		$800			Standard Deviation		$50	
6									
7									
8	**Simulation**					**Results**			
9		Contractor	Contractor	Lowest		Contractor's	Number	Probability	
10	Trial	A's Bid	B's Bid	Bid		Bid	of Wins	of Winning	
11	1	$673	$720	$673		$650	628	0.628	
12	2	$757	$655	$655		$625	812	0.812	
13	3	$706	$791	$706		$615	875	0.875	
14	4	$638	$677	$638					
15									

Chapter 13

1. a.

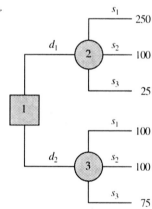

b.

Decision	Maximum Profit	Minimum Profit
d_1	250	25
d_2	100	75

Optimistic approach: Select d_1
Conservative approach: Select d_2

Regret or opportunity loss table:

Decision	s_1	s_2	s_3
d_1	0	0	50
d_2	150	0	0

Maximum regret: 50 for d_1 and 150 for d_2; select d_1

2. a. Optimistic: d_1
   Conservative: d_3
   Minimax regret: d_3
   c. Optimistic: d_1
   Conservative: d_2 or d_3
   Minimax regret: d_2

3. a. Decision: Choose the best plant size from the two alternatives—a small plant and a large plant.
   Chance event: market demand for the new product line with three possible outcomes (states of nature)—low, medium, and high

   b. Influence diagram:

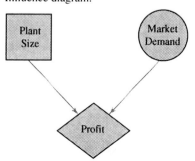

c.

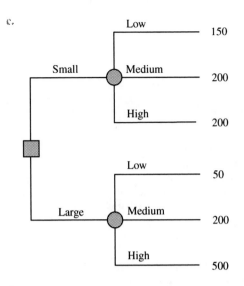

d.

Decision	Maximum Profit	Minimum Profit	Maximum Regret
Small	200	150	300
Large	500	50	100

Optimistic approach: Large plant
Conservative approach: Small plant
Minimax regret: Large plant

4. $EV(d_1) = 0.65(250) + 0.15(100) + 0.20(25) = 182.5$
$EV(d_2) = 0.65(100) + 0.15(100) + 0.20(75) = 95$
The optimal decision is d_1.

6. a. Decision: Which lease option to choose
   Chance event: Miles driven

   b. **Annual Miles Driven**

	12,000	15,000	18,000
Forno	10,764	12,114	13,464
Midtown	11,160	11,160	12,960
Hopkins	11,700	11,700	11,700

   c. Optimistic: Forno Saab
   Conservative: Hopkins Automotive
   Minimax: Hopkins Automotive

   d. Midtown Motors

   e. Most likely: $11,160; Probability = 0.9

   f. Midtown Motors or Hopkins Automotive

7. a. EV(own staff) = 0.2(650) + 0.5(650) + 0.3(600) = 635
   EV(outside vendor) = 0.2(900) + 0.5(600) + 0.3(300) = 570
   EV(combination) = 0.2(800) + 0.5(650) + 0.3(500) = 635
   Optimal decision: Hire an outside vendor with an expected cost of $570,000.

b.

	Cost	Probability
Own staff	300	0.3
Outside vendor	600	0.5
Combination	900	0.2
		1.0

8. a. $EV(d_1) = p(10) + (1 - p)(1) = 9p + 1$
   $EV(d_2) = p(4) + (1 - p)(3) = 1p + 3$

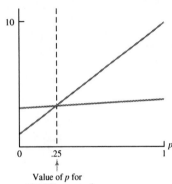

Value of p for
which EVs are equal

   $9p + 1 = 1p + 3$ and hence $p = 0.25$
   d_2 is optimal for $p \leq 0.25$, d_1 is optimal for $p \geq 0.25$

   b. d_2

   c. As long as the payoff for $s_1 \geq 2$, then d_2 is optimal.

10. b. Space Pirates
    EV = $724,000
    $84,000 better than Battle Pacific

    c. $200   0.18
       $400   0.32
       $800   0.30
       $1600   0.20

    d. $P(\text{Competition}) > 0.7273$

12. a. Decision: Whether to lengthen the runway
    Chance event: The location decisions of Air Express and DRI
    Consequence: Annual revenue

    b. $255,000

    c. $270,000

    d. No

    e. Lengthen the runway.

14. a. If s_1, then d_1; if s_2, then d_1 or d_2; if s_3, then d_2

    b. EVwPI = 0.65(250) + 0.15(100) + 0.20(75) = 192.5

    c. From the solution to Problem 4, we know that $EV(d_1) = 182.5$ and $EV(d_2) = 95$; thus, recommended decision is d_1; hence, EVwoPI = 182.5.

    d. EVPI = EVwPI − EVwoPI = 192.5 − 182.5 = 10

16. a.

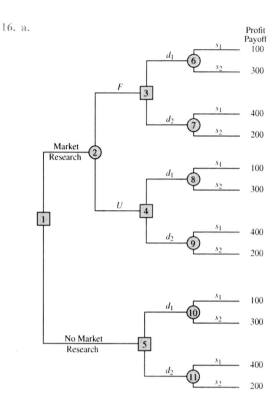

b. EV (node 6) = 0.57(100) + 0.43(300) = 186
   EV (node 7) = 0.57(400) + 0.43(200) = 314
   EV (node 8) = 0.18(100) + 0.82(300) = 264
   EV (node 9) = 0.18(400) + 0.82(200) = 236
   EV (node 10) = 0.40(100) + 0.60(300) = 220
   EV (node 11) = 0.40(400) + 0.60(200) = 280

   EV (node 3) = Max(186,314) = 314 d_2
   EV (node 4) = Max(264,236) = 264 d_1
   EV (node 5) = Max(220,280) = 280 d_2

   EV (node 2) = 0.56(314) + 0.44(264) = 292
   EV (node 1) = Max(292,280) = 292
   ∴ Market research
   If favorable, decision d_2
   If unfavorable, decision d_1

18. a. 5000 − 200 − 2000 − 150 = 2650
       3000 − 200 − 2000 − 150 = 650
    b. Expected values at nodes:
       8: 2350   5: 2350   9: 1100
       6: 1150   10: 2000   7: 2000
       4: 1870   3: 2000   2: 1560
       1: 1560
    c. Cost would have to decrease by at least $130,000.

d.

Payoff (in millions)	Probability
−$200	0.20
800	0.32
2800	0.48
	1.00

20. b. If Do Not Review, Accept
       If Review and F, Accept
       If Review and U, Accept
       Always Accept
    c. Do not review; EVSI = $0
    d. $87,500; better method of predicting success

22. a. Order 2 lots; $60,000
    b. If E, order 2 lots
       If V, order 1 lot
       EV = $60,500
    c. EVPI = $14,000
       EVSI = $500
       Efficiency = 3.6%
       Yes, use consultant.

23.

State of Nature	$P(s_j)$	$P(I/s_j)$	$P(I \cap s_j)$	$P(s_j/I)$
s_1	0.2	0.10	0.020	0.1905
s_2	0.5	0.05	0.025	0.2381
s_3	0.3	0.20	0.060	0.5714
	1.0	$P(I) = 0.105$		1.0000

24. a. 0.695, 0.215, 0.090
       0.98, 0.02
       0.79, 0.21
       0.00, 1.00
    c. If C, Expressway
       If O, Expressway
       If R, Queen City
       26.6 minutes

Chapter 14

2. a. Let x_1 = number of shares of AGA Products purchased
      x_2 = number of shares of Key Oil purchased

   To obtain an annual return of exactly 9%:

   $$0.06(50)x_1 + 0.10(100)x_2 = 0.09(50,000)$$
   $$3x_1 + 10x_2 = 4500$$

   To have exactly 60% of the total investment in Key Oil:

   $$100x_2 = 0.60(50,000)$$
   $$x_2 = 300$$

Therefore, we can write the goal programming model as follows:

Min $P_1(d_1^-) + P_2(d_2^+)$

s.t.

$$50x_1 + 100x_2 \leq 50{,}000 \quad \text{Funds available}$$
$$3x_1 + 10x_2 - d_1^+ + d_1^- = 4{,}500 \quad P_1 \text{ goal}$$
$$x_2 - d_2^+ + d_2^- = 300 \quad P_2 \text{ goal}$$
$$x_1, x_2, d_1^+, d_1^-, d_2^+, d_2^- \geq 0$$

b. In the following graphical solution, $x_1 = 250$ and $x_2 = 375$.

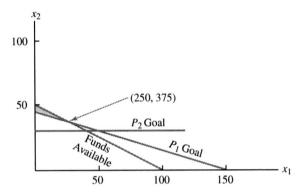

4. a. Min $P_1(d_1^-) + P_2(d_2^1) + P_2(d_3^-) + P_2(d_4^-) + P_3(d_5^-)$

s.t.

$$20x_1 + 30x_2 - d_1^+ + d_1^- = 4800$$
$$20x_1 + 30x_2 - d_2^1 + d_2^- = 6000$$
$$x_1 - d_3^+ + d_3^- = 100$$
$$x_2 - d_4^+ + d_4^- = 120$$
$$x_1 + x_2 - d_3^1 + d_5^- = 300$$
$$x_1, x_2, \text{all deviation variables} \geq 0$$

b. $x_1 = 120, x_2 = 120$

6. a. Let x_1 = number of letters mailed to group 1 customers

x_2 = number of letters mailed to group 2 customers

Min $P_1(d_1^-) + P_2(d_2^-) + P_2(d_3^+)$

s.t.

$$x_1 - d_1^+ + d_1^- = 40{,}000$$
$$x_2 - d_2^+ + d_2^- = 50{,}000$$
$$x_1 + x_2 - d_3^1 + d_3^- = 70{,}000$$
$$x_1, x_2, \text{all deviation variables} \geq 0$$

b. $x_1 = 40{,}000, x_2 = 50{,}000$

c. Optimal solution does not change.

8. a. Min $d_1^- + d_1^+ + e_1^- + e_1^+ + d_2^- + d_2^+ + e_2^- +$
$$e_2^+ + d_3^- + d_3^+ + e_3^- + e_3^+$$

s.t.

$$x_1 + d_1^- - d_1^+ = 1$$
$$x_2 + e_1^- - e_1^+ = 7$$

$$x_1 + d_2^- - d_2^+ = 5$$
$$x_2 + e_2^- - e_2^+ = 9$$
$$x_1 + d_3^- - d_3^+ = 6$$
$$x_2 + e_3^- - e_3^+ = 2$$
$$\text{all variables} \geq 0$$

b. $x_1 = 5, x_2 = 7$

9. Scoring calculations

Criterion	Analyst Chicago	Accountant Denver	Auditor Houston
Career advancement	35	20	20
Location	10	12	8
Management	30	25	35
Salary	28	32	16
Prestige	32	20	24
Job security	8	10	16
Enjoyment of the work	28	20	20
Totals	171	139	139

The analyst position in Chicago is recommended.

10. 178, 184, 151
Marysville

12. 170, 168, 190, 183
Handover College

14. a. 220 Bowrider (194)
b. 240 Sundancer (144)

16. Step 1: Column totals are $\frac{17}{4}$, $\frac{31}{21}$, and 12.
Step 2:

Style	Accord	Saturn	Cavalier
Accord	$\frac{4}{17}$	$\frac{7}{31}$	$\frac{4}{12}$
Saturn	$\frac{12}{17}$	$\frac{21}{31}$	$\frac{7}{12}$
Cavalier	$\frac{1}{17}$	$\frac{3}{31}$	$\frac{1}{12}$

Step 3:

Style	Accord	Saturn	Cavalier	Row Average
Accord	0.235	0.226	0.333	0.265
Saturn	0.706	0.677	0.583	0.656
Cavalier	0.059	0.097	0.083	0.080

Consistency Ratio
Step 1:

$$0.265 \begin{bmatrix} 1 \\ 3 \\ 1/4 \end{bmatrix} + 0.656 \begin{bmatrix} 1/3 \\ 1 \\ 1/7 \end{bmatrix} + 0.080 \begin{bmatrix} 4 \\ 7 \\ 1 \end{bmatrix}$$

$$\begin{bmatrix} 0.265 \\ 0.795 \\ 0.066 \end{bmatrix} + \begin{bmatrix} 0.219 \\ 0.656 \\ 0.094 \end{bmatrix} + \begin{bmatrix} 0.320 \\ 0.560 \\ 0.080 \end{bmatrix} = \begin{bmatrix} 0.802 \\ 2.007 \\ 0.239 \end{bmatrix}$$

Step 2: $0.802/0.265 = 3.028$
$2.007/0.656 = 3.062$
$0.239/0.080 = 3.007$
Step 3: $\lambda_{max} = (3.028 + 3.062 + 3.007)/3 = 3.032$
Step 4: CI $= (3.032 - 3)/2 = 0.016$
Step 5: CR $= 0.016/0.58 = 0.028$
Because CR $= 0.028$ is less than 0.10, the degree of consistency exhibited in the pairwise comparison matrix for style is acceptable.

18. a. 0.724, 0.193, 0.083
    b. CR $= 0.057$, yes

20. a.

Flavor	A	B	C
A	1	3	2
B	1/3	1	5
C	1/2	1/5	1

b. Step 1: Column totals are $^{11}\!/_{6}$, $^{21}\!/_{5}$, and 8.
   Step 2:

Flavor	A	B	C
A	6/11	15/21	2/8
B	2/11	5/21	5/8
C	3/11	1/21	1/8

Step 3:

Flavor	A	B	C	Row Average
A	0.545	0.714	0.250	0.503
B	0.182	0.238	0.625	0.348
C	0.273	0.048	0.125	0.148

c. Step 1:

$$0.503 \begin{bmatrix} 1 \\ 1/3 \\ 1/2 \end{bmatrix} + 0.348 \begin{bmatrix} 3 \\ 1 \\ 1/5 \end{bmatrix} + 0.148 \begin{bmatrix} 2 \\ 5 \\ 1 \end{bmatrix}$$

$$\begin{bmatrix} 0.503 \\ 0.168 \\ 0.252 \end{bmatrix} + \begin{bmatrix} 1.044 \\ 0.348 \\ 0.070 \end{bmatrix} + \begin{bmatrix} 0.296 \\ 0.740 \\ 0.148 \end{bmatrix} = \begin{bmatrix} 1.845 \\ 1.258 \\ 0.470 \end{bmatrix}$$

Step 2: $1.845/0.503 = 3.668$
$1.258/0.348 = 3.615$
$0.470/0.148 = 3.123$
Step 3: $\lambda_{max} = (3.668 + 3.615 + 3.123)/3 = 3.469$
Step 4: CI $= (3.469 - 3)/2 = 0.235$
Step 5: CR $= 0.235/0.58 = 0.415$
Because CR $= 0.415$ is greater than 0.10, the individual's judgments are not consistent.

22. a.

	D	S	N
D	1	1/4	1/7
S	4	1	1/3
N	7	3	1

b. 0.080, 0.265, 0.656
c. CR $= 0.028$, yes

24. Criteria: Yield and Risk
Step 1: Column totals are 1.5 and 3.
Step 2:

	Yield	Risk	Priority
Yield	0.667	0.667	0.667
Risk	0.333	0.333	0.333

With only two criteria, CR $= 0$; no need to compute CR; preceding calculations for Yield and Risk provide

Stocks	Yield Priority	Risk Priority
CCC	0.750	0.333
SRI	0.250	0.667

Overall Priorities:
CCC $0.667(0.750) + 0.333(0.333) = 0.611$
SRI $0.667(0.250) + 0.333(0.667) = 0.389$
CCC is preferred.

26. a. Criterion: 0.608, 0.272, 0.120
Price: 0.557, 0.123, 0.320
Sound: 0.137, 0.239, 0.623
Reception: 0.579, 0.187, 0.046
b. 0.446, 0.162, 0.392
System A is preferred.

Chapter 15

1. The following table shows the calculations for parts (a), (b), and (c).

Week	Time Series Value	Forecast	Forecast Error	Absolute Value of Forecast Error	Squared Forecast Error	Percentage Error	Absolute Value of Percentage Error
1	18						
2	13	18	−5	5	25	−38.46	38.46
3	16	13	3	3	9	18.75	18.75
4	11	16	−5	5	25	−45.45	45.45
5	17	11	6	6	36	35.29	35.29
6	14	17	−3	3	9	−21.43	21.43
			Totals	22	104	−51.30	159.38

a. MAE = 22/5 = 4.4
b. MSE = 104/5 = 20.8
c. MAPE = 159.38/5 = 31.88
d. Forecast for week 7 is 14.

2. The following table shows the calculations for parts (a), (b), and (c).

Week	Time Series Value	Forecast	Forecast Error	Absolute Value of Forecast Error	Squared Forecast Error	Percentage Error	Absolute Value of Percentage Error
1	18						
2	13	18.00	−5.00	5.00	25.00	−38.46	38.46
3	16	15.50	0.50	0.50	0.25	3.13	3.13
4	11	15.67	−4.67	4.67	21.81	−42.45	42.45
5	17	14.50	2.50	2.50	6.25	14.71	14.71
6	14	15.00	−1.00	1.00	1.00	−7.14	7.14
			Totals	13.67	54.31	−70.21	105.86

a. MAE = 13.67/5 = 2.73
b. MSE = 54.31/5 = 10.86
c. MAPE = 105.89/5 = 21.18
d. Forecast for week 7 is (18 + 13 + 16 + 11 + 17 + 14)/6 = 14.83.

3. By every measure, the approach used in problem 2 appears to be the better method.

4. a. MSE = 363/6 = 60.5
   Forecast for month 8 is 15.
   b. MSE = 216.72/6 = 36.12
   Forecast for month 8 is 18.
   c. The average of all the previous values is better because MSE is smaller.

5. a. The data appear to follow a horizontal pattern.

b.

Week	Time Series Value	Forecast	Forecast Error	Squared Forecast Error
1	18			
2	13			
3	16			
4	11	15.67	−4.67	21.78
5	17	13.33	3.67	13.44
6	14	14.67	−0.67	0.44
			Total	35.67

MSE = 35.67/3 = 11.89.
The forecast for week 7 = (11 + 17 + 14)/3 = 14.

c.

Week	Time Series Value	Forecast	Forecast Error	Squared Forecast Error
1	18			
2	13	18.00	−5.00	25.00
3	16	17.00	−1.00	1.00
4	11	16.80	−5.80	33.64
5	17	15.64	1.36	1.85
6	14	15.91	−1.91	3.66
			Total	65.15

MSE = 65.15/5 = 13.03
The forecast for week 7 is 0.2(14) + (1 − 0.2)15.91 = 15.53.

d. The three-week moving average provides a better forecast because it has a smaller MSE.

e.

Alpha   0.367694922

Week	Time Series Value	Forecast	Forecast Error	Squared Forecast Error
1	18			
2	13	18	−5.00	25.00
3	16	16.16	−0.16	0.03
4	11	16.10	−5.10	26.03
5	17	14.23	2.77	7.69
6	14	15.25	−1.25	1.55
			Total	60.30

MSE = 60.30/5 = 12.061

6. a. The data appear to follow a horizontal pattern.
   b. MSE = 110/4 = 27.5
      The forecast for week 8 is 19.
   c. MSE = 252.87/6 = 42.15
      The forecast for week 7 is 19.12.

d. The three-week moving average provides a better forecast because it has a smaller MSE.
e. $\alpha = 0.351404848$ MSE = 39.61428577

8. a.

Week	4	5	6	7	8	9	10	11	12
Forecast	19.3	21.3	19.8	17.8	18.3	18.3	20.3	20.3	17.8

b. MSE = 11.49
   Prefer the unweighted moving average here; it has a smaller MSE.
c. You could always find a weighted moving average at least as good as the unweighted one. Actually, the unweighted moving average is a special case of the weighted ones where the weights are equal.

10. b. The more recent data receives the greater weight or importance in determining the forecast. The moving averages method weights the last n data values equally in determining the forecast.

12. a. The data appear to follow a horizontal pattern.
    b. MSE(3-month) = 0.12
       MSE(4-month) = 0.14
       Use 3-month moving averages.
    c. 9.63

13. a. The data appear to follow a horizontal pattern.

b.

Month	Time-Series Value	3-Month Moving Average Forecast	(Error)^2	$\alpha = 0.2$ Forecast	(Error)^2
1	240				
2	350			240.00	12100.00
3	230			262.00	1024.00
4	260	273.33	177.69	255.60	19.36
5	280	280.00	0.00	256.48	553.19
6	320	256.67	4010.69	261.18	3459.79
7	220	286.67	4444.89	272.95	2803.70
8	310	273.33	1344.69	262.36	2269.57
9	240	283.33	1877.49	271.89	1016.97
10	310	256.67	2844.09	265.51	1979.36
11	240	286.67	2178.09	274.41	1184.05
12	230	263.33	1110.89	267.53	1408.50
			17,988.52		27,818.49

MSE(3-Month) = 17,988.52/9 = 1998.72
MSE($\alpha = 0.2$) = 27,818.49/11 = 2528.95
Based on the above MSE values, the 3-month moving average appears better. However, exponential smoothing was penalized by including month 2, which was difficult for any method to forecast. Using only the errors for months 4–12, the MSE for exponential smoothing is

$MSE(\alpha = 0.2) = 14{,}694.49/9 = 1632.72$

Thus, exponential smoothing was better considering months 4–12.

c. Using exponential smoothing,

$F_{13} = \alpha\, Y_{12} + (1 - \alpha)F_{12} = 0.20(230) + 0.80(267.53)$
$\quad = 260$

14. a. The data appear to follow a horizontal pattern.

b. Values for months 2–12 are as follows:
   105.00 114.00 115.80 112.56 105.79 110.05 120.54
   126.38 118.46 106.92 104.85
   MSE = 510.29

c. $\alpha = 0.032564518$ MSE = 5056.62

16. a. The time series plot indicates a possible linear trend in the data. This could be due to decreasing viewer interest in watching the Masters. But, closer inspection of the data indicates that the two highest ratings correspond to years 1997 and 2001, years in which Tiger Woods won the tournament. The pattern observed may be simply due to the effect Tiger Woods has on ratings and not necessarily on any long-term decrease in viewer interest.

b. The methods discussed in this section are only applicable for a time series that has a horizontal pattern. So, if there is really a long-term linear trend in the data, the methods disucssed in this are not appropriate.

c. The time series plot for the data for years 2002–2008 exhibits a horizontal pattern. It seems reasonable to conclude that the extreme values observed in 1997 and 2001 are more attributable to viewer interest in the performance of Tiger Woods. Basing the forecast on years 2002–2008 does seem reasonable. But, because of the injury that Tiger Woods experienced in the 2008 season, if he is able to play in the 2009 Masters then the rating for 2009 may be significantly higher than suggested by the data for years 2002–2008.

17. a. The time series plot shows a linear trend.

b.

	b0	4.70		
	b1	2.10		
Year	Sales	Forecast	Forecast Error	Squared Forecast Error
1	6.00	6.80	−0.80	0.64
2	11.00	8.90	2.10	4.41
3	9.00	11.00	−2.00	4.00
4	14.00	13.10	0.90	0.81
5	15.00	15.20	−0.20	0.04
6		17.30	**Total**	9.9

$MSE = 9.9/5 = 1.98$

c. $T_6 = 4.7 + 2.1(6) = 17.3$

18. a.

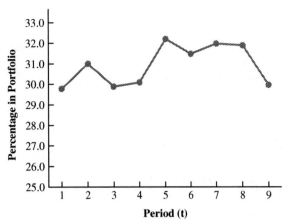

The time series plot indicates a horizontal pattern.

b. $\alpha = 0.467307293$; MSE = 1.222838367

c. Forecast for second quarter 2009 = 30.93

20. a. The time series plot exhibits a curvilinear trend.

b. $T_t = 107.857 - 28.9881\,t + 2.65476\,t^2$

c. 45.86

21. a. The time series plot shows a linear trend.

b.

			b0	4.72	
			b1	1.46	
Period	Year	Enrollment	Forecast	Forecast Error	Squared Forecast Error
1	2001	6.50	6.17	0.33	0.11
2	2002	8.10	7.63	0.47	0.22
3	2003	8.40	9.09	−0.69	0.47
4	2004	10.20	10.54	−0.34	0.12
5	2005	12.50	12.00	0.50	0.25
6	2006	13.30	13.46	−0.16	0.02
7	2007	13.70	14.91	−1.21	1.47
8	2008	17.20	16.37	0.83	0.69
9	2009	18.10	17.83	0.27	0.07
10	2010		19.28	**Total**	3.427333

$T_t = 4.72 + 1.46t$

c. $T_{10} = 4.72 + 1.46(10) = 19.28$

22. a. The time series plot shows a downward linear trend.

b. $T_t = 13.8 - 0.7t$

c. 8.2

d. If SCC can continue to decrease the percentage of funds spent on administrative and fund-raising by 0.7% per year, the forecast of expenses for 2015 is 4.70%.

24. a. The time series plot shows a linear trend.
    b. $T_t = 7.5623 - .07541t$
    c. 6.7328
    d. Given the uncertainty in global market conditions, making a prediction for December using only time is not recommended.

26. a. A linear trend is not appropriate.
    b. $T_t = 5.702 + 2.889t - .1618t^2$
    c. 17.91

28. a. The time series plot shows a horizontal pattern. But, there is a seasonal pattern in the data. For instance, in each year the lowest value occurs in quarter 2 and the highest value occurs in quarter 4.

b.

Year	Quarter	Period	Seasonality QTR1	QTR2	QTR3	Series	Forecast	Forecast Error	Squared Forecast Error
1	1	1	1	0	0	71	67.00	4.00	16.00
	2	2	0	1	0	49	47.00	2.00	4.00
	3	3	0	0	1	58	57.00	1.00	1.00
	4	4	0	0	0	78	77.00	1.00	1.00
2	1	5	1	0	0	68	67.00	1.00	1.00
	2	6	0	1	0	41	47.00	−6.00	36.00
	3	7	0	0	1	60	57.00	3.00	9.00
	4	8	0	0	0	81	77.00	4.00	16.00
3	1	9	1	0	0	62	67.00	−5.00	25.00
	2	10	0	1	0	51	47.00	4.00	16.00
	3	11	0	0	1	53	57.00	−4.00	16.00
	4	12	0	0	0	72	77.00	−5.00	25.00
								Total	166.00
		b0	b1	b2	b3				
		77.00	−10.00	−30.00	−20.00				

c. The quarterly forecasts for next year are as follows:
   Quarter 1 forecast = 77.0 − 10.0(1) − 30.0(0) − 20.0(0) = 67
   Quarter 2 forecast = 77.0 − 10.0(0) − 30.0(1) − 20.0(0) = 47
   Quarter 3 forecast = 77.0 − 10.0(0) − 30.0(0) − 20.0(1) = 57
   Quarter 4 forecast = 77.0 − 10.0(0) − 30.0(0) − 20.0(0) = 77

30. a. There appears to be a seasonal pattern in the data and perhaps a moderate upward linear trend.
    b. $Sales_t = 2492 - 712 Qtr1_t - 1512 Qtr2_t + 327 Qtr3_t$
    c. The quarterly forecasts for next year are as follows:
       Quarter 1 forecast = 1780
       Quarter 2 forecast = 980
       Quarter 3 forecast = 2819
       Quarter 4 forecast = 2492
    d. $Sales_t = 2307 - 642 Qtr1_t - 1465 Qtr2_t + 350 Qtr3_t + 23.1 t$

The quarterly forecasts for next year are as follows:
   Quarter 1 forecast = 2058
   Quarter 2 forecast = 1258
   Quarter 3 forecast = 3096
   Quarter 4 forecast = 2769

32. a. The time series plot shows both a linear trend and seasonal effects.
    b. $Revenue_t = 70.0 + 10.0 Qtr1_t + 105 Qtr2_t + 245 Qtr3_t$
       Quarter 1 forecast = 80
       Quarter 1 forecast = 175
       Quarter 1 forecast = 315
       Quarter 1 forecast = 70
    c. The equation is
       $Revenue = -70.1 + 45.0 Qtr1 + 128 Qtr2 + 257 Qtr3 + 11.7 Period$
       Quarter 1 forecast = 221
       Quarter 1 forecast = 315
       Quarter 1 forecast = 456
       Quarter 1 forecast = 211

Chapter 16

2. a. 0.82
    b. $\pi_1 = 0.5, \pi_2 = 0.5$
    c. $\pi_1 = 0.6, \pi_2 = 0.4$

3. a. 0.10 as given by the transition probability
    b. $\pi_1 = 0.90\pi_1 + 0.30\pi_2$ (1)
       $\pi_2 = 0.10\pi_1 + 0.70\pi_2$ (2)
       $\pi_1 + \pi_2 = 1$ (1)
       Using (1) and (3),
       $$0.10\pi_1 - 0.30\pi_2 = 0$$
       $$0.10\pi_1 - 0.30(1 - \pi_1) = 0$$
       $$0.10\pi_1 - 0.30 + 0.30\pi_1 = 0$$
       $$0.40\pi_1 = 0.30$$
       $$\pi_1 = 0.75$$
       $$\pi_2 = (1 - \pi_1) = 0.25$$

4. a. $\pi_1 = 0.92, \pi_2 = 0.08$
    b. $85

6. a.

	City	Suburbs
City	0.98	0.02
Suburbs	0.01	0.99

    b. $\pi_1 = 0.333, \pi_2 = 0.667$
    c. City will decrease from 40% to 33%; suburbs will increase from 60% to 67%.

7. a. $\pi_1 = 0.85\pi_1 + 0.20\pi_2 = 0.15\pi_3$ (1)
       $\pi_2 = 0.10\pi_1 + 0.75\pi_2 = 0.10\pi_3$ (2)
       $\pi_3 = 0.05\pi_1 + 0.05\pi_2 = 0.75\pi_3$ (3)
       $\pi_1 + \pi_2 + \pi_3 = 1$ (4)
       Using (1), (2), and (4) provides three equations with three unknowns; solving provides $\pi_1 = 0.548, \pi_2 = 0.286$, and $\pi_3 = 0.166$.
    b. 16.6% as given by π_3
    c. Quick Stop should take
       $667 - 0.548(1000)$ $= 119$ Murphy's customers
       and $333 - 0.286(1000) = \underline{\ \ 47}$ Ashley's customers
            Total 166 Quick Stop customers
       It will take customers from Murphy's and Ashley's.

8. a. MDA
    b. $\pi_1 = \frac{1}{3}, \pi_2 = \frac{2}{3}$

10. $3 - 1(0.59), 4 - 1(0.52)$

11. $I = \begin{bmatrix} 1 & 0 \\ 0 & 1 \end{bmatrix}$ $Q = \begin{bmatrix} 0.25 & 0.25 \\ 0.05 & 0.25 \end{bmatrix}$

    $$(I - Q) = \begin{bmatrix} 0.75 & -0.25 \\ -0.05 & 0.75 \end{bmatrix}$$

$$N = (I - Q)^{-1} = \begin{bmatrix} 1.3636 & 0.4545 \\ 0.0909 & 1.3636 \end{bmatrix}$$

$$NR = \begin{bmatrix} 1.3636 & 0.4545 \\ 0.0909 & 1.3636 \end{bmatrix}\begin{bmatrix} 0.5 & 0.0 \\ 0.5 & 0.2 \end{bmatrix} = \begin{bmatrix} 0.909 & 0.091 \\ 0.727 & 0.273 \end{bmatrix}$$

$$BNR = \begin{bmatrix} 4000 & 5000 \end{bmatrix}\begin{bmatrix} 0.909 & 0.091 \\ 0.727 & 0.273 \end{bmatrix} = \begin{bmatrix} 7271 & 1729 \end{bmatrix}$$
Estimate $1729 in bad debts.

12. 3580 will be sold eventually; 1420 will be lost.

14. a. Graduate and Drop Out
    b. $P(\text{Drop Out}) = 0.15, P(\text{Sophomore}) = 0.10$, $P(\text{Junior}) = 0.75$
    c. 0.706, 0.294
    d. Yes; $P(\text{Graduate}) = 0.54$
       $P(\text{Drop Out}) = 0.46$
    e. 1479 (74%) will graduate.

Appendix A

2. =F6*$F$3

4.

	A	B
1	Nowlin Plastics	
2		
3	Fixed Cost	$3,000.00
4		
5	Variable Cost Per Unit	$2.00
6		
7	Selling Price Per Unit	$5.00
8		
9	Capacity	1500
10		
11	Forecasted Demand	1200
12		
13	Model	
14		
15	Production Volume	1200
16		
17	Total Cost	$5,400.00
18		
19	Total Revenue	$6,000.00
20		
21	Total Profit (Loss)	$600.00
22		

	A	B
14		
15	Production Volume	=IF(B11<B9,B11,B9)
16		
17	Total Cost	=B3+B5*B15
18		
19	Total Revenue	=B7*B15
20		
21	Total Profit (Loss)	=B19-B17
22		

6.

Cell	Formula
D14	=C14*$B$3
E14	=C14*$B$7
F14	=C14*$B$9
G14	=$B$5
H14	=SUM(E14:G14)
I14	=D14-H14

	A	B	C	D	E	F	G	H	I
1	Cox Electric Breakeven Analysis								
2									
3	Revenue per Unit	$0.63							
4									
5	Fixed Costs	$10,000.00							
6									
7	Material Cost per Unit	$0.15							
8									
9	Labor Cost per Unit	$0.10							
10									
11									
12	Model								
13				Volume	Total Revenue	Material Cost	Labor Cost	Fixed Cost	Total Cost	Profit
14				10000	$6,300.00	$1,500.00	$1,000.00	$10,000.00	$12,500.00	-$6,200.00
15				20000	$12,600.00	$3,000.00	$2,000.00	$10,000.00	$15,000.00	-$2,400.00
16				30000	$18,900.00	$4,500.00	$3,000.00	$10,000.00	$17,500.00	$1,400.00
17									

8.

Grade	Count
F	1
D	2
C-	1
C-	1
C+	0
B-	2
B	1
B+	0
A-	1
A	3

10. Error in SUMPRODUCT range in cell B17
Cell A23 should be Lexington.

Index